Second Edition

This book is a substantial revision of the First Edition of *Principles of Fluid Mechanics.* The author has rewritten the entire manuscript to include vectors where appropriate. Throughout the book, the concepts are presented in a precise and lucid fashion, and illustrative examples clarify each new consideration. Basic relationships in each chapter are first developed in a general way and then followed by various applications in component form.

Salamon Eskinazi

Professor of Mechanical Engineering
Syracuse University

Principles of Fluid Mechanics

Second Edition

Allyn and Bacon, Inc.
Boston

To Ruth

Library of Congress Catalog Card Number: 68-20414

Printed in the United States of America

Preface first edition

Teaching a course or learning is not exclusively an elegant display of knowledge. The method of teaching or learning, as the case may be, must manifest a logical and rigorous continuity. In general, it is this logical rigor of thought that makes a course interesting and consequently appealing to the mind that has a desire to learn. Logic is essential for reasoning. Furthermore, accurate reasoning requires accurate usage of the rules of logic. Today, every field of study has developed its own specialized operational logic which enables reasoning in specialized terms. To the scientist and the engineer, mathematics is a symbolic or shorthand form of logical thinking enabling him to reason his premise to a satisfactory conclusion. If experimentation of the physical phenomenon is possible to perform, it will yield the same conclusion, provided the same conditions prevail in both cases. However, it would be wise for scientists and engineers to remember the thoughts of Albert Einstein on logical thinking as related to science. He said, "*Pure* logical thinking cannot yield us any knowledge of the empirical world; all knowledge of reality starts from experiment and ends in it." Furthermore, he warns us also that "experience remains, of course, the sole criterion of the physical utility of mathematical construction. But the creative principle resides in mathematics." [1]

This book is intended for the beginning student in mechanics of fluids. It will provide him with the basic and fundamental concepts so necessary for advancement in the fields of general fluid dynamics (hydro- and aerodynamics). Throughout the book an attempt has been made to present the concepts and notions as simply as possible, without distortion of meaning or significance. First, the most important con-

[1] Albert Einstein, "On the Method of Theoretical Physics," from *Essays in Science*, Philosophical Library, New York, 1934.

cepts, variables, constants, and parameters necessary for the formulation of the most basic axioms and theorems are presented in a logical sequence. Without the clear understanding of these concepts, axioms, and theorems, the student cannot hope to grasp clearly the nature, mechanism, and scope of applied problems related to the dynamics of flowing fluids.

The same general laws of equilibrium already encountered in the mechanics of solids will be found to apply for fluids as well. Some concepts in kinematics and dynamics pertaining to solids will be used for fluids also. Some concepts will require certain alterations in order to include fluids. Finally, some new concepts will be introduced which will have a meaning for fluids but not for solids. In essence, it may be said that solid mechanics as well as fluid mechanics are limited studies of a broad field in general mechanics. In elementary books it is common practice to cover fluid statics in great length at the beginning of the course. This practice is not followed here for two reasons: Since good treatments of fluid statics are available in many textbooks, any extended effort on the part of the present author would be merely a duplication of material. Furthermore, since the behavior of fluids under static conditions is similar to that of solids, they are generally treated together in an earlier course.

In mechanics of rigid bodies, the relative positions of the elemental masses constituting the body always remain unchanged. This can be accomplished only when the elemental mass behaves as the body itself. In mechanics of deformable bodies, however, the deformation within the entire body must be distributed uniformly in order to say that the behavior of the elemental mass is a small-scale replica of the body's behavior. A *fluid* substance deforms under the influence of external forces. This deformation is often nonuniformly distributed throughout the extent of the fluid without causing separation of mass. Under these circumstances the over-all deformation, being the sum of the nonuniform elemental deformations, will not be a scale replica of the deformation of any elemental mass. In fluid mechanics a knowledge of the behavior of the elemental mass is essential in order to deduce the behavior of larger masses. It was just mentioned that every fluid portion throughout the flow field does not necessarily move in precisely the same amount; therefore, since small fluid portions must be examined in detail, the use of partial and total differentiation is inevitable. In most instances it is not unreasonable to postulate that the fluid properties vary in a smooth, continuous fashion in a given region of consideration.

The differential equation expressing the motion of a fluid element may, in most instances, involve more than one dependent variable. In that case, as in algebraic equations, as many independent equations are needed as independent variables in order to obtain a solution in terms of the independent variables alone. In mechanics of fluids these additional equations are obtained from axiomatic laws such as the conservation of mass and energy and the equation of state of the substance. This availability of the exact number of equations does not necessarily guarantee a solution; it merely defines the problem. The engineers and scientists are dependent on available mathematical information on how to obtain solutions in a form that is easily handled in practice. Most fluid-dynamic problems are well defined; this means that the physical set of conditions required to define the problem is complete. Some of them are unsolvable today, however, on account of the lack of mathematical tools. Where mathematical tools are not abundant, the scientist and engineer must resort to experimental means. The experimental approach is comparatively slower, more expensive, and generally more tedious. In essence, theory and experiment depend on each other for sensible progress in a given field.

During the past years, extensive contributions have been made in the field of fluid dynamics. A student, after having been exposed to general mechanics of fluids or aerodynamics, will be able to follow the basic concepts of viscous, nonviscid, rotational, irrotational, compressible, and incompressible states of fluid motion. Needless to say, less prepared students must devote extra effort to grasp the basic fundamentals they lack if they wish to assimilate their graduate courses satisfactorily. In a similar fashion, the less well-prepared student who chooses to work for industry will find it difficult to follow his industrial leaders working on contemporary research, design, or development problems. Generally speaking, the author believes that this book will give the undergraduate student the quality of knowledge in mechanics of fluids that is expected from a prospective graduate student.

Salamon Eskinazi

Preface second edition

We are living in an era when the time scale between our present to the "foreseeable future" has shrunk considerably. A half century ago, when one projected a view or an idea to a foreseeable future one expected it to be valid, at least, for one generation. Because of the rapidity with which changes are taking place today, the future we are immediately concerned with is of the order of two to five years. In some instances, and when dealing with certain problems, we are not able to make predictions beyond this foreseeable future. Other times, although it is possible to foresee deeper into the future; affecting present changes to reflect a far too distant future may be too premature, indeed.

It is common knowledge, today, that the average effective life of a textbook in engineering and science is approximately three years. Beyond this time, the educational pedagogy and the material that constitute the book are somewhat out of phase with the current demands and practices. What is interesting and at the same time complex to an author of textbooks is that the time of average obsolescence of a book and the time of the so-called "foreseeable future" are nearly the same. This poses a number of difficult problems to authors. For example, if through some prophetic powers an author is capable of seeing through a farther distant future and produces a work to reflect the needs of that time, he risks the chance of having completed a book that may not be appreciated until the period intended. Furthermore, the book may not be appreciated during this very same period, either, for it carries an antiquated publishing date. The following is a very good example of this case.

In 1934, L. Prandtl and O. G. Tietjens published an English version of two magnificent volumes in Fundamentals of Hydro- and Aeromechanics and Applied Hydro- and Aeromechanics. In general, the pedagogy and material in this work did not reflect our needs at the time. In fact, the material was so far advanced that our higher education in engineering did not make these books available to the student until three or four years ago. Roughly speaking, the books were, then, thirty years ahead of their time in this country. We must grant the fact that these volumes were favorites among teachers as sources of reference and constant influence. Nevertheless, they were never popular as standard textbooks at any period. Presently, there are many new successful books written in the spirit of Prandtl and Tietjens, including this one, and yet because of the reasons given, it is inconceivable that they could be placed in the market to compete with the new ones. They are now thirty years old. Authors do not necessarily write only for commercial reasons. Prandtl and Tietjens wrote their books because they had a far-reaching message to deliver, and this they did. They stand today, among the giants in Fluid Mechanics and Aerodynamics for having had the most influence in shaping our present state of the art.

The urge to be read by many during one's lifetime is natural. This desire is even more significant when it concerns the production of a textbook, for without the success of appealing to students, the whole enterprise becomes meaningless.

From its inception, the writing of this book has been influenced, to one degree or another, by the various considerations presented here. A summary of events that led to the publication of this book is indicative of the demands of our time.

In the year 1960, the original manuscript of this book was completed in vector notation and contained essentially the same material. It was felt at that time that an undergraduate Fluid Mechanics book in vector notation was very much in need. When the manuscript was presented to the publishers, the question arose whether schools across the country were ready to accept the language of vector mechanics at the undergraduate level. Although the implications of the launching of Sputnik had just jolted our educational system, most students did not have a good background in Vector Analysis at the undergraduate level. The editors suggested preparing a questionnaire asking various Fluid Mechanics teachers across the nation if they would prefer a text in vector notation. To the author's surprise, out of forty-eight replies the answer was overwhelmingly against the idea of using vectors in an undergraduate book. One must believe that this almost unanimous expression of preference was perhaps true in 1960. In the light of this, it was reasonable to transcribe the manuscript into scalar algebra and calculus. The first edition of the book appeared in 1962 in that form. The author is indebted to many of his colleagues for having given the first edition a measure of success.

It wasn't long after the first edition was published that a number of books on the same subject appeared at the same level and in vector notation. Approximately two years after, a large majority of schools were convinced of the value of vector analysis in Fluid Mechanics. This author will not forget the positive remark made to him by one of his colleagues: "Now, why couldn't you have gone a step further, writing your book in vector notation? Frankly, if a second edition does not appear in vector form, its adoption will be discontinued in my classes." Since then, many forms of the same question were registered. In fact, the author did not need convincing, he was ready before the first edition appeared.

Recently, a new book entitled *Vector Mechanics of Fluids and Magnetofluids* appeared by the same author. This book is more advanced in scope than this second edition. Rather than going back to the original manuscript of 1960, this edition uses essentially the material in the first edition enlarged by an exposé of the general subject in vector mechanics in almost every chapter. For the convenience of the student, a second appendix has been added entitled Survey in Vector Analysis. It is intended for a quick refresher. New problems have been added to reflect the new changes. There have been some criticisms on the need of Chapter III entitled Similarity of Motion in Fluid Mechanics in the first edition. This has been removed in the second edition and the concepts in that chapter have been divided between the chapter on Kinematics and Dimensional Analysis.

Salamon Eskinazi

Acknowledgments

The author acknowledges his appreciation to Academic Press for allowing him to use for Appendix A, a condensed form of Chapter 2 in the book *Vector Mechanics of Fluids and Magnetofluids* by the same author. A few illustrations were also borrowed from that book.

Mr. and Mrs. Howard F. Hamm have helped, as in the previous books, produce the revised illustrations. The excellent quality of their work is, in the author's opinion, an attractive aspect of the overall work.

In many respects, the work of a major revision is not a simple one, at all. The author is indebted to Mrs. Edith S. Brigham for the overall typing, pasting and editing of the entire revised manuscript. Her fine quality of work has been a major factor in the smooth production of this book.

Contents

Symbols

The following is a list of the most commonly used symbols in the book.

$\boldsymbol{a}$, a	Acceleration
a	Speed of Sound in the fluid
$\boldsymbol{A}$, A	Cross-section area
b	Width
B	Integration constant
c	Speed of pressure wave
c_p	Specific heat at constant pressure
c_v	Specific heat at constant volume
C	Dimensional constant in Newton's law of gravitation
C_p	Pressure coefficient
C_v	Velocity coefficient
C_d	Discharge coefficient
C_c	Contraction coefficient
C_D	Drag coefficient
d	Distance
d	Diameter
D	Diameter of pipe
D	Drag
e	Internal energy per unit mass
E	Modulus of elasticity
E	Energy
f	Frequency
f	Resistance coefficient
$\boldsymbol{F}$, F	Force
$\mathfrak{F}r$	Froude number
$\boldsymbol{g}$, g	Gravitational acceleration
g_0	Gravitational acceleration at 45° latitude and sea level
g_c	Dimensional constant in Newton's law of inertia
$\mathcal{G}$	Grashoff number
h	Enthalpy

h	Heat transfer coefficient
h	Height
H	Head loss
$\boldsymbol{i}$	Unit vector
I_{xy}	Product moment of inertia
I_{xx}	Moment of inertia about x-axis
$\boldsymbol{j}$	Unit vector
J	Mechanical equivalent of heat
k	Size of roughness
k	Strength of point source
$\boldsymbol{k}$	Unit vector
K	Strength of line source
l	Linear length
L	Characteristic length
L	Lift force
L_e	Equivalent length
m	Mass
M	Momentum
$\mathfrak{M}$	Mach number
$\overline{MG}$	Metacentric height
N	Nasselt number
n	Exponent in polytropic process
$\boldsymbol{n}$	Outward unit normal
p	Pressure
p_t	Total pressure
P	Power
$\mathcal{P}$	Péclet number
p	Prandtl number
q	Heat transferred
Q	Rate of mass flow
r	Radius
R	Radius of the earth
R	Dimensional gas constant
R	Radius of curvature
$\mathcal{R}$	Reynolds number
s	Length of path
s	Entropy
S	Surface area
$\mathbf{S}$	Stress tensor
t	Time
T	Surface-tension force
T	Period

T	Temperature
$\boldsymbol{T}$	Moment of momentum
u	x-component of velocity
u'	x-component of turbulent velocity fluctuation
u_*	Shearing velocity
$\boldsymbol{U}$, U	Velocity
U_s	Steady-state velocity
U_u	Unsteady-state velocity
$\overline{U}$	Temporal mean velocity
$U_\perp$	Velocity component normal to s
U_∞	Velocity of undisturbed flow
v	y-component of velocity
v_r	Radial component of velocity
v_θ	Peripheral component of velocity
v'	y-component of turbulent velocity fluctuation
V	Velocity
w'	z-component of turbulent velocity fluctuation
w	z-component of velocity
W	Work
W	Weight
$\mathcal{W}$	Weber number
x	Cartesian coordinate
x_p	Coordinate of center of pressure
$\bar{x}$	Coordinate of centroid
y	Cartesian coordinate
y_p	Coordinate of center of pressure
$\bar{y}$	Coordinate of centroid
z	Cartesian coordinate
z_p	Coordinate of center of pressure
$\bar{z}$	Coordinate of centroid
α	Angle
$\ddot{\alpha}$	Angular acceleration
β	Coefficient of compressibility
β_1	Coefficient of thermal expansion
β_2	Coefficient of tension
β	Angle
γ	Ratio of specific heats
Γ	Circulation
δ	Boundary-layer thickness
δ^*	Displacement thickness
ϵ	Resultant small pressure
ϵ	Ratio of bearing width

ζ	Vorticity
η	Dimensionless variable
θ	Angle of deformation
θ	Angle
θ	Momentum thickness
λ	Temperature-lapse rate
μ	Absolute viscosity
ν	Kinematic viscosity
Π	Dimensionless grouping
ρ	Density
σ	Surface-tension coefficient
σ	Normal viscous stress
τ	Shear stress
ϕ	Dimensionless pressure gradient
ϕ	Potential function
ϕ_l	Load factor
ϕ_d	Drag factor
ψ	Stream function
ω	Angular velocity

Subscripts

x	Pertaining to x-direction
y	Pertaining to y-direction
z	Pertaining to z-direction
i	Inlet or input
o	Outlet or output
s	Along streamline
max	Maximum value
av	Spatial average
w	Pertaining to wall
L	Along length
δ	Across boundary layer

Superscript

$^\circ$	Pertaining to stagnation point
$*$	Property at sonic point

Fundamental Concepts

chapter I

1.1 Solid, Liquid, and Gas

All matter in nature is found in the form of *solid*, *liquid*, or *gas* and often in a mixture of these forms. These basic forms are identified thermodynamically as *phases* which represent a form of matter that is physically and chemically stable. Because of their similarity in dynamic behavior, the two phases—liquid and gas—are designated as *fluids*. The *solid* is generally conceived as a substance that offers resistance to change of shape. In contrast, the *fluid*—representing the liquid and the gas—does not offer any resistance to change of shape.[1] A simple experiment can demonstrate the difference in behavior between a free volume of solid and a free volume of liquid when they are subjected to similar forces. A glass of water is quickly turned upside down on a flat, level surface. The water trapped between the walls of the glass and the flat surface imposes, owing to its own weight, a force on the glass wall as well as on the flat surface. If the glass is quickly lifted upward, the body of water originally restrained by the glass walls will deform continuously under its own weight. The surface tension finally limits this indefinite deformation to a puddle of water of minimum height. This experiment may be repeated with the same amount of

[1] Here, change of shape is conceived as a change of form without a change of volume.

water frozen within the glass. We know from experience that the solid will not deform continuously when the glass is removed upward. Owing to the relief of restraint imposed by the glass walls, the ice will deform slightly under the influence of its own weight. This deformation will be small and will remain the same indefinitely, provided that all conditions remain unchanged. Like ice, all solids will display the same finite deformation in the elastic regime.

The principal distinction between a *solid* and a *fluid* is, then, the mode of resistance to change of shape. This distinction is definitely dependent on the type of force imposed. For instance, if the glass of water and the glass of ice were not turned upside down, but if a compressive force were imposed on the water and on the ice with the help of a piston fitting snugly into the glass, the water and the ice would compress slightly. We can generalize, then, that *under pure compressive loads, the solid and the fluid will display a finite deformation proportional to the load.* This deformation will generally be accompanied by a change in volume. This proportionality between the load and the deformation is called *Hooke's law.*

What makes the first experiment different from the second experiment is the type of force applied in each case. In the first experiment the sudden relief of restraint from the glass wall induces forces in a direction perpendicular to the glass wall. These forces increase with depth, since the weight of the fluid above the layer increases with depth. Because of this, the layers of water at greater depths will move sideways faster than do the upper layers. The difference of velocity between layers will develop frictional forces between them. Since the water deforms continuously, it cannot resist any change of shape owing to frictional or shear forces. The solid, under the same conditions, will show a finite deformation under the same tangential shear forces. Therefore, *the fluid, unlike a solid, cannot sustain a finite deformation under the action of tangential shear forces. Under shear forces it cannot, like the solid, resist a change of shape.*

Based on experimental evidence, Newton showed[2] empirically that for most fluids *the time rate of change of the deformation of a fluid element is proportional to the shear force per unit area applied on the surfaces of the element.* He expressed this behavior of the fluid in his *Principia* in the form of the following hypothesis:[3]

[2] Sir Isaac Newton, "On the Attrition of Liquids," *Principia*, Book II, Sec. IX, S. Pepys, London, 1686.

[3] Sir Isaac Newton, *Principia in Modern English* (Motte's translation, revised by Cajori), University of California Press, Berkeley, 1946.

The resistance arising from the want of lubricity [slipperiness] in the parts of a fluid, is, other things being equal, proportional to the velocity with which the parts of the fluid are separated from one another.

This difference of behavior between a solid and a fluid now becomes clear. Under a tangential shear force the solid undergoes a finite *deformation* proportional to the force per unit area, and the proportionality factor is the shearing modulus of elasticity. A fluid, under the same force, will deform indefinitely, while the *rate of change of the deformation* will be proportional to the shearing force per unit area, and the proportionality factor is the *viscosity coefficient.*[4] It can be verified easily—with a third experiment—that, for fluids with equal shear forces, the viscosity determines the rate of deformation. Two equal volumes of liquids with approximately the same density, originally contained in separate identical glasses, are overturned on a flat surface, as in the previous experiments. At the start of the experiment, the internal-force distribution at corresponding levels in both liquids was the same, because of equal weights of fluid at equal depths owing to equal densities. Nevertheless, if the two liquids have different viscosities, it will take the more viscous liquid a longer time to reach its final "puddle" state. This experiment indicates that, for the same shear force, the viscosity determines the time it takes for a given deformation. More qualitative as well as quantitative descriptions on viscosity will follow later in this chapter.

A *gas* is a fluid and consequently obeys the type of behavior discussed in this section. It, however, differs from a liquid in its compressibility. This implies that a given mass of gas under a given compressive load will change its volume considerably more than does the liquid. Furthermore, unlike a liquid, a gas does not display a free surface; it expands and occupies the entire space of any size container.

1.2 System, Property, and State

A *system* is an arbitrary volume within the substance to be analyzed, across whose boundaries no mass is exchanged. The system, like a

[4] For a concise historical introduction to the development of the concept of viscous fluids, read H. Bateman's introduction to Chap. III in his book *Hydrodynamics*, Dover Publications, Inc., New York, 1956. Also read C. Truesdell, "Notes on the History of the General Equations of Hydrodynamics," *J. Am. Soc. Naval Engrs.*, Vol. 66, No. 1, February, 1954.

solid body, may experience a change in its momentum and energy but no change in mass. A system can be stationary or moving. In a moving system the boundaries will move with the system, and the mass within the system will always be the same.

In contrast, a *control volume* is an arbitrary volume across whose boundaries mass as well as momentum and energy are transferred. The control volume may thus be stationary with respect to the motion of the fluid. The fluid enters the boundaries of the control volume on one side and leaves through the other. The air inside a leaktight automobile tire represents a system, whereas an arbitrary length of exhaust pipe through which exhaust gases are blowing is considered to be a control volume.

The boundaries separate the system and the control volume from their *surroundings*. The surroundings are important in the analysis, since they exchange mass, momentum, and energy, as the case may be, with the system or control volume.

A *property* is an observable quantity of a system. If measured, its value is always the same when the system is brought to the same conditions, *regardless of the way in which it was brought to those conditions*. The properties of the system determine the state of that system. In essence, a property is a value or a set of values[5] within the system describing the state of that system. The four basic properties from which stem all other dynamic and energy properties are the mass, the length, the time, and the temperature. Of these four, the temperature is the only *intensive* property, meaning that it does not depend primarily on the extent of the system. For instance, two systems at the same temperature, when brought together into one, will still have the same temperature. The same reasoning does not apply to two systems with the same mass when brought together; that combined system will have twice the mass. This is because mass is an *extensive* property.

Certain properties are characterized by magnitude alone. For instance, when speaking of volume or temperature, a number of cubic feet or a number of degrees completely characterizes the volume or the temperature. These types of properties are called *scalar* properties. Other properties, such as velocity and acceleration, cannot be completely described by magnitude alone, since the direction of action is as important as the magnitude itself. These properties are called *vector* properties, and they are subject to a different form of algebra called *vector algebra*. In cases when *vector analysis* is not used, the algebra of

[5] The degree of involvement in describing a property will be discussed in Sec. 6.2.

vector quantities is handled in scalar component form. In that case, for three-dimensional problems, a vector is replaced by three scalar quantities, and each scalar equation is treated individually.

1.3 Properties in a Continuum

The general laws of mechanics, together with those of thermodynamics, establish the basic working principles of the mechanics of fluid motion. The meaning attached to most of these properties depends upon systems in which *continuum* exists. For instance, the meaning of *pressure* in a closed vessel is often explained as the total force per unit area imposed on the walls of a tank by the continuous impinging and bouncing off of molecules at the walls. A given mass of gas in a constant volume at a constant temperature is always under the same pressure.[6] This law naturally begins to lose its meaning when the constant-volume container is filled with a very small mass such that only a few molecules are present. If pressure is still defined as the reaction force per unit area on the walls of the tank owing to the bouncing off of molecules, the fewer the molecules, the more the pressure will depend on the probability of molecules bouncing off a particular wall at a particular time. Consequently, the pressure inside the tank will not be *continuous*—constant or smoothly varying—at a given time. At a given time this reaction force per unit area will vary in jumps or in a *discontinuous* fashion along the walls of the tank, depending on whether a molecule has been bounced off at a given point. This same argument holds for very small volumes of a dense gas where only a few molecules are present. How small a volume within a substance is then considered a continuum? Instead of establishing a concrete scale—which could be done for a given substance[7]—a qualitative measure is proposed. *Continuum* is said to exist in a given volume of a substance when the volume contains a large enough number of molecules so that the averaged effects of molecules on the properties

[6] This is true for the thermodynamically so-called "pure substances." In particular, this statement may be verified from Boyle's or Charles's laws pertaining to perfect gases. Boyle's law states that during an isothermal process the ratio of the pressure to the density is a constant. In a similar fashion Charles's law states that during an isobaric (constant-pressure) process the product of the density and the absolute temperature is a constant.

[7] For an estimate of dimensions, see Manfred Rauscher, *Introduction to Aeronautical Dynamics*, John Wiley & Sons, Inc., New York, 1953, pp. 108–111.

within the volume are constant or change smoothly with time and the dimensions of the volume. In essence, the smallest volume to be considered a continuum is one with enough molecules so that the statistical average of the molecular effects, such as pressure, is no longer dependent on the probable state of the molecules. In fact, this smallest volume of substance is referred to as a *point* in the substance having properties varying continuously with time and space. In a continuum the molecule has no significance; the smallest permissible division of the substance is a volume containing a substantial number of molecules.

As an illustration for this concept of continuum, the mass per unit volume—the *density*—in a substance may be examined in connection with the size of the sample volume considered. Consider a very large tank of air at a constant pressure and temperature. From this tank various sizes of samples are removed, and their mass per unit volume is determined.

When the samples have an extremely small volume—say in the neighborhood of 10^{-20} in^3—the sample removed may or may not have air molecules in it, since the molecule count in air at standard conditions is about 4×10^{20}/in^3. Since molecules are in constant agitation throughout the substance, these small-size samples, when removed, may not contain a single molecule, in which case the density within that sample will be zero. Accidentally, the same samples may contain two or more, in which case the density within that sample may be high or low, depending on whether the molecule count is above or below the expected average. These measurements of density in the very-small-volume samples will be extremely erratic. This trend is shown in Fig. 1.1 for sample volumes less than $\mathcal{V}_c$. As the sample volume becomes many times larger than the cube of the distance between molecules, a major number of the molecules will be within the sample; only a few along the boundaries of the sampling volume may or may not be included in the sample at the time of sampling. Since this variation is small compared with the mass already in the sampling volume, the density will be essentially constant for every sampling as the sampling volumes become larger and larger. When the size of the sampling volume becomes extremely large, the lower layers of air in the direction of the gravitational pull will be under higher pressure from the weight of the upper layers, and consequently the density at the bottom of the sampling volume will be larger than at the top. Equal increments of volume in the upper layers will contribute less to the over-all density than do the same increments of volume in the lower layers. If the sampling volume increases in a direction opposite to the gravitational accelera-

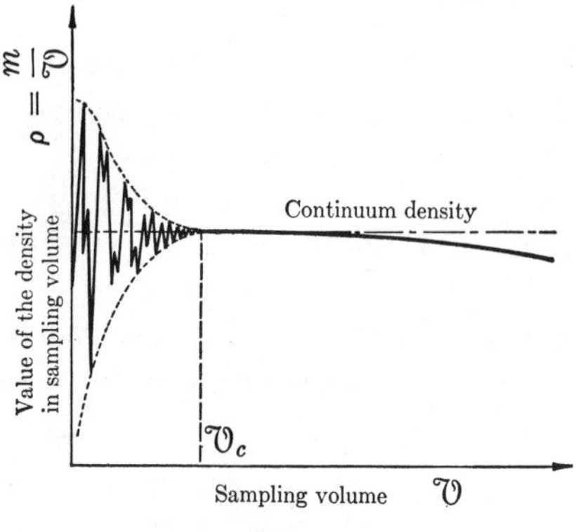

Figure 1.1
Influence of the size of sample on the value of the density.

tion, the over-all density of the sample will decrease, as shown to the right of $\mathcal{V}_c$ in Fig. 1.1. Naturally, the opposite will occur if the sampling volume is increased from a high to a low altitude. According to the foregoing discussions on continuum, the sizes of volumes to the right of $\mathcal{V}_c$ satisfy the requirements discussed.

Molecules inside the substance are in constant agitation and collision with one another. Their average motion between collisions, called the "mean free path," is about 2×10^{-6} in. for the standard air considered in the illustration. This distance becomes larger as density, or the number of molecules per unit volume, is reduced. In the upper altitudes of the atmosphere, this distance between collisions can easily increase to feet or yards because of the rarity of the air. In order for the *motion* of a system to be considered continuous, a second requirement must be established such that the motion is not dependent on the state of agitation of the molecules within the system. This second requirement is similar to the previous one in that a characteristic dimension—such as the dimension of a body around which the over-all motion is to take place—is many times larger than the mean free path of the fluid.

The concept of continuum is an arbitrary concept imposed on substances because of the simplicity of mathematical analysis associated with the concept. It should not be inferred that if continuum did not exist there would not be other methods of analyzing the situation. The essential advantage of the existence of continuum can be seen readily.

To justify continuum let us postulate that the properties at any one point are constant in time and that they vary in a smooth and continuous fashion in a given area of consideration. Therefore, provided that these variations and their derivatives are continuous, a property of the fluid at a given point can be expressed in terms of the property at another neighboring point. This interrelation between properties at two neighboring points in a continuum comes to us from calculus and is generally identified as *Taylor's series expansion.*

This famous theorem states that if a property P and its derivatives are known at a given point x_0, then the same property at a neighboring point x_1 is evaluated from the relation

$$P(x_1) = P(x_0) + (x_1 - x_0)\left(\frac{dP}{dx}\right)_{x_0} + \frac{(x_1 - x_0)^2}{2!}\left(\frac{d^2P}{dx^2}\right)_{x_0} + \cdots$$

The use of total differentiation in the above equation implies that the property P is a function of x alone. If it were a function of other variables as well, then a similar expression could be written for every variable in terms of the partial derivatives with respect to that variable. For a finite variation $(x_1 - x_0)$ the series expansion for $P(x_1)$ is infinite. This means that the accuracy with which $P(x_1)$ can be evaluated from $P(x_0)$ and its derivatives will depend on the number of terms considered in the expansion. Naturally, the smaller the difference $(x_1 - x_0)$, the smaller will be the contribution of the higher-order terms. It is therefore conceivable that if $(x_1 - x_0)$ approaches an infinitesimally small variation dx, second-order and higher terms are made negligible compared with the first two terms on the right-hand side of the equation. This implies, then, that the variation of property is in the form of a straight line in the interval dx. Actually, the milder the variation of P on x, the stronger the justification to neglect higher-order terms. These facts are of great help in the mathematical analysis of any physical phenomenon treated in a continuum.

1.4 Mass and Force

Mass is defined as the quantity of matter or substance. This quantity is a function of the internal structure of the substance and of its dimensions. When a given mass is chosen, its value remains unaffected by external influences such as the geographical location, the temperature, or the pressure. This concept of indestructibility of mass is extremely important when dealing with physical phenomena associated with matter. In the study of mechanics of fluids, this is generally known as the concept of *continuity of mass.*

Mass can be measured comparatively with the balance shown in Fig. 1.2. An equal mass on each platform of the scale will keep the scale balanced everywhere and at all times, provided that external forces other than the gravitational pull of the earth do not affect each platform in a different fashion. The comparative use of this scale depends on a gravitational pull or on the resistance to acceleration of both platforms. If one conceives a space without a gravitational pull or acceleration, a different type of scale can be devised so that it is sensitive to mass. Since the volume of a substance is a function of temperature and pressure, 1 cubic centimeter (cc) of water at 76 centimeters of mercury (cm Hg) pressure and 4°C temperature is defined to represent 1 gram (gm) of mass. At the same pressure and temperature, in the English system, 1 cubic foot (ft^3) of water will represent 1.941 slugs or 62.42 pound-mass (lb_m). The *slug* is a larger unit of mass equivalent to 32.174 lb_m.

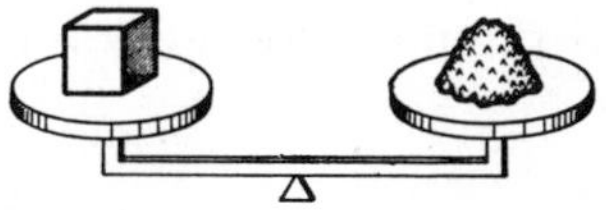

Figure 1.2
Mass-measuring balance.

In 1686, Sir Isaac Newton stated his law of inertia, claiming that *in the absence of external influences a given mass tends to remain at rest or move in a straight line with a uniform velocity.* This law is often considered axiomatic, since its certainty rests upon the fact that it has never been disproved; actually, it rests upon verifications of our physical experiences. This external influence that sets a body in motion or that changes the direction of motion is an action called *force. When a mass m is moved from rest to a given velocity, or when the direction of its velocity $\boldsymbol{U}$ is changed, it can be verified that the force $\boldsymbol{F}$ necessary to perform this change is proportional to the rate of change of momentum $m\boldsymbol{U}$.* This represents Newton's second law of motion

$$\boldsymbol{F} = \frac{d}{dt}(m\boldsymbol{U}) \tag{1.1}$$

For systems, the mass remains constant, and this equation reduces to the more conventional form

$$\boldsymbol{F} = m\frac{d\boldsymbol{U}}{dt} = m\boldsymbol{a} \qquad [1.1(a)]$$

The quantity $\boldsymbol{a}$ represents the acceleration which, like the velocity and the force, is a directed vector quantity. Equation [1.1(a)] for the case of the gravitational acceleration $\boldsymbol{g}$ can also be derived from Newton's gravitational law. This law was formulated from Kepler's planetary observations. It states that the magnitude of the *force* of attraction between two masses m_1 and m_2 is directly proportional to their product and inversely proportional to the square of their distance $\boldsymbol{r}$ apart. If the proportionality constant is C, then

$$\boldsymbol{F} = C\,\frac{m_1 m_2}{r^3}\,\boldsymbol{r}$$

The constant C has been measured in the laboratories and found to be not a function of the substances used. The quantity $\boldsymbol{r}/r$ is the unit vector in the direction of $\boldsymbol{r}$ and $\boldsymbol{F}$. If m_1 is the mass of the earth and $r = R$ the radius of the earth, then the quantity Cm_1/R^2 must represent the gravitational acceleration as seen from the comparison of the gravitational equation and the inertial equation, Eq. [1.1(*a*)]. From Eq. [1.1(*a*)], in the cgs system, a *dyne* is defined as the unit force accelerating 1 gm at 1 cm/sec^2. In the same fashion, in the English system, a *pound-force* ($\mathrm{lb_f}$) is a unit force accelerating 1 slug at 1 ft/sec^2. The *poundal* is a smaller unit of force equivalent to 1/32.174 $\mathrm{lb_f}$ which would accelerate 1 $\mathrm{lb_m}$ at 1 ft/sec^2. The constant C calculated from the gravitational equation is 6.66×10^{-8} dyne $\times$ cm^2/gm^2 in the cgs system or 1.068×10^{-9} poundal $\times$ ft$^2/\mathrm{lb_m^2}$ in the English system. For free-falling bodies which are not affected by the earth's rotation, the gravitational acceleration of free fall $Cm_1/R^2 = 32.225 - 0.026 \cos 2L$. The second term is a correction for the oblateness of the earth where L is the latitude. For a system at the surface of the earth, the rotation of the earth contributes to a component of acceleration in a direction opposite to the gravitational attraction. Its value is maximum at the equator and zero at the geometric poles. If this quantity, which is the product of the earth's angular velocity squared times the latitude radius, is vectorially added to the gravitational free-falling acceleration Cm_1/R^2, the gravitational acceleration with reference to the surface of the earth at sea level is[8]

$$g = 32.174 - 0.085 \cos 2L$$

The symbol L is used again for the latitude. At 45° latitude and sea level $g = g_0 = 32.174$ ft/sec^2. In cgs units this corresponds to 980.66 cm/sec^2.

To illustrate the contribution of the earth's rotation on the gravitational acceleration, the following example is worked out.

[8] These corrections have been taken from William D. McMillan, *Statics and the Dynamics of a Particle*, Dover Publications, Inc., New York, 1958, p. 39.

Illustrative Example 1.1

Determine the radial component of the centrifugal acceleration owing to the earth's rotation. Calculate for 45° latitude and an approximate earth's radius of 4,000 miles.

Since the earth revolves around its axis 1 revolution per day, the angular velocity ω in radians per second is

$$\omega = \frac{2\pi}{24 \times 60 \times 60} = 0.727 \times 10^{-4} \text{ radian/sec}$$

The centrifugal acceleration $a_r = \omega^2 r$ is

$$a_r = \omega^2 R\sqrt{2}/2 = 2a_R/\sqrt{2}$$

Consequently, the radial component of the centrifugal acceleration is

$$a_R = \omega^2 R/2 = \frac{(0.727 + 10^{-4})^2 4{,}000 \times 5{,}280}{2} = 0.0557 \text{ ft/sec}^2$$

which explains the difference between g and Cm_1/R^2.

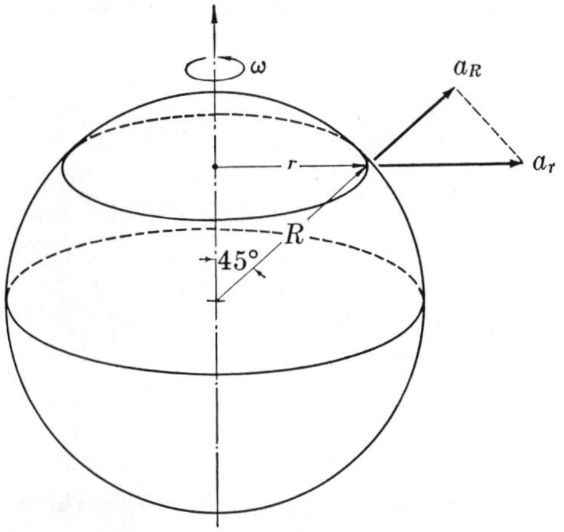

Figure 1.3
Centrifugal acceleration owing to earth's rotation.

1.5 Dimensions in Newton's Law of Inertia

There are four fundamental units in Newton's law of inertia, Eq. [1.1(*a*)]. These are the unit of *force*, the unit of *mass*, and, since the acceleration is the time rate of change of the velocity, it is composed of a unit of *length* and a unit of *time*.[9] Since each one of these units can be expressed in many unitary scales, a controversy often arises as to which scales represent the proper dimensional value.

In engineering practice, three dimensional unit systems have developed in connection with the law of inertia.[10]

(a) The Absolute Dimensional System

In this system the *mass*, the *length*, and the *time* are defined and the unit of force is derived from Eq. [1.1(*a*)]. In the European cgs system these three units will correspond to the *gram*, the *centimeter*, and the *second*. In the English system they will be the *pound-mass*, the *foot*, and the *second*. Consequently, the derived unit of force in the cgs system will be the *dyne*, and in the English system the *poundal*. So when a quantity of pound-mass is accelerated in any number of feet per second squared, then according to Eq. [1.1(*a*)], the resultant product can express a force only in poundals. The same reasoning applies in the cgs system concerning the dyne.

(b) The Technical Dimensional System

The *force*, the *length*, and the *time* are the units defined in this dimensional system. The unit of force is chosen as the *pound-force* (lb_f), the length as the *foot*, and the time as the *second*. The derived unit of mass is the *slug*. So 1 lb_f accelerates 1 slug at a value of 1 ft/sec^2. Comparing these two systems, since a slug is equivalent to 32.174 lb_m, in turn the lb_f is equivalent to 32.174 poundals.

(c) The Engineering Dimensional System

This system adopts all four units of force, mass, length, and time as the *pound-force*, the *pound-mass*, the *foot*, and the *second*. Since the use of these four units in Eq. [1.1(*a*)] will not be compatible with the two previous systems, Eq. [1.1(*a*)] is modified by a constant g_c. This modification makes Newton's inertial law compatible with the other two systems and dimensionally homogeneous.

[9] Scale units of time are generally based on periods of repeating or periodic motions, for instance, the period of vibration of a reed or the period of revolution of the earth around its own axis or around the sun. The second is defined as $(1/365 \times 24 \times 60 \times 60)$th of the earth's revolution around the sun or $(1/24 \times 60 \times 60)$th of the earth's revolution around its own axis. Time can also be measured by nonperiodic phenomena, such as an arbitrary decay level of radioactive substances.

[10] Read E. F. Obert, *Thermodynamics*, McGraw-Hill Book Company, Inc., New York, 1948, Chap. 1.

$$F = \frac{1}{g_c} ma$$

The magnitude of g_c must be 32.174, and the units according to the previous equation must be $\frac{\text{lb}_\text{m} \times \text{ft}}{\text{lb}_\text{f} \times \text{sec}^2}$.

To make Newton's inertial law dimensionally homogeneous in the two previous systems, a similar constant can be introduced appropriately. Its magnitude will be unity in the first two systems. The units of the constant in the absolute system will be $\frac{\text{lb}_\text{m} \times \text{ft}}{\text{poundal} \times \text{sec}^2}$, and those in the technical system will be $\frac{\text{slug} \times \text{ft}}{\text{lb}_\text{f} \times \text{sec}^2}$.

Table 1.1 gives the relationship between the dimensional units of the three basic systems. The inertial law becomes identical to the earth's gravitational law when the acceleration in the inertial law is that due to the free fall caused by the attraction of the earth. The resisting or the reaction force in that case is called the *weight* of a substance. The weight is then expressed in units of force. According to the gravitational law, the weight of a given mass is a function of its distance from the center of the earth. It varies inversely as the square of that distance. Since a force is conveniently measured by the compression or expansion of a coil spring, a scale for measuring weight could be that shown in Fig. 1.4. Weights can also be measured comparatively with the use of the balance shown in Fig. 1.2. This book will use the technical system unless stated otherwise.

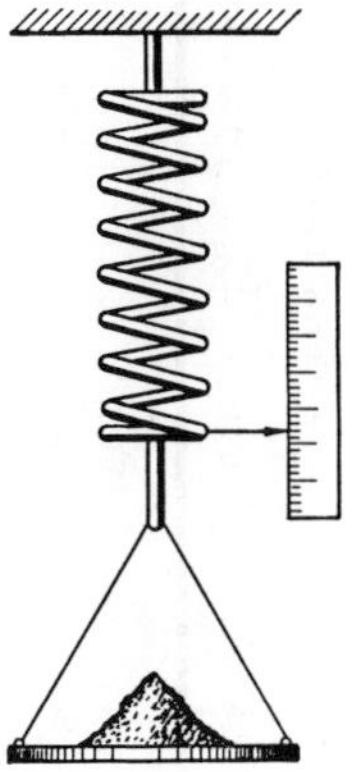

Figure 1.4 Weight-measuring scale.

1.6 Density, Specific Weight, Specific Gravity, and Specific Volume

The *density* is the property of the substance that denotes its mass per unit volume. Consequently, if Newton's inertial law is divided on both sides of the equation by the volume, the weight per unit volume—or the *specific weight*—can be related to the density through the gravitational acceleration. The appropriate units for the density and the spe-

Table 1.1
Dimensional units of the three basic dimensional systems.

DIMENSIONAL SYSTEMS	Defined units	DIMENSIONS OF UNITS: Length	Time	Mass	Force	Constant	Work	Power
Absolute metric	Mass Length Time	cm	sec	gm	$\boxed{\text{dyne}}$ equivalent to $\frac{\text{gm} \times \text{cm}}{\text{sec}^2}$	$F = ma/k$ $k = 1 \frac{\text{gm} \times \text{cm}}{\text{dyne-sec}^2}$	dyne × cm or erg	erg/sec watt = 10^7 ergs/sec
Absolute English	Mass Length Time	ft	sec	lb_m	$\boxed{\text{poundal}}$ equivalent to $\frac{\text{lb}_m \times \text{ft}}{\text{sec}^2}$	$F = ma/k$ $k = 1 \frac{\text{lb}_m \times \text{ft}}{\text{poundal-sec}^2}$	ft × poundal	$\frac{\text{ft} \times \text{poundal}}{\text{sec}}$
Technical English	Force Length Time	ft	sec	$\boxed{\text{slug}}$ equivalent to $\frac{\text{lb}_f \times \text{sec}^2}{\text{ft}}$	lb_f	$F = ma/k$ $k = 1 \frac{\text{slug} \times \text{ft}}{\text{lb}_f \times \text{sec}^2}$	$\text{ft} \times \text{lb}_f$	$\frac{\text{ft} \times \text{lb}_f}{\text{sec}}$
Engineering English	Force Mass Length Time	ft	sec	lb_m	lb_f	$F = ma/g_c$ $\boxed{g_c} = 32.17 \frac{\text{lb}_m \times \text{ft}}{\text{lb}_f \times \text{sec}^2}$	$\text{ft} \times \text{lb}_f$	$\frac{\text{ft} \times \text{lb}_f}{\text{sec}}$

☐ Denotes derived quantities obtained from Newton's inertial law.

cific weight will correspond to those for a unit volume of mass and weight, already discussed in the previous section. The *specific gravity* of a substance is the ratio of its density to that of pure water at 4°C and 76 cm Hg. The *specific volume* is the reciprocal of the density.

Illustrative Example 1.2

Find the relationship between the specific weight in pound-weight per cubic foot and the density in pound-mass per cubic foot.

Since the engineering system uses both units of pound-force and pound-mass, in the case of gravitational acceleration the density–specific-weight relationship is

$$\frac{F}{\mathcal{V}} = \frac{m}{\mathcal{V}}\frac{g}{g_c} = \rho g/g_c$$

where $F/\mathcal{V}$ is the specific weight, ρ the density, and g_c the dimensional constant having the magnitude and units of 32.174 $\text{lb}_\text{m} \times \text{ft}/\text{lb}_\text{f} \times \text{sec}^2$. It is evident from the equation appearing above, that the magnitude of the specific weight will be the same as that of the density only when g is the standard sea-level gravitational acceleration at the latitude of 45°. Although in that particular case the magnitudes are the same, the units should not be confused, since the specific weight has the units of force per unit volume and the density the units of mass per unit volume.

1.7 The Equation of State

The primary scope of fluid mechanics is to apply the general laws of mechanics to fluid substances. During the consideration of such laws, the substance called "fluid" often experiences some thermodynamic changes as well. These thermodynamic changes occur in the fluid system if conversion of fluid energy from one form to another takes place within the system and also if energy in the form of work or heat is exchanged between the system and its surroundings. These thermodynamic changes, in turn, affect the state of the substance and consequently its motion. A basic equation that describes the relationship of thermodynamic properties at all states of the system is called the *equation of state*. Depending on the substance, this equation can be simple or complicated and must be considered together with laws of mechanics if the thermodynamic state of the substance undergoes a change. Fortunately, for most substances having an engineering interest, the equation of state takes a simple mathematical form

$$\rho = f(p, T) \tag{1.2}$$

When the density ρ is a function of two independent[11] properties such as the pressure p and the absolute temperature T, the substance is generally known as *pure*[12] or *simple homogeneous.* In most applications, gases and liquids are in the category of pure substances. The simplicity of Eq. (1.2) stems from the fact that it contains only two independent variables p and T. The functional relationship of the density to these two independent properties may, however, be extremely complicated, as is the case for solids and liquids and during thermodynamic phase changes. In the continuum range of most gases, Eq. (1.2) can be derived from the independent experimental observations of Boyle and Mariotte and those of Charles and Gay-Lussac.

Experimenting with air at ordinary temperatures, Boyle and Mariotte arrived separately at the following conclusion: during any constant-temperature (*isothermal*) process the ratio of the pressure to the density is a constant. The pressure here is considered absolute, and consequently it is measured from perfect vacuum. Boyle's observation implies that when a gas is expanded or compressed, if the temperature of the gas is kept constant by the addition or removal of heat to or from the system, the ratio of the absolute pressure to the density will remain constant throughout an expansion or compression.

Charles's and Gay-Lussac's independent observations were with a constant-pressure (*isobaric*) system. For their case the product of the density and the absolute temperature was constant. As shown in Fig. 1.5, any two points 1 and 3 on the p-ρ diagram can be connected with the two processes mentioned, namely the isothermal process 1–2 and the isobaric process 2–3. According to Boyle's observation, the relation between the properties of points 1 and 2 is

$$\frac{p_1}{\rho_1} = \frac{p_2}{\rho_2} = \frac{p_3}{\rho_2} \quad \text{since} \quad p_2 = p_3$$

Also during the second isobaric process

$$\rho_2 T_2 = \rho_3 T_3 = \rho_2 T_1, \quad \text{since} \quad T_1 = T_2$$

Dividing these two sets of relations, the equation of state for a *perfect gas* is obtained:

$$\frac{p_1}{\rho_1 T_1} = \frac{p_2}{\rho_2 T_2} = \frac{p_3}{\rho_3 T_3} = \text{constant}$$

[11] During a change of phase, the pressure and temperature are generally dependent, and consequently a second independent property such as the entropy can be used.
[12] The word "pure" has nothing to do with the chemical purity of the substance; it characterizes a group of substances with a simple property dependence.

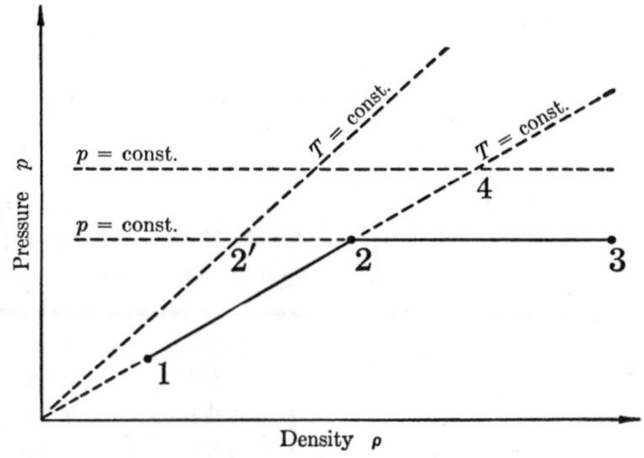

Figure 1.5
Isothermal and isobaric processes on the p-ρ diagram.

If the constant is denoted by R, in the engineering system its units will be $lb_f \times ft/lb_m \times$ °Rankine, and the density will be in lb_m/ft^3. In the technical system the units of R are $lb_f \times ft/slug \times$ °R or $ft^2/sec^2 \times$ °R and the density in $slugs/ft^3$.

$$\rho = p/RT \tag{1.3}$$

This equation is a special case of the pure-substance equation Eq. (1.2) and is generally identified as the *perfect-gas law*. Most common gases used in engineering applications obey to a fair degree of approximation the equation of state of a perfect gas at not too elevated pressures. The law of Boyle-Mariotte is readily satisfied by a large number of gases called permanent gases. The law of Charles and Gay-Lussac is obeyed provided the coefficient of expansion of the gas is a constant and consequently not a function of pressure. Since the end points 1 and 3 on the p-ρ diagram were chosen arbitrarily, then the perfect-gas law can be written for any point (state) such as 2′ and 4 of this pure substance. Consequently, Eq. (1.3) is not a process equation but an equation describing the thermodynamic equilibrium state for all processes of a perfect gas. The process equation is p/ρ^n = constant, where the exponent n determines the type of process.[13] The exponent $n = \gamma = c_p/c_v$ when the process is isentropic.

[13] Consult Sec. 8.2(d) of this text for derivation of this equation for the case of an isentropic process.

Table 1.2
Gas constants and adiabatic coefficients for perfect gases.

Gas	Chemical formula	Gas constants R' $\frac{lb_f \times ft}{lb_m \times °R}$	Gas constants $R = R'g_c$ $ft^2/sec^2 \times °R$ or $\frac{lb_f \times ft}{slug \times °R}$	Adiabatic coefficient* $\gamma = c_p/c_v$
Air		53.36	1,716.59	1.40
Ammonia	NH_3	90.7	2,917.82	1.29
Argon	A	38.73	1,245.94	1.68
Carbon dioxide	CO_2	35.12	1,129.81	1.29
Carbon monoxide	CO	55.19	1,775.46	1.40
Ethane	C_2H_6	51.43	1,654.50	1.19
Helium	He	386.33	12,428.23	1.67
Hydrogen	H_2	766.53	24,659.27	1.41
Methane	CH_4	96.40	3,101.19	1.30
Nitrogen	N_2	55.15	1,774.18	1.40
Octane	C_8H_{18}	13.54	435.58	1.04
Oxygen	O_2	48.29	1,553.49	1.39
Sulfur dioxide	SO_2	24.12	775.94	1.25
Water vapor	H_2O	85.60	2,753.75	1.33

* These values are for standard temperatures. For variations of γ with temperature, for air, consult J. H. Keenan and J. Kaye, *Gas Tables*, John Wiley & Sons, Inc., New York, 1945, Table 2, p. 34.

1.8 Coefficient of Compressibility, Coefficient of Thermal Expansion, and Coefficient of Tension

Since the density is the reciprocal of the specific volume and if a system is considered with a given mass, Eq. (1.3) can be rewritten in terms of the volume instead of the density:

$$p = \phi(\mathcal{V}, T)$$

According to the rules of differentiation, the change of pressure of a system is evaluated in terms of the corresponding changes in temperature and volume of the system.

$$\Delta p = \left(\frac{\partial p}{\partial \mathcal{V}}\right)_T \Delta \mathcal{V} + \left(\frac{\partial p}{\partial T}\right)_{\mathcal{V}} \Delta T \tag{1.4}$$

For changes of pressure approaching zero, $\Delta p \to 0$, this equation becomes

$$\lim_{\substack{\Delta p = 0 \\ \Delta T \to 0}} \left(\frac{\Delta \mathcal{V}}{\Delta T}\right) = -\left(\frac{\partial p}{\partial T}\right)_{\mathcal{V}} \bigg/ \left(\frac{\partial p}{\partial \mathcal{V}}\right)_T = \left(\frac{\partial \mathcal{V}}{\partial T}\right)_p \qquad [1.4(a)]$$

In the limit the left-hand side of the equation is the partial derivative $(\partial \mathcal{V}/\partial T)_p$. In essence, Eq. [1.4($a$)] can be considered as the differential form of the equation of state for a pure substance. The three partial derivatives appearing in this equation have a special physical significance. By definition, the quantity

$$\beta = -\frac{1}{\mathcal{V}}\left(\frac{\partial \mathcal{V}}{\partial p}\right)_T = -\frac{1}{\mathcal{V}}\left(\frac{d\mathcal{V}}{dp}\right)_T$$

is the *coefficient of compressibility* which measures the per cent change of volume per change of pressure when the process is carried at a constant temperature. Since the process is identified as isothermal, it is easy to verify from Eq. (1.4) that the partial derivative can be replaced by the total derivative for that particular process.

In a similar fashion the *coefficient of thermal expansion* is defined as

$$\beta_1 = \frac{1}{\mathcal{V}}\left(\frac{d\mathcal{V}}{dT}\right)_p$$

This coefficient describes the change of volume produced by the change of temperature when the process is isobaric. The volume coefficient of thermal expansion is three times the value of the linear coefficient of thermal expansion, provided the linear coefficient is the same (isotropic) in all three perpendicular directions.

Finally, the third derivative in Eq. [1.4(a)] is the *coefficient of tension*

$$\beta_2 = \frac{1}{p}\left(\frac{dp}{dT}\right)_{\mathcal{V}}$$

If the volume is maintained constant, this coefficient indicates the change of pressure owing to a change of temperature. Substitution of these coefficients into Eq. [1.4(a)] yields

$$p\beta = \frac{\beta_1}{\beta_2} \qquad (1.5)$$

Illustrative Example 1.3

Calculate the three coefficients β, β_1, and β_2 for a perfect gas at standard pressure and temperature.

If the density ρ is substituted for the mass per unit volume $m/\mathcal{V}$, Eq. (1.3) becomes

$$p\mathcal{V} = mRT$$

Since the compressibility coefficient is obtained at constant temperature, for a constant-mass system the differential form of the previous equation is

$$p\,d\mathcal{V} + \mathcal{V}\,dp = 0$$

Consequently,

$$\beta = -\frac{1}{\mathcal{V}}\left(\frac{d\mathcal{V}}{dp}\right)_T = \frac{1}{p}$$

$$= 1/14.7 \text{ sq in./lb}_f$$

The other two coefficients are the same:

$$\beta\mathrm{i} = \beta_2 = \frac{1}{T}$$

$$= 1/(460 + 60)\ {}^\circ\mathrm{R}^{-1}$$

It is easy to verify that Eq. (1.5) is satisfied by these particular values.

1.9 Compressible and Incompressible Fluids

The compressibility coefficient β, described in the previous section, is a measure of the compressibility of a substance. The larger its value, the more compressible is the substance. *Compressibility* actually implies that the volume of a substance is a function of the pressure level. This term is sometimes erroneously identified as the ability of the substance to change shape. Constrained[14] bodies generally change shape under the influence of external forces; nevertheless, the substance of the body may be incompressible if the volume of the substance did not change. Conversely, it can be said that *incompressibility* is the inability to change the volume of a given mass by the action of external pressure. It follows, therefore, that the density of a substance is not a function of pressure if the substance is incompressible.

Liquids are generally considered to be incompressible substances, since their density is very insensitive to changes of pressure. *Hydrodynamics* is the general study of the dynamics of liquids as well as incompressible gases under the influence of very small pressure changes. *Gas dynamics* is the general study of compressible gases under the influence of pressures causing comparatively larger density variations.

Often, as in the case of solids, the *bulk modulus of elasticity* is used

[14] The word "constrained" is used in a sense directly opposite to the word "free" used in mechanics.

as a measure of incompressibility, and therefore it is the reciprocal of the coefficient of compressibility β:

$$E = \frac{1}{\beta} = -\left(\frac{dp}{d\mathcal{V}/\mathcal{V}}\right)_T \tag{1.6}$$

Since for an increase of pressure the volume decreases, the derivative $dp/d\mathcal{V}$ is negative, and consequently the minus sign on the right-hand side of Eq. (1.6) makes the coefficient of compressibility and the modulus of elasticity positive.

In general, the coefficient of compressibility is a function of pressure and temperature. In Illustrative Example 1.3 it was found that it is a function of pressure alone for a perfect gas. In fact, the coefficient of compressibility is the inverse of the absolute pressure, and consequently the bulk modulus of elasticity is the pressure itself when the compression or expansion process is isothermal. Table 1.5 shows that at ordinary pressures and temperatures, water has a modulus of elasticity $E =$ 300,000 pounds per square inch (psi). This is, indeed, a very large number compared with that of perfect gases, which is just the atmospheric pressure for an isothermal compression.

Eq. (1.6) is made more general when the coefficient of compressibility and the modulus of elasticity are defined for all processes rather than the isothermal process alone. The relationship will be simply

$$E = \frac{1}{\beta} = -\frac{dp}{d\mathcal{V}/\mathcal{V}}$$

This generality implies that the values derived from the equation will depend on the type of processes as well. As an example, if a perfect gas is considered again, and if the compression or expansion process is polytropic, then, according to Sec. 1.7, the process equation is

$$p\mathcal{V}^n = \text{constant}$$

and, after differentiating this equation, the bulk modulus of elasticity for a polytropic process is

$$E = -\frac{dp}{d\mathcal{V}/\mathcal{V}} = np$$

This result is in accordance with that in Illustrative Example 1.3, since $n = 1$ for an isothermal process.

Illustrative Example 1.4

Find the increase of pressure necessary to produce a 1 per cent reduction in the volume of water at ordinary pressure and temperature. Compare the findings with those of air undergoing an isentropic compression.

For water at about 45°F, the value of E is 300,000 psi (Table 1.5). Then, for a finite pressure rise,

$$\Delta p = -E(\Delta \mathcal{V}/\mathcal{V}) = -300{,}000(-0.01)$$
$$= 3{,}000 \text{ psi}$$

Since air can be considered a perfect gas, for an isentropic process the modulus of elasticity is $kp = 1.4 \times 14.7$ psi. Then again, the finite pressure rise is

$$\Delta p = -1.4 \times 14.7(-0.01)$$
$$= 0.206 \text{ psi}$$

1.10 Viscosity and Shearing Stress

At the beginning of this chapter, the *viscosity* was considered as a characteristic property distinguishing a fluid from a solid. The influence of viscosity in fluids demonstrates itself only when the fluid is undergoing a frictional or shearing motion. Since the fluid must be in motion for the viscosity to play a role, it is meaningless to consider viscosity in fluids at rest. It will be shown in this discussion that it is also meaningless to consider viscosity as an influential property when the motion of fluids is such that there is no relative motion between layers of fluid.

Viscosity is often identified with the stickiness or sometimes the "thick" appearance of liquids. Although these two descriptive concepts do, in general, indicate a measure of relative viscosity of liquids, they are not completely adequate in fully describing viscosity for all fluids. In accordance with the discussion of fluids and solids presented in Sec. 1.1, *the viscosity must be defined as the property of a fluid to resist the rate at which deformation takes place when the fluid is acted upon by tangential shear forces.* According to Newton's law of viscosity, for a given shear stress acting on a fluid element, the rate at which the fluid deforms is inversely proportional to the value of the viscosity. This implies that, when keeping the shear stress constant, the rate at which deformation takes place is larger for fluids having small values of viscosity. For a solid, the resistance to *deformation* is the modulus of elasticity, and for a fluid, the resistance to the rate of deformation is the viscosity. It was discussed in Secs. 1.8 and 1.9 that a fluid can sustain, like a solid, a deformation under a normal compressive load. In essence, the coefficient of compressibility was a measure of the deformation for a given compressive load. Unlike the solid, a fluid cannot sustain a

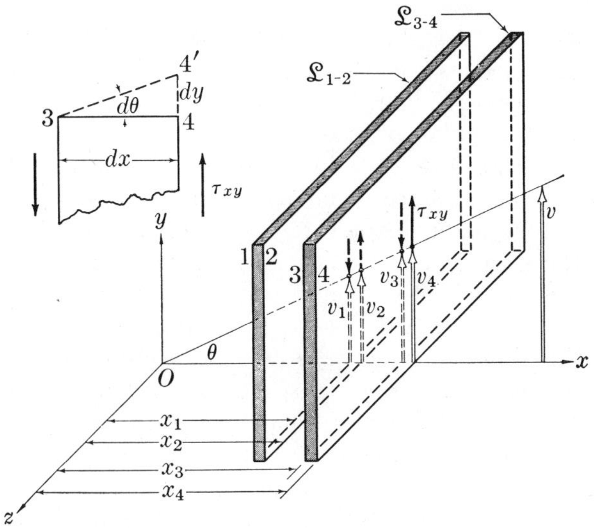

Figure 1.6
Representation of a shearing motion.

finite deformation under a tangential shear stress. The fluid will deform continuously, and for a constant shear stress the rate of deformation of a fluid system will be constant, provided that the viscosity remains constant. For ordinary fluid motions the viscosity is not a function of pressure but depends on temperature. Owing to the difference in molecular structure between a gas and a liquid, the viscosity of a gas increases with temperature and that of a liquid decreases with temperature. Tables 1.4 and 1.5 show variations of viscosity for air and water at various temperatures.

In order to help visualize the nature of viscosity and shearing stress, the following example will be considered. Figure 1.6 represents a right-handed Cartesian-coordinate system with its origin at O through which a fluid is considered in motion. For simplicity, let it be assumed that the resultant velocity of the fluid is in the y-direction and that its magnitude varies lineally with x alone. In general, the velocity field may have components in all three directions.[15] Consider two thin layers $\mathfrak{L}_{1\text{-}2}$ and $\mathfrak{L}_{3\text{-}4}$ of this viscous fluid moving in the y-direction at speeds v varying along the coordinate x. Since the fluid is viscous, a friction or shear stress will develop at the interface of fluid layers owing

[15] This problem will be generalized in Chap. IX.

to the relative velocity $(v_3 - v_2)$ of one interface with respect to the other. The frictional stress τ_{xy} is such that the high-velocity face 3 will try to accelerate the low-velocity face 2, and the low-velocity face, in turn, will exert a retarding action on the high-velocity face 3. The conventional direction of τ_{xy} in Fig. 1.6 is in agreement with this explanation. Each layer $\mathfrak{L}$ will be acted upon by shear stresses having opposite directions at corresponding parallel faces. As in solid mechanics, the subscript on the shear stress τ indicates an orientation.[16] The first subscript x indicates that the stress is on a plane perpendicular to x. The second subscript y indicates that the stress is in a direction parallel to y. According to this representation, it is possible to establish five other shear stresses acting on the three perpendicular planes $x = c$; $y = c$; $z = c$. The first $x = c$ plane will be acted on by the two shear stresses τ_{xy} and τ_{xz}. The second plane $y = c$ will contain τ_{yx} and τ_{yz}; finally, the third plane $z = c$ will contain τ_{zx} and τ_{zy}.

Referring to Fig. 1.6, under the action of the shear stress τ_{xy} an originally rectangular fluid layer $\mathfrak{L}_{3\text{-}4}$ will eventually suffer an angular deformation $d\theta = \tan d\theta = \dfrac{dy}{dx}$. This relationship will be true, provided that small deformations are considered in a unit of time. Now, according to Newton's law of viscosity enunciated in Sec. 1.1, the shear stress τ_{xy} must be proportional to the time rate of change of the angular deformation, and the proportionality constant is the *absolute viscosity* μ_f.

$$\tau_{xy} = \mu_f \frac{d}{dt}\left(\frac{dy}{dx}\right)$$

and, if the order of differentiation is interchanged,

$$\tau_{xy} = \mu_f \frac{d}{dx}\left(\frac{dy}{dt}\right)$$

Since $dy/dt = v$, the shear stress for the problem in Fig. 1.6 is

$$\tau_{xy} = \mu_f \frac{dv}{dx} \tag{1.7}$$

This equation can be derived also by considering velocities on the surfaces of the layer $\mathfrak{L}_{3\text{-}4}$ (Fig. 1.7). As was mentioned, the shear stress is

$$\tau_{xy} = \mu_f \frac{d\theta}{dt} \qquad [1.7(a)]$$

[16] For a more precise concept consult Sec. 9.4.

The element shown deforms continuously, but, in a small deformation time dt, the quantity $d\theta = dv\,dt/dx$, and its substitution in the equation above yields the same result as Eq. (1.7).

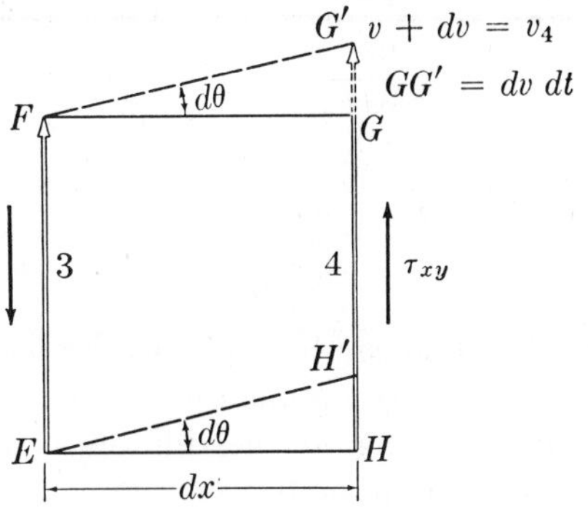

Figure 1.7
Deformation of a fluid layer under the action of shear stresses.

This equation, derived from Newton's empirical reasoning, constitutes the basis for viscous-flow theory. An analysis of this equation reveals that the units of the absolute viscosity as shown are those of $(\tau x/v)$ or $lb_f \times sec/ft^2$. The subscript f under the coefficient of viscosity refers to the fact that the units are being expressed in terms of force. A similar coefficient in terms of mass can be obtained by a multiplication with g_c. The result will be $\mu_m = \mu_f g_c$. The units of μ_m are $lb_m/ft \times sec$. In the cgs system the absolute viscosity is expressed in dynes $\times$ sec/cm^2 or gm/sec $\times$ cm and both are equivalent to a third unit called a *poise*.[17] A unit 1/100 the size of a poise is called a *centipoise*. In kinematics and dynamics of fluids, the viscosity appears divided by the density. This ratio is called the *kinematic viscosity* $\nu = \mu_m/\rho$ and therefore has the units of ft^2/sec. In the cgs system the appropriate units for the kinematic viscosity are cm^2/sec, and this is sometimes referred to as a *stoke*.[18] A smaller unit called the *centistoke* is 1/100 of a stoke.

[17] After the name of J. L. M. Poiseuille, a French experimenter whose work in the years 1840–1845 has been very important in the development of the theory of viscous fluids.
[18] After G. G. Stokes, a British mathematician and scientist who, in the years 1840–1850, contributed a great deal to the theory of viscous fluids.

Table 1.3
Units of Viscosity

	μ_f	$\mu_m = \mu_f g_c$	$\nu = \mu_m/\rho$
English System	$\frac{lb_f \times sec}{ft^2}$	$\frac{lb_m}{ft \times sec}$	$\frac{ft^2}{sec}$
CGS System	$\frac{dyne \times sec}{cm^2}$ = poise	$\frac{gm}{cm \times sec}$	$\frac{cm^2}{sec}$ = stoke

The influence of viscosity in a moving fluid can be explained by the kinetic theory of molecules. It is the process of momentum exchange between the molecules in adjacent layers owing to the difference of velocity between the layers. Since the agitation, or the average velocity, of the molecules is a function of the temperature, as already stated, the viscosity is a function of the temperature.

Table 1.4
Physical properties of air.

Temperature (°F)	Density* lb_m/ft^3 (ρ)	Viscosity† $\frac{lb_f \times sec}{ft^2}$ (μ_f)	Kinematic viscosity ft^2/sec (ν)
32	0.0806	3.60×10^{-7}	1.39×10^{-4}
50	0.0785	3.70	1.47
100	0.0710	3.98	1.75
150	0.0652	4.25	2.09
200	0.0604	4.50	2.40

* At standard pressure.
† Viscosities computed from Sutherland's relation.

The temperature dependence of the absolute viscosity μ_f can be obtained from Sutherland's relation, which fits most gases for a wide range of temperatures. This relationship is given by

$$\mu_f = a \frac{\sqrt{T}}{1 + b/T}$$

Table 1.5
Physical properties of water.

Temperature (°F)	Density lb_m/ft^3 (ρ)	Viscosity $\frac{lb_f \times sec}{ft^2}$ (μ_f)	Kinematic viscosity ft^2/sec (ν)	Surface tension coefficient lb_f/ft (σ)	Bulk modulus of elasticity lb_f/in^2 (E)
32	62.4	3.75×10^{-5}	$1.93 + 10^{-5}$	0.0052	29×10^4
50	62.4	2.74	1.41	0.0051	31
100	62.0	1.42	0.74	0.0048	33
150	61.2	0.91	0.48	0.0045	33
200	60.1	0.64	0.34	0.0041	31

The quantity T is the absolute temperature in degrees Rankine, and a and b are constants that depend on the gas as shown.[19]

Gas	a	b
Air	2.22×10^{-8}	180
Carbon dioxide	2.42	420
Carbon monoxide	2.18	196
Helium	2.36	176
Hydrogen	1.01	127
Methane	1.53	279
Nitrogen	2.16	184

To show the opposite behavior of the kinematic viscosity with temperature for a gas such as air and a liquid such as water, the values of the viscosity are plotted in Fig. 1.8 from Tables 1.4 and 1.5. At ordinary temperatures a comparison of absolute viscosities shows that the viscosity of water is about 50 times that of air. With reference to that of water, castor oil's viscosity is 1,000 times greater, that of crude oil 10 times greater, and that of gasoline about 3 times smaller.

Finally, a property of real fluids is that it assumes the velocity of a solid boundary right at the boundary when the direction of the flow is completely guided by the boundary. For instance, if fluid flows

[19] Newman A. Hall, *Thermodynamics of Fluid Flow*, Prentice-Hall, Inc., Englewood Cliffs, N.J., 1956, pp. 20–23, gives a more detailed description of Sutherland constants at various pressures and temperatures for a larger number of gases.

through a straight pipe, the relative velocity of the fluid with respect to the pipe at the pipe wall is zero. As in the following illustration, it is not necessary for the solid boundary to be straight; the only condition is that the flow does not separate from the boundary. From here on, the symbol μ will be used to represent the absolute viscosity in the technical system whose units will be $lb_f \times sec/ft^2$.

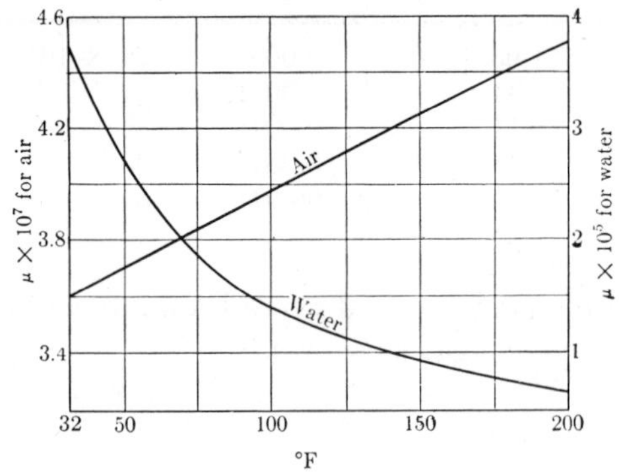

Figure 1.8
Typical temperature dependence of the viscosity for a gas and a liquid.

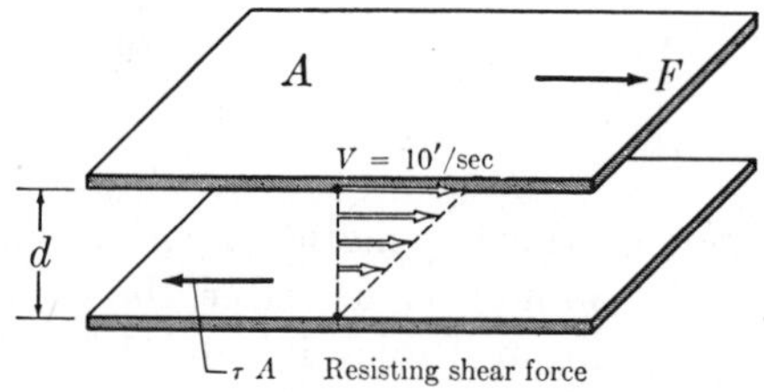

Figure 1.9
Shear motion between two plates moving relative to each other.

Illustrative Example 1.5
If the space between two plates, as shown in Fig. 1.9, is lubricated with water, find the shear stress at the plates and the power necessary to move the upper plate at a constant velocity $V = 10$ ft/sec relative to the lower plate.

Consider the lower plate to be fixed and the upper plate moving. Assume the lubricating film to be 0.025 in. deep and, for this small distance, the velocity of the fluid between the plates to be linearly increasing from a value of zero at the lower plate to 10 ft/sec at the upper plate. According to the description in Fig. 1.6 and Eq. (1.7), the shear stress at every layer of the lubricating film at 50°F is

$$\tau = \mu \frac{dV}{dx} = \mu \frac{V}{d} = \frac{2.74 \times 10^{-5} \times 10 \times 12}{0.025}$$

$$= 0.131 \text{ lb}_f/\text{ft}^2$$

Since the upper plate moves at a constant velocity, the force F necessary to move the upper plate must be balanced by an equal and opposite force contributed by the fluid friction at the plate surface. This force will be

$$F = 0.131A \text{ lb}_f$$

The work required per unit time is

$$FV = \mu \frac{V^2 A}{d} = 1.31A \text{ lb}_f \times \text{ft/sec}$$

Correspondingly, the power per unit volume of fluid will be

$$\frac{FV}{Ad} = \mu \left(\frac{V}{d}\right)^2 = 630 \frac{\text{lb}_f \times \text{ft}}{\text{sec} \times \text{ft}^3}$$

This energy will be dissipated into heat raising the temperature of the water and the plates.

In this section the linear relationship between the shearing stress and the rate of deformation of a fluid system was emphasized. This linear relationship, proposed by Newton, holds for most viscous fluids used in engineering applications. Fluids demonstrating this linear relationship are called *Newtonian fluids.* There are some fluids, such as molasses, molten rubber, cake mixes, printer's ink, blood, etc., that do not obey this simple linear relationship of the shear stress and the rate of deformation. Such fluids have relatively smaller application in general fluid mechanics and consequently are part of the study of a special field called *rheology*.

For measurement of viscosity of Newtonian fluids, an apparatus such as that shown in Illustrative Example 1.5 or the one shown in Fig. 1.10, based on the same principle, is used. The latter is made of two concentric cylinders with the inner cylinder rotating with an electric motor at a constant speed. The fluid is placed between the concentric cylinders, and the torque on the rotating cylinder is measured from the power input: power = torque × radians per unit time. For a narrow gap between cylinders, the velocity distribution of the fluid in the gap approaches a linear relation. The viscosity of the fluid can then be computed from Newton's viscosity law. The theory for the viscometer just discussed will be treated in Chap. X. A third and useful method of measuring viscosity from capillary viscous motion also will be discussed.

1.11 Frictionless Motion

By definition, *frictionless motion* implies that frictional or shear stresses are not present in the motion of a substance. According to Eq. (1.7), for a fluid in motion this condition is achieved when the viscosity of the fluid is zero or when the velocity components of the fluid motion do not exhibit any magnitude variations in the directions perpendicular to that velocity component. In other words, a frictionless motion is present when the fluid is *inviscid* ($\mu = 0$) or when its relative deformation between layers does not change with time, as in the case of statics or uniform motion. Of these two conditions that permit frictionless motion, the inviscid condition is the most ideal. This is because nature does not provide us with fluids that are truly inviscid. The second condition of velocity gradients of zero value in directions perpendicular to the velocity can be easily achieved for the examples already cited, but they are very limited and comparatively unimportant as far as general fluid motions are concerned. The absence of shear stresses in the motion of a fluid considerably simplifies the mathematical treatment of that motion. It is for this reason, and also because some qualitative information can be derived from this simple treatment concerning real viscous motions, that the theory on frictionless motion is noteworthy.

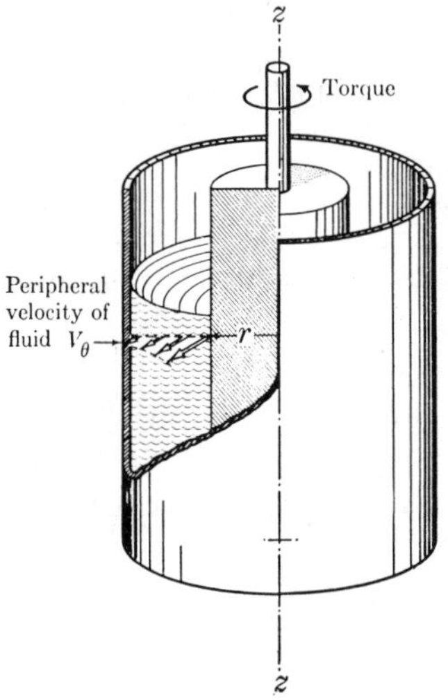

Figure 1.10
Viscometer.

1.12 Perfect Fluid

By definition, a *perfect fluid* is one that is inviscid[20] and whose density is a constant. Although such a fluid is ideal and therefore cannot be found in nature, under certain conditions it gives valuable information about a real viscous fluid.

A perfect fluid indicates an absence of shear stresses between the fluid layers. It follows, therefore, that two adjacent layers of an ideal fluid can move at two different velocities (slip flow) without affecting each other by internal frictional forces. The only influence they exert on each other is through their geometry, which must conform with the geometry of the solid boundaries. With perfect fluids a slip condition exists between the fluid and the solid boundaries; the sole purpose of the boundary is to guide the flow without any viscous (frictional) interference. Consequently, in the absence of viscosity, any layer of a perfect fluid can be removed from the flow and replaced by a solid boundary of the same geometrical shape as the removed layer. This change will not alter the remaining flow pattern. It may, therefore, be concluded that shear stresses are the properties that communicate dynamic information from one layer to another. In the absence of these stresses this communication is completely missing. The study of perfect fluids will be important when applied to flow regions where the viscous forces are negligible compared with the inertial forces. Chapter VIII deals with the study of perfect fluids.

1.13 Real Fluids

The presence of viscosity is unavoidable when dealing with *real fluids*. Unlike perfect fluids, *real fluids* cannot slip with a finite velocity difference over adjacent layers or over solid boundaries. The amount of viscosity that governs the stickiness of fluid layers will be responsible for making gradual the velocity variation across the layers. Near a stationary boundary the velocity of a real fluid must gradually increase from zero at the boundary to a finite stream velocity in a finite fluid

[20] It is more appropriate to define a perfect fluid as an irrotational and constant density fluid. Since rotation of fluids is a concept not defined until Sec. 3.14, and since an inviscid fluid originally irrotational remains irrotational, the inviscid condition has been used here.

layer generally known as *Prandtl's*[21] *boundary layer*. Unlike perfect fluids, a fluid layer cannot be replaced by a layer of a different fluid or by a solid boundary with the same geometry with the expectation that conditions will remain the same. The effects of the change will be felt readily, since the replaced layer will impose new dynamic conditions (shear stress) at the new interface. In the neighborhood of solid boundaries—in the boundary layer itself—the velocity variations across the layer are large, and therefore the viscous effects are large compared with those in the free stream. The treatment of the boundary layer near the solid boundary as a viscous fluid and the flow outside the boundary layer as a frictionless fluid was one of Prandtl's important contributions. Frequently, in the absence of solid boundaries, the flow may be considered ideal, but this type of flow alone has hardly any engineering applications.

Figure 1.11 demonstrates the influence of viscosity near the solid boundaries of blunt and thin bodies at low and high speeds. The solid lines around the solid bodies represent the trajectory of fluid elements as they proceed downstream, if the fluid is inviscid. In the case of the cylinder, since the solid boundary is symmetrical with respect to the y-plane, the flow is also symmetrical for the inviscid case. The dotted lines represent the modified flow field owing to shear stresses induced by the presence of viscosity. In the real case the influence of the viscosity starts at the leading edge of the solid body and increases in a downstream direction. This fact brings the unsymmetry about the y-plane, since the viscosity influence is cumulative in the downstream direction. One fact is apparent from these figures—that the flow field upstream of the solid body for the viscous case is very nearly the same as for that of the inviscid case. The effects of viscosity are more apparent at the rear of the bodies. The viscosity effects caused by the solid boundary of the thin body show a narrower extent of influence than is found around the blunt body. From this, one may conclude that the thin-body surface creates less of a departure from perfect fluid motion than does the corresponding surface of a blunt body.

The extent of the viscosity influence in the y-direction is also related to the speed of the fluid relative to the solid body. As an analogy, the viscosity influence spreads around the body in the same manner as heat would, if the body were hotter than the fluid. The slower the velocity of the body relative to the fluid, the larger the extent of this so-called "contamination" from heat into the fluid. As shown in Fig.

[21] Professor L. Prandtl, a scientist and teacher with highest principles, whose illuminating work from himself and from his students at Göttingen forms the framework of today's modern principles of hydro- and aeromechanics.

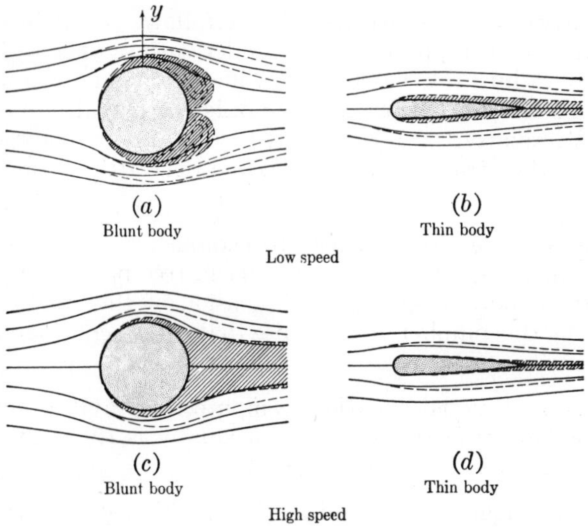

Figure 1.11
Influence of viscosity on real fluids past different solid bodies at different speeds.

1.11, at higher speeds, viscous-layer effects of viscosity become narrower in the y-direction.

The viscous region behind the bodies, blunt or thin, extends very far downstream and is called the *wake*. In this wake the effects of viscosity decrease in intensity but increase in area as the fluid proceeds downstream from the body.

The drag forces affecting bodies such as cylinders and spheres when submerged in a moving fluid will be discussed in Sec. 9.12. The influence of the speed and viscosity of the fluid and the size of the object on the drag will be analyzed.

Problems

1.1 Verify that both relations $y = Ax + B$ and $y = Ax^2 + B$ satisfy Taylor's expansion when expanding from $x = 0$ to a neighboring x value. From the value of y and its derivatives evaluated at $x = 1$ for the two relations given, reconstruct the relations at any neighboring point x by substitution into the Taylor series.

1.2 Consider a property p varying with distance x as follows: $p = x^2 + 1$. Evaluate first the value of the property and its derivatives at $x = 1$. Substituting these values into the Taylor series, find the value of p at a neighborhood point $x = 1.1$. Determine the order of magnitude of the error if the second derivative term is neglected. If p is now required at $x = 1.01$, determine the error again if the second derivative term is neglected.

1.3 If 1,000 molecules of air are sufficient to establish a reasonable statistical average of any property, and if the "mean free path" of air is 2×10^{-6} in., what is the average linear dimension of the smallest cubic volume containing this number of molecules that can be considered a continuum?

1.4 From Newton's gravitational equation, compute the gravitational acceleration Cm/R^2 if the earth's diameter at the equator is 7,926 miles and the mean specific gravity of the earth is 5.52.

1.5 Compute the centrifugal acceleration at the earth's equator and determine from Prob. 1.4 the total acceleration at the equator.

1.6 If the polar diameter is $(1 - \frac{1}{297})$ that of the equatorial diameter of the earth, find the gravitational acceleration at the poles owing to a free fall. Use the data given in Prob. 1.4.

1.7 Assuming the earth's diameter to be a constant and equal to 7,926 miles, determine the variation with latitude of the radial acceleration owing to the earth's rotation.

1.8 If a dimensional system were devised so that the force, the mass, and the length were defined as 1 lb_f, 1 lb_m, and 1 ft, and if the derived time unit were called the "era," find the relationship between an era and a second. Do not contradict the accepted definitions.

1.9 A spaceship is to leave the earth, taking with it 50,000 lb_f of fuel weighed before take-off. The destination of the ship is a planet with a gravitational acceleration one half that of the earth. If the same mass of fuel is consumed for the trip to the planet and for the way back, what weight of fuel should the pilot have, when he lands on the other planet, in order to make sure that he has enough for returning to earth?

1.10 If a system has a volume $\mathcal{V}$ and a density ρ and is moving at a uniform velocity U, establish the kinetic energy of the system in the cgs system of units and the three English unit systems discussed.

1.11 Compute the attraction of the moon on a unit mass at the surface of the earth. The mean distance between the center of the earth and that of the moon is 238,857 miles. The diameter of the moon is 2,160 miles; that of the earth is 7,926 miles. The specific gravity of the moon is 3.34.

1.12 At the same pressure and temperature, compare the weight in 1 ft^3 of oxygen and methane.

1.13 Evaluate the density of dry air at 68°F and 14.7 psia in the engineering English system. Find its specific weight at 45° latitude in the same dimensional system.

1.14 At 68°F and 1/8 atmosphere (atm) the coefficient of thermal expansion for nitrogen is 0.0037. The coefficient of tension at the same condition is also 0.0037. Compute the coefficient of compressibility.

1.15 Compare the compressibility coefficient and the modulus of elasticity of argon, helium, and hydrogen at standard pressure. The compression in all three cases is adiabatic.

1.16 A concrete bin 1,000 ft^3 in volume is full of water at atmospheric pressure. Find the weight of the water at standard temperature. Compare the weight of water at 1,000 psi and also at 2,000 psi.

1.17 By increasing the pressure of a liquid from 1,000 psi to 2,000 psi, the volume of a liquid decreases by 1 per cent. What is the bulk modulus of the liquid?

1.18 If the original volume of Prob. 1.17 was 1 ft^3, find the work necessary for the compression. If the tank is to be filled completely at 2,000 psi pressure, calculate the additional work necessary to fill the 1 per cent gap with liquid taken from another tank at 1,000 psi.

1.19 Derive a relation similar to Eq. (1.6) in terms of the pressure and density ρ.

1.20 Establish the equivalence in absolute viscosity between 1 $lb_f \times sec/ft^2$ and 1 poise. Similarly, for the kinematic viscosity, find the equivalence between the English units and the stoke.

1.21 The absolute viscosity of mercury is 1.7 centipoises and the specific gravity is 13.6 at standard pressure and temperature. Find the kinematic viscosity in the English system.

1.22 Compute the density, absolute viscosity, and kinematic viscosity of helium at 5 atm and 60°F.

1.23 The bearing on an engine is 10 in. in diameter and 12 in. long. Ignoring the eccentricity of the shaft, the clearance between the bearing and the journal is 0.020 in. The lubricating oil at the temperature of the bearing has an absolute viscosity of 7.5×10^{-4} $lb_f \times sec/ft^2$. Assume that the velocity of the lubricating oil varies linearly with radius in the small gap. If the machine rotates at 3,600 rpm, find the drag on the journal and the horsepower dissipated into it at the bearing. (Neglect curvature of flow.)

1.24 What is the rate of angular deformation in the previous problem?

1.25 Consider the two plates in Illustrative Example 1.5. The distance between the plates is maintained 0.025 in., and castor oil is used for lubrication. The absolute viscosity of the oil is 2.06×10^{-2} $lb_f \times sec/ft^2$. The upper plate moves 10 ft/sec to the right and the lower plate moves 10 ft/sec to the left. (*a*) Find the rate of angular deformation. (*b*) Find the shear stress on both plates if the velocity varies linearly from one plate to the other.

1.26 At about 60°F, mercury has the same absolute viscosity as water. Find their corresponding kinematic viscosities.

1.27 Compute the density, the absolute viscosity, and the kinematic viscosity of carbon dioxide at 600°F.

1.28 A house 40 ft long, 25 ft wide, and 10 ft high is to be painted with a paint for which $\mu_f = 3 \times 10^{-3}$ $lb_f \times sec/ft^2$. For one coat of paint 0.020 in. thick applied with a 5-in. brush and an inch-thick bristle, the painter keeps the speed of painting at 2 ft/sec. Find (*a*) the opposing force on the motion of the brush; (*b*) the total work necessary to complete the painting; (*c*) the power necessary for painting under the prescribed conditions. Assume here that the paint is thin enough so that it can be considered a Newtonian fluid, and that, since the paint layer is small, the velocity of the paint in the layer vanishes at the wall in a linear fashion. Also assume that there are no doors or windows.

1.29 If the meniscus of a fluid in a vertical tube is semispherical in shape, express the total surface-tension force in terms of σ and the diameter d. Discuss the direction of the surface-tension force when the meniscus is concave or convex. What weight of fluid in the tube can this force support? Express the height of the capillary column in terms of σ, d, and the specific weight.

1.30 A capillary tube is bent over the edge of a beaker half filled with a fluid, as shown in the figure. (*a*) Discuss whether the fluid could go over the edge of the beaker owing to the surface tension on the capillary column. (*b*) With any free choice of fluid, capillary-tube diameter, and level of fluid in the beaker, can the fluid drip out of the tube?

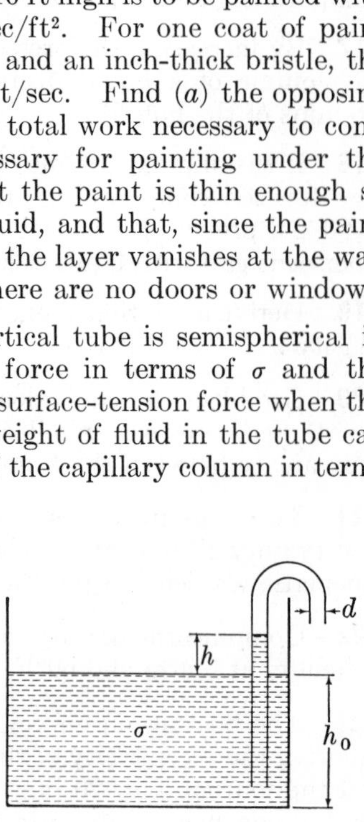

Statics of Fluids

chapter II

2.1 Static Equilibrium

The word *static* is derived from the Greek word *statikos*, meaning causing to stand still. The Latin word *equilibrium* implies a state of balance among the forces acting on a system. Therefore, when this state of balance is applied to a system that is at rest with respect to a suitable system of reference, the system is then considered to be in *static equilibrium*. The relativity to a system of reference is of importance, since every physical system considered in this universe has some absolute motion.

Since fluid elements in motion or at rest are subjected to forces, as a refresher it will be worth while to enunciate Newton's equilibrium laws in general mechanics.

First Law: A fluid element on which no external resultant forces are acting has zero acceleration.

Second Law: If a force is applied to a fluid element, it experiences an acceleration in the direction of the force. In the absence of friction, the magnitude of the force *applied* is proportional to the mass and the magnitude of the acceleration. In the presence of friction opposing the motion, it is the *resultant* force that is proportional to the mass and the corresponding acceleration.

Third Law: Action equals reaction. For every force acting from the surroundings onto a system, there is a reaction from the system to the surroundings equal in magnitude and opposite in direction. Consequently, the forces acting on two adjacent faces of two neighboring systems are equal in magnitude and opposite in direction.

In static equilibrium, in addition, the sum of the moments of these forces about an arbitrary axis must be zero.

It was emphasized in the previous chapter that a fluid element has no resistance to change of shape produced by tangential forces. Consequently, for static equilibrium, since tangential forces must be zero, all resultant forces are normal to the surface of the fluid system considered. Finally, by the nature of equilibrium or balance of forces, since the sum of the external forces is zero, the sum of all internal forces between the elements of the system must also be zero.

2.2 Types of Forces on Fluid Systems

The types of forces acting on fluid systems are generally classified into three essential categories, according to the geometry on which they act.

The *body force* or the *volume force* is a force that acts upon a system because of the mass extent of the system. This force is proportional to the mass of the system. For example, the weight of a system is a body force acting on the mass center of the system in the direction of the gravitational pull. Electric and magnetic potential forces also fall in this classification.

The *surface force* acts on the extent of the surface of a system and consequently is proportional to the extent of that surface. For instance, the shear forces, discussed in the previous chapter, act in a direction tangential to the surface, and their magnitude depends on the extent of the surface area of the system. Since all surface forces can be resolved into tangential and normal components, the normal surface force per unit area is called the *pressure*.

A third classification of force is that discussed at the end of the previous chapter. The surface-tension force can be called a *line force*, since its magnitude depends on the extent of the line perpendicular to which it acts.

2.3 Concept of Pressure in Fluids in Equilibrium

In the absence of motion, the normal force per unit area is called the *pressure*. Let Fig. 2.1 represent a fluid system in static equilibrium whose depth AA' is unity. Consequently, the external forces on this system must be perpendicular to the surface of the system, and the body force or the weight must balance the resultant of these surface forces. Let p_a, p_b, and p_c represent the external pressures on the faces of the prism opposite the edges AA', BB', and CC'. The smaller the size of the system, the more likely it will be that these pressures will be uniform over the surfaces on which they act. Since the limiting case will be considered shortly, these pressures can be considered uniform over their respective surfaces.

If $\boldsymbol{n}$ is the outward unit normal on each of the faces in the elementary fluid system in Fig. 2.1, for equilibrium the vector summation[1] of all forces must be zero.

$$-\boldsymbol{n}_a p_a c - \boldsymbol{n}_b p_b b - \boldsymbol{n}_c p_c a + \rho \mathcal{V} \boldsymbol{g} = 0$$

Here $\mathcal{V}$ is the volume of the element equal in this case to $hb/2$, $\boldsymbol{g}$ is the gravitational acceleration or the body force per unit mass and ρ is the density of the fluid. By the scalar product of this equation with $\boldsymbol{n}_b$

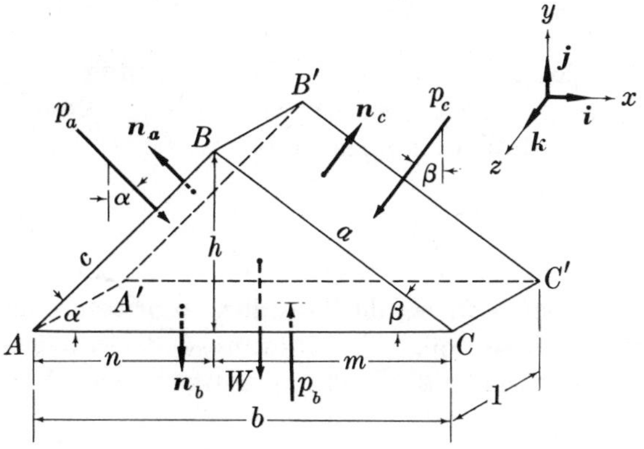

Figure 2.1
Equilibrium of an elementary fluid system.

[1] The student should be reminded that the pressure forces act opposite in direction to the positive outward normal and for this reason should carry a negative sign. Unlike the scalar algebraic summations, in vector summations vectors carry directions that must be taken into account.

the summation of forces along y is obtained. The scalar product of the same equation with $\boldsymbol{i}$ provides the x summation

$$\Sigma F_x = p_a c \sin \alpha - p_c a \sin \beta = 0$$
$$\Sigma F_y = p_b b - p_a c \cos \alpha - p_c a \cos \beta - W = 0$$

remembering that

$$\boldsymbol{n}_b \cdot \boldsymbol{n}_a = -\cos \alpha \qquad \boldsymbol{n}_b \cdot \boldsymbol{n}_c = -\cos \beta$$
$$\boldsymbol{i} \cdot \boldsymbol{n}_a = -\sin \alpha \qquad \boldsymbol{i} \cdot \boldsymbol{n}_b = \boldsymbol{i} \cdot \boldsymbol{g} = 0, \qquad \boldsymbol{i} \cdot \boldsymbol{n}_c = \sin \beta$$
$$W = \rho g h b/2 \qquad (m + n) = b$$
$$\sin \beta = h/a \qquad \cos \beta = m/a$$
$$\sin \alpha = h/c \qquad \cos \alpha = n/c$$

Because the surface ABC is taken the same as $A'B'C'$, the third summation of forces in the z-direction will show that the pressures on these two faces are the same. The equilibrium relations become

$$h(p_c - p_a) = 0$$
$$p_b b - p_a n - p_c m - \frac{\rho g h b}{2} = 0$$

In other words,

$$p_c = p_a$$
$$p_b - p_a = \frac{\rho g h}{2}$$

Now, for fluids with moderate densities, the following interesting results can be obtained. By letting the size of the elemental system approach smaller and smaller dimensions, the pressures remain finite while $h \rightarrow 0$. In the limit

$$p_a = p_b = p_c \tag{2.1}$$

This is known as Pascal's[2] principle.

In conclusion, a fluid system in equilibrium gives a pressure at every point independent of orientation. The pressure of the fluid is therefore, unlike the velocity of the fluid, a scalar quantity independent of orientation.

Although Eq. (2.1) was derived for a system in static equilibrium, it is not difficult to realize that the same conclusion would be reached for moving fluids with moderate density and acceleration, provided that the surface forces are normal, as in the case previously considered. In other words, the independence of pressure on orientation is also valid for moving fluids, provided that the motion is frictionless.

[2] Blaise Pascal (1623–1662) was a French scientist and philosopher whose achievements in his youth surprised many great contemporary scientists, such as Leibniz.

Illustrative Example 2.1

Show that the free surface of a liquid at rest is always perpendicular to the direction of the gravitational acceleration.

Considering the opposite to be true, as shown in Fig. 2.2, a line *AC* is drawn to intersect the nonhorizontal surface. The free-body diagram of the fluid element *ABC* cannot be in equilibrium, since the summation of surface forces along *AC* will always give an unbalanced component in a direction perpendicular to *g*, and therefore a motion in that direction. Consequently, the free surface shown cannot be in static equilibrium.

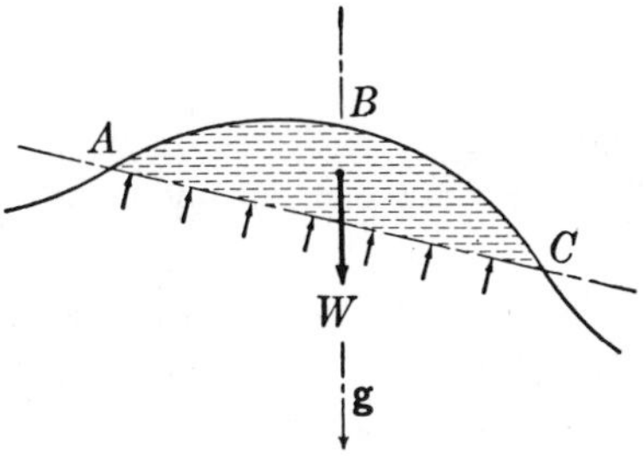

Figure 2.2
Free body of a liquid surface.

2.4 Relationship Between the Body Forces and the Surface Forces for a Fluid in Static Equilibrium

Since the gravitational force is the most common body force encountered in fluid mechanics, its relationship to the surface forces on a fluid element in equilibrium will be studied. Two essential theorems give an account of the pressure distribution on a fluid element in equilibrium under the action of gravity.

Theorem I: Given a field of body force such as the gravitational field, acting on a fluid element in static equilibrium, the pressure is constant along a surface perpendicular to the gravitational-force field.

Proof: Consider, in Fig. 2.3, a cylindrical fluid element with cross-sectional area dA subjected to the gravitational body force per unit mass $\boldsymbol{g}$ perpendicular to the axis of the cylindrical element. Since the element is considered to be in equilibrium, the surface forces are all perpendicular to the surface. In the absence of resultant moments,

$$-\boldsymbol{n}pS - \boldsymbol{n}_2 p_2 dA - \boldsymbol{n}_1 p_1 A + \rho \mathcal{V} \boldsymbol{g} = 0$$

where the unit normals are taken positive in the outward direction. The scalar multiplication with $\boldsymbol{i}$ yields

$$p_1 = p_2$$

or that the pressure along the axis of the cylinder perpendicular to $\boldsymbol{g}$ is constant. If the axis of the cylinder is displaced parallel to itself to any plane perpendicular to $\boldsymbol{g}$, the pressure on that plane will again be

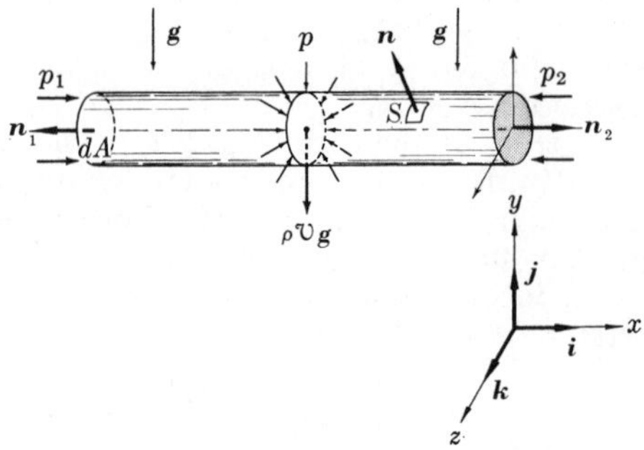

Figure 2.3
Thin horizontal element under the action of gravity.

constant. The constants will have different values at different planes. This relationship will be established in the next theorem.

Theorem II: Given a gravitational field of force acting on a fluid element in equilibrium, the pressure change per unit length in the direction of the force field is equal to the density times the magnitude of the force per unit mass or $\boldsymbol{g}$ in the case of the gravitational field.

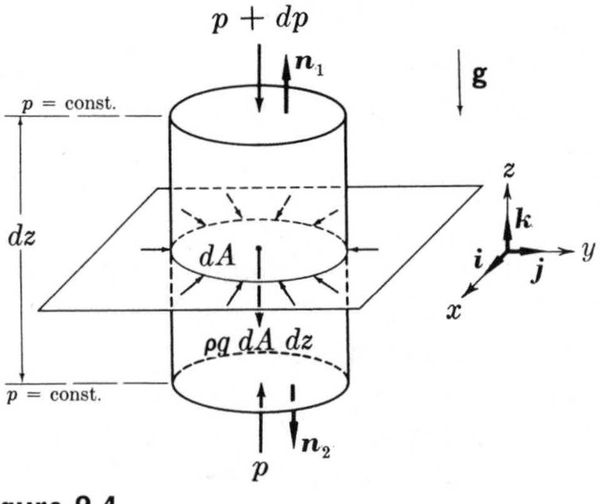

Figure 2.4
Vertical fluid element under the action of gravity.

Proof: Theorem I has just shown that the pressure on the plane perpendicular to the gravitational field of force is a constant. As shown in Fig. 2.4, let the cylindrical-volume element be placed so that its axis is along $\boldsymbol{g}$. On any plane P normal to $\boldsymbol{g}$, the pressure around the periphery of the cylinder is a constant, and therefore the summations of forces in the x- and y-directions are zero if equilibrium conditions are to be satisfied. If z is measured positively in the direction opposite to $\boldsymbol{g}$ (elevation), then, to complete the equilibrium conditions, the summation of forces gives

$$[-\boldsymbol{n}_1(p + dp) - \boldsymbol{n}_2 p]dA + \rho dA dz \boldsymbol{g} = 0$$

Since $\boldsymbol{n}_1 = -\boldsymbol{n}_2$ after simplifying

$$\boldsymbol{n}_1 \frac{dp}{dz} = \rho \boldsymbol{g}$$

or[3]

$$\nabla p = \rho \boldsymbol{g} \tag{2.2}$$

This equation implies that $dp/dz < 0$ since $\boldsymbol{n}_1$ has a direction opposite to $\boldsymbol{g}$; in other words, ∇p is in the direction of $\boldsymbol{g}$ and thus for equilibrium p must increase with depth (negative altitude). In a scalar form

$$\frac{dp}{dz} = -\rho g \qquad [2.2(a)]$$

The gravitational field on this earth is visualized as a force field pulling all masses in a direction toward the center of the earth. It should not be very difficult, however, to visualize a force field attracting masses in three component directions. In that case, Eq. [2.2(a)] is still valid, and this can be shown when the axis of the cylinder is oriented along the gravitational force. Since the pressure is then a function of the three coordinates, Eq. (2.2) has for components three partial differential equations:

$$\frac{\partial p}{\partial x} = -\rho g_x$$

$$\frac{\partial p}{\partial y} = -\rho g_y$$

$$\frac{\partial p}{\partial z} = -\rho g_z$$

2.5 The Hydrostatic Equation

In general, the differential equation, Eq. [2.2(a)], cannot be integrated unless the natures of ρ and g are specified. One very special case which

[3] See Sec. A.14.

applies to incompressible columns of liquids is obtained when both ρ and g are treated as constants. In that case the integration can be carried out at two different levels z and z_0;

$$p - p_0 = -\rho g(z - z_0) \tag{2.3}$$

This equation is known as the *hydrostatic equation* or *Torricelli's*[4] *principle*. It relates the pressure variation of a static incompressible fluid to the variations of altitude. This equation can be written in the following manner:

$$p + \rho g z = p_0 + \rho g z_0 = \text{constant} \qquad [2.3(a)]$$

which indicates that at every elevation the *static pressure* plus the head

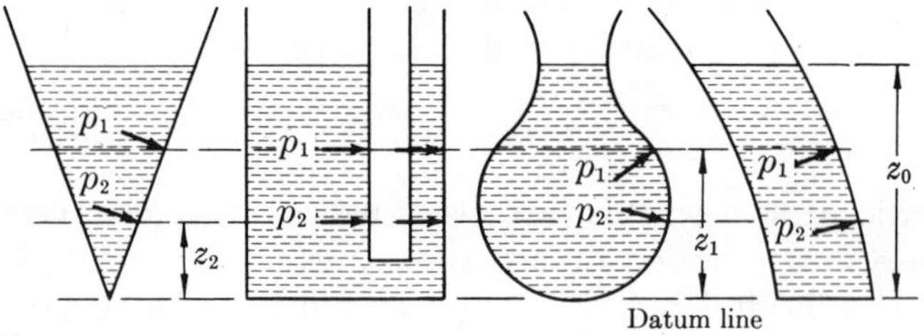

Figure 2.5
Hydrostatic pressure in various-shaped vessels.

of fluid above a given datum line is a constant. The deduction in Theorem I is therefore only a special case of Torricelli's principle, since, for a constant elevation z, the pressure p is a constant. The illustration in Fig. 2.5 shows that, at the same elevation z, the pressure in the various vessels is the same, no matter what the shape of the vessel. *This pressure is not a function of the total volume of fluid above the point but is proportional only to the height of the vertical column of fluid above the point.*

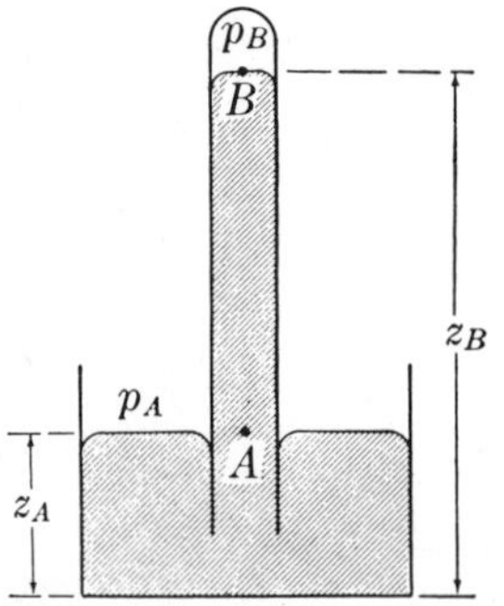

Figure 2.6
The mercury barometer.

Illustrative Example 2.2

A mercury barometer is obtained when a long tube, open at one end, is filled with mercury and its open end is submerged in a mercury

[4] Evangelista Torricelli (1608–1647), Florentine physicist and student of Galileo. His work on mercury barometers is based on this principle.

vessel without admitting air into the tube. The mercury in the tube will seek a level B which, as will be shown, depends on the ambient pressure p_A. Since the mercury level dropped in the tube from its closed end to the level B, the space above B is a vacuum if air was not admitted in the submerging process. Considering the bottom of the vessel as the datum line, Eq. [2.3(a)] states that

$$p_A + \rho g z_A = p_B + \rho g z_B = \text{constant}$$

and since $p_B = 0$, then the atmospheric pressure p_A is

$$p_A = \rho g(z_B - z_A)$$

Illustrative Example 2.3

The pressure in the tank A of Fig. 2.7 is to be determined at the central elevation E with the help of a mercury manometer. The fluid in the tank is water and fills the manometer on the left-hand side up to the mercury level B. The datum line can be arbitrarily chosen at BC, since the configuration below BC is the same on both sides of the manometer. The total pressure at B is the pressure at E, p_E, plus the pressure owing to the head of water from E to B. On the right-hand side of the manometer, the pressure at C is the pressure at D (atmospheric at elevation D) plus the head of mercury DC; therefore,

$$p_B = p_E + \rho_w g h_1 = p_C = p_D + \rho_m g h_2$$

But the atmospheric pressure at D is smaller than that at elevation E by the atmospheric head $\rho_a g(h_2 - h_1)$. The subscripts for the densities are the first letters of the fluid involved. Consequently, the equilibrium equation becomes

$$p_E + \rho_w g h_1 - p_E' - \rho_a g(h_2 - h_1) + \rho_m g h_2$$

In the last equation, p_E' is the atmospheric pressure at elevation E and, consequently, the pressure at E in the tank with reference to the atmospheric pressure at the same elevation is

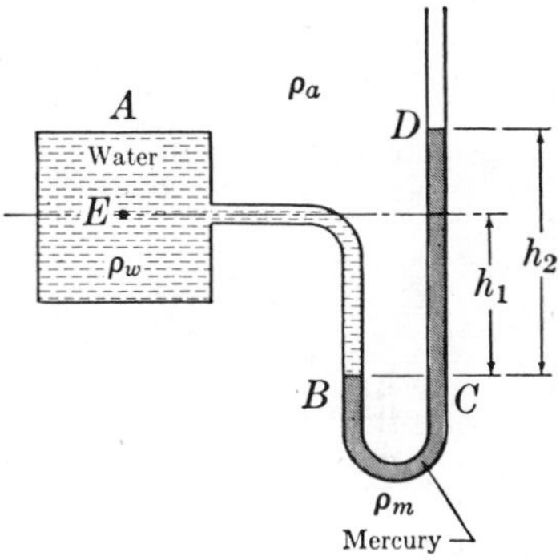

Figure 2.7

Pressure-measuring manometer.

$$p_E - p_E' = (\rho_m - \rho_a)gh_2 - (\rho_w - \rho_a)gh_1$$

2.6 Stability of Static Equilibrium

By definition, a fluid element is said to be in *stable equilibrium* when, if displaced slightly from its existing equilibrium position, it returns right back to its original state. In other words, when the equilibrium is slightly disturbed, the net forces resulting from this disturbance are such that they act in a direction to restore the original state of the element. Conversely, a fluid element is said to be in *unstable equilibrium* when, displaced slightly, it tends to move farther away from the original position in the direction of the disturbance. Finally, a *neutral equilibrium* exists when the fluid element, given a slight displacement, finds itself again in equilibrium in its new position.

For example, consider a fluid in a tall tank whose pressure increases with depth. Since all fluids are compressible to some extent, the density of the fluid will increase with depth, depending on the compression process discussed in Sec. 1.9. In Fig. 2.8, let a fluid element at elevation z_2 and density ρ_2 be displaced and brought to a higher level z_1 where the density of the surrounding fluid is ρ_1. For this case $\rho_1 < \rho_2$. Since the displaced element originally at 2 was in equilibrium at 2, then

$$p_5 - p_4 = \rho_2 g \Delta z$$

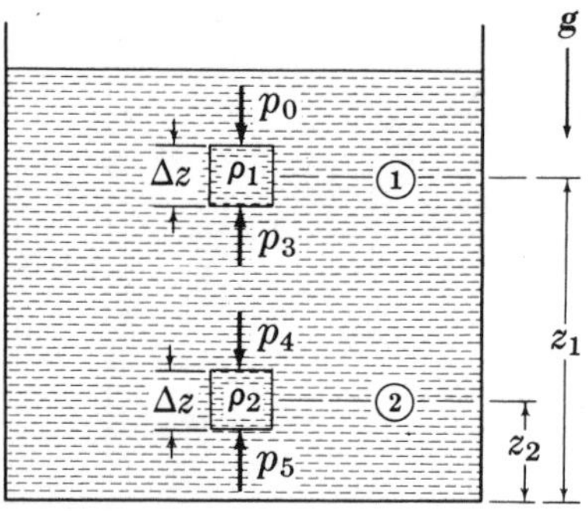

Figure 2.8
Stability of equilibrium.

which is the weight per unit area of the element at 2. When this element is displaced to its new position at 1, because of the change of the ambient pressure, the dimensions of the element will expand to a new dimension $\Delta z'$ such that its mass remains the same with the new change of density. The volume of the element must increase by the ratio of ρ_2/ρ_1 and $\Delta z' = \Delta z \left(\frac{\rho_2}{\rho_1}\right)^{1/3}$. The resultant ambient pressure difference at this new location is $p_3 - p_0 = \rho_1 g \Delta z'$, and, in general, it may not be able to support the weight of element 2, which is $\rho_2 g \Delta z$. Consequently, the element at this new location will be acted upon with a resultant force

$$\begin{aligned} \epsilon &= \rho_2 g \Delta z - (p_3 - p_0) \\ &= g(\rho_2 \Delta z - \rho_1 \Delta z') \\ &= \rho_2 g \Delta z \left[1 - \left(\frac{\rho_1}{\rho_2}\right)^{2/3}\right] \end{aligned}$$

This resultant force may be positive, zero, or negative. When $\rho_1 < \rho_2$, which is the case considered, and if the change of pressure from one elevation to another produces any change of the density inversely proportional to its volume, then the residual resultant force ϵ will be positive and in the direction of the weight. The restoring residual force ϵ opposes the original displacement, and therefore the element was in *stable equilibrium*. Consequently, $\partial\rho/\partial z < 0$ would correspond to a stable system. When $\rho_1 = \rho_2$ or $\partial\rho/\partial z = 0$, the residual restoring force will be zero and the element will find itself in equilibrium everywhere it is placed. This corresponds to *neutral equilibrium*. Finally, when $\rho_1 > \rho_2$ or $\partial\rho/\partial z > 0$, the residual force ϵ will continue to move the element in the direction in which it was originally displaced. The system would be in an *unstable equilibrium*.

If carefully done, water can be made to rest in equilibrium over a layer of oil. The system as a whole is unstable because, if slightly disturbed, the oil will change places with the water level.

2.7 Equilibrium of the Atmosphere

For the aerodynamicist and the meteorologist the study of atmospheric properties is of considerable importance. For most engineering applications the properties of the atmosphere, deduced from the assumption of an atmosphere in static equilibrium, are noteworthy. Since air is a compressible gas, its density is a function of pressure and temperature. Consequently, for complete equilibrium one must consider thermal equilibrium as well. The system will be considered to be in thermal equilibrium if its thermodynamic equation of state is satisfied everywhere in the system at all times. Except for rarefied regions in the atmosphere, air obeys the equation of state of a perfect gas $p = \rho RT$. This is Eq. (1.3), discussed in Sec. 1.7. This equation indicates that the pressure is a function of the density and temperature. Consequently, since the pressure of the atmosphere varies with altitude according to Eqs. (2.2) and [2.2(a)], the density and the temperature will also vary with altitude through the relationship of the equation of state. Equation [2.2(a)] has two dependent variables p and ρ and the independent variable z. In order to solve this equation explicitly in p or ρ as a function of z, another independent equation in p and ρ is necessary. Unfortunately, the equation of state, if used, brings a third dependent variable T for which a third equation in T, p, or ρ will be necessary. For the third equation, one must establish the *thermal process* which an atmospheric particle must follow when moved from one elevation to the other. For instance, if the atmosphere is considered *isothermal*, the temperature is no longer a variable, T = constant or p = constant $\times \rho$, which gives the third relationship required. The atmosphere, if considered *adiabatic*, also brings together, with the equation of state and Eq. [2.2(*a*)], a third relationship for another explicit mathematical solution of p, ρ, and T as a function of z. The word *adiabatic* implies that the atmosphere does not exchange heat with the surroundings.

In general, the thermal process of air being moved from one elevation to the other varies from elevation to elevation. This is the reason why, for the general cases, the polytropic law described in Sec. 1.7 is used.

2.8 The Polytropic Atmosphere

In the general case the pressure and density of the atmosphere vary polytropically according to

$$\frac{p}{p_0} = \left(\frac{\rho}{\rho_0}\right)^n$$

The subscript 0 refers here to the altitude at sea level, and n is the polytropic expansion exponent. The density at any level can then be expressed as

$$\rho = \rho_0 \left(\frac{p}{p_0}\right)^{1/n}$$

Upon substituting this relation in the hydrostatic differential equation, Eq. (2.2), and for small altitudes when the gravitational acceleration can be considered constant, the following differential equation is obtained:

$$\frac{dp}{dz} = -\rho_0 g \left(\frac{p}{p_0}\right)^{1/n}$$

After separation of variables, the equation becomes

$$p^{-1/n}\, dp = -\frac{\rho_0 g}{p_0}\, p_0^{n-1/n}\, dz$$

This can be readily integrated into the form

$$\frac{n}{n-1}\left[p^{n-1/n} - p_0^{n-1/n}\right] = -\frac{\rho_0 g}{p_0}\, p_0^{n-1/n}(z - z_0)$$

The following results are obtained:

$$z - z_0 = \frac{nRT_0}{g(n-1)}\left[1 - \left(\frac{p}{p_0}\right)^{n-1/n}\right]$$

The units of the gas constant R are on a per slug basis; the elevation in feet and the density are in slugs per cubic feet.

$$\frac{p}{p_0} = \left[1 - \frac{g(n-1)}{nRT_0}(z - z_0)\right]^{n/n-1} \qquad [2.4(a)]$$

From the polytropic density-pressure relationship, the density variation with altitude is

$$\frac{\rho}{\rho_0} = \left[1 - \frac{g(n-1)}{nRT_0}(z - z_0)\right]^{1/n-1} \qquad [2.4(b)]$$

For the same process, the temperature varies with pressure according to

$$\frac{T}{T_0} = \left(\frac{p}{p_0}\right)^{n-1/n}$$

and the temperature altitude variation becomes

$$\frac{T}{T_0} = \left[1 - \frac{g(n-1)}{nRT_0}(z - z_0)\right] \qquad [2.4(c)]$$

For the polytropic atmosphere the temperature variation with altitude is linear, as shown by Eq. [2.4(*c*)]. In reality, this is approximately true up to altitudes of 36,000 ft, or about 6.8 miles from sea level. This first layer of the atmosphere is called the *troposphere*. Equation [2.4(*c*)] can be written in the form

$$T = T_0 - \frac{g(n-1)}{nR}(z - z_0)$$

where the coefficient $\lambda = \frac{g(n-1)}{nR}$ is the *temperature-lapse rate*. According to measurements in the troposphere, $\lambda = 0.00363°\text{F/ft}$. From this value a polytropic exponent can be evaluated, $n = 1.24$.

With a sea-level temperature of 60°F, Eqs. [2.4(*a*)] and [2.4(*b*)] become

$$\frac{p}{p_0} = [1 - 6.97 \times 10^{-6}(z - z_0)]^{5.167}$$

$$\frac{\rho}{\rho_0} = [1 - 6.97 \times 10^{-6}(z - z_0)]^{4.167}$$

Above the troposphere is a layer of air that is more or less constant in temperature. This isothermal layer is called the *stratosphere* and has a temperature around −70°F. Its height is in the neighborhood of 12 miles beyond the troposphere.

2.9 The Isothermal Atmosphere

In this case the density in the hydrostatic differential equation can be replaced by the isothermal value $\rho = p/RT_0$

$$\frac{dp}{p} = -\frac{g}{RT_0}\,dz$$

and consequently,

$$\ln\frac{p}{p_0} = -\frac{g}{RT_0}(z - z_0)$$

$$\frac{p}{p_0} = e^{-\frac{g(z-z_0)}{RT_0}} \qquad [2.5(a)]$$

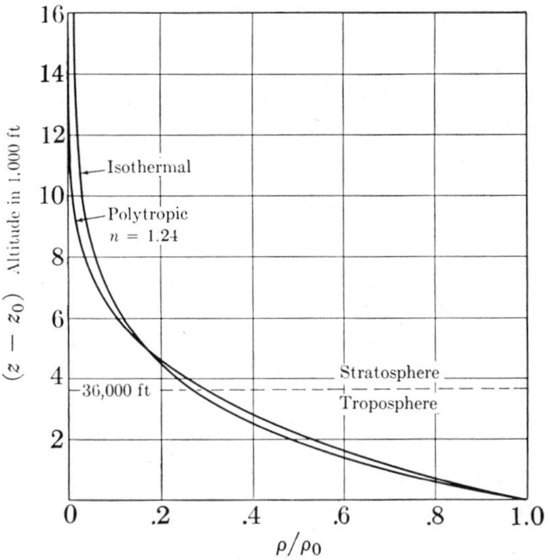

Figure 2.9
Density variation with altitude.

Since, for the isothermal case $p/p_0 = \rho/\rho_0$, then

$$\frac{\rho}{\rho_0} = e^{-\frac{g(z-z_0)}{RT_0}} \qquad [2.5(b)]$$

When the acceleration of gravity is standard and $T_0 = 520°R$,

$$\frac{\rho}{\rho_0} = e^{-3.604\times 10^{-5}(z-z_0)}$$

It can be seen from Eq. [2.5(*b*)], plotted in Fig. 2.9, that if the atmosphere were all isothermal its height would be infinite. The polytropic type of atmosphere always gives a finite height.

Illustrative Example 2.4

It is often necessary to evaluate the error introduced in the variation of properties with height when, as was done in the previous two cases, the gravitational acceleration was considered to be constant with elevation. Actually, it varies inversely proportional to the square of the distance from the center of the earth:

$$g = g_0\left(\frac{r_0}{r_0 + z}\right)^2 \tag{2.6}$$

Here g is the local acceleration at any altitude, g_0 is the sea-level acceleration at standard latitude of 40°, and r_0 is the earth's mean radius, 3,959 miles. The value of z is measured from sea level. Expanding Eq. (2.6) in a *binomial* form, it can be represented in the approximate form

$$g = g_0\left(1 - \frac{2z}{r_0}\right)$$

If this value is introduced in the hydrostatic equation, Eq. (2.2), for the polytropic atmosphere, for instance,

$$p^{-1/n}\,dp = -\frac{\rho_0 g_0}{p_0}\,p_0^{n-1/n}\left(1 - \frac{2z}{r_0}\right)dz$$

and, after integration,

$$\frac{p}{p_0} = \left[1 - \frac{g_0(n-1)}{nRT_0}\left(z - \frac{z^2}{r_0}\right)\right]^{n/n-1}$$

The difference between this equation and Eq. [2.4(*a*)] is the additional term z^2/r_0. If the atmosphere is treated as isothermal, the correction $-z^2/r_0$ will appear after the z term in the exponent. If the atmosphere is considered up to an altitude of 20 miles, the correction $-z^2/r_0$ for that altitude will be approximately 0.1 mile, which can become significant.

2.10 Thermodynamic Consideration in the Stability of the Atmosphere

In Sec. 2.8 it was concluded that in order for a polytropic atmosphere to be mechanically stable, the temperature had to drop with altitude at the rate of $dT/dz = -0.00363°F/ft$. For complete equilibrium, and since temperature, pressure, and density variations are taking place, one should investigate the conditions for thermal equilibrium. In other words, do the temperature gradients set up in the atmosphere generate convective currents that may upset the mechanical equilibrium? What temperature gradients are permissible to preserve mechanical equilibrium?

Following the reasoning in Sec. 2.6, let us consider a volume of air at pressure p and entropy s with a density $\rho(s,p)$. Let us move this volume of air a small altitude. This volume of air will take a new density $\rho(s_1,p_1)$, and its weight will be larger than that of the displaced fluid at pressure p_1 and entropy s_2. Then

$$\rho(s_1,p_1) - \rho(s_2,p_1) > 0$$

Since the displacement was small between states 1 and 2, then by Taylor's expansion

$$\rho(s_2,p_1) = \rho(s_1,p_1) + \left(\frac{d\rho}{ds}\right)_p ds + \cdots$$

Dividing by dz

$$\frac{\rho(s_2,p_1) - \rho(s_1,p_1)}{dz} = \left(\frac{d\rho}{ds}\right)_p \frac{ds}{dz}$$

and thus

$$\left(\frac{d\rho}{ds}\right)_p \frac{ds}{dz} < 0$$

The combination of First and Second Laws of Thermodynamics gives[5]

$$T ds + \frac{1}{\rho} dp = c_p dT \qquad (2.6)$$

At constant pressure this can be rewritten as

$$\left(\frac{dT}{ds}\right)_p = \frac{T}{c_p}$$

Multiplying both sides by $\left(\frac{d\rho}{dT}\right)_p$

$$\left(\frac{d\rho}{dT}\right)_p \left(\frac{dT}{ds}\right)_p = \frac{T}{c_p}\left(\frac{d\rho}{dT}\right)_p = \left(\frac{d\rho}{ds}\right)_p$$

[5] Consult any introductory thermodynamics textbook. For instance, E. F. Obert, *Thermodynamics*, McGraw-Hill Book Company, Inc., New York, 1948, pp. 138–139.

Then from the inequality it becomes apparent that

$$\frac{T}{c_p}\left(\frac{d\rho}{dT}\right)_p \frac{ds}{dz} < 0$$

It is well known that for most substances $\left(\frac{d\rho}{dT}\right)_p < 0$, and that T and c_p are always positive. So, from the previous equation we can deduce that the entropy must increase with altitude

$$\frac{ds}{dz} > 0 \tag{2.7}$$

This is the condition on the entropy for thermal gradients not to upset mechanical equilibrium. To find the allowable temperature gradient for mechanical equilibrium not to be disturbed, we represent the entropy in terms of the pressure and temperature $s = f(p,T)$. Then

$$\frac{ds}{dz} = \left(\frac{ds}{dT}\right)_p \frac{dT}{dz} + \left(\frac{ds}{dp}\right)_T \frac{dp}{dz} > 0 \qquad [2.7(a)]$$

It was already stated that $\left(\frac{ds}{dT}\right)_p = c_p/T$ and from the hydrostatic equation, Eq. [2.2(*a*)], $dp/dz = -\rho g$ then

$$\frac{dT}{dz} > \frac{T\rho g}{c_p}\left(\frac{ds}{dp}\right)_T \tag{2.8}$$

The quantity $(ds/dp)_T$ can be evaluated from Eq. (2.6) by taking an isothermal process

$$\left(\frac{ds}{dp}\right)_T = -\frac{1}{\rho T}$$

Using the equation of state of a perfect gas $p = \rho RT$

$$\left(\frac{ds}{dp}\right)_T = -\frac{R}{p}$$

Then the inequality in Eq. (2.8) becomes

$$\frac{dT}{dz} > -\frac{T\rho gR}{pc_p}$$

$$> -\frac{g}{c_p} \tag{2.9}$$

So for stability of the atmosphere, the entropy must increase with altitude which yields according to Eq. (2.9) that the temperature cannot decrease with altitude faster than g/c_p. If we substitute the limit $dT/dz = -g/c_p$ into Eq. [2.7(*a*)] and use other available relations for

$(ds/dT)_p$, $(ds/dp)_T$, and dp/dz, we find that $ds/dz = 0$. This is then the adiabatic reversible case.[6] Thus, if we call $\lambda_a = g/c_p$ the limiting temperature lapse rate, we conclude

$$\frac{dT}{dz} > -\lambda_u$$

Substituting the values of g and c_p for air

$$\frac{dT}{dz} > -0.00535°\text{F/ft}$$

for stable equilibrium, $dT/dz = -0.00535°\text{F/ft}$ for neutral equilibrium, and $dT/dz < -0.00535°\text{F/ft}$ for unstable equilibrium. The polytropic process discussed in Sec. 2.8 for which $\lambda = 0.00363°\text{F/ft}$ is within the limiting condition. The negative sign with λa implies temperature *drop* with altitude. In other words, temperature drops larger in ab-

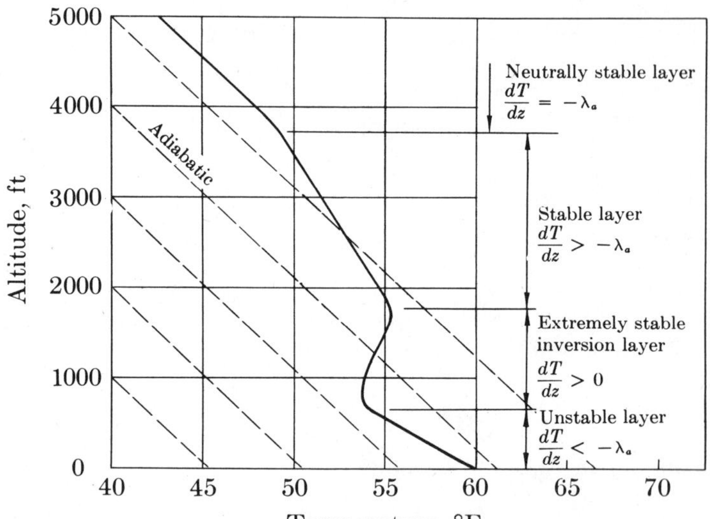

Figure 2.10
Temperature variation in the atmosphere.

[6] In Sect. 2.8 if we substitute $n = c_p/c_v$, $R = (c_p - c_v)$ in the temperature lapse rate λ for the adiabatic case we obtain $\lambda = g/c_p$.

solute value than 0.00535°F/ft produce unstable layers that will make them rise because their weight is smaller than the net pressure forces. Figure 2.10 shows four different layers in the atmosphere with different temperature-lapse rates. The dotted lines represent the maximum temperature drop for stability.

2.11 Origin of Clouds

Having discussed the conditions for stability of an air column with respect to pressure and temperature drops with altitude, we proceed to explain a few meteorological situations that control our weather.

The previous section demonstrated that temperature drops with altitude less than 0.00535°F/ft produce stable layers. In Fig. 2.11

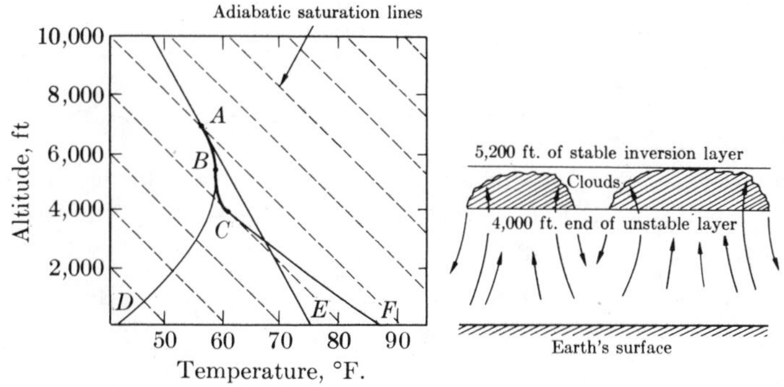

Figure 2.11
Stability of atmospheric layers.

let us pick such a stable layer *AE* during a spell of prolonged mild weather. If at night time the earth's temperature cools rapidly to approximately 40°F, a layer *ABD* of the total column may cool as shown. We know that from the temperature gradient this night-cooled layer is extremely stable. If the following day is sunny and warm, the layer of the atmosphere close to the earth's surface may take the temperature distribution *ABCF* as shown. According to the stability criteria, the temperature drop with altitude *CF* is too large to be stable. Warm layers near the surface of the earth will be rising to upper layers carrying humidity with them. There will be corresponding down-currents of colder air as shown in Fig. 2.11. At a sufficient height, the rising air currents reach a region C cold enough to produce condensation in the form of mist or cloud. Since the drier air at this height is slightly stable and since it is heavier than the uprising damp air, it will descend to lower layers creating a continual growth of cloud formation up to a point B where there is an inversion which marks the beginning of a very stable upper layer. The rising air currents are invisible up to the layer C, and above it they appear as clouds shown in Fig. 2.11.

The mechanism just described is one among others producing clouds. Ordinarily, the atmosphere is not in a state of static equilibrium. Low pressure regions are affected by winds which tend to lift the damp and warm air already there. This tends to make larger temperature gradients and consequently less stable upper layers. Then the process of cloud formation up to the inversion point is the same.

2.12 Forces on Submerged Surfaces

For any arbitrary submerged surface in a fluid, the total force on the surface can be obtained by integrating the pressure over the entire area of the surface[7]

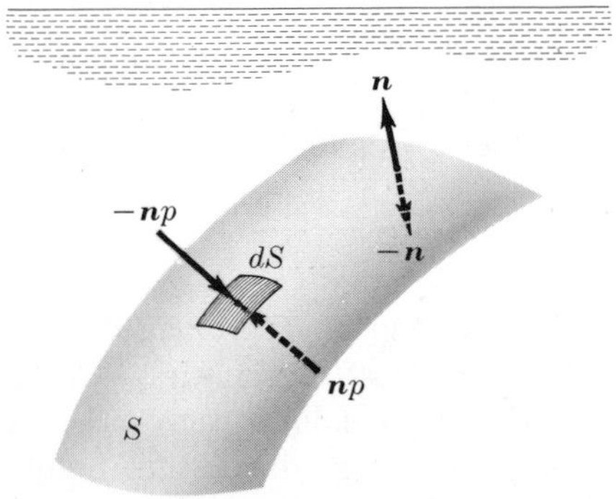

Figure 2.12
Forces on a submerged surface S.

[7] Throughout this book the unit normal is defined positive when pointing outward (along the radius of curvature).

$$\boldsymbol{F} = -\int_S \boldsymbol{n}p\, dS \tag{2.10}$$

If the surface is totally submerged (the same fluid on both sides of it), the resultant integrated force on one side of the surface will equal the integrated force on the other side. *Since a surface has no thickness, and therefore no weight, it will always remain in neutral equilibrium when totally submerged.* (See Fig. 2.12.) If a thickness, and therefore a weight, is prescribed to it, then the only force that can set it in motion is its own weight inside the fluid.

Often, the fluids exert larger forces on one side of the surface alone, such as on the walls of a container holding a fluid. Then, according to *Pascal's principle*, the pressure on surfaces perpendicular to $\boldsymbol{g}$ will be constant and, according to Torricelli's equation, equal to

$$p - p_0 = -\rho g(z - z_0) \tag{2.11}$$

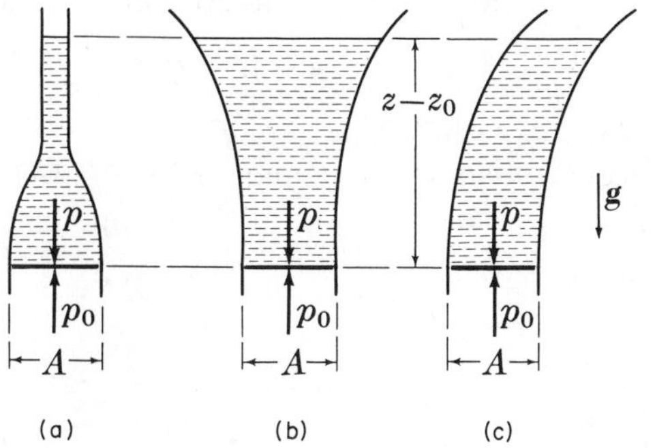

Figure 2.13
Equal areas supporting equal columns of fluid.

for an incompressible liquid of small heights where ρ and g are considered constant. Figure 2.13 illustrates, then, for the same area A and the same liquid elevation $(z - z_0)$, that the total force on the plates at the bottom of the three containers is the same, regardless of the total weight of liquid they support. It is, however, a function of the density of the liquid. The fact that different quantities of fluid above a plate can produce the same force on the plate is known as the *hydrostatic paradox*. This can be explained by examining Fig. 2.14. The total force supported by the plate at the bottom of the container is the fluid directly above the plate *aefb*. This is given by Eq. (2.11). The weight of the fluid *ca''e* and *fb''d* is supported by the surfaces of the container *ca''* and db''. Consequently, these parts of the liquid can be considered as frozen and as part of the walls of the container but still at the same density of the liquid. Consider now the imaginary fluid surfaces $a'g'g$ and $b'h'h$. If the fluid in the volumes $a'g'gca''a'$ and $b'h'hdb''b'$ is frozen at the same density as the liquid and is made part of the vessel, the pressure on the bottom plate and consequently the total force will remain unaltered.

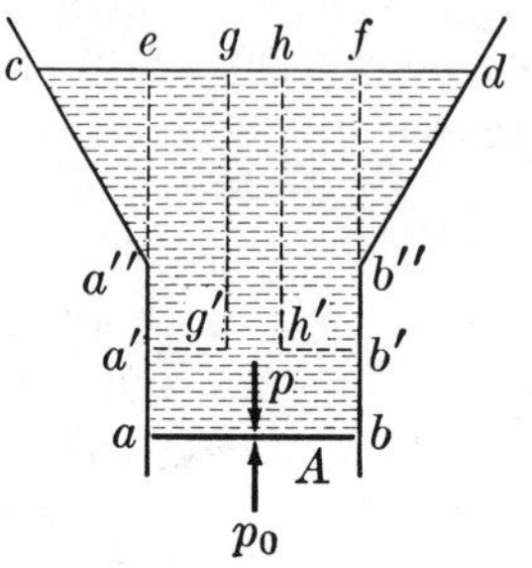

Figure 2.14
Hydrostatic paradox.

To evaluate the forces on one side of an arbitrary surface shown in Fig. 2.15 we proceed as follows. The total force on the surface S is given by Eq. (2.10); its location from an arbitrary origin O from where the position vector $\boldsymbol{r}$ is measured can be found from the solution of the moment equation that must be satisfied for complete equilibrium

$$\boldsymbol{r}_p \times \boldsymbol{F} = -\int_S (\boldsymbol{r} \times \boldsymbol{n})\, p dS \qquad (2.12)$$

Here $\boldsymbol{r}_p$ is called the *center of pressure* or the location of $\boldsymbol{F}$.

Until S is given, the two previous equations cannot be evaluated. However some interesting relationships can be found in the component

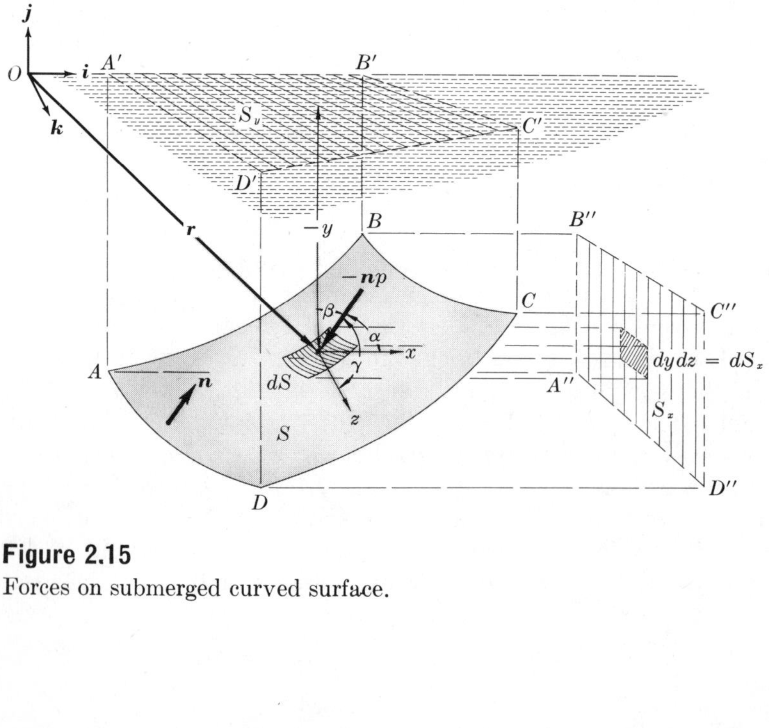

Figure 2.15
Forces on submerged curved surface.

equations. To find the component equations, Eq. (2.10) is dotted to $\boldsymbol{i}$, $\boldsymbol{j}$, and $\boldsymbol{k}$ and for a liquid the value of $p = -\rho g y$ above atmospheric pressure is used from Eq. (2.11) where $y_0 = 0$, and p_0 is atmospheric.

$$\boldsymbol{F}\cdot\boldsymbol{i} = -\int_S (\boldsymbol{n}\cdot\boldsymbol{i})\, p dS$$

$$F_x = \int_S \rho g y \cos\alpha\, dS$$

Similarly

$$F_y = \int_S \rho g y \cos\beta\, dS$$

$$F_z = \int_S \rho g y \cos\gamma\, dS$$

The angles α, β, and γ are the angles of $\boldsymbol{n}$. From the geometry, it is evident that $dS\cos\alpha = dS_x = dydz$, $dS\cos\beta = dS_y = dxdz$, and $dS\cos\gamma = dS_z = dxdy$. Then

$$F_x = \rho g \int_{S_x} y dS_x, \qquad F_y = \rho g \int_{S_y} y dS_y \quad \text{and} \quad F_z = \rho g \int_{S_z} y dS_z \tag{2.13}$$

If y is to be used as depth then the signs of y and S_x and S_z must be changed since the coordinate y is contained in S_x and S_z and not in S_y. *The sign of F_x and F_z will depend not on y but on dz and dx. Since S_y can always be chosen positive, the direction of F_y will depend on that of y. In this text we shall consider positive y in the direction of increasing altitude.* From calculus the y-component of the centroid of these two surfaces is defined as

$$\bar{y} = \frac{1}{S_x}\int_{S_x} y dS_x = \frac{1}{S_z}\int_{S_z} y dS_z \tag{2.14}$$

then

$$\begin{aligned} F_x &= \rho g \bar{y} S_x \quad \text{and} \quad & F_z &= \rho g \bar{y} S_z \\ &= \bar{p} S_x & &= \bar{p} S_z \end{aligned} \tag{2.15}$$

This is a very interesting relation. It states that for no matter which surface S as long as it has the same projection S_x *the x-component of the force is equal to the hydrostatic pressure $\bar{p}$ at the centroid of S_x times the surface S_x.* The same is true for the z-component. The component normal to the surface of the water F_y shows a different relation. From Eq. (2.13) it is seen that

$$\begin{aligned} F_y &= \rho g \int_{S_y} y dS_y \\ &= \rho g \mathcal{V} \end{aligned} \tag{2.16}$$

where $\mathcal{V}$ is the volume of liquid above the surface S. Therefore the value of F_y, even if the projection S_y remains the same, depends on the position of the surface S from the free surface of the liquid. Equation (2.12) can be handled in a similar fashion. The following is also true

$$x_p\boldsymbol{F} = -\int_S x\,\boldsymbol{n}\,p dS$$

Dotting this equation by $\boldsymbol{j}$ or $\boldsymbol{k}$ we obtain

$$x_p(\boldsymbol{F}\cdot\boldsymbol{j}) = -\int_S x(\boldsymbol{n}\cdot\boldsymbol{j})\,p dS$$

$$x_pF_y = -\int_S xp\cos\beta\,dS$$

But from Eq. (2.13)

$$F_y = \rho g\int_{S_y} ydS_y = \rho g\mathcal{V}$$

where $\mathcal{V}$ is the volume of fluid above the submerged surface and since $dS\cos\beta = dS_y$ and $p = -\rho gy$

$$x_p = \frac{\int_{S_y} xydS_y}{\int_{S_y} ydS_y} = \frac{\int_{S_z} xydS_z}{\int ydS_z} = \frac{\int_{S_x} xydS_x}{\int_{S_x} ydS_x} \tag{2.17}$$

In a similar fashion the z-component of the center of pressure is

$$z_p = \frac{\int_{S_y} zydS_y}{\int_{S_y} ydS_y} = \frac{\int_{S_x} zydS_x}{\int ydS_x} = \frac{\int_{S_z} zydS_z}{\int_{S_z} ydS_z} \tag{2.18}$$

and for y_p

$$y_p = \frac{\int_{S_y} y^2dS_y}{\int_{S_y} ydS_y} = \frac{\int_{S_x} y^2dS_x}{\int_{S_x} ydS_x} = \frac{\int_{S_z} y^2dS_z}{\int_{S_z} ydS_z} \tag{2.19}$$

Illustrative Example 2.5

In the case of flat submerged surfaces as shown in Fig. 2.16, the force components and the location of the center of pressure becomes simpler to evaluate. Let the depth (negative of elevation) be measured from the free surface of the liquid in the tank. Then, at any point on both surfaces *ab* and *cd*, the elemental force will be

$$dF = \rho gy\,dA = \rho gz\sin\alpha\,dA \tag{2.20}$$

where α is the angle between the free surface of the liquid and the walls. Then the total force on any surface is

$$F = \rho g\sin\alpha\int_A z\,dA$$

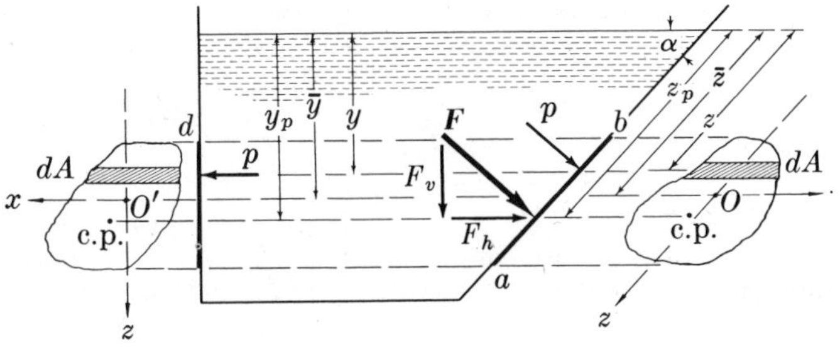

Figure 2.16
Fluid forces on plane areas.

Since the centroidal coordinate of the flat surface A is $\bar{z} = \dfrac{1}{A}\displaystyle\int_A z\, dA$, then the total force on the wall surfaces becomes

$$F = \rho g z A \sin \alpha = \rho g \bar{y} A \tag{2.21}$$
$$= p_{\bar{y}} A$$

Therefore, *the magnitude of the force acting on the walls is the product of the pressure at the centroid of the area times the extent of the area.* From intuition, since the magnitude of the pressure increases with depth, the lower half of the wall surfaces will contribute more to the total force, and consequently the point where this total force will act will not necessarily coincide with the center of gravity. This point of action of the total force is called the *center of pressure* (c.p.). Its location is found by evaluating the total moment owing to elemental forces on the surfaces and equating it to the moment of the total resultant force. Thus

$$\begin{aligned} x_p F &= \int_A xp\, dA \\ z_p F &= \int_A zp\, dA \end{aligned} \tag{2.22}$$

Upon substitution of the force F from Eq. (2.21) and the pressure p from Eq. (2.20),

$$\begin{aligned} x_p &= \frac{1}{\rho g \bar{z} A \sin \alpha} \int_A x(\rho g z \sin \alpha)\, dA \\ &= \frac{1}{\bar{z} A} \int_A xz\, dA \\ &= \frac{I_{xz}}{\bar{z} A} \end{aligned}$$

In the same manner the moments around the x-axis give

$$z_p = \frac{1}{\bar{z}A} \int_A z^2 \, dA$$

$$= \frac{I_{xx}}{\bar{z}A}$$

The coordinate system can be translated into the centroids O and O'. Denoting the moments of inertia with reference to the centroid by $\bar{I}_{xx}$ and $\bar{I}_{xz}$, the translational relations are also true:

$$I_{xx} = \bar{I}_{xx} + \bar{z}^2 A$$

$$I_{xz} = \bar{I}_{xz} + \bar{x}\bar{z}A$$

Substituting these transformation equations into the values derived for x_p and z_p

$$x_p = \frac{\bar{I}_{xz}}{\bar{z}A} + \bar{x}$$

$$z_p = \frac{\bar{I}_{xx}}{\bar{z}A} + \bar{z} \tag{2.23}$$

The center of pressure is located from the center of gravity at the distances

$$\bar{I}_{xz}/\bar{z}A \quad \text{and} \quad \bar{I}_{xx}/\bar{z}A$$

From Eq. (2.21), the horizontal component of the force on the inclined surface is $F_h = \rho g A \bar{y} \sin \alpha$, but $A \sin \alpha$ is the vertical projection of the inclined surface area or is equal to the surface on the left-hand side of the container.

Illustrative Example 2.6

Find the forces acting on the walls of the water channel shown. Find their location. The problem will be worked out on the basis of a unit depth in the direction perpendicular to the plane of the paper. The force on the surface OA is

$$F_{OA} = \int_O^A p \, dA = \rho g \int_0^1 \sqrt{2}(1 - y) \, dy$$

$$= \frac{\sqrt{2}}{2} \rho g = 44.1 \text{ lb}_f$$

According to Eq. (2.21), this same force must be the pressure at the centroid of OA (halfway between O and A) $\rho g/2$ times the area of the surface OA, $\sqrt{2} \times 1$. This is identical with the value just found.

Along the surface OB, $y = x^2$, $2x \, dx = dy$, $\tan \theta = dy/dx$ and $dA = \sqrt{dx^2 + dy^2} = dx \sqrt{1 + 4x^2}$, and $\sin \theta \, dA = 1 \times dy$, $\cos \theta \, dA = dx$

$$F_{OB_x} = \int_O^B p \sin \theta \, dA = \rho g \int_O^B (1 - y) \sin \theta \, dA$$

$$F_{OB_x} = \rho g \int_0^1 (1 - y)\, dy = \frac{\rho g}{2}$$

This is the same value as that of the x-component for the surface OA or any other surface, provided that the limits remain the same.

$$F_{OB_y} = \int_O^B p \cos\theta\, dA = \rho g \int_0^1 (1 - y)\, dx$$

$$= \rho g \int_0^1 (1 - x^2)\, dx = \frac{2\rho g}{3}$$

This component can also be obtained from Eq. (2.16) if the volume above the surface OB is known. According to that equation, the volume must be 2/3. The total force F_{OB} is then the vectorial sum of the two components, or 52 $\text{lb}_f = \frac{5\rho g}{6}$.

The location of the forces is found by direct integration

$$F_{OA}s_p = \sqrt{2}\, \rho g \int_0^1 (1 - y)s\, dy$$

since $s = \sqrt{x^2 + y^2}$, and for this surface, since $y = -x$,

$$F_{OA}s_p = 2\rho g \int_0^1 y(1 - y)\, dy = \frac{\rho g}{3}$$

Solving for s_p the location of the center of pressure along the length OA,

$$s_p = \frac{\sqrt{2}}{3}$$

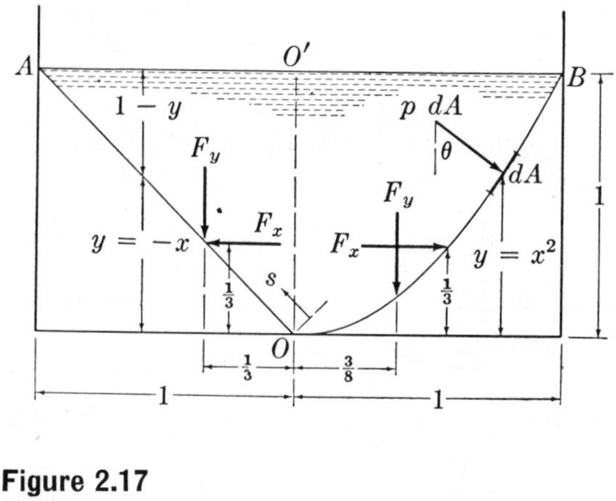

Figure 2.17
Water channel.

This value can be found to be identical when evaluated from Eqs. (2.23), (2.17) and (2.18). For instance, the center of pressure x_p was found to be the centroid of the area AOO' which is located at $x = -1/3$ from O. When y_p is evaluated from Eq. (2.18), it must be remembered that the distances are from the level of the free surface. Therefore, $y_p = 2/3$ the distance from the free surface or 1/3 the distance from the bottom of the tank. Consequently, s_p has the value already found.

The coordinates of the center of pressure for the surface OA are found in the same fashion. It is seen from Eq. (2.18) that y_p measured from O must be the same as that of OA, since the limits have not changed. Therefore, $y_p = 1/3$. The value of x_p can be found, for instance, from the location of the centroid of the area $OO'B$, which is

$$x_p = \frac{\int_0^1 x(1-y)\,dx}{\int_0^1 (1-y)\,dx} = \frac{\int_0^1 x(1-x^2)\,dx}{\int_0^1 (1-x^2)\,dx} = \frac{3}{8}$$

2.13 Buoyant Forces on Submerged Bodies

Consider again the discussion in Sec. 2.4 and the forces involved as applied to the arbitrary body shown in Fig. 2.18. Then for the body to be in static equilibrium in the submerged position,

$$-\oint_S \boldsymbol{n}\, p dS + \int_{\mathcal{V}} \rho_b \boldsymbol{g} d\mathcal{V} = 0 \tag{2.24}$$

where p is the pressure at any depth $-y$, and ρ_b is the density of the body of volume $\mathcal{V}$ and surface S. The left-hand side term is the buoyant force from the pressure around the body and the right-hand side is the weight of the body. From the hydrostatic equation Eq. (2.3)

$$p = p_0 + \rho_f g y$$

Here ρ_f is the density of the fluid around the body and $\boldsymbol{g}$ is in the $-y$ direction. Then Eq. (2.24) becomes

$$-\oint_S \boldsymbol{n}(p_0 + \rho_f g y) dS + \int_{\mathcal{V}} \rho_b \boldsymbol{g} d\mathcal{V} = 0$$

Applying Gauss's theorem in Sec. A.23 to the left-hand surface integral,

$$-\int_{\mathcal{V}} \boldsymbol{\nabla}(p_0 + \rho_f g y) d\mathcal{V} + \int_{\mathcal{V}} \rho_b \boldsymbol{g} d\mathcal{V} = 0$$

Since p_0 is the atmospheric pressure which is constant, its gradient is zero, and then

$$-\int_{\mathcal{V}} \rho_f g \boldsymbol{j} d\mathcal{V} + \int_{\mathcal{V}} \rho_b \boldsymbol{j} g d\mathcal{V} = 0 \tag{2.25}$$

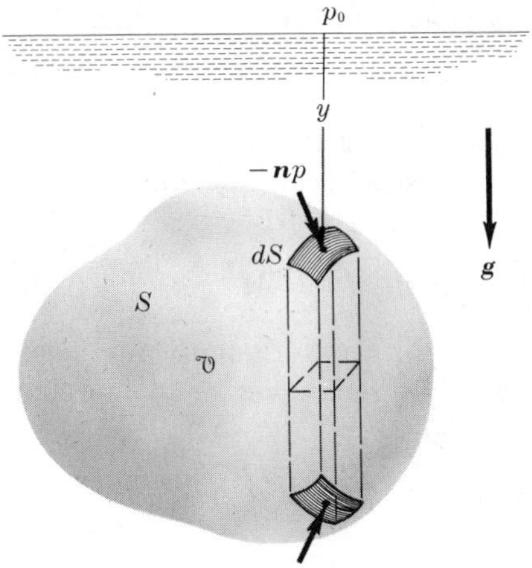

Figure 2.18
Forces on a submerged body.

This is a very interesting equation. The left-hand side term was deduced from the buoyant force and it is seen that this total buoyant force is opposite the direction of $\boldsymbol{g}$. Both forces are along the y-axis as indicated by $\boldsymbol{j}$ in the equation but they are in opposite directions. Another interesting result from the last equation states that the left-hand side representing *the weight of the displaced fluid due to the presence of the volume* $\mathcal{V}$ *is equal to the weight of the body with the same volume* $\mathcal{V}$. This is known as the *principle of Archimedes*.

It is obvious then for this body to be in equilibrium, its average density must equal the average density of the surrounding fluid. For a submarine to remain submerged at a constant depth it must have the right combination of air, water, and cargo to average the density of the sea at that depth. If its density is higher than that of the sea around it, it will sink. If the body is not in equilibrium, then the restoring lift force is

$$\boldsymbol{L} = \int_{\mathcal{V}} (\rho_f - \rho_b)\boldsymbol{g}\, d\mathcal{V} \tag{2.26}$$

$$= \boldsymbol{W}_f - \boldsymbol{W}_b$$

where $\boldsymbol{W}_f$ is the weight of the displaced fluid and $\boldsymbol{W}_b$ is the weight of the body.

For complete mechanical equilibrium the acting forces must not only sum to zero but the moments must be zero. Since the density distribution in the volume for the body may not be the same as that for the displaced fluid, although the buoyant force is equal and opposite to the weight of the body, they may not be colinear. This will result into a moment that will rotate the body. For this it is necessary to locate *the center of buoyancy* as one locates *the center of gravity*. The moment equation of the force system of Eq. (2.24) is

$$\int_{\mathcal{V}} \rho_b(\boldsymbol{r}_1 \times \boldsymbol{g})d\mathcal{V} - \oint_S (\boldsymbol{r}_2 \times \boldsymbol{n})p\,dS = \boldsymbol{M} \tag{2.27}$$

where $\boldsymbol{r}_1$ is the radius vector from an arbitrary origin to any mass-point in the volume of the body, and $\boldsymbol{r}_2$ is the radius vector to any point on the surface. Since $\boldsymbol{g}$ is a constant then

$$\int_{\mathcal{V}} (\boldsymbol{g} \times \boldsymbol{r}_1)\rho_b\, d\mathcal{V} = -\int_{\mathcal{V}} (\boldsymbol{r}_1 \times \boldsymbol{g})\rho_b\, d\mathcal{V} = \boldsymbol{g} \times \int_{\mathcal{V}} \boldsymbol{r}_1\rho_b\, d\mathcal{V}$$

But

$$\int_{\mathcal{V}} \boldsymbol{r}_1\rho_b\, d\mathcal{V} = \int_{\mathcal{V}} \boldsymbol{r}_1\, dm_b$$

$$= \boldsymbol{r}_{g_b} m_b$$

gives the location $\boldsymbol{r}_{g_b}$ of the *center of mass* or *center of gravity* of the body with a mass $m_b = \int_{\mathcal{V}} \rho_b\, d\mathcal{V}$. Now the buoyant force can be transformed also in a similar fashion:

$$\oint_S \boldsymbol{n} \times (p\boldsymbol{r}_2)\, dS = -\oint (\boldsymbol{r}_2 \times \boldsymbol{n})p\,dS$$

By Eq. 2.71(a)

$$\oint_S \boldsymbol{n} \times (p\boldsymbol{r}_2)\, dS = \int_{\mathcal{V}} \boldsymbol{\nabla} \times (p\boldsymbol{r}_2)\, d\mathcal{V}$$

If one expands $\boldsymbol{\nabla} \times (p\boldsymbol{r}_2)$ according to Eq. [A.53(b)]

$$\boldsymbol{\nabla} \times (p\boldsymbol{r}_2) = p(\boldsymbol{\nabla} \times \boldsymbol{r}_2) + (\boldsymbol{\nabla} p) \times \boldsymbol{r}_2$$

But $\boldsymbol{\nabla} \times \boldsymbol{r}_2 = 0$ and then from Eq. (2.2)

$$\oint_S \boldsymbol{n} \times (p\boldsymbol{r}_2)\, dS = \int_{\mathcal{V}} \rho_f \boldsymbol{g} \times \boldsymbol{r}_2\, d\mathcal{V}$$

$$= \boldsymbol{g} \times \int_{\mathcal{V}} \rho_f \boldsymbol{r}_2\, d\mathcal{V}$$

$$= \boldsymbol{g} \times m_f \boldsymbol{r}_{g_f}$$

where $\boldsymbol{r}_{g_f}$ is the center of gravity of the displaced fluid or the *center of buoyancy*. Then Eq. (2.27) becomes

$$\boldsymbol{M} = \boldsymbol{g} \times (m_f \boldsymbol{r}_{g_f} - m_b \boldsymbol{r}_{g_b}) \tag{2.28}$$

If the body is floating $m_f = m_b$ and then

$$\boldsymbol{M} = \boldsymbol{W} \times (\boldsymbol{r}_{g_f} - \boldsymbol{r}_{g_b}) \tag{2.29}$$

For $\boldsymbol{M} = 0$ the center of gravity of the body and the center of buoyancy must be from Eq. (2.28) along $\boldsymbol{g}$. For a closed surface, the center of pressure becomes the center of buoyancy and its coordinate location from Eqs. (2.17), (2.18), and (2.19) can be found. For instance, since $ydS_y = d\mathcal{V}$

$$y_p = \frac{\int_{\mathcal{V}} y\,d\mathcal{V}}{\mathcal{V}} \tag{2.30}$$

Illustrative Example 2.7

From Eq. (2.28) it is seen that if $m_f\boldsymbol{g} = m_b\boldsymbol{g}$ then for no turning moment $\boldsymbol{r}_{g_b}$ must be colinear with $\boldsymbol{r}_{g_f}$ and $\boldsymbol{g}$. Since $|\boldsymbol{g} \times \boldsymbol{r}_{g_f}| = gr_{g_f}\sin\beta$, $|\boldsymbol{g} \times \boldsymbol{r}_{g_b}| = gr_{g_b}\sin\alpha$ then $r_{g_f}\sin\beta = \gamma_{g_b}\sin\alpha$. For this to be true the points B and G of the center of buoyancy and gravity must be along $\boldsymbol{g}$ and $r_{g_f}\sin\beta = r_{g_f}\sin\alpha = OA$.

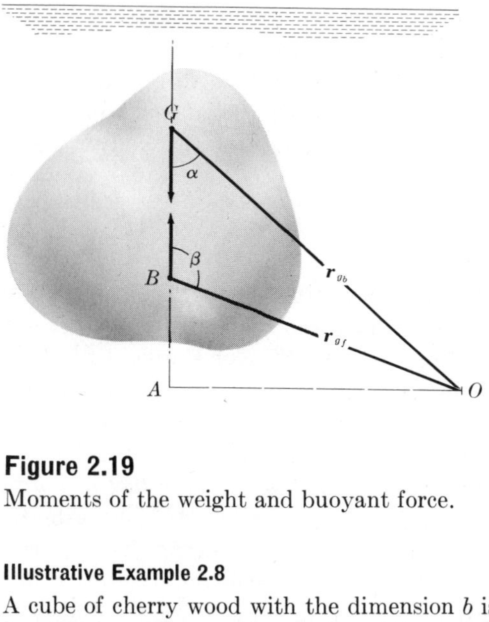

Figure 2.19
Moments of the weight and buoyant force.

Illustrative Example 2.8

A cube of cherry wood with the dimension b is submerged in water at a depth $l = 16.1$ in. The specific gravity of the wood is 0.5. Find the acceleration of the block toward the surface when the block is released. The viscous drag is neglected.

In the submerged position, the resultant hydrostatic pressure acting on the block is $b\rho_0 g$. The density of the water is ρ_0. The hydrostatic-lift force is then $b^3\rho_0 g$. If the density of the wood is denoted by ρ_w, then the weight of the block is $b^3\rho_w g$, and the resultant upward force is

$$L = g(\rho_0 - \rho_w)b^3$$

Since the mass of the block is $\rho_w b^3$, then the acceleration when the block is released is the force divided by the mass

$$a = g\left(\frac{\rho_0 - \rho_w}{\rho_w}\right) = g\left(\frac{\rho_0}{\rho_w} - 1\right) = g$$

The time required for the block to reach the surface is $t = \sqrt{2l/g}$, or 1 sec.

2.14 Floating Bodies—Metacenter and Metacentric Height

The equilibrium conditions for floating bodies at the surface of a liquid are the same as those for a submerged body. *The weight of the body must equal the weight of the fluid displaced.* If the average density of the body is less than that of the liquid, the body will float on the surface in such a way as to displace a smaller volume of liquid with weight equal to that of the body. There is no need to repeat the analysis for equilibrium; Eq. (2.26) applies except that the volume of displaced fluid is no longer equal to the volume of the body. Then

$$\int_{\mathcal{V}_b} \rho_b \mathbf{g}\, d\mathcal{V}_b = \int_{\mathcal{V}_f} \rho_f \mathbf{g}\, d\mathcal{V}_f$$

$$\mathbf{B} = \mathbf{W} \tag{2.31}$$

where the subscripts b and f identify quantities pertaining to the body and fluid. For equilibrium, the buoyant force $\mathbf{B}$ is equal to the weight of the body $\mathbf{W}$. The volume $\mathcal{V}_b$ represents that of the floating body shown in Fig. 2.20 and the volume $\mathcal{V}_f$ represents the volume of displaced fluid BCA in the a-position and $B'CA'$ in the b-position.

A floating body is said to be in *stable equilibrium, if, when displaced slightly, the forces and moments at the new position are such that they tend to return the body to its original position.* In Fig. [2.20(b)] the body, in the shape of a boat, has been displaced on angle $d\alpha$ and its center of buoyancy P has been displaced to P' by an angle $d\alpha$ relative to the line MC on which G and P are located. At this tilted position the forces $\mathbf{W}$ and $\mathbf{B}$ form a couple with a counterclockwise moment $|\overrightarrow{GF} \times \mathbf{W}| = Wm\, d\alpha$ in the direction opposing the original displacement. The boat was therefore in stable equilibrium. The point M of intersection of $\mathbf{B}$ and $\overrightarrow{GP}$ is called the *metacenter* or the center of rolling of the boat. The distance $\overline{MG} = m$ which enters in the restoring moment $Wm\, d\alpha$ is called the *metacentric height.* The quantity can be evaluated in terms

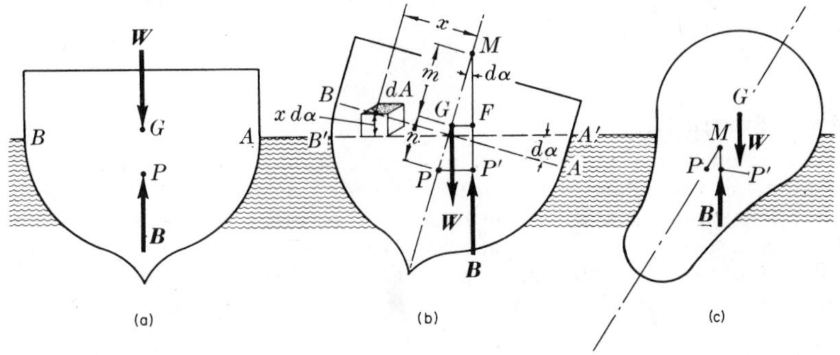

Figure 2.20

of the geometry of the boat if the density of the fluid around the boat can be considered uniform.

The shift of the center of buoyancy from P to P' was caused by the *change* in the displaced volume. An elementary change in the displaced volume of the liquid is $x\, d\alpha dA$, where dA is an elemental cross-section area of the boat at the water line. Its weight is $\rho g x\, d\alpha\, dA$, and according to Eq. (2.17), this shift of volume should cause a change of the center of buoyancy PP'

$$(\overline{PP'})B = \rho g\, d\alpha \int_A x^2\, dA$$

Here $x\, d\alpha = dy$ and $dA = dS_y$. Since $\mathbf{B} = \mathbf{W}$

$$PP' = \frac{I}{|\mathbf{W}|}\, d\alpha$$

$$= \frac{I}{\mathcal{V}}\, d\alpha \tag{2.32}$$

I is the moment of inertia of the water-line cross-section and is the volume of the fluid displaced. The quantity $I/\mathcal{V}$ represents then the length $\overline{MP}$ and therefore the metacentric height m is found from

$$m = \frac{I}{\mathcal{V}} - n \tag{2.33}$$

It can be seen from Eq. (2.33) that the floating body is in stable equilibrium as long as $I/\mathcal{V} > n$ or $\overline{MP} > \overline{GP}$. In the case of the body in Fig. [2.20(c)] $\overline{MP} < \overline{GP}$ and therefore the moment of the couple $(\mathbf{B}, \mathbf{W})$ is in a direction of the original displacement and consequently unstable. Therefore for stable equilibrium the metacenter must be above the center of gravity.

Illustrative Example 2.9

Consider a spherical shell as shown in Fig. (2.21) floating on a liquid. The outer radius of the sphere is r and its thickness t is small compared with the radius. The specific gravity of the spherical shell is 8. If h is the submerged depth, it is necessary to find a relationship between r, t, and h for equilibrium.

The volume of the submerged sphere can be calculated by integrating the elemental volume $\pi \times x^2\, dy$. This volume is

$$\frac{\pi}{3} h^2(3r - h)$$

For equilibrium, the weight of the thin shell must equal the weight of the displaced fluid. Then

$$4\pi r^2 t\, \rho_m g = \frac{\pi}{3} \rho_w g h^2(3r - h)$$

From this

$$t = \frac{h^2(3r - h)}{96r^2}$$

Now if the sphere is half submerged then $h = r$ and

$$t = \frac{r}{48}$$

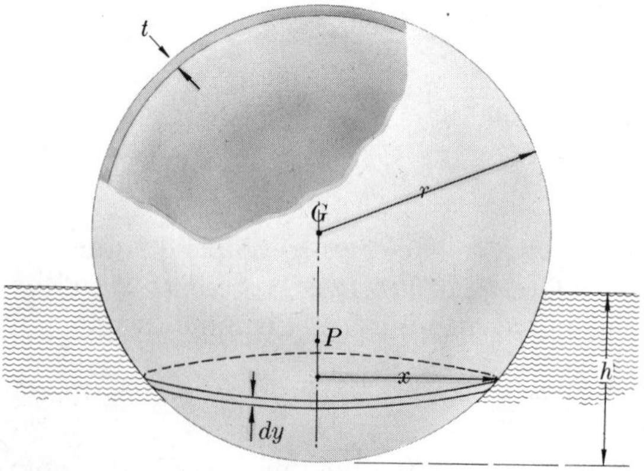

Figure 2.21
A floating spherical shell.

This answer is compatible with the assumption made at the beginning that the thickness is small compared to the radius. Here it is approximately 2 per cent.

Now, at the half-submerged position, the center of buoyancy P from Eq. (2.30) is at $3r/8$ from the surface. Now the value of $I/\mathcal{V}$ is found easily since I through the center of the circle is $\pi r^4/4$ and the submerged volume $\mathcal{V} = 2\pi r^3/3$. Then $I/\mathcal{V} = 3r/8$, and therefore the metacenter from Eq. (2.33) is at the center of gravity. The sphere is then in a *neutral equilibrium*. It turns out that for no matter what depth the sphere is submerged the metacenter is at the center of gravity and there no metacentric height. Therefore it is in neutral equilibrium. For instance, if $h = r/2$, the center of buoyancy is calculated to be $7r/40$ from the surface of the water. I for the cross-sectional surface of the sphere at the water level is $9\pi r^4/64$, and the displaced volume

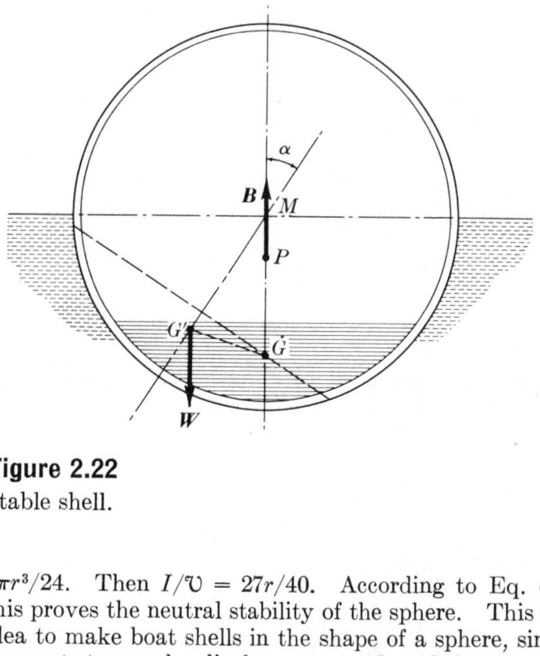

Figure 2.22
Stable shell.

$5\pi r^3/24$. Then $I/\mathcal{V} = 27r/40$. According to Eq. (2.33), n is $GP = 27r/40$; this proves the neutral stability of the sphere. This shows that it is not a good idea to make boat shells in the shape of a sphere, since they have no restoring moments to angular displacements unless their center of gravity is moved away from the center. For instance, a floating spherical shell with some weight at the bottom as shown in Fig. 2.22 when rotated on angle α proves to be stable. The center of buoyancy P does not change position in this case since the metacenter turns out to be the center of the sphere. This is seen to be true since it was already found that $MP = I/\mathcal{V} = 3r/8$ is the same as OP the location of the center of buoyancy. The restoring moment is

$$\mathbf{M} = \overrightarrow{MG} \times \mathbf{W}$$

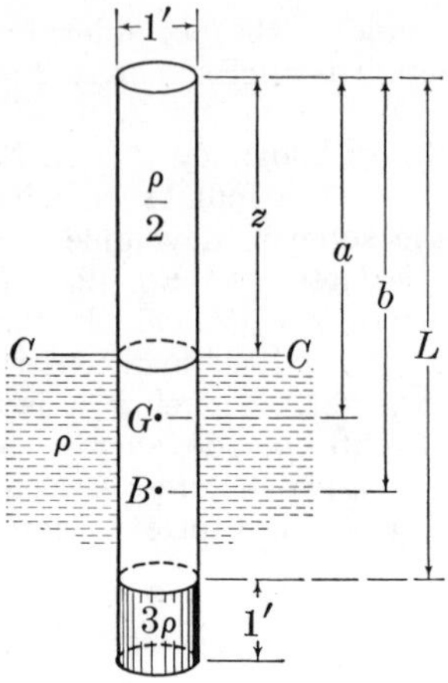

Figure 2.23
Floating pole.

Illustrative Example 2.10

A cylindrical pole 1 ft in diameter and L long has a specific gravity of 0.5. A cylindrical concrete mold 1 ft in diameter and 1 ft high is attached at the bottom for the purpose of floating the pole vertically as a marker buoy. The concrete has a specific gravity of 3.0. The purpose of this problem is to find the maximum and minimum pole length which will cause the pole to float vertically above the surface of water. (Fig. 2.23)

The total weight of the buoy is

$$\rho g \frac{\pi}{4}\left[\frac{L}{2} + 3\right]$$

The submerged volume is $\frac{\pi}{4}(L - z + 1)$

For floating conditions, the weight must always equal the buoyant force, and

$$\rho g \frac{\pi}{4}\left[\frac{L}{2} + 3\right] = \rho g \frac{\pi}{4}[L - z + 1]$$

$$z = \frac{L}{2} - 2$$

The center of buoyancy, measured from the top of the pole is $b = z + (L - z + 1)/2 = (L + z + 1)/2 = (3L - 2)/4$.

The distance a to the center of gravity can be found by taking moments of the weights with respect to the end of the pole:

$$\rho g \frac{\pi}{4}\left[\frac{L}{2} + 3\right] a = \frac{\rho g}{2}\frac{\pi}{4} L \frac{L}{2} + 3\rho g \frac{\pi}{4}(L + \tfrac{1}{2})$$

$$a = \frac{13L + 6}{2L + 12}$$

The distance $\overline{GB} = b - a = \dfrac{6L^2 - 20L - 48}{8L + 48}$

The metacentric height $\overline{MG}$ can then be found from Eq. (2.33):

$$\overline{MG} = \frac{I_{cc}}{\mathcal{V}} - \overline{GB}$$

The moment of inertia of the pole cross section at CC with respect to the axis CC is $\pi d^4/64$; in this case $d = 1$, the diameter of the cross section.

$$\overline{MG} = \frac{\pi/64}{\pi(L - z + 1)/4} - \frac{6L^2 - 20L - 48}{8L + 48}$$

$$= \frac{1}{8L + 48} - \frac{6L^2 - 20L - 48}{8L + 48}$$

$$= -\frac{6L^2 - 20L - 49}{8L + 48}$$

The pole will be considered to be stably floating when $\overline{MG} > 0$ or the metacenter is above the center of gravity. This limit is found when all L values are below the one solved for $\overline{MG} = 0$. The solution of $-6L^2 + 20L + 49 > 0$ gives $L < 4.98$. For the pole to be floating vertically above the surface of the water, z cannot be less than zero. $z = \frac{L}{2} - 2 > 0$ gives the lower limit of $L > 4$.

2.15 The Period of Rolling

In Fig. 2.18, for a finite angle α, the restoring moment, that of the couple acting on G and P, was found to be $W \times \overline{GF}$ or $W \times \overline{MG} \sin \alpha$. When this restoring torque acts freely on the floating body, it acts in such a way as to decrease the original angle. In general mechanics it was shown that this torque will be responsible for changing the angular momentum of the motion of the floating body with respect to its axis of roll O. This rate of change of angular momentum is $-I_m \frac{d^2\alpha}{dt^2}$. The quantity I_m is the mass moment of inertia of the ship at the axis of roll, and $d^2\alpha/dt^2$ is the angular acceleration. The minus sign indicates that the restoring torque $W \times \overline{MG} \times \alpha$, for small α, acts in the direction of reducing α. Then

$$-W \times \overline{MG} \times \alpha = I_m \frac{d^2\alpha}{dt^2}$$

$$\frac{d^2\alpha}{dt^2} = \ddot{\alpha} = -\frac{W \times \overline{MG}}{I_m} \alpha$$

This simple linear differential equation of a simple vibrating system is called the *pendulum equation*, because it is similar to that of the oscillation of a simple pendulum. It can be verified that the solution of this differential equation is

$$\alpha = \alpha_0 \cos \left(\frac{W \times \overline{MG}}{I_m} \right)^{1/2} t$$

This is done by substituting the solution back into the differential equation and making sure that it satisfies. The coefficient α_0 is the original or initial angular displacement at time $t = 0$. The quantity $(W \times \overline{MG}/I)^{1/2}$ is the frequency in radians per second or $2\pi f = (W \times \overline{MG}/I)^{1/2}$. The period of roll is the reciprocal of the frequency. Consequently, the time it will take for one complete oscillation of the floating body will be

$$t = 2\pi \sqrt{I_m/W \times \overline{MG}}$$

$$= 2\pi k \sqrt{g\,\overline{MG}} \text{ where } k \text{ is the radius of gyration.}$$

2.16 Surface Tension

The phenomenon of surface tension displays itself when dealing with problems involving the interface between two fluids. The interface behaves in a way similar to a thin stressed membrane under tension. From the molecular point of view, this difference of behavior of the interface can be explained by the fact that, at the interface, the cohesive forces between the molecules on one side of the interface are different from those on the other side of the interface. The surface-tension property of an interface can be readily changed by dissolving at the interface different fluids with different surface-tension properties.

The surface a liquid displays at the top of a container is sometimes referred to as the *free surface*. The surface-tension phenomenon on

Figure 2.24
Thin soap film on a loop.

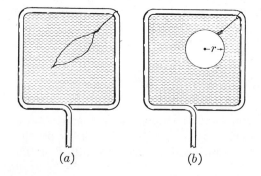

this free surface is displayed by the slight rise or depression of the level near the wall of the container. The formation of droplets and soap bubbles and the equilibrium of a drop of liquid on a dry solid surface depend upon surface tension. Fat lenses on the surface of a good broth are maintained in equilibrium because of the surface tension.

The fact that the surface-tension force will act to stretch the surface of a liquid film can be shown by the following example. A thin loop of thread is tied to a rigid loop of wire, as shown in Fig. 2.24. In the left figure, the soap film in the wire loop is shown to have formed all the way through the thread loop. If the soap film inside the thread loop is pierced, the rest of the remaining film will pull the string all the way around, owing to the surface-tension force, until the soap film attains its smallest possible surface, as shown in Fig. 2.24(*b*). In the same fashion, in the absence of external forces, owing to the surface tension a liquid will take a spherical shape which is the volume with the minimum area. A drop resting on a solid, dry surface is slightly out of round because of its own weight; a falling drop is deformed from its spherical shape as a result of the drag resistance during the fall.

The surface of a free liquid behaves somewhat like a stretched membrane, in such a manner that work must be done to the liquid system in order to alter the shape of its free surface. A free-fluid system has the tendency to assume as small a surface as possible for its given volume. It can be shown in elementary calculus that the volume having the smallest surface area is the sphere. Since a fluid assumes a minimum surface, the surface of this fluid must experience a force toward its center in order to prevent it from taking on any other form. This force, called the *surface-tension force,* is associated with the cohesion or attractive forces between the fluid molecules. The attraction between the molecules decreases with increasing distance between them, and consequently it can be neglected in the case of gases. In a group of molecules the cohesive forces will be such that the average distance between molecules is a minimum. This configuration corresponds to a sphere when the group of molecules is considered to be shielded from external forces. Inside the liquid, the molecular forces compensate each other, but those on the surface are acted upon by an inward force preventing the molecules from escaping. Thus this inner force is responsible for keeping the two halves of a soap bubble together. It is also this force that keeps the two halves of a liquid drop together and maintains the height of a liquid column in a capillary tube, as shown in Fig. 2.25.

The *surface-tension coefficient* is defined, then, as the force per unit length of any line on the free surface of a liquid necessary to hold that surface together at that line.

$$F = \int \sigma \, dl \tag{2.34}$$

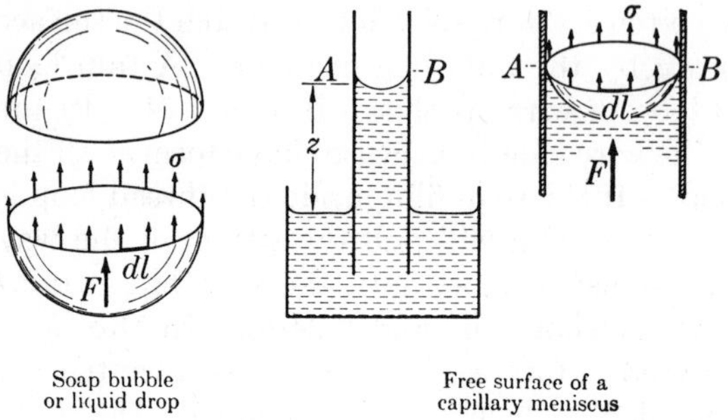

Figure 2.25
Free-liquid surfaces.

The quantity σ is the surface-tension coefficient and depends on the properties of the free surface of a liquid and its surroundings. This phenomenon of surface tension occurs as well at interfaces between liquids. The fat drops in a soup bowl constitute an example of liquid interfaces displaying a difference of cohesive forces at the interface. Since the spacing between molecules is a function of temperature, the surface-tension coefficient is therefore a function of temperature (Table 1.5). The value of σ varies with the materials making up the film and with the temperature.

Illustrative Example 2.11

Calculate the force necessary to divide an oil drop in water in two identical halves. Assume that the drop is spherical in shape, with a radius of $\frac{1}{2}$ in. The surface tension of the oil in water is 0.0024 lb_f/ft.

To divide the oil drop in half, a force must be exerted on the drop equal and opposite to that holding the two spherical halves together. According to Eq. (2.34) and Fig. 2.25 this force will be

$$F = \int_0^{2\pi} \sigma \, dl = 2\pi r \sigma$$

$$= \frac{2 \times 3.14 \times \frac{1}{2} \times 0.0024}{12}$$

$$= 0.000628 \text{ lb}_f$$

Now consider a completely closed surface like a soap bubble, and establish the forces involved for the equilibrium of a liquid film. As shown in Fig. 2.26 let an infinitesimal portion of a liquid film be considered as a free body for establishing the equilibrium. A general case

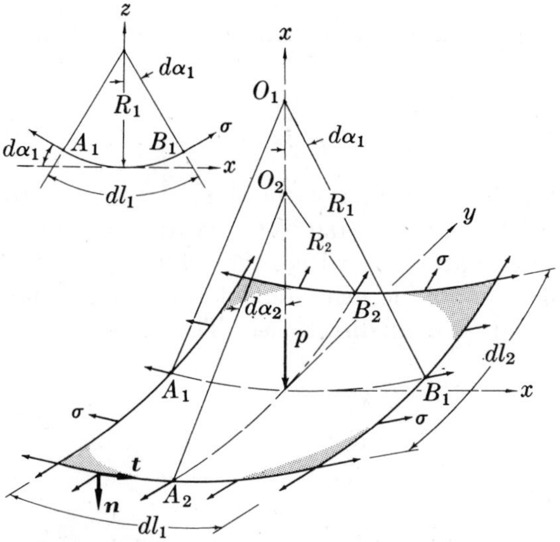

Figure 2.26
Forces on a curved fluid film.

is considered, for the curvature in the A_1B_1-direction may not necessarily be the same as that in the A_2B_2-direction. The forces keeping the film in its original shape are the surface-tension forces on all four sides of the film and the internal-pressure force of the film that must be there in order to balance the forces in the z-direction and keep the surface curved. Let p be the internal pressure of the film and p_0 the outside ambient pressure. Owing to symmetry, the contribution of the surface-tension force in the x- and y-directions must cancel all around the element $A_1A_2B_1B_2$. The equilibrium conditions in the z-direction give[7]

[7] This is one case where vector approach to the equilibrium of the surface forces is more cumbersome. If $\boldsymbol{n}$ is the outward unit normal, $\boldsymbol{t}$ the unit tangent to the contour C of the film with surface S. Then

$$\int_S \boldsymbol{n} p dS = \oint_C (\boldsymbol{n} \times \boldsymbol{t}) \sigma \, dc$$

$$(p - p_0)\, dl_1\, dl_2 = 2\sigma\, dl_2 \sin d\alpha_1 + 2\sigma\, dl_1 \sin d\alpha_2$$

For infinitesimal geometry, $\sin d\alpha_1 = d\alpha_1 = \frac{dl_1}{2R_1}$, and, in the same manner, $d\alpha_2 = \frac{dl_2}{2R_2}$. When these values are substituted in the equilibrium equation, the internal pressure of the film related to the radii of curvature is found to be

$$p - p_0 = \sigma\left(\frac{1}{R_1} + \frac{1}{R_2}\right) \tag{2.35}$$

This indicates that the bigger the radius of the film, the smaller the pressure inside the film. The principal radii of curvature R_1 and R_2 are positive if the center of curvature lies within the volume of the fluid film or drop. In general, a bubble is made out of two parallel films with the same radius of curvature in all directions. The excess pressure inside the bubble is then

$$p - p_0 = \frac{4\sigma}{R} \tag{2.36}$$

Illustrative Example 2.12

To find the work necessary to blow a soap bubble to a radius R_0, it is necessary to use the relation for reversible work and Eq. (2.36).

$$W = \int (p - p_0)\, d\mathcal{V}$$

According to Eq. (A.61) and Eq. (A.29)

$$\boldsymbol{pn} = \sigma(\boldsymbol{n} \bullet \boldsymbol{\nabla})\boldsymbol{t}$$

If both sides are multiplied by a differential length dc then

$$pndc = \sigma\, dt$$

From *Frenet's Formula.* (See, for instance, L. Brand, *Vector and Tensor Analysis*, John Wiley and Sons, Inc., New York, 1947, p. 92.)

Then $$dt/dc = \frac{1}{R}\boldsymbol{n}$$

$$p = \sigma\frac{1}{R}$$

This approach is limited to surfaces with one radius of curvature.

where $d\mathcal{V} = 4\pi R^2\,dR$.

$$W = \int_0^{R_0} \frac{4\sigma}{R}\, 4\pi R^2\, dR = 16\pi\sigma \int_0^{R_0} R\, dR$$
$$= 8\pi\sigma R_0^2$$
$$= 2\sigma S$$

where S is the surface area of the bubble.

2.17 Wetting and Nonwetting Fluids

When a drop of liquid rests on top of a dry, solid surface, three surface-tension forces enter into the equilibrium of the drop—the surface tension between the liquid and the solid, that between the liquid and the ambient air, and that in the film between the air and the solid surface. At points A or A', shown in Fig. 2.27, all three of these forces are present. The force shown on the diagram is that at A and A' owing to the film

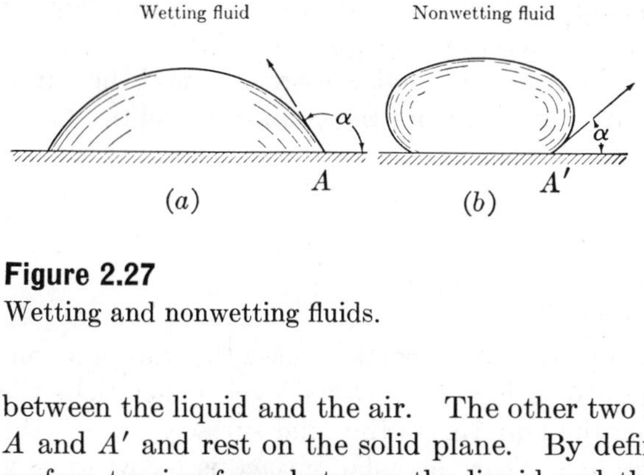

Figure 2.27
Wetting and nonwetting fluids.

between the liquid and the air. The other two forces are concurrent at A and A' and rest on the solid plane. By definition, if, as shown, the surface-tension force between the liquid and the ambient air makes at A or A' an angle α larger than 90° with the solid surface on the ambient-air side, then the fluid is said to be *wetting*. Water is a wetting fluid. Like mercury, if $\alpha < 90°$, then the fluid is called a *nonwetting* fluid.

The equilibrium of the wetting fluid near the wall of a container depends on the balance between its weight and the force owing to surface tension. According to Eq. (2.35), the pressure difference at the fluid surface is

$$p_1 - p = \sigma \frac{1}{R}$$

Here the container shown in Fig. 2.28 is considered to be very long in the direction normal to the paper, so that at any point of consideration the radius of curvature in the other direction is infinite. The hydrostatic equation also establishes this pressure difference in terms of the elevation z. Consequently, $p_1 = p_0 - g\rho_0 z$ and $p = p_0 - g\rho_w z$. Therefore, the pressure difference across the free surface $p_1 - p = g(\rho_w - \rho_0)z$. Equating these two relations, the equation of the elevation becomes

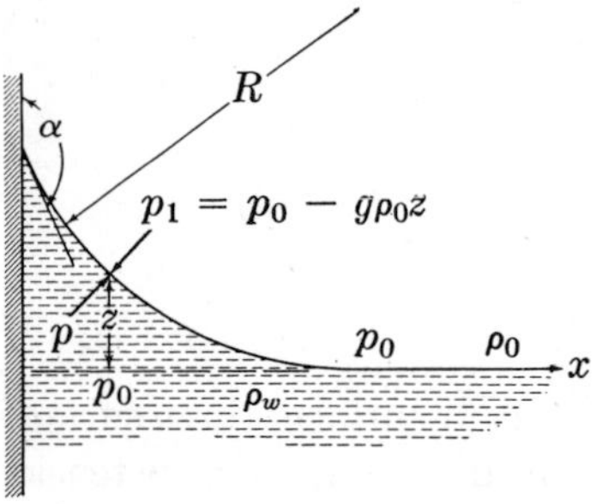

Figure 2.28
The free surface of a contained wetting fluid.

$$z = \frac{\sigma}{g(\rho_w - \rho_0)R}$$

From calculus, the radius of curvature of a curve is given in terms of the derivatives of the contour $z = f(x)$ of the free surface; therefore the previous equation is a differential equation that will need to be solved in order to find the variation of the water level with distance from the container wall.[8]

2.18 Capillarity

In the previous discussion it was observed that, near the wall of a container, the surface tension of a liquid raises its level higher than the rest of its free level when the liquid wets the solid surface. When the liquid is nonwetting, the level near the solid surface is below that of most of the fluid in the container. In either case the total surface-tension force is the surface-tension coefficient σ multiplied by the film periphery in the container. For instance, if the container is cylindrical in form, the film periphery is that of the cross section of the container.

[8] For solutions of surface contours, see S. Eskinazi, *Vector Mechanics of Fluids and Magnetofluids*, Academic Press, New York, 1967.

The weight of the fluid raised above the free surface must be equal to the component of the surface-tension force in the direction of the weight. Now, if the diameter of the cylinder is reduced, the surface-tension force reduces in the same proportion as the diameter. The cross-sectional area reduces as the square of the diameter. In order for the weight of fluid supported above the free surface to reduce in the same proportion as the surface-tension force, the height of this supported liquid must increase in the inverse ratio of the decrease of the diameter.

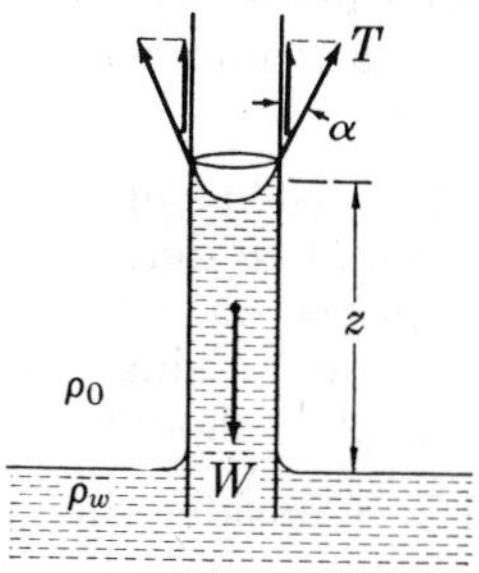

Figure 2.29 Capillarity in a narrow container.

For instance, let the container be a small-diameter tube, of radius r, open at both ends. This is shown in Fig. 2.29. When one end of the tube is introduced into a fluid, the total surface tension force is

$$T = 2\pi\sigma r$$

The vertical component of this force is

$$T \cos \alpha = 2\pi\sigma r \cos \alpha$$

Naturally, this force can support the buoyant force of the liquid in the ambient air $\pi r^2 z g(\rho_w - \rho_0)$. Therefore,

$$z = \frac{2\sigma \cos \alpha}{g(\rho_w - \rho_0)r} \tag{2.37}$$

This equation is similar to that derived for the one-dimensional case at the end of Sec. 2.16. One can see that this method is fairly adaptable for the determination of the surface-tension coefficient of a liquid. The geometry and the density of the column can be easily measured, and, from Eq. (2.37), the surface-tension coefficient σ can be computed. Surface-tension coefficients of water are tabulated in Table 1.5.

Problems

2.1 The mathematical enunciation of equilibrium was presented in Sec. 2.3. The surface force was assumed, in the static case, to be exclusively a pressure force always normal to any immersed surface.

This implies that the normal to the surface is in the direction of the surface force and that the difference between them is simply a scalar p called pressure. Can you discuss how, in your opinion, it would have been necessary to handle the summation of forces had there been tangential components of the surface force owing to frictional motion, for instance?

2.2 Instead of considering Theorems I and II in Sec. 2.4, separately, attempt to derive Eq. (2.2) by taking a completely arbitrary volume $\mathcal{V}$ as in Sec. 2.13 and writing the equilibrium equation for the entire *finite* volume. Using the divergence Theorem in Sec. A.22, the result of Eq. (2.2) should be apparent.

2.3 Consider the geometry of Eq. (2.2). Taking an arbitrary surface where p = const., what is the relationship of the gravitational acceleration $\boldsymbol{g}$ to that surface? Can Theorem I be deduced from this relationship?

2.4 In the case of a gravitational force, we know that, as in the case of $\boldsymbol{g}$, it can be represented as the gradient of a potential energy. If Ω represents the potential energy per unit mass, then $\boldsymbol{g} = -\nabla\Omega$ and where $\Omega = gz$. Replacing in Eq. (2.2), $\boldsymbol{g}$ by the gradient of Ω an integrable simple differential equation can be obtained. Consult Sect. A.13 for integration. For a constant density, obtain the hydrostatic equation, readily.

2.5 The gauge pressure on the water surface in a tank A is $(p - p_0) = 2.0$ psi. The water and the ambient atmosphere are at 50°F. Find the height of water z. Find the pressure p_0'. (For densities of water and air, consult Tables 1.4 and 1.5.)

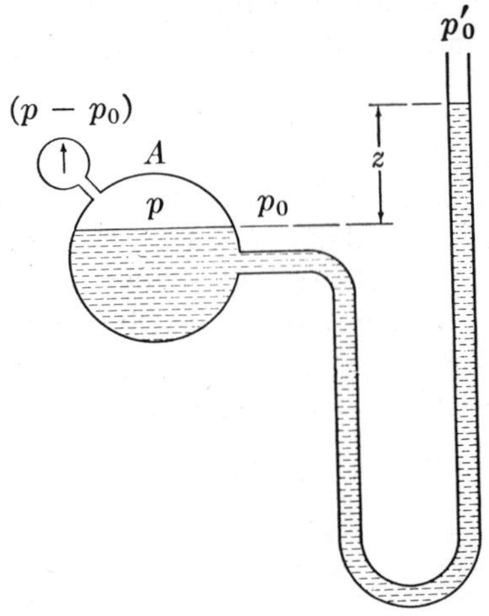

2.6 When the atmospheric pressure reads 14.7 psia, find the equivalent in feet of water and inches of mercury at 50°F.

2.7 Assuming that the density of the atmosphere does not change with height, what would be the height of the atmospheric column if the atmospheric pressure on the earth's surface was 14.7 psia and the density of the air at 50°F?

2.8 A tank contains a quantity of water of height h and an equally tall layer of an oil with specific gravity of 0.8. If the gauge pressure at the bottom of the tank (referred to ambient atmosphere) is to be 0.78 psi, what should be the height of each column h?

2.9 As shown, the pressure in the container at 1 is 2 atm. The difference of elevation ($z_2 - z_1$) is 2 ft, and the difference of density between the two fluids 2 and 1 is 10 lb_m/ft^3. What is the pressure at 3 in psi?

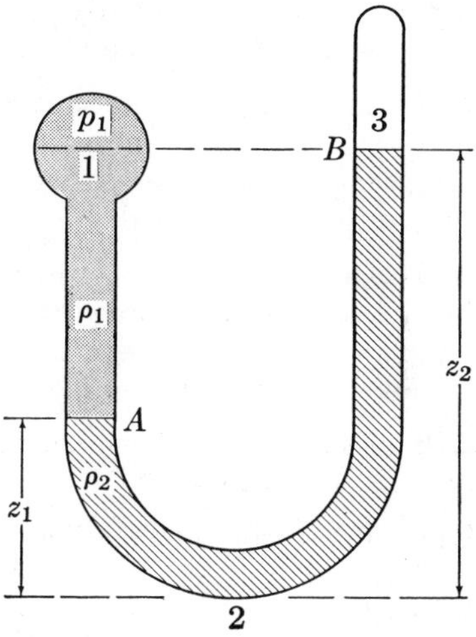

2.10 The short leg of a U-tube manometer is 10 in. Originally, 6 in. of water are poured into the U-tube, and then the short leg is scaled at the open end. More water is poured into the other leg until the level of the water in the short leg rises 1 in. What is the difference of elevation of the liquid surface in the two legs?

2.11 The sensitive differential manometer shown below has two liquids

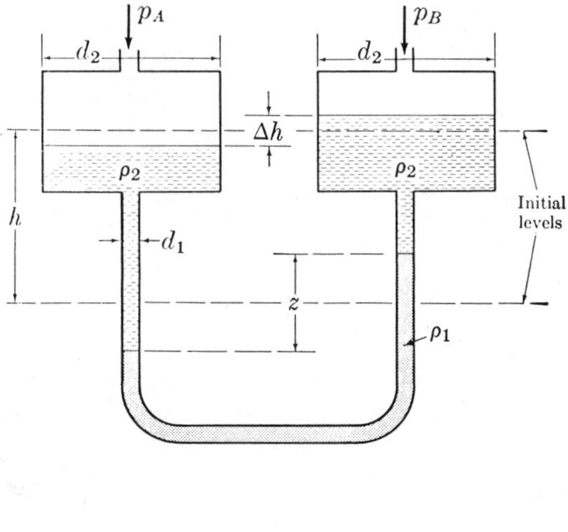

of density ρ_1 and ρ_2. Find an expression for the pressure difference $p_A - p_B$ in terms of ρ_1, ρ_2, z, d_1, and d_2.

2.12 What would be the height of the atmosphere if it were incompressible and the conditions at the earth's surface are $T_0 = -30°F$ and $p_0 = 14.7$ psia?

2.13 If the temperature-lapse rate in the troposphere is 3.57°F per 1,000 ft and consequently the polytropic exponent $n = 1.24$, express the pressure, density, and temperature as a function of altitude.

2.14 The pressure and the temperature at sea level are 14.7 psia and 60°F. If the troposphere is 36,000 ft high, find the atmospheric pressure, temperature, and density at 10 miles altitude. Assume the stratosphere to be isothermal.

2.15 Derive an expression for the pressure ratio if the temperature in the atmosphere is assumed to vary linearly with altitude. The absolute temperature $T = T_0 - a(z - z_0)$. T_0 is the absolute temperature at sea level and a is the temperature gradient.

2.16 For Prob. 2.15, show that the pressure-density variation is polytropic.

2.17 What would be the temperature-lapse rate if the atmosphere were adiabatic $\gamma = c_p/c_v = 1.4$? What, then, is the height of this troposphere?

2.18 What would be the difference in the pressure ratio p/p_0 for the polytropic atmosphere ($n = 1.24$), when the following two cases are considered: (*a*) variation of gravitational acceleration with altitude; (*b*) the gravitational acceleration is a constant and equal to that of sea level $g_0 = 32.17$ ft/sec². The radius of the earth is 3,959 miles.

2.19 What percentage of error is introduced in case (*b*) of Prob. 2.18 when the variation of g with z is neglected?

2.20 The dam shown holds 90 ft of water. The specific weight of the dam is 150 lb_f/ft^3. Find the reaction forces F_1 and F_2 holding the dam in equilibrium.

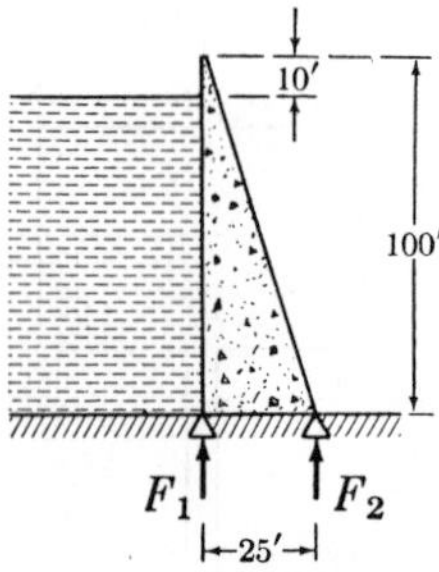

2.21 A horizontal circular pipe, sealed at both ends, with radius a and length b is half filled with a liquid of density ρ. (*a*) Find the force on either half of the pipe when sectioned with a vertical plane running along the full length b. (b) If the bottom of the pipe along the length b were hinged, what would be the moment necessary to keep both halves together?

2.22 A plane OA is supported by water at an angle θ, as shown. The plane OA is hinged at O. It has a weight W, a width a, and a depth normal to the paper b. What would be the height of water z above O as a function of the plane position θ?

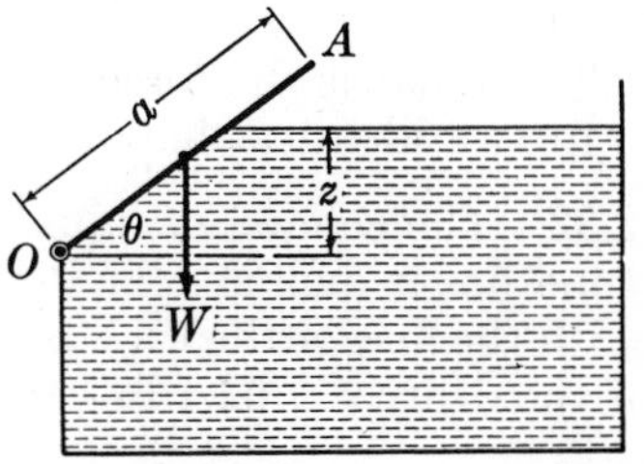

2.23 Locate the resultant force on half the cylinder of Prob. 2.21.

2.24 A circular gate 12 ft in diameter is submerged in a vertical position just below the surface of the water. Find the center of pressure from the surface of the water.

2.25 A spherical shell of diameter d completely floats on water. (a) Find the increase in buoyant force as a function of submerged depth until completely submerged. (b) Find the distance from the water surface to the center of buoyancy in terms of the submerged depth.

2.26 Find the forces on the walls of the parabolic channel shown. The channel is used for water. Also determine the location of the center of pressure.

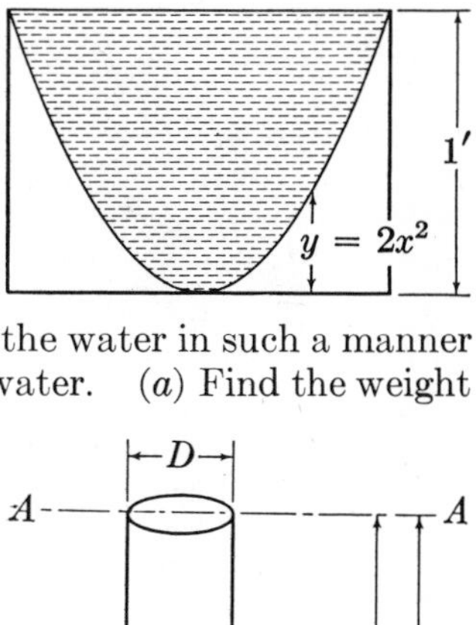

2.27 A 12-in.-square log 12 ft long floats on the water in such a manner that 1.0 in. remains above the surface of the water. (a) Find the weight of the log. (b) Find the righting couple and the metacentric height if the log is tipped with one side flush with the water level.

2.28 A buoy, as shown, consists of a wooden pole 1 ft in diameter and 5 ft long, with a semispherical weight at the bottom. The specific weight of the wood is 0.6 and of the bottom 1.5. (a) Find the positions of the center of gravity and the center of buoyancy from the top of the buoy. (b) Find the metacentric height. (c) Find the period of roll.

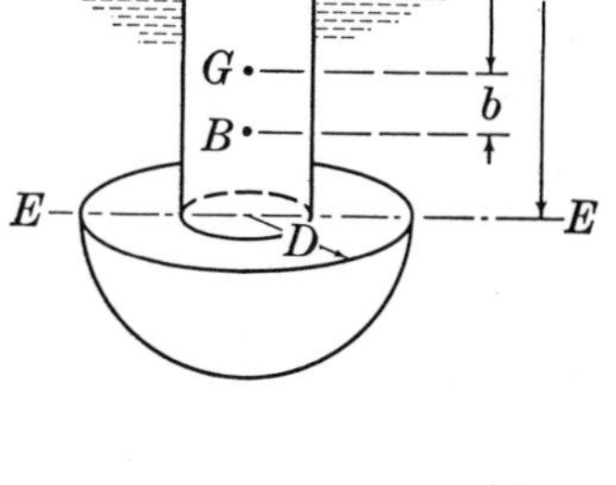

2.29 Find the period of roll for Prob. 2.27.

2.30 If it takes 0.00355 ft $\times$ lb_f to form a bubble with soapy water, what is the size of the bubble formed if $\sigma = 0.0051$ lb_f/ft?

2.31 What is the force necessary to separate the bubble in Prob. 2.30 into two identical halves? What was the pressure inside the bubble?

2.32 The column of liquid supported in a capillary tube is 2 in. The tube has a diameter of 0.030 in., and the inclination of the meniscus with the axis of the tube is 45°. What is the surface tension of the fluid if the density is 62.4 lb_m/ft^3?

2.33 In Prob. 2.32, if the diameter of the tube is increased to 0.060 in., what will be the height of the liquid column in the capillary?

Kinematics of Fluid Motion

chapter III

3.1 Introduction

Kinematics is that part of mechanics which deals with quantities derivable from units of space and time. Although forces are the causes responsible for accelerated or decelerated motions, kinematics is solely concerned with the effects of the motion on the displacement, time, velocity, acceleration, or any other quantity derivable from displacement and time. Before undertaking the study of forces responsible for the motion of fluids, it is desirable to acquire some understanding of the types of motion from the kinematic point of view.

It is worth while to review the following concepts of general mechanics pertaining to kinematics. The displacement, velocity, and acceleration of an elemental fluid mass is described relative to some coordinate system, fixed or moving. An observer on a bridge will describe the motion of a river with respect to a fixed coordinate system—fixed on the space of the earth. A fisherman drifting in a boat will describe the motion of the same river with respect to the moving boat. The description by these two observers will not be the same, since each description

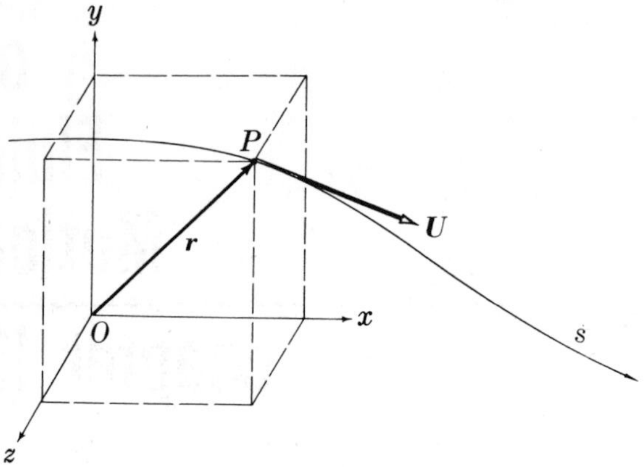

Figure 3.1
Motion at P with respect to O.

is relative to a coordinate system that does not have the same position, velocity, or acceleration. The description of both observers, however, can be made the same, provided that the displacement, velocity, and acceleration of one coordinate system are known relative to the other.

For convenience, in most engineering applications, the motion of a fluid at a given point x,y,z fixed with reference to a stationary coordinate system, is described as a function of time t. This method of motion representation, applied to every point in the flow field, is called *the Eulerian*[1] *coordinate representation.*

Following the diagram in Fig. 3.1, if O is chosen as the origin of such a system, any point P on the trajectory of a fluid-mass element having the coordinate x,y,z from O can also be represented by a single vector distance $\mathbf{r}$, which is the vector sum of the three coordinate distances x,y,z. The position, displacement, velocity, and acceleration of P are vector quantities, and, in general, they can be expressed in terms of the position vector $\mathbf{r}$ and the time t.

[1] After Leonhard Euler, a Swiss mathematician who, in the middle of the 18th century, was responsible for notable advances in hydrodynamics.

3.2 Basic Concepts and Dimensions

The state of a physical phenomenon is generally described by its properties; to be more exact, by a complete set of independent properties. Properties, in turn, are described by *basic fundamental dimensions* which form the skeleton of our entire dimensional system. For instance, the motion of an object is described in terms of its momentum at a given time. This description can be divided into more basic units such as the *mass*, the *velocity*, and the *time*. In turn, the velocity can be further described by two more fundamental quantities, namely the *length* and *time*. Consequently, in the case of mechanics cited, *mass length* and *time* are the most basic fundamental dimensions involved. For phenomena treated in general dynamics, these three basic fundamental dimensions are sufficient. A fourth dimension, that of a force, was also discussed in Chap. I, but it was shown that it is a unit that is derivable from mass length and time.

3.3 Geometric, Kinematic, and Dynamic Similitude

Two flow fields are said to be *geometrically similar* when the geometry of the motion of one is merely a constant scale of the other, throughout corresponding points of the entire motion. This condition implies that the flow field and its boundaries show the same geometrical scaling. If the coordinate axes in the two flow fields are similarly oriented, the two flow fields will be geometrically similar if their geometric corresponding angles are equal. In other words, the scaling does not alter the angles in the geometry of the motion. For geometrical similitude the ratio of characteristic lengths L_1/L_2 is a constant at corresponding parts of the two flow fields.

In a similar fashion, *kinematic similarity* implies that the velocity ratio at corresponding points throughout the motion of various systems is a constant. Therefore, U_1/U_2 is a constant for all corresponding points of the two systems.

It was mentioned in Sec. 1.12 that the geometry of the boundaries of a perfect fluid determine the geometry of the flow field. It follows, therefore, that complete similarity exists between two perfect fluids, provided that the geometric similarity is satisfied. For instance, if a perfect fluid flows around a cylinder and if the diameter of the cylinder is suddenly doubled, corresponding properties of the flow will move to new positions twice the original distance from the origin. The geometry of the flow field, however, will remain unaltered if the velocity of the flow field is suddenly doubled. In that case all the points in the flow field will assume a velocity twice as large.

In the case of real fluids, satisfying the geometrical and the kinematical similarity is not sufficient in order to ensure dynamic similarity as well. This is readily understood, for instance, in the case of viscous motion when different viscous fluids produce different viscous effects, even with the same boundary geometries. To conclude, increasing the scale of the boundaries or increasing the velocity level does not increase the viscous effects of a real fluid in the same proportion. In that case, for similarity to exist between two flow fields, *dynamic similitude* must also be satisfied.

Dynamic similitude is said to exist in flow fields when the ratio of corresponding forces F_1/F_2 in both flow fields is the same. In general, the forces that influence the motion of a real fluid are forces of inertia, viscosity, pressure, gravitation, elasticity, surface tension, and electric and magnetic forces if the fluid is permeable to electric and magnetic fields. In general, if all these forces are present in the movement of a fluid, then, for complete similitude to exist in two flow fields, the ratio of all these forces must be the same in both fields.

(*a*) *Reynolds Number*

In most incompressible flow fields for which the density remains essentially constant, the pressure forces are uniquely determined by the balance of viscous and inertial forces. In such flow fields, where the other types of forces either are not present or can be neglected, for equilibrium, the component summation of forces will read

$$F_p = F_i - F_v$$

The subscript on the force F indicates pressure, inertia, and viscosity in the order of the equation. If the equation is divided by the inertial force F_i, the result is

$$F_p/F_i = 1 - F_v/F_i$$

The left-hand side of this dimensionless equation gives the dependent variable F_p/F_i, which is defined as the *pressure coefficient*. The independent variable on the right-hand side F_v/F_i, which is the ratio of the viscous forces to the inertial forces, is defined as the reciprocal of the *Reynolds*[1] *number*. Consequently, this independent dimensionless num-

[1] In honor of Osborne Reynolds, who first applied the idea that his dimensionless number is essential for identifying viscous similitude. *Phil. Trans. Roy. Scc. London*. Vol. 174, 1883, pp. 935–982.

ber, called *Reynolds number, is determined by the ratio of the inertial forces to the viscous forces.*

L, U, and t represent a characteristic length, velocity, and time of the flow system. For instance, for flow inside a pipe, the characteristic length can be the diameter; the characteristic velocity, the average velocity in the pipe, and the characteristic time can be taken from the origin where the pipe flow began. The inertial force being the product of the mass and the acceleration, at a point in the flow field it will be proportional to

$$F_i \propto \rho L^3 \frac{U}{t} \propto \rho L^2 U^2$$

Since L/t has the dimensions of velocity, this ratio has been substituted for U in the previous equation. Similarly, according to Eq. (1.7), the viscous force which represents the product of the shear stress and the characteristic area L^2 will be proportional to

$$F_v \propto \tau L^2 \propto \mu \frac{U}{L} L^2 = \mu U L$$

The characteristic Reynolds number $\mathcal{R}$ is then

$$\mathcal{R} \propto \frac{\text{inertial force}}{\text{viscous force}} = \frac{F_i}{F_v}$$

$$\frac{\text{Inertial force}}{\text{Viscous force}} \propto \frac{\rho L^2 U^2}{\mu U L} = \frac{UL}{\nu} = \mathcal{R} \tag{3.1}$$

The Reynolds number will be derived in Sec. 9.5 from the equations of motion of a viscous fluid.

(*b*) *Mach Number*

If a fluid is considered to be compressible, that is, the density varies with the pressure level throughout the flow field, elastic forces in the fluid elements become as important as the inertial forces. In that case the equilibrium equation divided by the inertial force will give another ratio of forces which is important when comparing compressible fluids.

According to Eq. (1.6), the characteristic dimensions of the elastic force are obtained when that equation is multiplied by the characteristic area L^2. Therefore, the elastic force is proportional to EL^2. The quantity E is the modulus of elasticity of the fluid.

$$\frac{\text{Inertial force}}{\text{Elastic force}} \propto \frac{\rho L^2 U^2}{E L^2} = \frac{\rho U^2}{E}$$

Considering Eq. (1.6) again, after multiplying and dividing by the mass of the system the modulus of elasticity in terms of the density is

$$E = \rho \frac{dp}{d\rho}$$

The quantity $dp/d\rho$ has the units of a velocity squared. Precisely, it is the square of the velocity of sound in the fluid medium.[2] If the sound velocity is denoted by a, the modulus of elasticity relation becomes

$$E = \rho a^2$$

Substitution of this relation into the force-ratio equation yields

$$\frac{\text{Inertial force}}{\text{Elastic force}} \propto \left(\frac{U}{a}\right)^2 = \mathfrak{M}^2 \tag{3.2}$$

The quantity $\mathfrak{M}$ is the *Mach*[3] *number*, which represents the ratio of the velocity of the fluid to that of sound in the same fluid. When this number assumes the same value in two different flow fields, it indicates that the ratio of inertial forces to elastic forces is the same in both flow fields. Its value also indicates the importance of compressibility in the particular flow considered. For complete similarity to exist in flow fields whose density variations with pressure are large, the Mach numbers of these flows must also be the same.

3.4 Classification of Types of Motion

Chapter II included a discussion of the various forces that may, in general, contribute to the motion of a fluid. Besides these forces, if thermodynamic changes take place with the motion, the change of thermodynamic state also influences the motion. In addition, the kinematic conditions pertaining at the time origin of flow, as well as those at the boundaries of the flow, affect the over-all motion.

A *perfect fluid* already has been differentiated from a *real fluid* by

[2] See Sec. 8.3 for a detailed derivation.

[3] In honor of the Austrian physicist and philosopher, Ernst Mach, who was also a pioneer in the development of optical methods for visualizing high-speed flows. The term "Mach number" was first proposed by J. Ackeret, *Schweiz. Bauz.* Vol. 94, 1929, p. 179.

the fact that it does not sustain shear or changes in density owing to compressive forces. Naturally, the assumption of a perfect fluid simplifies the mathematical treatment of the motion, since it ignores shear and effects of compressive forces. Because all fluids are viscous, the assumption of a perfect fluid is unrealistic in all cases where shear forces are present. Fluid flows are also classified into two large fields of study, according to the behavior of the density in the fluid. These classifications take the names *compressible* and *incompressible* fluid motion. These two types of flow were discussed in Chap. I, and it should be understood that the presence or omission of elastic forces will, in general, alter the over-all character of the flow (Fig. 3.2). The Mach number was found to be a measure of the relative importance of compressibility. Consequently, since the Mach number is the ratio of the fluid velocity to that of the sound in that fluid, sometimes a more specific set of classifications is adopted instead, such as *subsonic, sonic, supersonic,* and *hypersonic* flows.

The classification *subsonic* simply indicates fluid speeds with a Mach number less than unity; this, however, does not imply that the elastic forces are not important or, in other words, that the motion is incompressible. *Sonic* flow occurs when the fluid velocity reaches that of sound in the fluid. The *supersonic* regime extends for flow speeds higher than that of sound. The regime of *hypersonic* flows embraces the motions of fluids at extremely high speeds—about five times the velocity of sound or greater.

Regardless of the level of elastic forces in the flow field, flows are also classified as *laminar* or *turbulent,* depending on the ratio of the inertia to viscous forces or, in other words, on the Reynolds number $\mathcal{R}$. At low values of $\mathcal{R}$ (the critical value will be established in Chap. X), the flow, compressible or not, is said to be *laminar* because the fluid layers flow in a smooth, laminated form. If a streak of dye is injected in the center at the mouth of a tube, as shown on Fig. 3.3(a), the dye will remain parallel to the walls of the tube when $\mathcal{R}$ is low and the flow is laminar. If the same experiment is repeated with an increase of speed in the tube, the streak of dye will break into *sinuous* or *turbulent* irregularity, diffusing the dye rapidly downstream of the breaking point, as shown in Fig. 3.3(b). The breaking point from laminar to turbulent moves in an upstream direction as the velocity of the fluid is increased. Eventually, at a given critical $\mathcal{R}$, the entire flow will become turbulent in the passage. Although Osborne Reynolds was not the first to experience this essential structural change in the flow, he was the first to

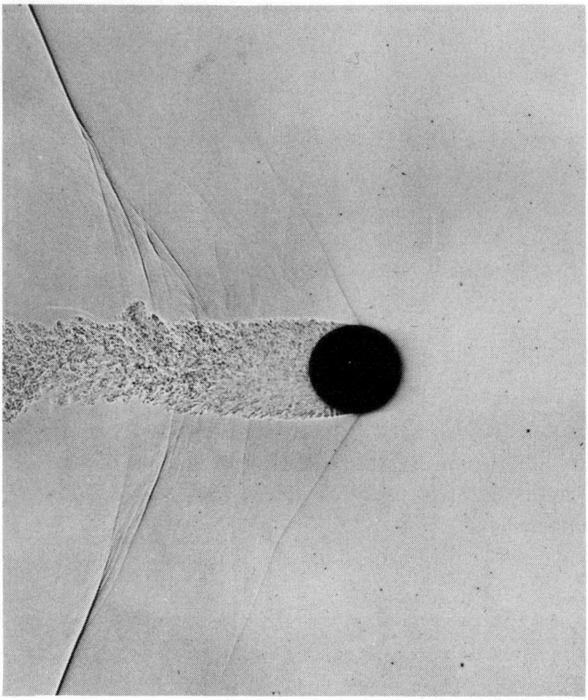

(a)

(b)

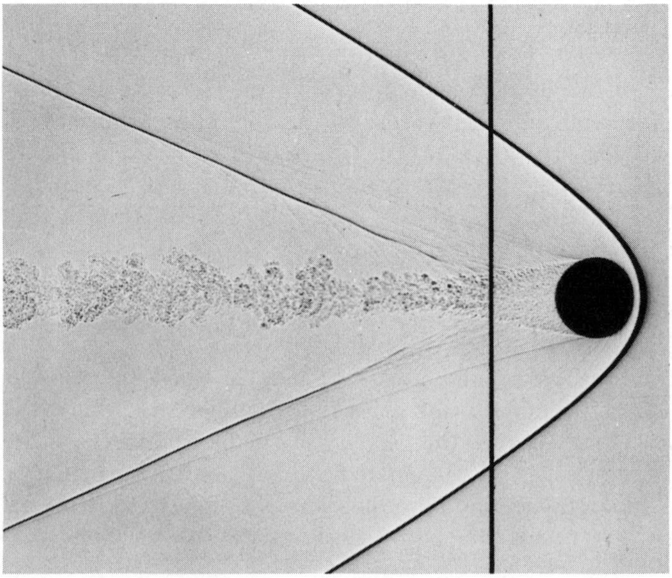

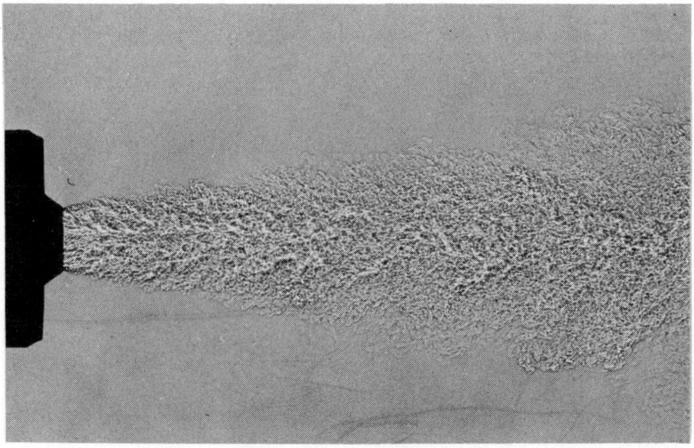

(*c*)

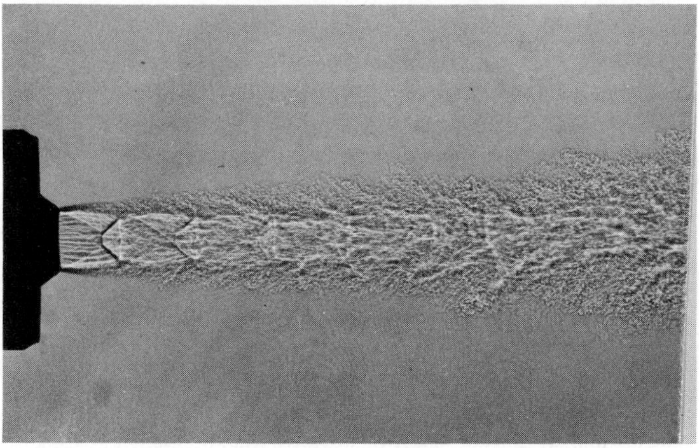

(*d*)

Figure 3.2

(*a*) Shadowgraph of decelerating $\frac{9}{16}$ in. steel ball moving to the right at a velocity of 1,116 ft/sec or slightly subsonic at $\mathfrak{M} = 0.992$. (Courtesy of A. C. Charters and R. N. Thomas, *Jour. Aero. Sci.*, Vol. 12, Oct. 1945.)
(*b*) Shadowgraph of motion from left to right of $\frac{9}{16}$ in. steel ball in still air. The velocity of the ball is 2,496 ft/sec or a $\mathfrak{M} = 2.23$. The vertical line is not part of the wave pattern of the supersonic flow. (Courtesy of A. C. Charters and R. N. Thomas, *Jour. Aero. Sci.*, Vol. 12, Oct. 1945.)
(*c*) Shadowgraph of subsonic, turbulent flow of gaseous Freon 12 from $\frac{1}{8}$ in. nozzle. (Courtesy of Mech. Eng. Dept. of Syracuse University.)
(*d*) Shadowgraph of wave pattern of supersonic jet of gaseous Freon 12. The jet throat diameter is $\frac{1}{8}$ in. and the pressure ratio is 3.72. (Courtesy of Mech. Eng. Dept. of Syracuse University.)

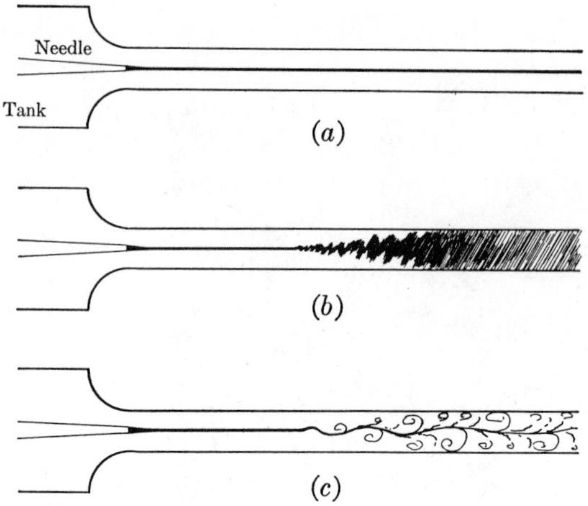

Figure 3.3
Streak of dye in a laminar and turbulent flow.

give a concise account for this change. This classic description by Reynolds[4] is worthwhile quoting:

> When the velocities were sufficiently low, the streak of color extended in a beautiful straight line across the tube. If the water in the tank had not quite settled to rest, at sufficiently low velocities, the streak would shift about the tube, but there was no appearance of sinuosity. As the velocity was increased by small stages, at some point in the tube, always at a considerable distance from the trumpet or the intake, the color band would all at once mix up with the surrounding water, and fill the rest of the tube with a mass of colored water. Any increase in the velocity caused the point of breakdown to approach the trumpet, but with no velocities that were tried did it reach this. On viewing the tube by the light of an electric spark, the mass of color resolved itself into a mass of more or less distinct curls showing eddies. [See Fig. 3.3(*c*).]

These are some of the classifications of flow fields most commonly encountered in general practice. The classes discussed are connected with the relative order of importance of the inertial, viscous, and elastic forces. It is clear that other classes of flow fields, showing marked differences in their general behavior, can be obtained by introducing

[4] Osborne Reynolds, "An Experimental Investigation of the Circumstances Which Determine Whether the Motion of Water Shall Be Direct or Sinuous, and of the Laws of Resistance in Parallel Channels," *Phil. Trans. Roy. Soc. London*, Vol. 174, 1883, pp. 935–982.

different types of forces. These classifications are introduced for purposes of identification. Actually, a flow field is neither completely incompressible nor completely compressible. The change is a gradual one, and consequently the classification of a flow into one group or another is a question of tolerance for neglecting one force or another.

3.5 Steady and Unsteady Motion

The concept of steadiness in physical problems does not imply the lack of motion. By *steady motion* it is meant that the properties of the fluid do not vary with time at a given Eulerian point in the space of the fluid. In other words, at a given position $\mathbf{r}$ from a coordinate system O, all the properties of the motion are constant with time. The variation of the properties with time, if any, is only *partial,* since, in general, properties are functions of position as well. Consequently, in *steady* motion the partial derivatives of the properties with respect to time are zero. Contrarily, an *unsteady motion* will exhibit variations of properties with time, and thus their partial derivative with respect to time will not be zero.

In practice, a modification is made in the definitions given above in order to be able to classify *turbulent* flows as *steady.* It was discussed in a previous section that the nature of turbulence was an unsteadiness or sinuosity in the flow field. Turbulence can be thought of as a laminar, smooth flow, sprinkled with eddies of all sizes spinning in the fluid at various peripheral velocities and being carried by the main laminar stream. This pictorial description is naturally not complete, but, for the time being, it will help extend the definition of steadiness to turbulent motions as well. Since a point in the turbulent flow will be influenced by different eddies at different times, the velocity of the fluid at the point being the vector sum of the laminar component and the peripheral velocity of the neighborhood vortices, its total velocity is inherently a function of time, since vortices around the point are not always the same in time. A turbulent flow will be called steady, provided that its average properties, like the velocity average, are constant values at all times at a given point in space. Steady and unsteady laminar and turbulent flows are shown in Fig. 3.4. A constant rate of flow of fluid, such as water through a pipe, whether laminar or turbulent, is an example of steady motion.

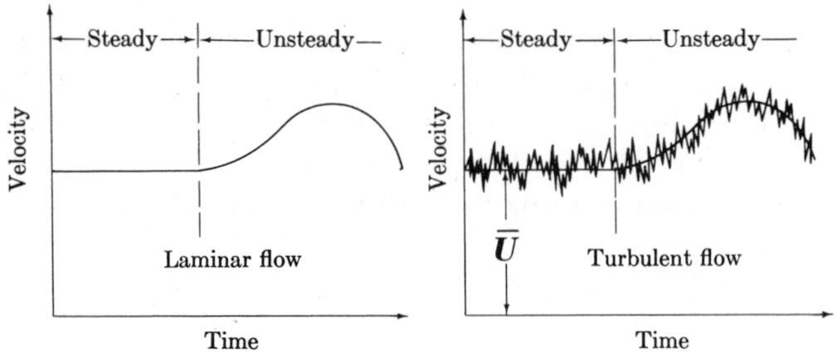

Figure 3.4
Steady and unsteady laminar and turbulent flows.

3.6 Representation of Turbulent Motion

It was mentioned in Sec. 3.5 that the physical concept of turbulent flow resembles that of a smooth streamline laminar flow on which small but extremely irregular motion is superimposed. This irregular motion, called *turbulence,* is always unsteady, since it changes with time at all points in the fluid and also varies in its irregular structure from point to point.

This flow is shown in Fig. 3.5, where the velocity has been chosen as the property describing the motion. At a given point $\boldsymbol{r}_0$ in a turbulent flow, the velocity fluctuates with time in an irregular fashion around the mean value $\boldsymbol{U}$. The word *irregular* implies here that the variations from $\boldsymbol{U}$ are neither smoothly increasing nor decreasing in time, nor are they periodic or repetitive in time. This means that, at the point $\boldsymbol{r}$, two traces of the velocity at different time intervals will never look identically the same.

For steady turbulent flow, $\boldsymbol{U}(\boldsymbol{r}_0)$ is constant with time and represents the temporal (time) average of the velocity at a given point. The irregular fluctuation in turbulence is always three-dimensional; that is, fluctuations in the velocity at x_0,y_0,z_0 occur in all three coordinate directions. Let u' represent the velocity fluctuation in the x-direction, v' in the y-direction, and w' in the z-direction. These values fluctuate at x_0,y_0,z_0 in time around the mean value $\boldsymbol{U}$. Since velocities are vector quantities, the total turbulent velocity will be the vector sum of the mean value and of the three fluctuating components u', v', and w'. This therefore indicates that the total velocity $\boldsymbol{U}$ at x_0,y_0,z_0 will vary with time in magnitude and direction, depending on the instantaneous components u', v', and w'. The vector addition reads

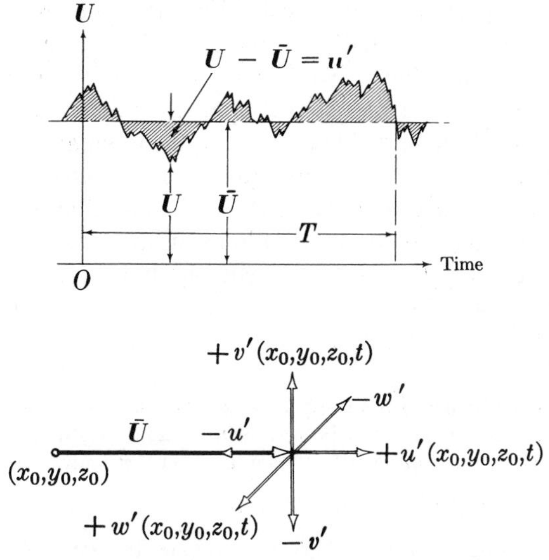

Figure 3.5
Representation of a turbulent motion.

$$\begin{aligned} \boldsymbol{U}(x_0,y_0,z_0,t) = \bar{\boldsymbol{U}}(x_0,y_0,z_0) &+ \boldsymbol{i}u'(x_0,y_0,z_0,t) \\ &+ \boldsymbol{j}v'(x_0,y_0,z_0,t) \\ &+ \boldsymbol{k}w'(x_0,y_0,z_0,t) \end{aligned} \tag{3.3}$$

The trace in Fig. 3.5 shows the time variation of the x-component of the total turbulent velocity.

The nature of these fluctuations is *random*, meaning that they vary in time above and below $\bar{\boldsymbol{U}}$ without repeating any finite portion of its history. The fluctuations u', v', and w' are such that a time average of them is zero. For this the area of the velocity trace above $\bar{\boldsymbol{U}}$ for a long period of time is the negative of the area of that trace under $\bar{\boldsymbol{U}}$. Since there is no periodicity in u', v', and w', the areas must be computed for extremely large periods of time—preferably infinite. If a time average of Eq. (3.1) is performed, then the average of the three fluctuating terms will be zero, and consequently the average of the total velocity $\boldsymbol{U}$ is really $\bar{\boldsymbol{U}}$; or, in a mathematical representation,

$$\lim_{T\to\infty} \frac{1}{2T} \int_{-T}^{T} \boldsymbol{U}(\boldsymbol{r}_0,t)\, dt = \bar{\boldsymbol{U}}(\boldsymbol{r}_0) \tag{3.4}$$

Actually, since there is no period T involved in the turbulent process, the averaging is taken to infinity. Finally, it is reasonable to assume that turbulence will be present in a flow field when the state of shear forces in the fluid is relatively high. In most turbulent-flow fields, the per cent of instantaneous variation of velocity with time is small, of the order between 0 and 20 per cent of the temporal mean velocity $\bar{U}$. When compared with laminar flows, the over-all effect of these fluctuations on the flow field is very large because of the additional stresses they impose on the flow field. For this reason, turbulent flows form a study separate from laminar flows.

Illustrative Example 3.1

If the turbulent fluctuation at a given point in space r_0 is sinusoidal in time, the turbulent fluctuating component $u'(r_0,t)$ can be represented as a (r_0) sin ωt. The maximum amplitude of the fluctuation with time is a, and ω is 2π times the frequency $f = \frac{1}{T}$. Show that the time average of u' is zero.

In this case the averaging through a period will be the same as any multiple number of periods. If an upper bar denotes a time average, then

$$u(r_0,t) = \bar{U}(r_0) + u'(r_0,t)$$

$$\overline{u'}(r_0,t) = \frac{1}{2T}\int_{-T}^{T} a(r_0)\sin\frac{2\pi}{T}t\,dt$$

$$= \frac{a}{4\pi}\left[\cos\frac{2\pi}{T}t\right]_{-T}^{T} = 0$$

Therefore, the temporal average of the total velocity $\overline{u(r_0)}$ is $\bar{U}(r_0)$ the temporal mean velocity itself. For turbulent steady flow, then, the temporal mean velocity is not a function of time.

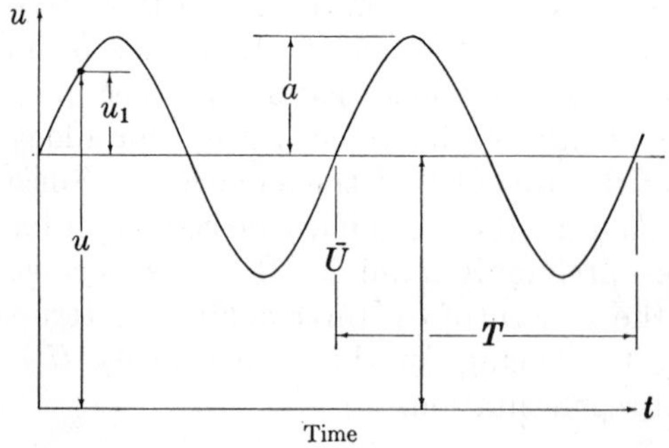

Figure 3.6

Sinusoidal fluctuation of the velocity.

3.7 Uniform Flow. One-, Two-, and Three-Dimensional Flow

By definition, a *one-dimensional flow* is one in which the properties of motion, such as the velocity, vary in one direction only. Consequently, the fluid properties do not vary on the surfaces perpendicular to the direction along which the properties are varying. This flow is often said to be *uniform* at every cross section normal to the main direction of flow. The flow of water down a gradual funnel approximates this situation. Owing to the constriction, the velocity of the water varies along the axis of the funnel, but it is essentially the same at each circular plane perpendicular to the axis. The friction of the water with the funnel walls will cause a slight departure from one-dimensionality.

In a similar fashion, a *two-dimensional flow* is one in which variations of flow properties occur in two directions. This indicates that there will be variations of flow properties on a surface, and that these variations will reproduce themselves on each surface perpendicular to the direction along which the flow properties are not varying. An example of this flow is that of a viscous fluid in a short circular pipe. Owing to the viscosity of the fluid, the boundary layer near the walls gives rise to velocity variations in the radial direction. As the fluid proceeds downstream, the boundary layer grows in thickness, and, at the same radius, the growth alters the velocity in the axial direction. The only variation that is not expected is with angular displacement.

A *three-dimensional flow* is one whose flow properties vary in all three directions. The flow of a river is a good example, where the water on a plane perpendicular to the direction of motion varies, since the velocity of the water at the surface is faster than that at the two banks and at the bottom. Also because of the expansion and contraction of the river bed, the velocity of the water varies in the direction of motion as well.

All real flows are more likely to be three-dimensional but they may approach the conditions of one- or two-dimensional flows. Since all properties of the fluid do not always vary in the same direction, the variations of the velocity are usually considered as the factor determining whether the flow is one-, two-, or three-dimensional.

3.8 Streamline, Path Line, and Streak Line

By definition, a *streamline* is an artificial line drawn in the fluid in such a manner that the tangent at *every point* on this line gives the direction of the fluid velocity at that point. Since all along the *streamline* the direction of the fluid velocity is tangential to the streamline, there could never be any flow normal to the streamline. In general, streamlines constitute the outline of the fluid layers in motion.

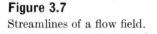

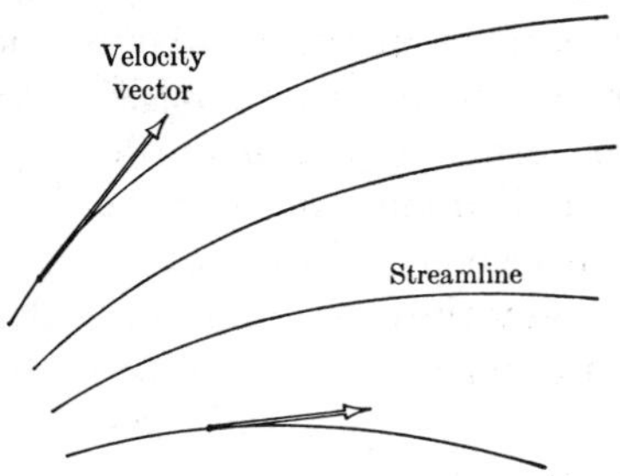

Figure 3.7
Streamlines of a flow field.

A *path line* is a line in the flow field describing the path or trajectory of a given fluid element.[5] The concept of this line is not different from the trajectory of a solid particle in solid mechanics.

Although the *streak line* represents the geometry of the motion that can be seen in the fluid, its description is physically more involved than the other two lines described. A *streak line* is a locus line in the flow field, at a given time t_0, that connects the temporary location of all the particles that have passed through a given contaminating point $\mathbf{r}$ in the flow field. A smokestack can be treated as a contaminating point in the motion of the air in the atmosphere, and the contaminated visible smoke trail at a given time represents the streak line pertaining to the motion of the air around the smokestack. Only when the flow is steady do all these three lines collapse into one, explaining, perhaps, why they are very often confused. The injection of smoke into gases and dye into liquids is common for outlining the streamlines of the fluid. This can be done only in steady motion where there is no geometrical distinction between the streamline, path line, and streak line.

Consider first a steady motion—for example, the flow around a ship moving at a uniform velocity, with an observer at a fixed point on the ship; or the motion of a river around a pier, with the observer on the pier. In such cases, at any point in the flow field the direction of the velocity at all times t is the same. Consequently, since the streamlines are lines drawn tangent to these velocity directions that are fixed in space, they will also have to be fixed in space with reference to the observer of the steady motion. Now, since the fluid particles move in the direction of the velocity at every point, and since those

[5] The word "element" is used here as an infinitesimal system containing the same mass and moving with the fluid. Often, "fluid particle" is used instead of "fluid element."

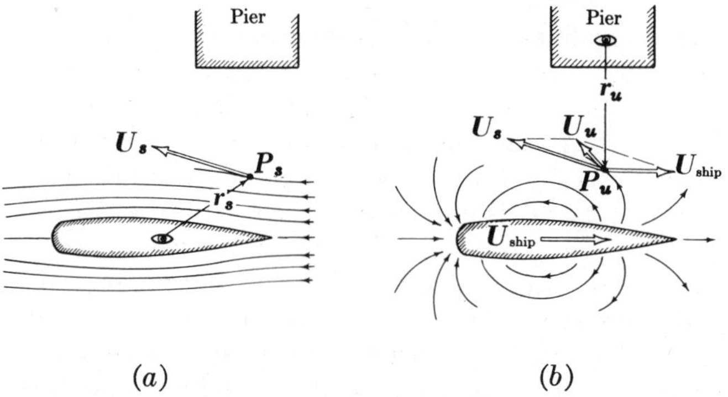

Figure 3.8
Streamlines for (*a*) steady and (*b*) unsteady motion from a uniform motion of a ship. The symbolic eye represents the position of the observer.

directions, in the steady-state case, are *molded* in the fluid space, the trajectory of the fluid particles must be the same as the streamline.[6] Furthermore, since a particle originating on a given streamline must follow the streamline, then, by the same token, all particles that pass through a given point $\boldsymbol{r}$ on a streamline must have originated at a given time somewhere along that streamline. Then, in conclusion, the locus of all the particles passing through $\boldsymbol{r}$ is the streamline which has already been shown to be the path line for a steady motion.

These observations are quite different when unsteady motion is observed. The geometry of the three lines described is entirely different. For instance, an observer standing on a pier, watching the motion of the water as a ship goes by, sees a case of unsteady motion. The conditions of flow at a given point in the water, with reference to the observer on the pier, change with time as the ship approaches or recedes from the observation point. Figure 3.8 shows the essential difference between the streamline patterns viewed from the ship or the pier with the ship moving at a uniform velocity. The direction of the velocity in the steady-state reference (*a*) is $\boldsymbol{U}_s$, which is found by drawing a tangent to the streamline at the point P a distance $\boldsymbol{r}_s$ from the observer. At the same point, however, in (*b*) the velocity at P is that claimed in (*a*) plus the relative velocity of the observer in (*a*) with respect to the observer in (*b*), which, in this case, is the vector addition of $\boldsymbol{U}_s$ to the velocity of the ship $\boldsymbol{U}_{\text{ship}}$. The velocity of the fluid at (*b*) is therefore $\boldsymbol{U}_u$. All

[6] It is impossible to see streamlines in a fluid, since velocity cannot be observed with the eye. It is with the path line or the streak line that streamlines are seen.

points of the steady streamlines at (*a*) can be changed into the unsteady streamline pattern in (*b*) by the vector addition of $\boldsymbol{U}_{\text{ship}}$ to all velocities in (*a*). In the case illustrated, the points P_s and P_u were chosen to be the same material point. As the ship moves to the right, the material point P_u will be represented by different points P_s at different distances $\boldsymbol{r}_s$ from the observer at (*a*). This implies that the conditions at P_u are changing with time as the ship moves. This is because the streamlines in the unsteady motion (*b*) are *molded* with the ship and consequently move away from the observer with the ship. In essence, in unsteady motion we can relate the streamline pattern to the fluid space only at one time. At a later time $t_0 + \Delta t$ the streamline passing through the same point will be different.

The fluid particle at P_s, $\boldsymbol{r}_s$ away from the observer, always moves in the direction of $\boldsymbol{U}_s$ and ultimately traces the streamline passing through P_s. A fluid particle P_u, $\boldsymbol{r}_u$ away from the observer, is directed in the direction of $\boldsymbol{U}_u$, but, as this velocity $\boldsymbol{U}_u$ changes with time at the point, the path of the particle will be governed by the successive streamlines moving to the right a distance $\boldsymbol{U}_{\text{ship}}t$. Since at different times the particle is affected by different unsteady streamlines, the trajectory of the particle or the path line will be geometrically different from the streamline.

As the motion of the ship progresses, there will be many particles that have originated at a given point, say P_u. At a given time the line joining the position of all such particles originating at P_u will describe the streak line. In unsteady motion the streak line will be geometrically different from a path line, which, in turn, will be geometrically different from a streamline. These differences are illustrated graphically in Illustrative Example 3.4.

3.9 Stream Filament, Stream Tube, and Stream Surface

A *stream filament* is a group of neighboring streamlines forming a cylindrical passage with an infinitesimal cross section. Since the surface of the stream filament is made out of streamlines, the motion of the fluid must be within the filament and therefore cannot cross its surface. The same is true for the surface of a *stream tube,* since it is made of a large number of stream filaments. The cross section of a stream tube is finite, and its surface, across which there is no flow, is called a *stream*

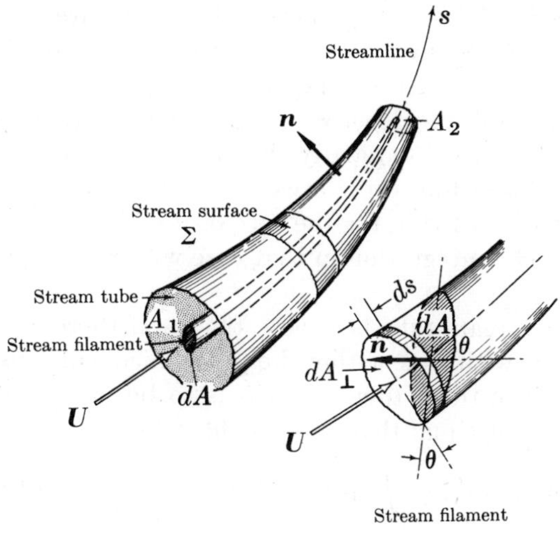

Figure 3.9
Stream tube, stream filament, and stream surface.

surface. Referring to Fig. 3.9, if the fluid starts entering the stream filament at the time t, after an infinitesimal time dt the volume that has flowed into the tube of cross-section $d\boldsymbol{A} = \boldsymbol{n}\, dA$ for an outward normal $\boldsymbol{n}$ is

$$(\boldsymbol{n}\cdot\boldsymbol{U})\, dA\, dt = dA_\perp \frac{ds}{dt}\, dt$$
$$= dA_\perp\, ds$$

where the subscript to dA is called *perpendicular*. The rate of mass flow in the stream filament is

$$\rho(\boldsymbol{n}\cdot\boldsymbol{U})\, dA = \rho U\, dA_\perp$$
$$= \rho U\, dA \cos\theta \tag{3.5}$$

If the cross section of the filament is not perpendicular to the velocity, then, in general, $dA \cos\theta = dA_\perp$ and, therefore, the rate of mass flow, a scalar quantity, is $\rho U\, dA \cos\theta$. The rate of mass flow entering the stream tube is obtained by integrating over the cross-sectional area

$$\left(\frac{dm}{dt}\right)_{\text{entering}} = \int_{A_1} \rho(\boldsymbol{n}\cdot\boldsymbol{U})\, dA_1$$
$$= \int_{A_1} \rho U \cos\theta\, dA \tag{3.6}$$

The angle θ is the one between $\boldsymbol{U}$ and the perpendicular to the area dA. Thus the rate of mass flow across any surface dA is the product of the density, the area of the surface, and the component of the velocity $\boldsymbol{U}$ perpendicular to dA. In general, the density and the velocity are functions of position on the area, and consequently the integral in Eq. (3.6) can be evaluated if their relationship to the area is known.

The same equation can be written for the rate of flow leaving the stream tube at section 2. The integration in that case will be over the area A_2.

If the flow through the stream tube is steady, that is, if there is no build-up or depletion of mass with time within the tube which will cause a change in the density in the tube, then, if mass is to be preserved, the rate of incoming mass must equal that leaving the tube:

$$-\int_{A_1} \rho(\boldsymbol{n}\cdot\boldsymbol{U})\,dA_1 = \int_{A_2} \rho(\boldsymbol{n}\cdot\boldsymbol{U})\,dA_2 \tag{3.7}$$

or

$$\int_{A_1} \rho\boldsymbol{U}\cos\theta\,dA = \int_{A_2} \rho\boldsymbol{U}\cos\theta\,dA \tag{3.8}$$

Because $(\boldsymbol{n}\cdot\boldsymbol{U})$ evaluated at A_1 is opposite in sign to that on A_2, since $\theta_1 > \frac{\pi}{2}$ and $\theta_2 < \frac{\pi}{2}$, in order for the scalar equation, Eq. (3.8) to be true, the first integral in Eq. (3.7) must carry a minus sign. It is understood that the values of ρ, $\boldsymbol{U}$ and θ are not necessarily the same at A_1 and A_2. By definition, the stream surface Σ is tangent to the velocity vector, thus $(\boldsymbol{n}\cdot\boldsymbol{U})$ on Σ is zero. Thus from Eq. (3.7)

$$\int_{A_1} \rho(\boldsymbol{n}\cdot\boldsymbol{U})\,dA_1 + \int_{A_2} \rho(\boldsymbol{n}\cdot\boldsymbol{U})\,dA_2 + \int_{\Sigma} \rho(\boldsymbol{n}\cdot\boldsymbol{U})\,d\Sigma = 0$$

or if the total enclosed surface $S = A_1 + A_2 + \Sigma$, then

$$\oint_S \rho(\boldsymbol{n}\cdot\boldsymbol{U})\,dS = 0 \tag{3.9}$$

Here the circle-like symbol on the integral implies closed contour integration on the entire surface S. This equation is called the *integral form of the mass-continuity equation for a steady flow.* Specifically, when the flow is one-dimensional so that ρ and U vary only in a direction perpendicular to A, and if the cross sections A are perpendicular to U, then Eq. 3.8 becomes

$$\rho_1 U_1 \int_{A_1} dA = \rho_2 U_2 \int_{A_2} dA \tag{3.10}$$

$$Q = \rho_1 U_1 A_1 = \rho_2 U_2 A_2$$

If the flow is not compressible at all, so that ρ is the same everywhere, then it cancels out of the last equation and

$$U_1A_1 = U_2A_2 \tag{3.11}$$

All these equations, Eqs. (3.8), (3.10), and (3.11), can be written for every cross section of the stream tube, and their evaluation yields the same result at each cross section. The unsteady case will be treated in the next section.

Illustrative Example 3.2

Because the viscous forces in the motion of a fluid reduce the momentum of the fluid near the solid boundaries, a flow originally uniform in a pipe will

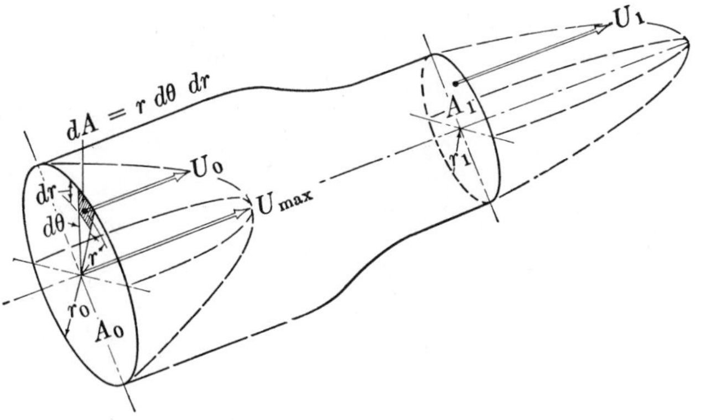

Figure 3.10
Velocity of fluid in converging pipe.

eventually have a nonuniform velocity, as shown in Fig. 3.10. If the flow is laminar, the velocity profile will eventually become a paraboloid

$$U = U_{\max}\left[1 - \left(\frac{r}{r_0}\right)^2\right]$$

a. To find the spatial mean velocity at the entrance of the converging section, the total mass rate of flow entering must be equated to a corresponding mass rate of flow which would have had a constant entering velocity U_{av}. If the density is considered constant,

$$\rho\pi r_0^2 U_{av} = \rho \int_0^{2\pi} \int_0^{r_0} (r\, d\theta\, dr) U$$

$$
\begin{aligned}
U_{av} &= \frac{1}{\pi r_0^2}\int_0^{2\pi}\int_0^{r_0} U_{max}\left[1-\left(\frac{r}{r_0}\right)^2\right] r\,dr\,d\theta \\
&= \frac{2U_{max}}{r_0^2}\int_0^{r_0}\left(r-\frac{r^3}{r_0^2}\right)dr \\
&= \frac{2U_{max}}{r_0^2}\left[\frac{r_0^2}{2}-\frac{r_0^2}{4}\right] \\
&= \frac{U_{max}}{2}
\end{aligned}
$$

b. If the cross section at the discharge of the section has a radius $r_1 = \frac{1}{2}r_0$, and if the velocity profile is still parabolic, from continuity of mass, the velocities at the discharge must all be four times as large, since the area reduced by a factor of four.

c. If a cylindrical stream surface is drawn at the interior of the tube so that the mass rate of flow in the converging pipe is divided into two equal parts, the radius of the inner stream surface will then be located at the following r:

$$
\tfrac{1}{2}\pi r_0^2 U_{av} = \tfrac{1}{4}\pi r_0^2 U_{max} = 2\pi U_{max}\int_0^r\left[1-\left(\frac{r}{r_0}\right)^2\right] r\,dr
$$

Solving further,

$$
\frac{r_0^2}{4} = r^2 - \frac{r^4}{2r_0^2}
$$

$$
\frac{r}{r_0} = \sqrt{1-\sqrt{1/2}}
$$

3.10 The Integral and Differential Form of the Continuity Equation

When the complete surface of the stream-tube section shown in Fig. 3.9 was considered, it could have been observed that it was composed of three distinct surfaces A_1, A_2 and Σ making up the total surface S. Since there was no flow across Σ, the exchange of flow took place at A_1 and A_2, consequently for the stream tube in steady state Eq. (3.9) was derived.

Had the flow in and out of the stream tube been transient, at one instant of time the flow entering the tube would not have been equal to that leaving the tube and consequently, there would have been an accumulation or depletion of mass with time inside the tube. This amount of mass variation inside the tube of fixed surface would have been

$$-\frac{\partial}{\partial t}\int_{\mathcal{V}} \rho \, d\mathcal{V} = \oint_S \rho(\boldsymbol{n}\cdot\boldsymbol{U}) \, dS \tag{3.12}$$

where $\mathcal{V}$ is the volume of the tube section shown in Fig. 3.9. This is the integral form of the continuity equation. This relation is not only valid for stream tubes but for any control volume through which an exchange of mass might have taken place. By definition, $\boldsymbol{n}$ is an outward normal. Thus, the integral on the right hand side is positive when the net flow is outward. It follows that if the surface integral is positive, then, for a fixed control volume, $\partial\rho/\partial t$ integrated through the volume must be negative. This implies that the density inside $\mathcal{V}$ decreases in time. Physically speaking, to preserve the mass, this is what one would expect. Conversely, if the surface integral is negative implying that more mass comes through S than exits, then $\partial\rho/\partial t > 0$ implying[7] an accumulation of mass in $\mathcal{V}$.

Now, Gauss's theorem (derived in Appendix A) becomes extremely useful. The surface integral in Eq. (3.12) can be changed into a volume integral to be combined with the left hand side. Then

$$\oint_S \boldsymbol{n}\cdot(\rho\boldsymbol{U}) \, dS = \int_{\mathcal{V}} \boldsymbol{\nabla}\cdot(\rho\boldsymbol{U}) \, d\mathcal{V} \tag{3.13}$$

and finally

$$\int_{\mathcal{V}} \left[\frac{\partial\rho}{\partial t} + \boldsymbol{\nabla}\cdot(\rho\boldsymbol{U})\right] d\mathcal{V} = 0 \tag{3.14}$$

The control volume in question is fixed in time. Since the volume $\mathcal{V}$ is arbitrary, and if the integrand in the brackets is continuously distributed in $\mathcal{V}$, then for Eq. (3.14) to be true for any volume, the integrand must be identically zero.

$$\frac{\partial\rho}{\partial t} + \boldsymbol{\nabla}\cdot(\rho\boldsymbol{U}) = 0 \tag{3.15}$$

This is the *differential form* of the continuity equation. In Cartesian coordinates is read

$$\frac{\partial\rho}{\partial t} + \frac{\partial(\rho u)}{\partial x} + \frac{\partial(\rho v)}{\partial y} + \frac{\partial(\rho w)}{\partial z} = 0 \qquad [3.16(a)]$$

This partial differential equation is valid at any point inside the control volume for a variable density fluid running through it with its properties

[7] For a formal proof of Eq. (3.12) pertaining to any control volume see, S. Eskinazi *Vector Mechanics of Fluids and Magnetofluids.* Academic Press, N.Y., 1967.

varying in time. This is, then, the most general form of the differential form of the continuity equation.

In particular, if the flow is steady but with variable density, Eq. (3.16) becomes

$$\nabla \cdot (\rho \boldsymbol{U}) = \frac{\partial(\rho u)}{\partial x} + \frac{\partial(\rho v)}{\partial y} + \frac{\partial(\rho w)}{\partial z} = 0 \qquad [3.16(b)]$$

and, if the flow is with constant density and commonly known as incompressible, then variations of the density are zero and consequently

$$\frac{\partial u}{\partial x} + \frac{\partial v}{\partial y} + \frac{\partial w}{\partial z} = 0 \qquad (3.17)$$

If the mass exchange was performed across a cylindrical element[8] of control volume, then in cylindrical coordinates the incompressible continuity equation would take the form

$$\frac{1}{r}\frac{\partial}{\partial r}(rv_r) + \frac{1}{r}\frac{\partial v_\theta}{\partial \theta} + \frac{\partial v_z}{\partial z} = 0 \qquad (3.18)$$

For two-dimensional incompressible flows, say with no variations of the properties in the z-direction, the equation of continuity at a point reads

$$\frac{\partial u}{\partial x} + \frac{\partial v}{\partial y} = 0 \qquad (3.19)$$

Illustrative Example 3.3

Show that rigid-body motion conserves mass. The velocity field in a rigid-body motion is given by

$$\boldsymbol{U} = \boldsymbol{\omega} \times \boldsymbol{r}$$

One axis of the coordinate system can be made to coincide with the axis of rotation or $\boldsymbol{\omega}$. Let this be the z-axis, for instance, the motion is then on the plane x-y in Cartesian coordinates or the plane $r - \theta$ in the cylindrical coordinate. According to Eq. (A. 33)

$$\boldsymbol{U} = \boldsymbol{i}u + \boldsymbol{j}v = \boldsymbol{i}(-\omega y) + \boldsymbol{j}(\omega x)$$

It is obvious, here, because of the coordinate orientation that $\omega_x = \omega_y = 0$ and $\omega_z = \omega$. Separating components, we have

$$u = -\omega y$$

$$v = \omega x$$

[8] The student will find this exercise very rewarding.

Since the motion is two-dimensional, we use Eq. (3.19) to test the conservation of mass

$$\frac{\partial u}{\partial x} = 0$$

$$\frac{\partial u}{\partial y} = 0$$

and the conservation equation is identically satisfied.

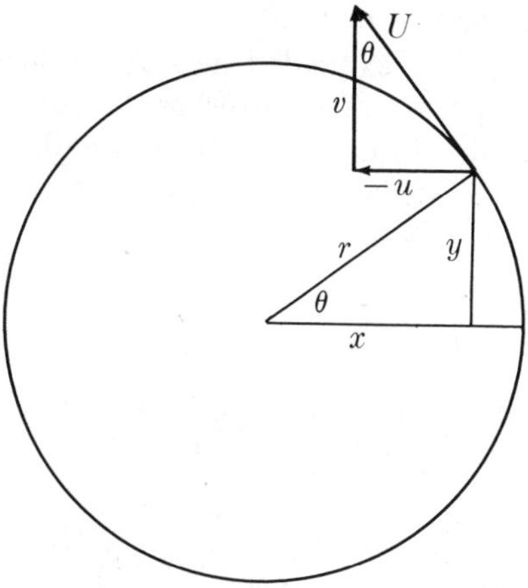

Figure 3.11
Rigid-body motion.

The conservation of mass equation in a differential form [Eq. (3.16)] was derived from the integral form of the continuity equation. Although elegant, this approach made no commitments to any size or shape of volume through which the mass flows. In order to give this important theorem of conservation of mass a stronger physical significance, an alternate approach is given here.

Consider, then, an elemental *control volume* in which the flow goes through this infinitesimal volume. Let the center point of this volume be x,y,z and an account of the rate of mass flow through the infinitesimal control volume be required. For generality, let the fluid be compressible and unsteady; then the density and the velocity components at the center point O of the elemental control volume will be a function of the coordinate x,y,z and time t. Then:

$$\rho = f_1(x,y,z,t)$$
$$u = f_2(x,y,z,t)$$
$$v = f_3(x,y,z,t)$$
$$w = f_4(x,y,z,t)$$

At a particular time t, the value of these velocities can be computed at all the mid-points of the rectangular faces of the element, as shown in Fig. 3.12. The displacement from the center to either face is half the elemental dimension. The motion is assumed to be in the direction of the coordinate system shown. Since the density is allowed to vary, the fluid in the volume may be compressed or expanded as a function of time. Therefore, it is not necessary that the mass entering the volume leave immediately; inside the elemental volume it may be accumulated or depleted as a function of time, hence causing an increase or decrease of density.

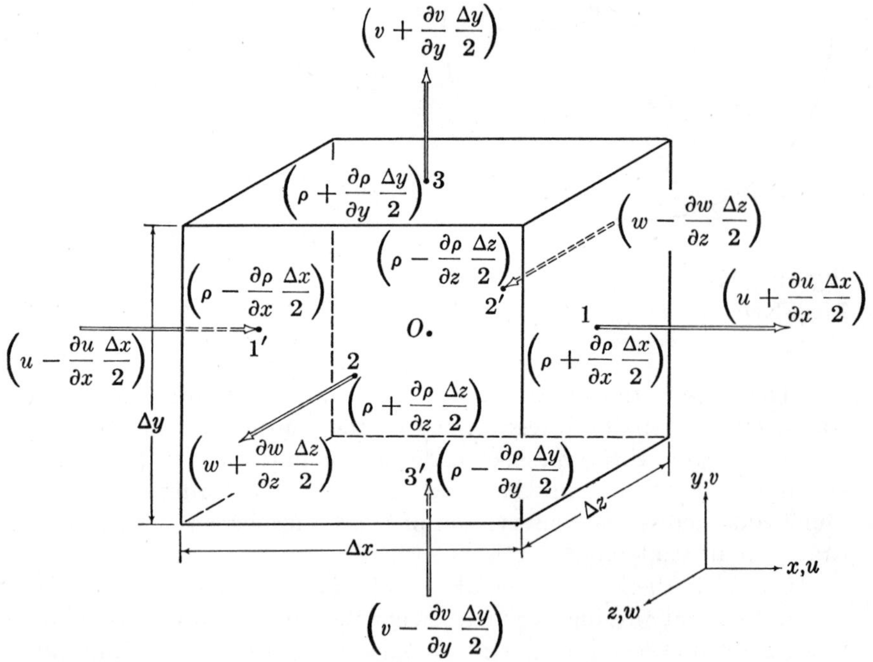

Figure 3.12
Value of density and velocity on faces of elemental volume.

In order to account for the rate of mass transfer in the elemental volume, the following possibilities must be considered. If the density in the elemental control volume is increasing, then so is the mass; hence the influx of fluid is larger than the outflux, and therefore there is a *storage* of mass in the volume. If the density is decreasing inside the volume, then the outflux is the sum of the influx and the *drainage*. Whatever case is considered, the final results will be the same, therefore consider here the first case when $\frac{\partial \rho}{\partial t}$ is positive.

According to Eq. (3.10), the rate of mass flow crossing any face of the elemental volume is the product of the density, the area, and the velocity normal to the face. The faces where outflux of mass occurs are 1, 2, and 3, and the faces through which mass enters are 1′, 2′, and 3′. The mass outflux per unit time through the three faces is

$$\begin{aligned} Q_o = &\left(\rho + \frac{\partial \rho}{\partial x}\frac{\Delta x}{2}\right)\left(u + \frac{\partial u}{\partial x}\frac{\Delta x}{2}\right)\Delta y\,\Delta z \\ &+ \left(\rho + \frac{\partial \rho}{\partial y}\frac{\Delta y}{2}\right)\left(v + \frac{\partial v}{\partial y}\frac{\Delta y}{2}\right)\Delta x\,\Delta z \\ &+ \left(\rho + \frac{\partial \rho}{\partial z}\frac{\Delta z}{2}\right)\left(w + \frac{\partial w}{\partial z}\frac{\Delta z}{2}\right)\Delta x\,\Delta y \end{aligned}$$

The mass influx per unit time through the three other faces is

$$\begin{aligned} Q_i = &\left(\rho - \frac{\partial \rho}{\partial x}\frac{\Delta x}{2}\right)\left(u - \frac{\partial u}{\partial x}\frac{\Delta x}{2}\right)\Delta y\,\Delta z \\ &+ \left(\rho - \frac{\partial \rho}{\partial y}\frac{\Delta y}{2}\right)\left(v - \frac{\partial v}{\partial y}\frac{\Delta y}{2}\right)\Delta x\,\Delta z \\ &+ \left(\rho - \frac{\partial \rho}{\partial z}\frac{\Delta z}{2}\right)\left(w - \frac{\partial w}{\partial z}\frac{\Delta z}{2}\right)\Delta x\,\Delta y \end{aligned}$$

The mass stored inside the element per unit time is the rate of change of mass within the elemental volume

$$Q_s = \left(\frac{\partial \rho}{\partial t}\right)\Delta x\,\Delta y\,\Delta z$$

The volume of the control elemental parallelepiped was taken as constant, and therefore it is not influenced by the differentiation in time.

For conservation of mass, the influx rate of flow must be equal to the outflux rate plus the storage within the elemental control volume.

After canceling identical terms, the equation for mass *continuity* becomes identical as in Eq. (3.16)

$$Q_i = Q_o + Q_s$$

$$\frac{\partial \rho}{\partial t} + \frac{\partial(\rho u)}{\partial x} + \frac{\partial(\rho v)}{\partial y} + \frac{\partial(\rho w)}{\partial z} = 0 \qquad [3.16(a)]$$

3.11 Stream Function in Two-Dimensional Flow

By definition, a *stream function* is a mathematical function representing the geometry of the stream surfaces at a given time. In two-dimensional incompressible and steady motion the stream function ψ can be related to the velocity field $\boldsymbol{U}$ in a simple manner. By definition, since the velocity vector is tangent to the stream surface ψ = *constant*, then

$$\boldsymbol{U} \cdot \nabla\psi = 0 \qquad (3.20)$$

The stream function $\psi(x,y)$ represents the stream surface, the gradient of ψ is normal to the surface ψ = *constant* and normal to $\boldsymbol{U}$; consequently, the dot product of $\boldsymbol{U}$ and $\nabla\psi$ is zero.

If the two-dimensional motion is represented on the x–y-plane as in Fig. 3.13 where u and v are the velocity components of the total velocity $\boldsymbol{U}$ respectively, in the x- and y-directions, according to Eq. (3.5) the rate of mass flow crossing the arbitrary line OMP_2,s_2 can be found. This being a two-dimensional motion, the third dimension represented by the unit normal $\boldsymbol{b}$ is perpendicular to the plane of the figure, and the flow field does not vary in that direction. If a unit dimension in that third direction is considered, the infinitesimal flow crossing the arbitrary surface OMP_2 at M is

$$\frac{dm}{dt} = \rho(\boldsymbol{n} \cdot \boldsymbol{U})\, ds$$

Here $(\boldsymbol{n} \cdot \boldsymbol{U})$ is $U \cos\theta$, or $U_\perp$, and the infinitesimal area is $dA = 1 \times ds$. The integration of this quantity along the path OMP_2 is in s alone, since there are no variations in the direction perpendicular to the plane x–y. The total rate of flow crossing OMP_2 is

$$\int_O^{P_2} \rho(\boldsymbol{n} \cdot \boldsymbol{U})\, ds = \int_O^{P_2} \rho U \cos\theta\, ds$$

$$= \int_O^{P_2} \rho U_\perp\, ds \qquad (3.21)$$

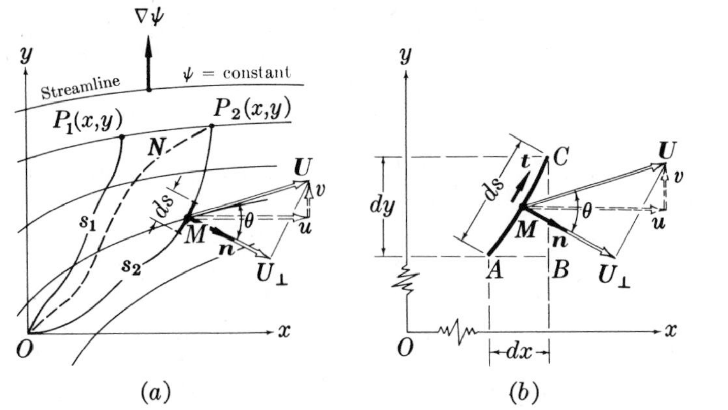

Figure 3.13
Streamline motion in two-dimensional flow.

Since the density has been postulated to be constant, it can be removed from the integrand and, by definition, let $\psi(x,y)$ be the rate of mass flow per unit density and per unit depth

$$d\psi = (\boldsymbol{n}\cdot\boldsymbol{U})\,ds = U_\perp\,ds$$

$$\psi_0 - \psi_{P_2} = \int_O^{P_2} U\cos\theta\,ds = \int_O^{P_2} U_\perp\,ds \tag{3.22}$$

According to Eq. (A.37) the total change of any scalar function is given by

$$\begin{aligned} d\psi &= \nabla\psi\cdot d\boldsymbol{s} \\ &= \nabla\psi\cdot\boldsymbol{t}\,ds \end{aligned}$$

where $\boldsymbol{t}$ is the unit vector along the path of integration. Thus,

$$\nabla\psi\cdot\boldsymbol{t} = \boldsymbol{n}\cdot\boldsymbol{U} \tag{3.23}$$

However, the three unit vectors $\boldsymbol{n}$, $\boldsymbol{t}$ and $\boldsymbol{b}$ have the following relationships

$$-\boldsymbol{t} = \boldsymbol{b}\times\boldsymbol{n}$$

Thus Eq. (3.23) becomes

$$-\nabla\psi\cdot(\boldsymbol{b}\times\boldsymbol{n}) = \boldsymbol{n}\cdot\boldsymbol{U} \tag{3.24}$$

The triple scalar product of Sec. A.9 can be applied here to give

$$\begin{aligned} \nabla\psi\cdot(\boldsymbol{b}\times\boldsymbol{n}) &= \boldsymbol{n}\cdot(\nabla\psi\times\boldsymbol{b}) \\ &= -\boldsymbol{n}\cdot(\boldsymbol{b}\times\nabla\psi) \end{aligned}$$

Then Eq. (3.24) becomes

$$\boldsymbol{b}\times\nabla\psi = \boldsymbol{U} \tag{3.25}$$

This means that the three vectors $\boldsymbol{b}$, $\nabla\psi$ and $\boldsymbol{U}$ form an orthogonal set.

In component form Eq. (3.25) is very useful. In Cartesian coordinates ∇ is given by Eq. [A.38(*a*)], $\boldsymbol{b}$ is $\boldsymbol{k}$, and Eq. (3.25) becomes

$$\boldsymbol{k}\times\left(\boldsymbol{i}\frac{\partial}{\partial x}+\boldsymbol{j}\frac{\partial}{\partial y}+\boldsymbol{k}\frac{\partial}{\partial z}\right)\psi=(\boldsymbol{i}u+\boldsymbol{j}v+\boldsymbol{k}w)$$

or

$$u=-\frac{\partial\psi}{\partial y},\qquad v=\frac{\partial\psi}{\partial x},\qquad \text{and}\qquad w=0 \tag{3.26}$$

In axisymmetric cylindrical coordinates using the definition of *del* in Eq. [A.38(*b*)]

$$v_r=-\frac{1}{r}\frac{\partial\psi}{\partial\theta},\qquad v_\theta=\frac{\partial\psi}{\partial r},\qquad \text{and}\qquad v_z=0 \tag{3.27}$$

In axisymmetric spherical coordinates

$$v_r=-\frac{1}{r^2\sin\theta}\frac{\partial\psi}{\partial\theta},\qquad v_\theta=\frac{1}{r\sin\theta}\frac{\partial\psi}{\partial r},\qquad \text{and}\qquad v_\alpha=0 \tag{3.28}$$

Returning to Fig. 3.13 and Eq. (3.22), it can easily be verified that, for the steady and incompressible case under study, this integral is always a constant, provided that the points O and P_2 are not changed. This is verified by assuming another arbitrary line ONP_2 joining the two points. If one considers the closed path OMP_2NO, since the flow is steady and incompressible, there could never be at any time any increase or decrease of mass within the closed path OMP_2NO, and consequently, as was discussed in Sec. 3.10, the amount of flow entering the two-dimensional surface ONP_2 must be the same as that leaving OMP_2. Thus Eq. (3.22) yields the same value, regardless of the path joining the two points. Mathematically speaking, then, $d\psi$ is an *exact differential*, and the *stream function* $\psi(x,y)$ is a *property* of the fluid which has one definite value at one point in space. This can be observed from Eq. (3.22). If arbitrarily $\psi_O = O$ or any other constant value, then ψ_{P_2} is always a constant. So, with reference to an arbitrary origin, the value of $\psi(x,y)$ is a constant at a given point.

Pursuing this discussion further, if points P_1 and P_2 are located on a stream surface, when continuity of mass is applied to the closed path OMP_2P_1O it can be deduced that the amount of flow per unit time crossing the arbitrary surface s_1 is the same as that leaving s_2, since the surface on which P_1 and P_2 are located is a stream surface and there could be no flow across it. The important conclusion that can be derived here is that $\psi(x,y)$ = *constant* describes the geometry of a stream surface in the steady two-dimensional incompressible flow considered.

If the continuity of mass is applied to the enlarged diagram in

Fig. 3.13(*b*), the rate of mass flow per unit depth from left to right entering at AC is $\rho U_\perp\, ds$. The quantity entering at AB is $\rho v\, dx$, and the amount leaving at BC is $\rho u\, dy$. Since what enters within the volume ABC must leave at the same time, after canceling ρ it follows that

$$U_\perp\, ds + v\, dx = u\, dy$$

From the definition in Eq. (3.22) and defining flow from left to right giving rise to $-d\psi$ this equation finally becomes

$$d\psi = v\, dx - u\, dy \tag{3.29}$$

It was deduced in this section that, since $\psi(x,y)$ was a property of the motion, $d\psi$ is an exact derivative and consequently can be written in the form

$$d\psi = \frac{\partial\psi}{\partial x}\, dx + \frac{\partial\psi}{\partial y}\, dy$$

Since this equation and Eq. (3.29) must be the same, the coefficients of dx and dy can be equated

$$u = -\frac{\partial\psi}{\partial y}$$

$$v = \frac{\partial\psi}{\partial x}$$

These equations were already found to be true in Eq. (3.26).

This last equation indicates that if, in a two-dimensional steady motion with constant density, the geometry of the streamlines is known, then the velocity field can be computed at every point in space from this geometry, and vice versa. It must be remembered that the direction of positive flow was considered here from right to left; otherwise, all the signs will change.

In cylindrical coordinates, Eq. (3.29) will become

$$d\psi = v_\theta\, dr - v_r r\, d\theta$$

and

$$v_r = -\frac{1}{r}\frac{\partial\psi}{\partial\theta}$$

$$v_\theta = \frac{\partial\psi}{\partial r}$$

where v_r and v_θ are the radial and peripheral velocity components. In the type of motion just discussed, a *stream function* always exists for real and ideal fluids, since mass must be preserved.[9] It was shown in

[9] For the case of compressible motion, see, for instance, J. C. Hunsaker and B. G. Rightmire, *Engineering Applications of Fluid Mechanics*, McGraw-Hill Book Company, Inc., New York, 1947, pp 218–220.

this section that ψ is a measure of the amount of flow per unit time from a given reference point to any other point. Accordingly, if two different flows, whose stream functions are known, are superimposed, then the value of the stream function of the combined flow at a given point is the algebraic sum of the stream functions that were superimposed.

Illustrative Example 3.4

It is claimed that the flow of an inviscid fluid around a very long cylinder has a stream function

$$\psi = U_\infty y\left(1 - \frac{a^2}{x^2 + y^2}\right) = U_\infty\left(r - \frac{a^2}{r}\right)\sin\theta$$

The two expressions for ψ are identical. The first one is in Cartesian rectangular coordinates and the second is in polar or cylindrical coordinates. The quantity a is the radius of the cylinder as shown in Fig. 3.14. The object is to find the velocity distribution on the surface of the cylinder. Because the cylinder itself is also a streamline, the velocity on its surface must be tangential and consequently peripheral. Therefore, it is inherently simpler to use the

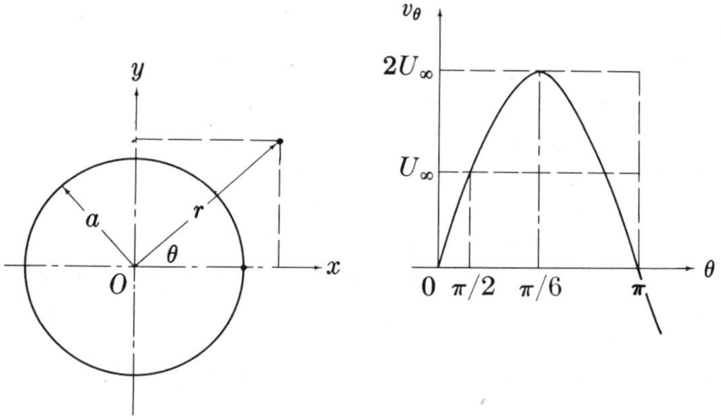

Figure 3.14

The cylinder and the cylindrical-coordinate system.

equations in the cylindrical form. The quantity U_∞ is the undisturbed velocity far away from the cylinder in a direction from right to left.

$$v_r\Big]_{r=a} = 0; \qquad v_\theta\Big]_{r=a} = -\frac{\partial\psi}{\partial r}\Big]_{r=a} = U_\infty \sin\theta\left[1 + \frac{a^2}{r^2}\right]_{r=a}$$

$$= 2U_\infty \sin\theta$$

According to this result, at $\theta = 0$ the peripheral and radial velocities are both zero. This point and the point at $\theta = 180°$ are both called the *stagnation points,* since the fluid stagnates there. Around the periphery of the cylinder, the velocity increases first to its initial value far downstream at $\theta = 30°$, and it continues to accelerate to a value $2U_\infty$ at the top and bottom of the cylindrical section where $\theta = 90°$ and $270°$. The conditions on the lower part of the cylinder are identical to the upper part.

In the same fashion, velocities at every point in the flow field besides the surface of the cylinder can be found by evaluating the results just found at different values of r.

At this point it becomes interesting to verify if this flow satisfies the conservation of mass equation, Eq. (3.18). The velocity components v_r and v_θ can be obtained through Eq. (3.27)

$$\begin{aligned} v_r &= -\frac{1}{r}\frac{\partial\psi}{\partial\theta} \\ &= U_\infty \cos\theta\left(\frac{a^2}{r^2} - 1\right) \end{aligned}$$

and

$$\begin{aligned} v_\theta &= \frac{\partial\psi}{\partial r} \\ &= U_\infty \sin\theta\left(\frac{a^2}{r^2} + 1\right) \end{aligned}$$

Now that the velocity components are obtained, the condition for continuity of mass can be checked with Eq. [4.20(*b*)].

$$\begin{aligned} \frac{1}{r}\frac{\partial}{\partial r}(rv_r) &= \frac{1}{r}\frac{\partial}{\partial r}\left[U_\infty \cos\theta\left(\frac{a^2}{r} - r\right)\right] \\ &= \frac{1}{r}\left[U_\infty \cos\theta\left(-\frac{a^2}{r^2} - 1\right)\right] \\ &= -U_\infty \cos\theta\left(\frac{a^2}{r^3} + \frac{1}{r}\right) \end{aligned}$$

Furthermore,

$$\frac{1}{r}\frac{\partial v_\theta}{\partial\theta} = U_\infty \cos\theta\left(\frac{a^2}{r^3} + \frac{1}{r}\right)$$

Since the sum of these two terms is zero, the continuity equation is satisfied; therefore, at every point in the flow field, the preservation of mass is not violated.

3.12 Linear Combination of Two-Dimensional Perfect Fluids

A *point source* is a fundamental flow emanating from a point in space and spreading radially outward in a uniform fashion. A *point sink* represents the same type of fundamental flow, except that the flow is inward toward the point. If a multitude of equal-strength sources are closely strung along a line of infinite extent, the resulting flow will again be

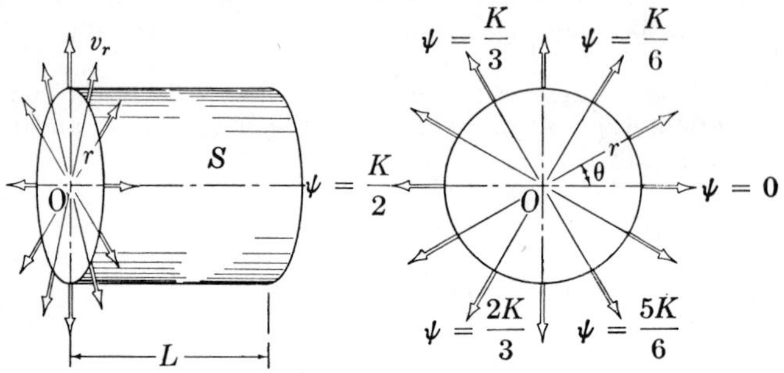

Figure 3.15
Two-dimensional line source.

radial but on a plane perpendicular to the line. The flow field will therefore be the same at all cross sections perpendicular to the line. This line of sources will give a two-dimensional-flow field called a *line source.* The *line sink* will be made of a similar array of infinitely packed point sinks of equal strength.

Let K be the strength of the line source per unit length. The strength here refers to the total flow emanating from the line source in a unit length. If any cylindrical surface S at a distance r from the center O is drawn as shown in Fig. 3.15, then the total amount of flow through this or any other surface is KL. If the flow is steady and with constant density using Eq. (3.11), this total flow is also equal to

$$KL = L(2\pi r)v_r$$

$$v_r = \frac{K}{2\pi r}$$

Since the flow is completely radial, according to Eq. (3.27),

$$v_\theta = 0$$

$$v_r = -\frac{1}{r}\frac{\partial \psi}{\partial \theta} = -\frac{1}{r}\frac{d\psi}{d\theta}$$

$$= \frac{K}{2\pi r}$$

Solving for $d\psi$,

$$d\psi = -\frac{K}{2\pi}\, d\theta$$

The integration of this linear first-order differential equation gives

$$\psi = -\frac{K}{2\pi}\theta + \text{constant}$$

As shown in Fig. 3.15, the constant can be arbitrarily made zero by letting $\psi = 0$ when $\theta = 0$. The streamlines are then radial lines denoting equal increment changes in ψ for equal increment changes in θ.

The stream function for a two-dimensional *parallel flow* can also be obtained in Cartesian notation from Eq. (3.26). For flow flowing in the positive x-direction,

$$v = 0$$

$$u = -\frac{\partial \psi}{\partial y} = -\frac{d\psi}{dy}$$

Upon integration, the stream function is found to be

$$\psi = -uy + \text{constant}$$

In the same manner, if $y = 0$ (the x-axis) is chosen as the reference streamline $\psi = 0$, the streamline equation for parallel flow becomes

$$\psi = -uy$$

If the source and the parallel flow are two flows to be superimposed,[10] their resultant solution is the sum of the individual solutions, since the differential equations for both flows are linear. Therefore, for the combined flows and $u = U_\infty$

$$\psi(r,\theta) = U_\infty y - \frac{K}{2\pi}\theta$$

$$= U_\infty r \sin\theta - \frac{K}{2\pi}\theta \qquad (3.30)$$

The *stagnation point* is defined as the point in the flow field where the motion stagnates; that is, the velocity is zero. This point can be found by evaluating from Eq. (3.30) the velocities v_r and v_θ and setting them equal to zero.

$$v_r = -\frac{1}{r}\frac{\partial \psi}{\partial \theta} = \frac{K}{2\pi r} - U_\infty \cos\theta = 0$$

$$v_\theta = \frac{\partial \psi}{\partial r} = U_\infty \sin\theta = 0$$

[10] This problem is discussed thoroughly in Sec. 7.12.

The solution of these two equations gives the position $\theta = 0$ and $r = r_0 = K/2\pi U_\infty$. The value of the stream function ψ at this point is seen to be zero [from Eq. (3.30)]. Therefore, the streamline that passes through the stagnation point is called, by definition, the *stagnation streamline.* The equation of this streamline is obtained when Eq. (3.30) is set to zero:

$$r = \frac{K}{2\pi U_\infty} \frac{\theta}{\sin \theta}$$

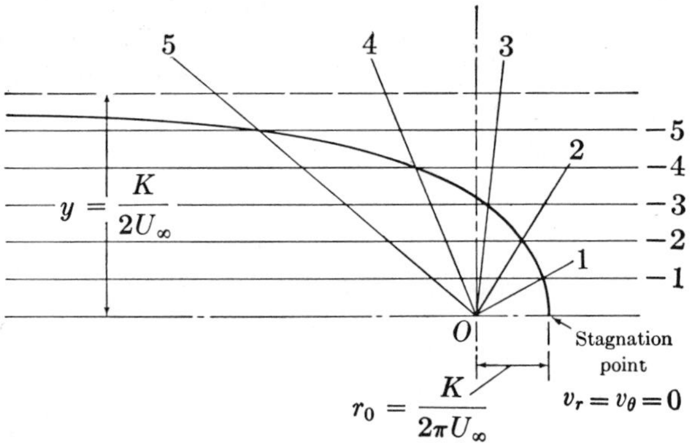

Figure 3.16
Two-dimensional Rankine half-body.

The shape of this stagnation streamline is represented in Fig. 3.16 by the curved line. On the left of the source center O, this streamline of the combined flow proceeds indefinitely and becomes asymptotic to a horizontal line $y = r \sin \theta = K/2U_\infty$. This can be shown from the previous equation when $\theta = \pi$. All other streamlines of the combined flow become parallel to the x-axis when $\theta = \pi$.

The flow field shown in Fig. 3.16 can be solved graphically as follows: Equal amounts of flow are represented between two consecutive radial streamlines of the source flow and between consecutive streamlines of the parallel flow. If, arbitrarily, the smallest division shown is called unity, then for the combined flow the streamline values at any point are the sum of the streamline values of both fields.

Since the flow considered is nonviscous, the flow in the internal part of the Rankine body can be considered solid without altering the configuration of the flow on the outside. This is because the perfect fluid, not having a viscosity, has no way of distinguishing two contours of the same geometry but different materials.

Illustrative Example 3.5

Using the principles of the stream function and its connections with the velocity of the fluid, this problem will illustrate the differences between the streamline, the streak line, and the path line in an unsteady motion.

Let the steady motion of fluid around a ship, described in Fig. 3.8(a), be represented by the stream function of a so-called two-dimensional "Rankine half-body." $\psi = U_\infty r \sin\theta - C\theta$ [Eq. (3.30)] describes, then, the equation of the steady-state streamlines around the Rankine body shown in Fig. 3.16. The full body extends identically on the lower side of $\psi = 0$, so, for convenience, only half of it is shown. U_∞ is again the value of the velocity far away from the body in the undisturbed flow. C is a constant such that C/U_∞ is a scale factor that determines the size of the body. $\psi = 0$ is the stagnation streamline that extends into the contour of the body. For different values of ψ, different streamlines are plotted in Fig. 3.17(a). Since the increment values of consecutive streamlines are the same, the same amount of flow per unit time passes between two consecutive streamlines. For $\psi = 0$ the contour of the body is obtained from the equation $U_\infty r \sin\theta - C\theta = 0$. When $\theta = 0$, by a limiting process $r = C/U_\infty$ represents the distance from the center O to the nose

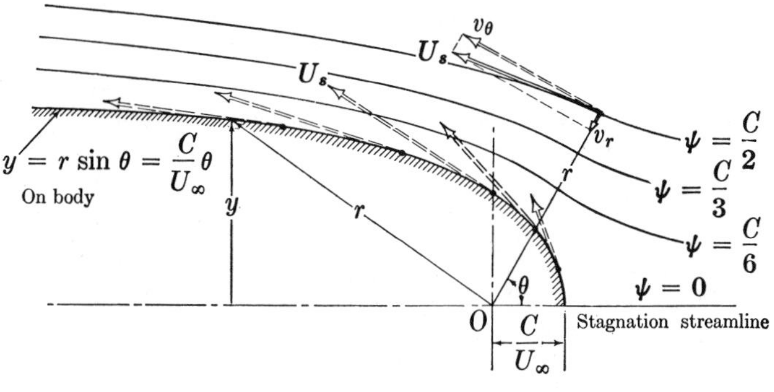

Figure 3.17

(a) Steady-state flow pattern of fluid over a half-body.

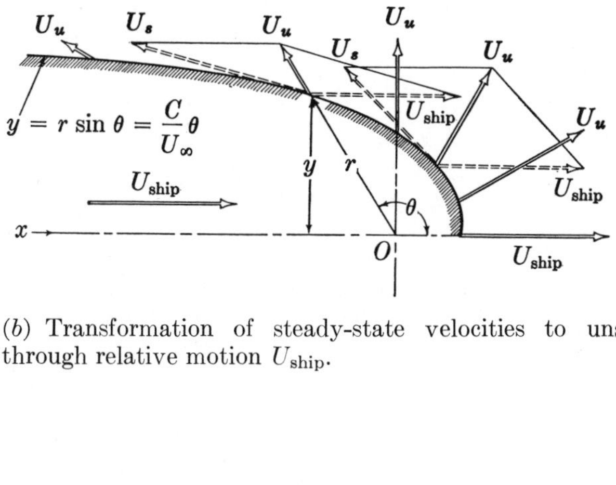

(b) Transformation of steady-state velocities to unsteady-state velocities through relative motion U_{ship}.

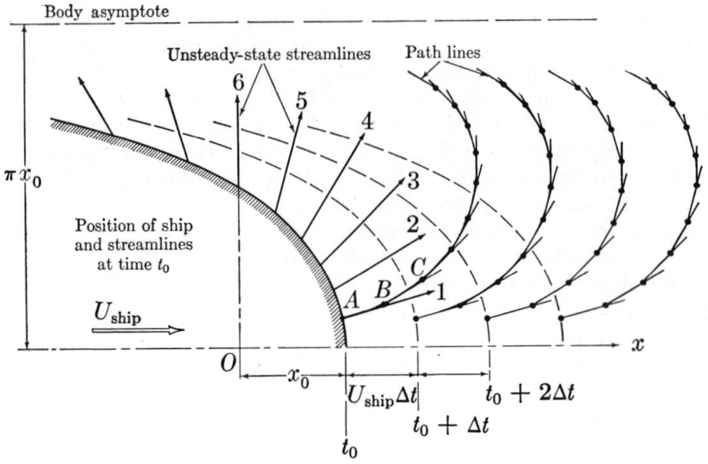

(c) Construction of path line as ship and unsteady-state streamlines move at a velocity U_{ship}.

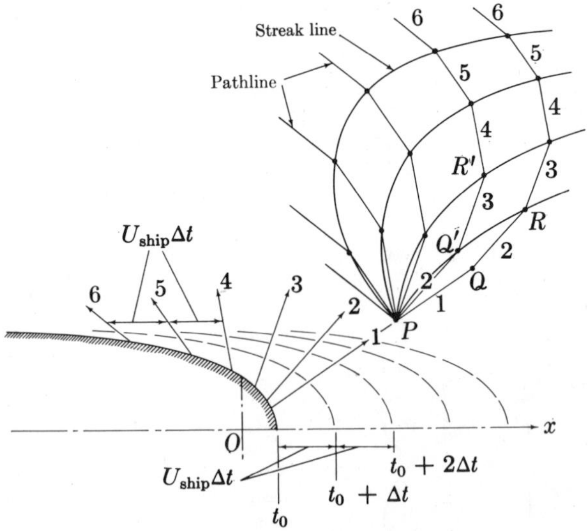

(d) Construction of streak lines as ship and unsteady-state streamlines move at a velocity U_{ship}.

of the body. When this distance is arbitrarily chosen as unity, the other radial distances from the center O for any angle θ can be determined in terms of the arbitrary length. From Sec. 3.11 the peripheral and radial velocities can be computed everywhere in the flow field from the partial derivative relationships of the stream function.

$$v_\theta = U_\infty \sin\theta \quad \text{and} \quad v_r = C/r - U_\infty \cos\theta$$

and the total velocity at any point r, θ measured from O would be

$$U_s = \sqrt{v_\theta^2 + v_r^2}$$

$$= U_\infty \sqrt{1 + \frac{C^2}{r^2U_\infty^2} + 2\frac{C}{rU_\infty}\cos\theta}$$

Particularly on the surface of the half-body where the contour is described by $C\theta - U_\infty r \sin\theta = 0$, the steady-state fluid velocity has the magnitude

$$U_s = U_\infty \sqrt{1 + \left(\frac{\sin\theta}{\theta}\right)^2 - \frac{\sin 2\theta}{\theta}}$$

Fig. 3.17(a) shows these velocities plotted for the steady-state case. These steady-state streamlines and velocities are determined with respect to an observer standing fixed on the half-body which travels at a steady velocity U_{ship}. Since the ship does not move with respect to the observer, the fluid will seem to move toward the ship with an undisturbed velocity U_∞ and a velocity field U_s just derived.

To achieve the unsteady motion of Fig. 3.8(b), the observer must move to the pier as in Fig. 3.8. (There, the relative velocity with the undisturbed fluid is zero.) The observer will now experience an entirely different flow field, because the motion he had observed originally was relative to the ship, but now the ship has a relative velocity U_{ship} with respect to the pier. Therefore, the velocity field, as observed from the pier, will be that of the steady motion as viewed from the ship shown in Fig. 3.17(a) plus a vector addition of the velocity of the ship relative to the pier U_{ship}. This new unsteady velocity field, as viewed from the pier, is shown in Fig. 3.17(b) for the flow on the surface of the body. The resulting velocity is U_u as observed from the pier. The flow field is now unsteady, because, as the ship moves, flow conditions at a given point with respect to the observer are no longer the same with time. Since, by definition, the velocity is tangential to the streamlines, the new set of streamlines in the proximity of the body have the new direction U_u, and they move constantly with the body.

The determination of the path lines is now a simple matter, since the direction of the velocity is known at a given point at all times. Referring to Fig. 3.17(c), a particle on the body at point A is considered at time t_0. This particle being on the streamline 1 will move along the streamline at the corresponding velocity, say for an increment of time Δt, until it reaches B. During this time the body has also moved a distance $U_{\text{ship}}\,\Delta t$ together with the streamline pattern. Consequently, when the particle has reached B, it will no longer be on streamline 1; streamline 2 will have caught up with it, giving the particle its own direction and speed. For the next increment of time Δt the particle will be moving along streamline 2 until streamline 3 catches up with it at C and imparts its own direction and speed. When the process is continued at infinitesimal times, the path of the particle will be the path lines shown in Fig. 3.17(c). Actually, the process just described does not happen in abrupt changes of directions and speeds but moves smoothly along the faired path lines shown. Since the velocity of the fluid decreases as we move away from the body, as time elapses the streamlines catch up with the particles faster than indicated and consequently bend sooner toward the rear of the half-body.

In Section 3.8 it was stated that the streak line is, at a given time, the locus of all the particles that have originated from a given point in the fluid space. In Fig. 3.17(d) the point P has been arbitrarily chosen where a source of dye is introduced. For convenience, consider the set of streamlines in that figure, located in such a manner that the horizontal spacing between them along the horizontal through P is the same. Starting at the instant t_0, streamline 1 will move a dyed particle from P in the direction of 1 and at the corresponding velocity at P. This particle will move along PQ, and the ship with the streamlines will move along the x-axis. After an interval of time Δt, streamline 2 will be at P and will move another particle from P in the direction of 2 at the new velocity at P. Shortly afterward, streamline 2 will catch up with the first particle at Q and will impart to it a new velocity in the direction of 2 which is QR. At time $t_0 + 2\,\Delta t$, streamline 3 will cross at P, and a new particle will start there in its direction; somewhat later, streamline 3 will meet the second particle at Q' and will give it a new direction $Q'R'$. Soon the same streamline 3 will catch up with the first particle at R and will give its own direction and speed to it.

The process continues indefinitely as long as the motion is present, and the set of moving streamlines will continuously influence the particles that originate from P or any other point. The locus of all these particles that have started at P is shown in Fig. 3.17(d) for times $t_0 + 5\,\Delta t$ and $t_0 + 6\,\Delta t$. They represent the streak lines originating at P. The respective path lines are also shown.

3.13 Existence and Visualization of Streamlines

The way the stream function ψ was defined in Eq. (3.22) implies that its existence depends on the fact that the fluid is incompressible and that continuity of mass is preserved in a region where the stream function is defined. The conditions are then solely kinematic, and therefore the validity of the stream function has nothing to do with forces. Consequently, the definition of the stream function is valid for the realm of viscous fluids as well.

If the stream function of a flow field is known, then the velocity field of the flow can be determined at every point by the differentiations given in Eqs. (3.26) and (3.27). In fact, the properties of motion of the entire flow field are known if ψ is known.

Sometimes the motion is very complex, and therefore an analytic expression for the stream function is not readily obtainable. Often, for problems of this nature, the experimental approach is used. Dyes,

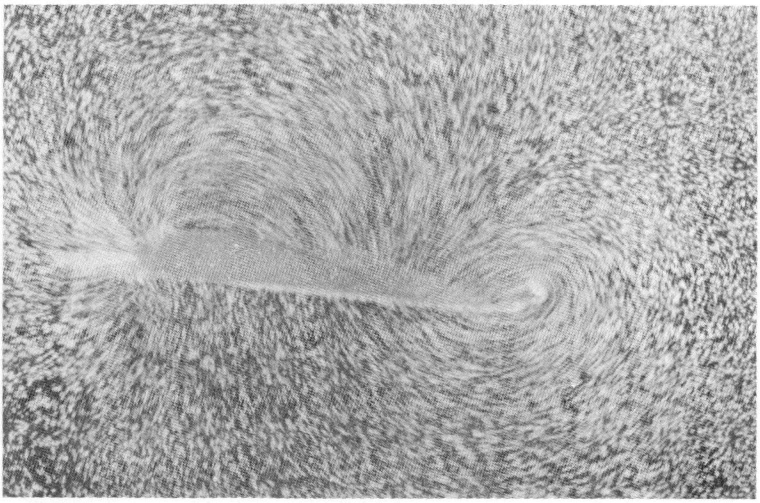

(*a*)

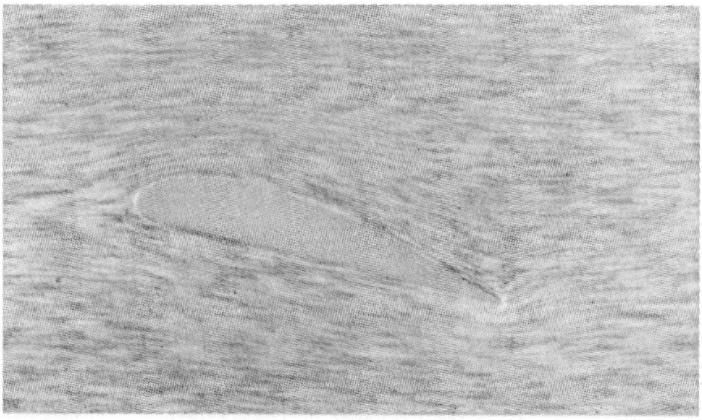

(*b*)

Figure 3.18
Flow fields viewed from different frames of reference. (*a*) Unsteady motion. Observer stationary. Airfoil moving to the left. (*b*) Steady motion. Observer stationary with respect to airfoil. Fluid moving to the right.

smokes, or suspensions are used in the fluid stream to trace the shape of the streamlines. This method of depicting streamlines is valid only for steady motions or motion with respect to a coordinate system such that it is considered steady. It was discussed in Sec. 3.8 that the streamline, the path line, and the streak line are one and the same when the flow is steady. The injection of dye or smoke at a given point in the stream, according to our previous definition, will describe the streak line, and, if the flow is steady, it can be considered to be the streamline. This is the reason why, for steady motions, the technique of streak lines is used for the representation of streamlines and path lines.

In the case of an unsteady motion, such as the motion of an airfoil past an observer at rest with respect to the fluid, at an instant of time as pictured with a camera, the flow field will look like Fig. 3.18(*a*). If this photograph were taken at a very high speed with respect to the motion of the airfoil, the photograph would then represent the instantaneous streamlines of this unsteady motion. The second photograph in Fig. 3.18(*b*) represents the same motion as viewed by an observer fixed in space with respect to the airfoil. The photographs shown were taken in water with floating aluminum powder as the visual medium.

3.14 The Concept of Fluid Rotation

In solid mechanics a *rigid body* is defined as a body in which the respective distances of the particles remain invariable, regardless of the force or motion applied to the body. This is not the case when the motion of fluids is considered. The respective distances of the fluid particles are constantly changing, and this is the reason it is called a fluid instead of a rigid body.

If a rigid body moves in such a way that an axis through the body remains fixed with respect to a coordinate system of reference, then the rigid body is said to be in *pure rotation.* Each particle of the body describes a circle about the *axis of rotation.* The particle speed is proportional to the *radius of rotation* that the particles describe. Every particle and every line on the body has the same angular velocity as any other. Since the respective distances between particles do not necessarily remain the same in a fluid, all parts of a fluid body do not necessarily rotate at the same angular velocity, nor do they have to rotate with respect to the same frame of reference. Consequently, the definition of rotation for solids must be reconsidered so as to make it applicable and consistent for fluids as well.

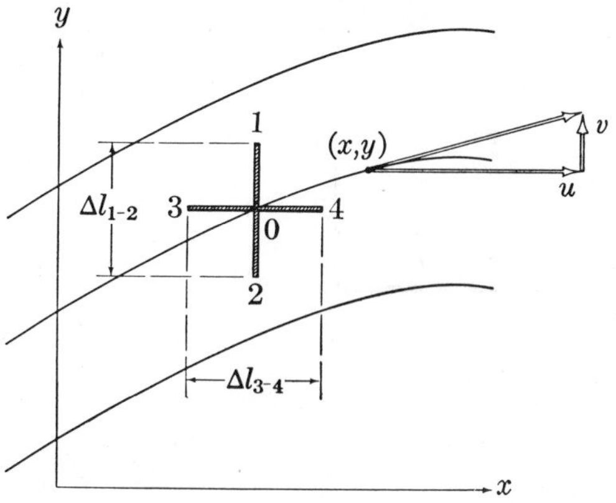

Figure 3.19
Motion of rigid linear elements in a two-dimensional-flow field.

Let *rotation* of a fluid *at a point* be defined as the average angular velocity of two rigid differential linear elements of fluid originally perpendicular to each other. The only difference, so far, from the definition of rotation of a rigid body is that two elements are involved, in the case of the fluid, instead of one as in the case of the rigid body. Rotation, as in solid mechanics, will again be a vector quantity whose *sense* is perpendicular to the plane formed by the two elements. By convention, its direction is given by the right-hand rule for the motion of a right-handed screw.

The discussion that follows is for a plane or two-dimensional motion. In order to obtain the total rotation for a three-dimensional flow, the three components of rotation must be determined in the same fashion and added vectorially. Consider the two rigid linear differential elements 1–2 and 3–4, as shown in Fig. 3.19. The two elements are in an arbitrary two-dimensional flow and are mutually perpendicular at the instant considered. Let $u(x,y)$ and $v(x,y)$ be the two components of the velocity in the x- and y-directions at every point in the flow field. In the configuration shown, the variation in the x-component of the velocity will contribute only to a rotation of element 1–2. In a similar fashion, variations in the component v will contribute only a rotation of the rigid element 3–4. At the same time, both elements will be translated downstream as well, but the main concern here is the study of rotation alone.

If the velocity $\boldsymbol{U}$ at point 0 is given, the corresponding velocities at points 1,2,3,4 can be evaluated by the Taylor series expansion. One can arbitrarily make the length of the rigid elements very small so that

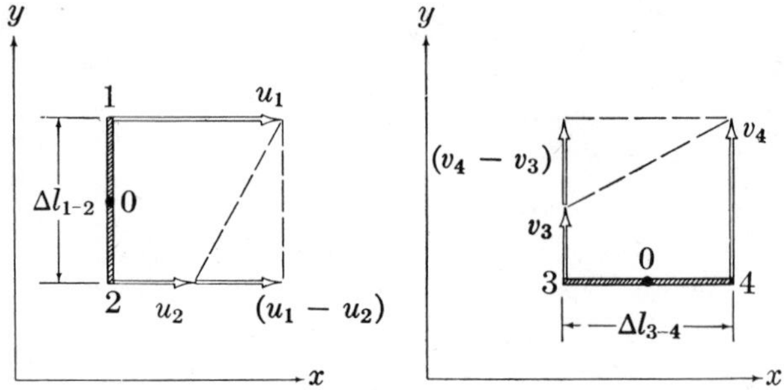

Figure 3.20
The rigid elements in a velocity gradient.
(*a*) Element 1-2.
(*b*) Element 3-4.

second-order or higher terms in the expansion are neglected because they become insignificantly small. Considering element 1–2, and also, for convention, assuming that the velocity increases with increasing coordinate direction, the velocities are readily found.

$$u_1 = u_0 + \left(\frac{\partial u}{\partial y}\right)_0 \frac{\Delta l_{1\text{-}2}}{2} + \cdots$$

$$u_2 = u_0 - \left(\frac{\partial u}{\partial y}\right)_0 \frac{\Delta l_{1\text{-}2}}{2} - \cdots$$

For u increasing with y, the difference $(u_1 - u_2)$ represents the relative velocity of the point 1 with respect to 2. This relative velocity will contribute to the rotation of point 1 with respect to point 2. The angular velocity of this rotation will be

$$\omega_{1\text{-}2} = \frac{u_1 - u_2}{\Delta l_{1\text{-}2}} = 2\left(\frac{\partial u}{\partial y}\right)_0 \frac{\Delta l_{1\text{-}2}}{2} \bigg/ \Delta l_{1\text{-}2}$$
$$= \left(\frac{\partial u}{\partial y}\right)_0 \curvearrowright$$

According to the assumption that u increases with y, element 1–2 rotates in a clockwise direction, and the vector representing the rotation is perpendicular to the paper in a direction piercing into the book. Element 3–4 can be analyzed in a similar fashion.

$$v_4 = v_0 + \left(\frac{\partial v}{\partial x}\right)_0 \frac{\Delta l_{3\text{-}4}}{2} + \cdots$$

$$v_3 = v_0 - \left(\frac{\partial v}{\partial x}\right)_0 \frac{\Delta l_{3\text{-}4}}{2} - \cdots$$

Therefore, the angular velocity of the element 3–4 is

$$\omega_{3\text{-}4} = \frac{v_4 - v_3}{\Delta l_{3\text{-}4}} = 2\left(\frac{\partial v}{\partial x}\right)_0 \frac{\Delta l_{3\text{-}4}}{2} \bigg/ \Delta l_{3\text{-}4}$$

$$= \left(\frac{\partial v}{\partial x}\right)_0 \curvearrowleft$$

Again for v increasing with x, element 3–4 indicates a counterclockwise rotation, and the vector, according to convention, pierces up from the book. The rotation of the fluid was defined as the average of the rotation of these two elements, and, since $\omega_{1\text{-}2}$ is in the negative direction compared to $\omega_{3\text{-}4}$, the rotation of the fluid will be

$$\omega_z = \left(\frac{\partial v}{\partial x} - \frac{\partial u}{\partial y}\right) \bigg/ 2 \tag{3.31}$$

This equation represents the rotation of the fluid in the x–y-plane, and consequently it is the z-component of the total rotation vector. In order to eliminate the factor 2 from the rotation equation, let, by definition, the *vorticity* be twice the value of the rotation. Consequently, the z-component of the vorticity will be

$$\zeta_z = \left(\frac{\partial v}{\partial x} - \frac{\partial u}{\partial y}\right) \tag{3.32}$$

The same method can be used to determine the vorticity of the fluid when in rotation in the other two planes.[11]

$$\begin{aligned} \zeta_y &= \left(\frac{\partial u}{\partial z} - \frac{\partial w}{\partial x}\right) \\ \zeta_x &= \left(\frac{\partial w}{\partial y} - \frac{\partial v}{\partial z}\right) \end{aligned} \tag{3.33}$$

In order to obtain the total vorticity of the fluid at a given point, the three components shown must be added vectorially.

$$\begin{aligned} \boldsymbol{\zeta} &= \boldsymbol{i}\zeta_x + \boldsymbol{j}\zeta_y + \boldsymbol{k}\zeta_z \\ &= \boldsymbol{\nabla} \times \boldsymbol{U} \end{aligned} \tag{3.34}$$

This is the *curl* of the velocity vector $\boldsymbol{U}$, and according to Eq. (3.31) it is twice the rotation vector. The *curl* is developed in Sec. A.18.

A fluid motion is said to be *irrotational* in a given region when the vorticity is zero at that region. Similarly, a fluid motion is said to be

[11] The student will find this exercise very helpful.

irrotational throughout when the vorticity is zero throughout the flow field. For example, a uniform parallel flow has no gradients in the velocities; thus the motion is said to be irrotational. In the case of irrotational motion, Eqs. (3.32) and (3.33) must be identically equal to zero.

In the case when the vorticity is constant everywhere, the motion corresponds to that of a rigid-body rotation, as will be shown in Illustrative Example 3.6.

Illustrative Example 3.6

When a fluid in a tank is made to rotate with the tank at a constant angular velocity ω, after an initial period the fluid will rotate in a so-called *rigid-body rotation*. The tangential velocity at a point will be

$$v_\theta = \omega r$$

When expressing the tangential velocity into Cartesian components u and v, it follows that

$$-u = v_\theta \sin\theta = \omega r \sin\theta = \omega y$$

$$v = v_\theta \cos\theta = \omega r \cos\theta = \omega x$$

According to Eq. (3.33), the value of the vorticity normal to the plane of the paper is then

$$\zeta_z = \left(\frac{\partial v}{\partial x} - \frac{\partial u}{\partial y}\right)$$

$$= \omega - (-\omega)$$

$$= 2\omega$$

This finding is in accordance with the definition that the vorticity is twice the value of the rotation. This illustrative example shows, then, that the definition of rotation set up for a fluid in this section is compatible with the definition of rotation for a rigid body. Equation (3.34) is, therefore, a measure of the rotation for deformable substances as well as for rigid bodies.

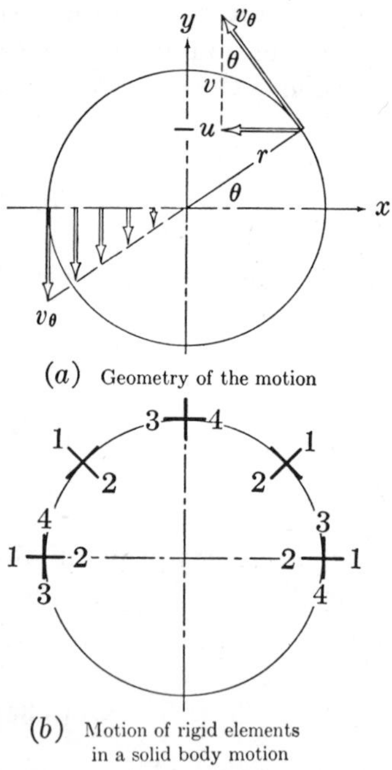

Figure 3.21
Solid-body motion.

3.15 Vorticity in Cylindrical Coordinates

The rotation of two originally perpendicular linear elements was considered in the previous section. If the flow is pure circulatory or polar, like the problem considered in the previous illustrative example, then the rotation and vorticity are more adequately expressed in polar coordinates.

In Sec. A.14, a method was presented on how to obtain the various parts of an operation with ∇. The cylindrical components of the vorticity $\nabla \times \boldsymbol{U}$ was easily determined by substituting the components of ∇ and those of $\boldsymbol{U}$.

$$\nabla = \boldsymbol{i}\frac{\partial}{\partial r} + \boldsymbol{j}\frac{1}{r}\frac{\partial}{\partial \theta} + \boldsymbol{k}\frac{\partial}{\partial z}$$

$$\boldsymbol{U} = \boldsymbol{i}v_r + \boldsymbol{j}v_\theta + \boldsymbol{k}v_z$$

Recalling the changes[12] of the unit vectors during the operation, we obtain in the cylindrical coordinates:

$$\begin{aligned}\boldsymbol{\zeta} &= \nabla \times \boldsymbol{U} \\ &= \boldsymbol{i}\left(\frac{1}{r}\frac{\partial v_z}{\partial \theta} - \frac{\partial v_\theta}{\partial z}\right) + \boldsymbol{j}\left(\frac{\partial v_r}{\partial \theta} - \frac{\partial v_z}{\partial r}\right) \\ &\quad + \boldsymbol{k}\left[\frac{1}{r}\frac{\partial}{\partial r}(rv_\theta) - \frac{1}{r}\frac{\partial v_r}{\partial \theta}\right]\end{aligned} \tag{3.35}$$

To show the physical significance of these components, we proceed to determine the rotation of the linear elements in cylindrical coordinates as was done in Sec. 3.14 for Cartesian coordinates. This is shown in Fig. 3.22.

Consider, then, the two rigid elements initially placed as shown in Fig. 3.22. Because of the components of v_θ normal element 3–4, the element will rotate in a counterclockwise direction owing to the radial component of the tangential velocity at 3 and 4

$$\begin{aligned} v_\theta \sin\frac{\Delta\theta}{2} &= v_\theta \frac{\Delta\theta}{2} \\ &= v_\theta \frac{\Delta s}{2r}\end{aligned}$$

The rotation of element 3–4 will also be influenced by the radial velocities $v_r - \frac{\partial v_r}{\partial \theta}\frac{\Delta\theta}{2}$ and $v_r + \frac{\partial v_r}{\partial \theta}\frac{\Delta\theta}{2}$ at both ends of the element. If v_r is again

[12] Students should attempt the development of this cross product as in the case of Sect. A.18.

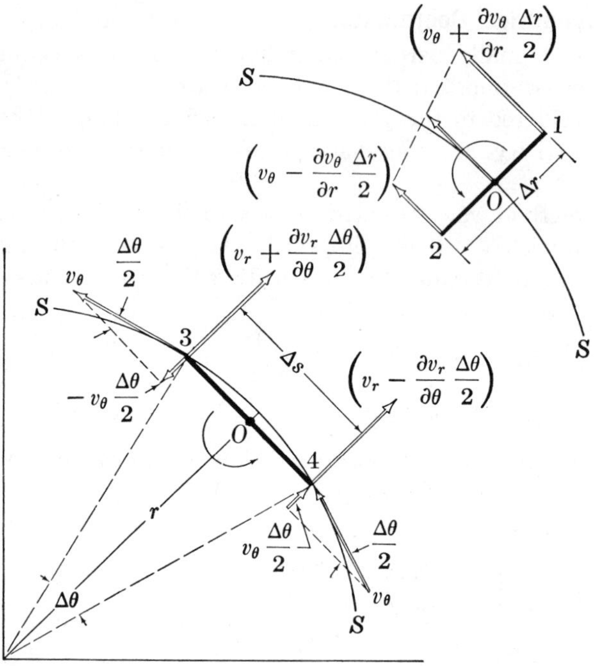

Figure 3.22
Motion of linear rigid elements in a circulatory two-dimensional motion.

assumed to increase with θ, the total rotation of element 3–4 can then be computed as

$$\omega_{3\text{-}4} = \frac{v_\theta \dfrac{\Delta s}{2r} - \left(-v_\theta \dfrac{\Delta s}{2r}\right)}{\Delta s} - \frac{\left(v_r + \dfrac{\partial v_r}{\partial \theta}\dfrac{\Delta\theta}{2}\right) - \left(v_r - \dfrac{\partial v_r}{\partial \theta}\dfrac{\Delta\theta}{2}\right)}{\Delta s}$$

$$= \frac{v_\theta}{r} - \frac{\partial v_r}{\partial \theta}\frac{\Delta\theta}{\Delta s}$$

$$= \frac{v_\theta}{r} - \frac{1}{r}\frac{\partial v_r}{\partial \theta}$$

since $\Delta s = r\,\Delta\theta$. The rotation of the normal element 1–2 can be obtained in the same fashion by considering again, by convention, an increase of the velocity with increase of the coordinate r so that the derivatives are assumed to be positive. The velocity at tip 1 is $v_\theta + \dfrac{\partial v_\theta}{\partial r}\dfrac{\Delta r}{2}$, and that at tip 2 is $v_\theta - \dfrac{\partial v_\theta}{\partial r}\dfrac{\Delta r}{2}$. The counterclockwise rotation of element 1–2 is the relative velocity of 1 with respect to 2 divided by the length Δr.

$$\omega_{1\text{-}2} = \frac{2 \dfrac{\partial v_\theta}{\partial r} \dfrac{\Delta r}{2}}{\Delta r} = \frac{\partial v_\theta}{\partial r}$$

The resultant rotation of O is the arithmetic average of $\omega_{1\text{-}2}$ and $\omega_{3\text{-}4}$. The vorticity component normal to the r–θ-plane is twice the rotation, or

$$\begin{aligned} \zeta_z &= \frac{\partial v_\theta}{\partial r} + \frac{v_\theta}{r} - \frac{1}{r}\frac{\partial v_r}{\partial \theta} \\ &= \frac{1}{r}\left[\frac{\partial}{\partial r}(r v_\theta) - \frac{\partial v_r}{\partial \theta}\right] \end{aligned} \tag{3.36}$$

This is exactly the $\boldsymbol{k}$ component of Eq. (3.35). The other components can be obtained with a similar reasoning. For a flow that is pure peripheral with $v_r = 0$, this equation simplifies to the form

$$\zeta_z = \frac{\partial v_\theta}{\partial r} + \frac{v_\theta}{r} \tag{3.37}$$

This equation is equivalent to Eq. (3.32).

As it was stated in Eq. (3.35), the three components of the vorticity in polar notation can be shown to be

$$\begin{aligned} \zeta_z &= \frac{1}{r}\left[\frac{\partial}{\partial r}(r v_\theta) - \frac{\partial v_r}{\partial \theta}\right] \\ \zeta_\theta &= \frac{\partial v_r}{\partial z} - \frac{\partial v_z}{\partial r} \\ \zeta_r &= \frac{1}{r}\frac{\partial v_z}{\partial \theta} - \frac{\partial v_\theta}{\partial z} \end{aligned} \tag{3.38}$$

3.16 Conditions for Irrotational Plane Motion

It can readily be shown that the differential equation for an irrotational plane motion is obtained from the condition already derived in Eqs. (3.26) and (3.32). If the quantities for u and v in Eq. (3.26) are substituted into Eq. (3.32), the following differential equation is found when $\zeta_z = 0$.

$$\frac{\partial}{\partial x}\left(-\frac{\partial \psi}{\partial x}\right) - \frac{\partial}{\partial y}\left(\frac{\partial \psi}{\partial y}\right) = 0$$

$$\frac{\partial^2 \psi}{\partial x^2} + \frac{\partial^2 \psi}{\partial y^2} = 0 \tag{3.39}$$

$$\nabla^2 \psi = 0$$

This is called *Laplace's Equation*, and, together with the prescribed boundary conditions of the flow, it can be solved for the particular problems. For a simple circulatory motion with axisymmetry and $v_r = 0$, the solution can be found more readily by considering Eq. (3.37). In the case considered, since v_θ is a function of r alone, for irrotational motion we have

$$\frac{dv_\theta}{dr} + \frac{v_\theta}{r} = 0$$

Its solution is obtained by separation of variables

$$\frac{dv_\theta}{v_\theta} + \frac{dr}{r} = 0$$

$$\ln v_\theta + \ln r = \text{constant} \tag{3.40}$$

$$v_\theta r = C$$

This type of motion, where the vorticity is zero and the peripheral velocity varies inversely as the radial distance, is called a *free vortex*. This circulatory irrotational flow is observed, for instance, when the fluid of a large container is set into peripheral motion with a stirring rod. The circulatory motion set up in the neighborhood of a drain at the bottom of a tank is of the same nature. The idealized flow around bends is also of the same type.

An interesting behavior of irrotational plane flows with constant density follows from Eqs. (3.19) and (3.32). With two dependent variables u, v and the two last equations, one can solve for u or v in the form of a partial differential equation. Taking the derivative of Eq. (3.19) with respect to x and that of Eq. (3.32) with respect to y and equating, the following equation is obtained:

$$\frac{\partial^2 u}{\partial x^2} + \frac{\partial^2 u}{\partial y^2} = 0$$

The same result can be obtained for the v-component if the order of differentiation is reversed. These equations are then similar to Eq. (3.39) and can be solved with known boundary conditions. The solution will be valid for incompressible and irrotational two-dimensional flows.

3.17 Relationship Between the Vorticity, the Velocity and the Stream Function

Equation (3.25) gave the relationship between the velocity $\boldsymbol{U}$ and the stream function ψ. Taking the curl of this equation yields

$$\boldsymbol{\zeta} = \nabla \times \boldsymbol{U} = \boldsymbol{b}\, \nabla^2 \psi \tag{3.41}$$

If we multiplied this equation with Eq. (3.25) we have

$$\boldsymbol{U} \times \boldsymbol{\zeta} = (\boldsymbol{b} \times \nabla\psi) \times (\boldsymbol{b}\, \nabla\psi^2)$$

For the right hand side we use the triple vector product rules discussed in Sec. A.10 and we obtain

$$\boldsymbol{U} \times \boldsymbol{\zeta} = (\nabla^2\psi)\, \nabla\psi \tag{3.42}$$

This equation has a very important significance in the geometry of the flow field. It shows the geometrical relationship between the velocity $\boldsymbol{U}$, the vorticity $\boldsymbol{\zeta}$ and the surface represented by the stream function ψ. Since the cross product of $\boldsymbol{U}$ and $\boldsymbol{\zeta}$ is along $\nabla\psi$ (normal to ψ = *constant* surface). Then both $\boldsymbol{U}$ and $\boldsymbol{\zeta}$ are on that surface ψ = *constant*. By definition, it was already known that $\boldsymbol{U}$ was tangent to ψ = *constant* surface. However, for a two dimensional constant density flow, it was not known that $\boldsymbol{\zeta}$ lies on the stream surface.

Equation (3.41) gives also some physical significance to the two-dimensional flow. Since $\boldsymbol{b}$ is the unit vector normal to the plane of the motion, $\boldsymbol{\zeta}$ is also in that direction from the vectorial sense of this equation. Furthermore, comparing Eqs. (3.39) and (3.41) we conclude that the Laplacian of ψ, $\nabla^2\psi$ is equal to the vorticity in a rotational flow, while it equals zero for an irrotational motion.

3.18 The Concept of Circulation

Given an arbitrary closed region R with a surface area A and bound by a closed contour C through which fluid is flowing, the circulation around the contour C is defined as the summation at every point on the contour of the velocity component tangential to the contour C times the elemental length of the contour ds. This is precisely the line integral of $\boldsymbol{U}$ as defined in Sec. A.20. Giving the circulation the symbol Γ, we have

$$\Gamma = \oint_c \boldsymbol{U} \cdot \boldsymbol{t}\, ds$$

$$= \oint_c U \cos\theta\, ds \tag{3.43}$$

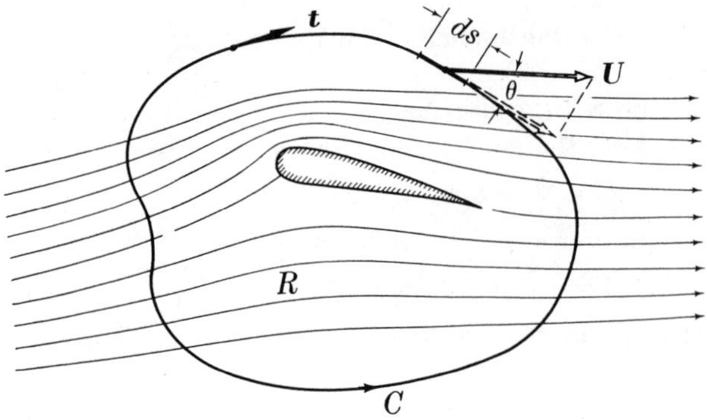

Figure 3.23
Concept of circulation.

The integral sign indicates summation all around the contour. By convention, the integration is considered positive when it is performed in a counterclockwise direction. The geometry for this integration is shown in Fig. 3.23. The concept of circulation is extremely important in the theory of lifting surfaces such as aircraft wings and blades of a turbomachine. The student, not having a preconceived knowledge of what is to follow in this course, must take Eq. (3.43) as a mere definition of the flow field.

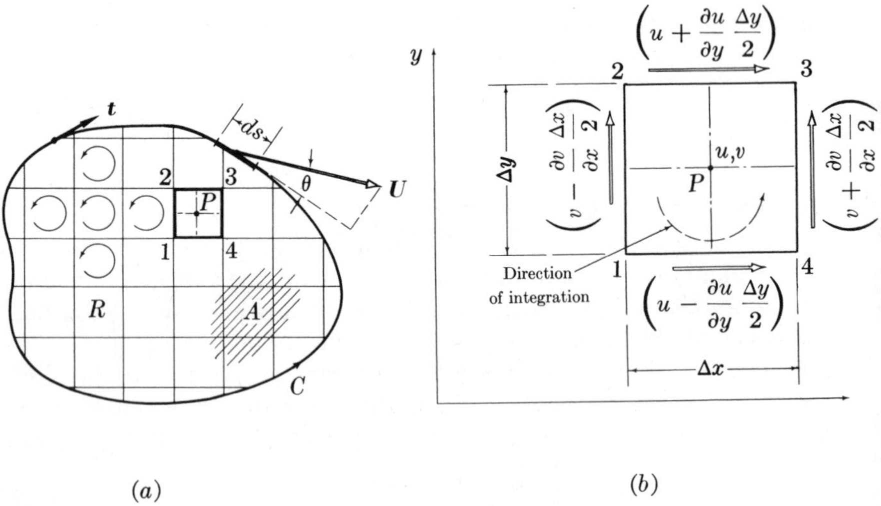

Figure 3.24
Analysis of circulation.

In general, the velocity U and the angle θ are functions of s, the position on the contour. This region, in general, need not be a plane as shown in the figure; it applies to any closed contour in space.

Stokes Theorem: Dependence of Circulation on the Vorticity. This theorem states that the circulation expressed in Eq. (3.43) is also equal to the sum of the vorticities at various points in the entire surface area A. Hence this theorem connects the fluid velocity at the contour of the region to the rotation inside the region R. In the two-dimensional problem shown in Figs. 3.23 and 3.24, we need consider only the vorticity on the x–y-plane or ζ_z. The proof of this theorem for a three-dimensional domain is presented in Sec. A.22. The theorem therefore states

$$\Gamma_C = \oint_C \boldsymbol{U} \cdot \boldsymbol{t}\, ds = \int_A \boldsymbol{\zeta}_z \cdot d\boldsymbol{A}$$

$$= \oint_C U \cos\theta\, ds = \int_A \zeta_z\, dx\, dy \tag{3.44}$$

Proof: Let the domain R in Fig. 3.23 be divided into infinitesimally small rectangular cells, as shown in Fig. 3.24(a). Let one of these cells P be considered separately in Fig. 3.24(b). If the velocity at the center of the cell is defined, then its components u and v are also known. The velocity components at the sides of the rectangular cell can also be found in terms of u and v through Taylor's expansion. For positive derivatives, by convention, velocities have been taken to increase with increasing coordinate direction. According to Eq. (3.43), the circulation around the small cell P is

$$\Delta\Gamma_P = \underbrace{\left[\left(u - \frac{\partial u}{\partial y}\frac{\Delta y}{2}\right)\Delta x\right]}_{1\text{–}4} + \underbrace{\left[\left(v + \frac{\partial v}{\partial x}\frac{\Delta x}{2}\right)\Delta y\right]}_{4\text{–}3}$$

$$- \underbrace{\left[\left(u + \frac{\partial u}{\partial y}\frac{\Delta y}{2}\right)\Delta x\right]}_{3\text{–}2} - \underbrace{\left[\left(v - \frac{\partial v}{\partial x}\frac{\Delta x}{2}\right)\Delta y\right]}_{2\text{–}1}$$

The integration was performed in a counterclockwise direction. If the fluid motion is in the direction of integration, the contribution to circulation is positive.

After simplifying the previous equation, the circulation around one cell becomes

$$\Delta\Gamma_P = \left(\frac{\partial v}{\partial x} - \frac{\partial u}{\partial y}\right)\Delta x\, \Delta y$$

$$= (\zeta_z)_P\, \Delta x\, \Delta y$$

This is part of the proof that applies to one cell alone. This proof can be extended to the entire domain R by the following reasoning: In the summation of this integration process in the entire region R, it can be noticed from Fig. 3.24(a) that the contour integration on a given cell side will be performed twice, once in each direction, because each side is common to two adjacent cells. This will be the case everywhere except for the outer contour C, which will be integrated only once. Therefore, in the limit when Δx, Δy tend toward the derivatives dx, dy, then $\Delta\Gamma$ also tends toward $d\Gamma$, and the summation over the entire surface A gives

$$\oint_C d\Gamma = \int_A \left(\frac{\partial v}{\partial x} - \frac{\partial u}{\partial y}\right) dx\,dy$$
$$\Gamma = \int_A \zeta_z \cdot dA \tag{3.45}$$

which is the proof of the theorem.

Illustrative Example 3.7

A circular tank, with radius r_0, containing fluid is rotated in a large body of the same fluid at a constant angular velocity ω. Neglecting viscous effects near the solid wall, find the velocity distribution, vorticity, and circulation in the fluid inside and outside the tank.

The fluid inside the tank is revolving with the tank; its angular velocity will be that of the tank, and the velocity of the fluid as a function of the radius is

$$v_\theta = \omega r$$

As explained in Sec. 3.17, the free fluid outside the tank will eventually take the

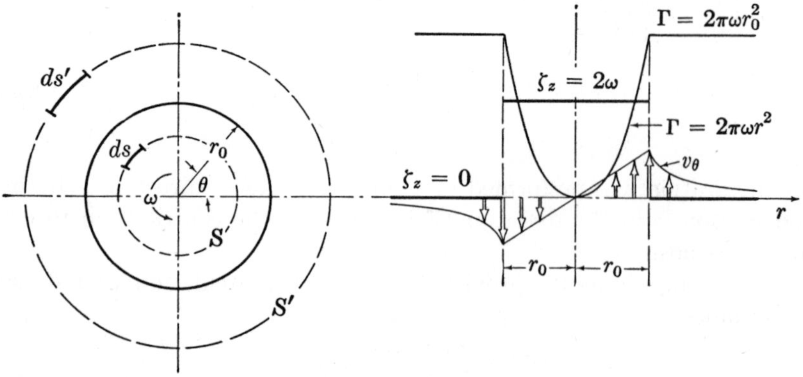

Figure 3.25
Velocity, vorticity, and circulation.

circulatory motion of the free vortex. The peripheral velocity will vary hyperbolically with the radius

$$v_\theta = \frac{C}{r}$$

Since, at both sides of the tank wall, the velocity of the fluid should have the peripheral velocity of the tank (no slip), the constant C can be evaluated.

$$\omega r_0 = \frac{C}{r_0}$$

$$C = \omega r_0^2$$

Since the fluid within the tank revolves like a rigid body, the vorticity is the same everywhere inside and equal to twice the rotation 2ω. In Sec. 3.17, it was shown that the free-vortex flow is an irrotational flow, and therefore the vorticity everywhere outside the tank is zero.

In order to compute the circulation inside and outside the tank as a function of the radius, for convenience two concentric streamlines S and S' are chosen. The circulation inside the tank for $r < r_0$ is, according to Eq. 3.43,

$$\begin{aligned} \Gamma_S &= \oint v_\theta \, ds = \int_0^{2\pi} v_\theta r \, d\theta \\ &= \int_0^{2\pi} (\omega r) r \, d\theta \\ &= 2\pi\omega r^2 \end{aligned}$$

This answer confirms Eqs. (3.44) and (3.45), the product of the vorticity times the area. Therefore Γ is a parabolic function of the radius for inside the tank. The circulation outside the tank along the contour S', $r > r_0$ is

$$\begin{aligned} \Gamma_{S'} &= \oint v_\theta \, ds' = \int_0^{2\pi} v_\theta r \, d\theta \\ &= \int_0^{2\pi} \frac{C}{r} r \, d\theta \\ &= 2\pi C = 2\pi\omega r_0^2 = \text{constant} \end{aligned}$$

This shows that, since the vorticity is zero outside the tank, there is no longer any contribution to the circulation for $r > r_0$.

Problems

3.1 Find the velocity of sound in adiabatic air at normal pressure and temperature.

3.2 Find the speed of sound in water at normal pressure and temperature.

3.3 A 16-ft outboard motorboat moves at 30 mph. Evaluate $\mathcal{R}$, $\mathcal{M}$. The temperature of the water is 50°F.

3.4 A 1-ft model is to be tested for evaluating the viscous resistance of the boat in Prob. 3.3. What should be its velocity?

3.5 A 1/10-size model of a high-speed fighter plane is to be tested for high-speed performance. If the fighter is to operate at $\mathcal{M} = 2$, what should be the speed of the model in relation to that of the fighter if the conditions of the air are the same in both cases?

3.6 The velocity of water near the discharge of a reciprocating pump fluctuates as a function of time approximately as $u = (10 + 2 \cos \omega t)$ ft/sec. The water is at 60°F, and the interval diameter of the discharge pipe is 6 in. State the time average of the velocity and the time average of the mass rate of flow.

3.7 An incompressible fluid flows through an elastic hose. The velocity and the area fluctuate as a function of time owing to the reciprocating action of the pump. If the velocity and area fluctuation are in phase, $u = (u_0 + a \sin \omega t)$ and $A = (A_0 + b \sin \omega t)$. Find the average volume flow per unit time out of the pipe.

3.8 In Prob. 3.7, instead of the area fluctuating as shown, let the radius fluctuate as $r = (r_0 + c \sin \omega t)$ and the velocity as before. Find the time average of the volume rate of flow.

3.9 Using Eq. (3.9) show that a line source such as described in Sec. 3.12 cannot conserve mass if the line source is inside the domain enclosed by the closed contour S. However, that mass is conserved if the line source is outside the domain enclosed by S. *Hint:* In the first case consider a circular cylindrical surface with the center being the origin of the source. In the second case consider the closed surface made up of two concentric cylindrical surfaces.

3.10 Again, by using Eq. (3.9) show that any circular flow, such as a vortex, in which the streamlines are circular satisfies the conservation of mass.

3.11 A perfect gas flows steadily in a horizontal pipe of constant cross-sectional area A. Assuming the flow to be isothermal and the ratio of the pressure downstream to that upstream to be 4:5, find the velocity ratio at the two locations.

3.12 Repeat Prob. 3.11 if the flow is considered to be adiabatic after insulation of the pipe. The expansion coefficient of the gas is 1.35.

3.13 Instead of a pipe as discussed in Illustrative Example 3.2, a two dimensional-channel, as shown with this problem, is considered. The velocity profile across the channel is parabolic according to the laminar profile

$$U = U_{\max}\left[1 - \left(\frac{2y}{d}\right)^2\right]$$

The flow being incompressible, find the relationship of the space average velocity U_{av} in terms of the maximum velocity $U_{\max}$. If a rectangular stream centered in the middle of the channel is to represent one half the volume rate of flow, what is the width of this stream?

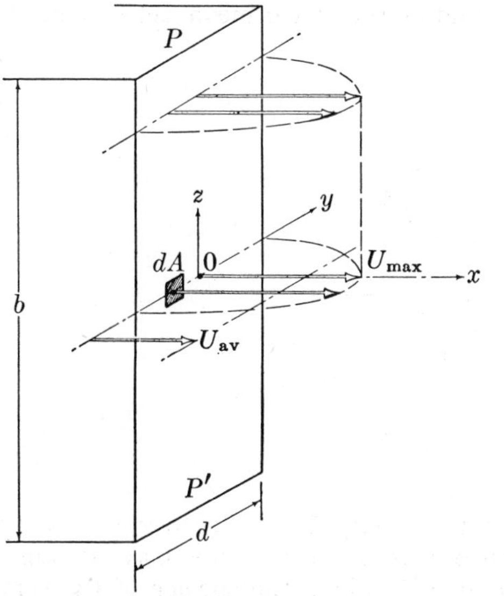

3.14 A tank 1 ft³ in volume has an inlet through which a gas is being pumped at the rate of 0.1 ft³/sec. The gas also escapes through an outlet at the same volume rate at which it is being pumped in, but at the same density as that in the tank and one half the density of that at the inlet. Derive an expression for the value of the density inside the tank as a function of time.

3.15 From Eq. (3.12), determine when the surface integral is positive and negative. In each case, show when the density in the volume increases or decreases in time.

3.16 Find the rate of density change in a tank 2 ft^3 in volume where a gas escapes through a pipe 1 in. in diameter at a velocity of 100 ft/sec. The density of the gas at the time of the test is 0.10 lb_m/ft^3.

3.17 A circular stack has a diameter of 50 ft at its base. It converges uniformly to a diameter of 10 ft at a height of 160 ft. Exhaust gas with a density of 0.02 lb_m/ft^3 enters the stack at the bottom. The gas cools on its way to the top, and the density increases uniformly to 0.03 lb_m/ft^3. Calculate the velocity in ft/sec and the discharge in ft^3/sec for every 40 ft up the stack if the velocity at the top is 20 ft/sec.

3.18 Water at 60°F enters a 2-in.-square channel at a velocity of 10 ft/sec. The channel diverges to a 4-ft by 4-ft section before the water is discharged. The outlet of the channel is cut at a 30° bias, as shown, but the velocity direction is still parallel to the channel axis. What is the rate of flow and what is the space mean velocity at the discharge?

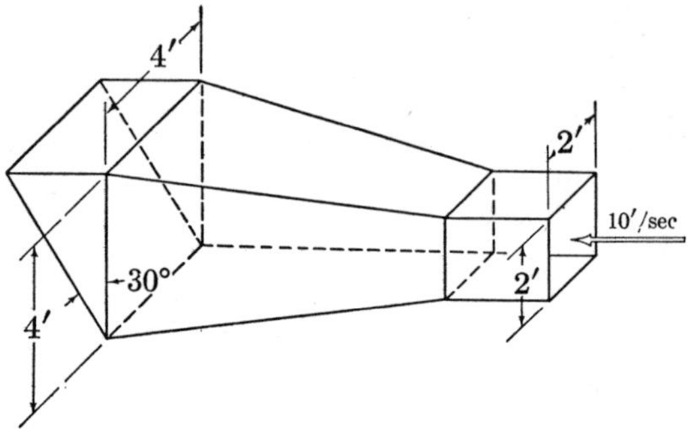

3.19 Consider a steady wind with velocity $\boldsymbol{U}$ parallel to the surface of the earth. Although a difference in regional pressures may be caused by winds, the variations of air density along the surface of the earth are generally much smaller than those normal to the earth and owing to the changes of hydrostatic pressure. Thus even with a strong wind consider $\nabla\rho$ to be in the direction of $\boldsymbol{g}$ the gravitational acceleration. From Eq. (3.15) show that Eq. (3.17) holds even though the density of the flow varies.

3.20 If flow is radial and $v_r = f(r)$, where r is the distance from a fixed point, show that for a variable density flow

$$v_r \frac{\partial \rho}{\partial r} + \frac{\rho}{r^2} \frac{\partial}{\partial r} (r^2 v_r) = 0$$

3.21 Show that a velocity field $\boldsymbol{U} = a\boldsymbol{r}$ is not a possible flow.

3.22 Show the vector geometry of Eq. (3.25) for a rigid body motion; in other words, show the proper relationship of $\boldsymbol{U}$, $\nabla\psi$, and $\boldsymbol{b}$. From Eq. (3.27), show that ψ must increase with r.

3.23 In Illustrative Example 3.4 the ideal flow around a cylinder was claimed to be represented by $\psi = U_\infty \sin\theta \left[\frac{a^2}{r} - r\right]\cdot$ As shown in the figure below, a is the radius of the cylinder, U_∞ is the velocity of the undisturbed stream, and θ is the angle of any point in the flow field to the direction of the undisturbed flow. Find a relation for the peripheral velocity v_θ at $\theta = \pi/2$ at the top of the cylinder. Plot the relationship as a function of r. Find the relationship for v_r at $\theta = 0$ as a function of r and plot it in the same graph.

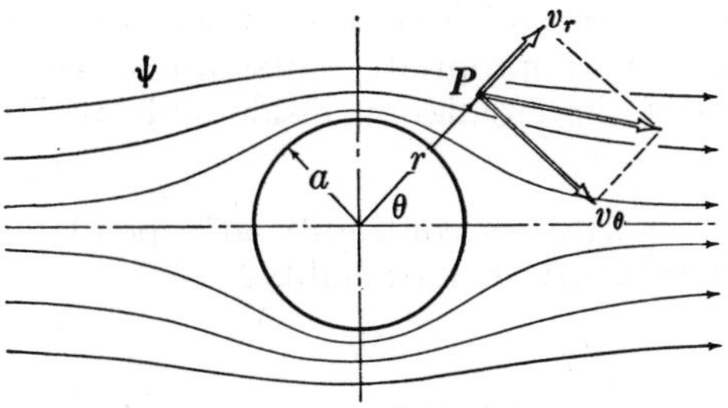

3.24 In the Rankine body discussed in Sec. 3.12, find the total velocity of the fluid on the surface of the body; that is, $\psi = 0$, as a function of the angle θ.

3.25 The velocity of the fluid on the surface of the Rankine half-body is derived in Illustrative Example 3.5 as

$$U_s = U_\infty\left[1 + \left(\frac{\sin\theta}{\theta}\right)^2 - \frac{\sin 2\theta}{\theta}\right]^{1/2}$$

U_s is the steady velocity of the fluid, U_∞ is the undisturbed velocity of the fluid far away from the body, and θ is the angle in the counterclockwise direction. Plot the body so that $r = C/U_\infty = 1$ in. when $\theta = 0$. Then, choosing the magnitude of U_∞ as 2 in., plot the relative magnitudes of U_∞ at 15° increments. If the observer is made stationary with respect to the undisturbed fluid, as shown in Fig. 3.17(*c*), draw the unsteady-state streamlines and construct the path lines in the vicinity of the body.

3.26 Verify from Eq. (3.34) that if $\boldsymbol{U} = \boldsymbol{j}\omega r$ (a rigid-body motion), the vorticity is $2\boldsymbol{k}\omega$. Also show that if $\boldsymbol{U} = \boldsymbol{j}/r$ that the flow is irrotational. *Hint:* In applying the component derivations of ∇ both $\boldsymbol{j}$ and $\boldsymbol{r}$ should be differentiated by parts. For instance $\partial/\partial r(\boldsymbol{j}) = 0$ but $\partial/\partial\theta = -\boldsymbol{i}$.

3.27 The previous problem should be worked out by taking $\boldsymbol{U} = \boldsymbol{\omega} \times \boldsymbol{r}$ and using the triple vector product show that the vorticity is $2\boldsymbol{k}\omega$.

3.28 Verify geometrically Eq. (3.42) for a plane rigid-body motion. What happens in the case of a two dimensional circular vortex? What can you deduce about the magnitude of $\nabla^2\psi$?

3.29 With two perpendicular linear elements in cylindrical coordinates, show that on the r–z- and θ–z-surfaces in cylindrical coordinates the components of the vorticity are the two last expressions given in Eq. (3.38).

3.30 If the tank in Illustrative Example 3.7 is rotated at 600 rpm and the tank diameter is 2 ft, plot, with appropriate units, the velocity distribution and the distribution of the circulation inside and outside the tank.

3.31 Which of the following flows satisfies continuity at a point for incompressible flows? Which ones satisfy irrotationality?

$$(a)\quad u = x^2y \qquad\qquad (b)\quad u = -x^2y$$
$$v = y^2x \qquad\qquad v = y^2x$$

Dynamics of an Ideal Motion

chapter IV

4.1 Methods of Representing the Motion of Fluids

In general, for three-dimensional flows and unsteady states, the motion of the fluid is represented in terms of four independent variables, namely, three space coordinates and a time coordinate. With these four coordinates there are two methods for describing the motion.

One method specifically focuses its attention on physical points occupied by the flow field and determines the properties of the motion at these points as a function of time. The coordinate system can be arbitrarily chosen at any one of these points, moving or stationary, and the motion of the flow field can be studied with reference to that point. This approach is given the name of *Eulerian method*, after the mathematician Euler.[1] This method has been used so far and will be used throughout the book.

[1] Leonhard Euler (1707–1783), Swiss mathematician and founder of the science of pure mathematics. He contributed notable work in mathematics, astronomy, hydrodynamics, and optics.

The second method describes the motion of fluid-material elements by following them and establishing their property as they move with time. Each element is conveniently identified by specifying the position it held at one particular time. This is called the *Lagrangian method*, named after the mathematician Lagrange.[2] The difference between these two methods can be illustrated by the following analogy.

Let us suppose that a complete survey of automobile traffic is to be performed in a large city. This study can be accomplished by the following two methods. First, a complete description of the traffic can be obtained by placing an observer at every intersection and recording the speed and direction of the traffic, makes of the cars, license numbers, etc., as they cross each intersection. The information gained by concentrating at various points in the city constitutes the Eulerian method of analysis. The same traffic information can also be obtained if a motorist observer is assigned to each vehicle in the city. The observer records the speed and direction as a function of time, together with the make of car and license number of the car he is assigned to observe. This is the Lagrangian method. Although the mode of observation in these cases is different, the same information can be derived, if necessary, from both methods.

4.2 Mathematical Representation of a Property in a Continuum

We are ready to formulate in mathematical notation the two modes of property description in space and time. Let $\boldsymbol{p}$ represent a property of the continuum in motion. The fact that this property was chosen to be a vector is coincidental; it could have been a scalar property. This property can be attributed either to a point in space or to a mass-particle moving with the substance. In the Lagrangian method, we fix our reference to the mass-particle. This mass-particle is distinguished from all others by the position, $\boldsymbol{s}_i$, it occupied at time $t = t_0$. Having thus identified the particle we maintain our reference on it and observe any possible changes of the property $\boldsymbol{p}$ with time t. Thus mathematically we can say

$$\boldsymbol{p} = \boldsymbol{p}(\boldsymbol{s}_i,t) \tag{4.1}$$

[2] Count Joseph Louis Lagrange (1736–1813), French mathematician and astronomer.

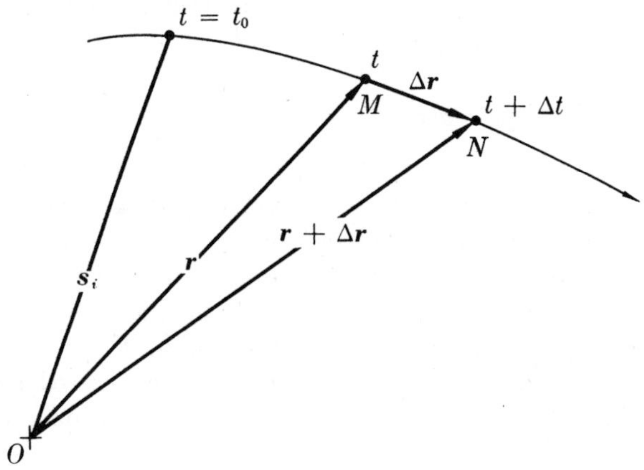

Figure 4.1
Time—history and location of particle.

This is shown in Fig. 4.1. Since $\boldsymbol{s}_i$ only serves to identify which particle we are talking about and thus cannot vary unless we change the particle, it is not a variable in the true sense of the word. In the Lagrangian method $\boldsymbol{s}_i$ is an identification parameter, and taking derivatives with respect to it is meaningless. The index i refers to the particle number among the very many in the continuum.

According to this description the only way the property can change is with respect to time

$$\frac{dp}{dt} = \lim_{\Delta t \to 0} \left(\frac{\Delta p}{\Delta t}\right)_{s_i} \tag{4.2}$$

This expression implies the rate of change of the property p of a given mass-particle i that had occupied the position $\boldsymbol{s}_i$ at time t_0. This rate of change is evaluated while our space reference *follows the particle.* Thus dp/dt is the total change of the property with respect to time measured by the Lagrangian method. Indeed, it is the simplest way to evaluate this change (if it is at all possible to chase a particle and all particles in a continuum). If p is, for instance, the position vector $\boldsymbol{r}$, as shown in Fig. 4.1, then Eq. (4.2) is the velocity of the particle. To obtain the acceleration, it is necessary to differentiate once more with respect to time.

The same property of the mass-particle identified in the Eulerian-method requires that we fix our coordinate system independently of the mass-particle, say at O in Fig. 4.1, and describe it in terms of the position $\boldsymbol{r}$ of the particle at a given time t. This immediately becomes a two-variable description

$$\boldsymbol{p} = \boldsymbol{p}(\boldsymbol{r},t) \tag{4.3}$$

When we fix $\boldsymbol{r}$, the property $\boldsymbol{p}$ is that of all particles passing at the position given by $\boldsymbol{r}$ at a varying time t. Conversely, if we fix the time t, we obtain the value of the property in all mass-particles throughout the entire space. At one value of t and at one value of $\boldsymbol{r}$ we get the property of a mass-particle at that location and time. Thus Eqs. (4.1) and (4.3) are equivalent. In the Eulerian description, the rate of change of $\boldsymbol{p}$ of a mass-particle, *following the particle,* is evaluated as follows: As the particle in Fig. 4.1 moved from M to N, the property changed to a new value

$$\boldsymbol{p} + \Delta\boldsymbol{p} = \boldsymbol{p}\left(\boldsymbol{r} + \frac{d\boldsymbol{r}}{dt}\Delta t,\, t + \Delta t\right) \tag{4.4}$$

Expanding the right hand side in a Taylor series and considering only first order changes,

$$\boldsymbol{p} + \Delta\boldsymbol{p} = \boldsymbol{p}(\boldsymbol{r},t) + \frac{d\boldsymbol{r}}{dt}\Delta t\frac{\partial\boldsymbol{p}}{\partial\boldsymbol{r}} + \Delta t\frac{\partial\boldsymbol{p}}{\partial t} + \cdots \tag{4.5}$$

Subtracting Eq. (4.3) from Eq. (4.5), dividing by Δt, and letting $\Delta t \rightarrow 0$, we obtain the rate of change of p as in Eq. (4.2)

$$\lim_{\Delta t\rightarrow 0}\frac{\Delta\boldsymbol{p}}{\Delta t} = \frac{d\boldsymbol{p}}{dt} = \frac{\partial\boldsymbol{p}}{\partial t} + \frac{d\boldsymbol{r}}{dt}\cdot\frac{\partial\boldsymbol{p}}{\partial\boldsymbol{r}}$$

In Sec. A.14, $\partial\boldsymbol{p}/\partial\boldsymbol{r}$ can be identified as $\nabla\boldsymbol{p}$. Thus, the previous equation representing the rate of change of $\boldsymbol{p}$ of a mass-particle in the Eulerian description is

$$\frac{d\boldsymbol{p}}{dt} = \frac{\partial\boldsymbol{p}}{\partial t} + (\boldsymbol{U}\cdot\nabla)\boldsymbol{p} \tag{4.6}$$

where $d\boldsymbol{r}/dt$ is replaced by the velocity $\boldsymbol{U}$ of the fluid at that point. So far, we have identified $\boldsymbol{p}$ as a general vector or scalar property. If $\boldsymbol{p}$ is identified with the velocity $\boldsymbol{U}$, then the acceleration of a mass-particle in Eulerian representation becomes

$$\boldsymbol{a} = \frac{d\boldsymbol{U}}{dt} = \frac{\partial\boldsymbol{U}}{\partial t} + (\boldsymbol{U}\cdot\nabla)\boldsymbol{U} \tag{4.7}$$

The acceleration is the total change of the velocity with time and therefore, from Eq. (4.7), the three components can be obtained.

$$a_x = \frac{\partial u}{\partial t} + u\frac{\partial u}{\partial x} + v\frac{\partial u}{\partial y} + w\frac{\partial u}{\partial z}$$

$$a_y = \frac{\partial v}{\partial t} + u\frac{\partial v}{\partial x} + v\frac{\partial v}{\partial y} + w\frac{\partial v}{\partial z} \qquad [4.8(a)]$$

$$a_z = \frac{\partial w}{\partial t} + u\frac{\partial w}{\partial x} + v\frac{\partial w}{\partial y} + w\frac{\partial w}{\partial z}$$

The acceleration here is made up of two essential parts. The first part $\partial/\partial t$ is the change of velocity with time alone at a given point; the second is the change of velocity with space in the neighborhood of a point. The three last terms in each of the preceding equations represent the variation of the velocity with space and therefore are called the *convective* part of the acceleration.

The convective part can be explained simply by the following illustration. Consider, as in Fig. 4.2, a converging tube where the velocity of the fluid increases downstream owing to the reduction of area. To avoid complications, consider the flow to be steady and at a point O the velocity of the fluid to be u. Because on either side of O the velocity of the fluid is not the same, there will be an acceleration at O. This acceleration can be evaluated by finding the change of velocity on either side of O in the time it takes the fluid to go from one side to the other. At the point 1, $\Delta x/2$ to the left of O, by Taylor's series expansion, the velocity will be $u - \frac{\partial u}{\partial x}\frac{\Delta x}{2}$, and the velocity at the right of O will be

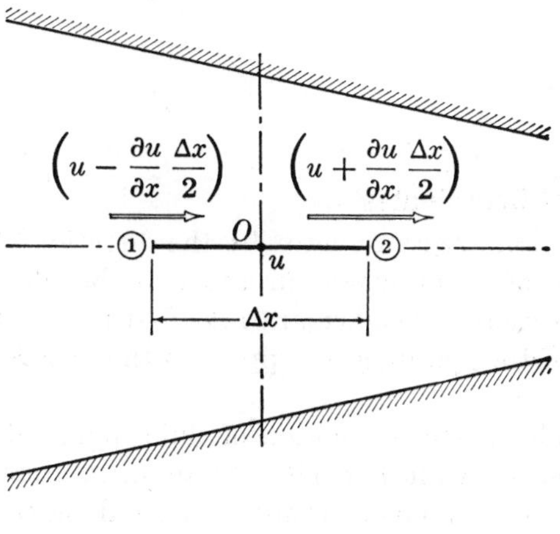

Figure 4.2
Convective acceleration.

$u + \frac{\partial u}{\partial x}\frac{\Delta x}{2}$. The time that the fluid took to go from point 1 to 2 is $\Delta t = \Delta x/u$. Since the acceleration is the change of velocity in a unit time, then

$$a_x = \frac{\left(u + \frac{\partial u}{\partial x}\frac{\Delta x}{2}\right) - \left(u - \frac{\partial u}{\partial x}\frac{\Delta x}{2}\right)}{\Delta x/u}$$

$$= u\frac{\partial u}{\partial x}$$

This is the first convective term of a_x in Eq. [4.8(*a*)]. The other terms in Eq. [4.8(*a*)] can be illustrated in the same fashion.

Using the expression for the del operator in Eq. [A.38(*b*)] in cylindrical coordinates and remembering that in this coordinate system the unit vectors change in direction with space as discussed in Sec. A.17, then the acceleration components in *cylindrical coordinates* are

$$\begin{aligned} a_r &= \frac{\partial v_r}{\partial t} + v_r\frac{\partial v_r}{\partial r} + \frac{v_\theta}{r}\frac{\partial v_r}{\partial \theta} - \frac{v_\theta^2}{r} + v_z\frac{\partial v_r}{\partial z} \\ a_\theta &= \frac{\partial v_\theta}{\partial t} + v_r\frac{\partial v_\theta}{\partial r} + \frac{v_\theta}{r}\frac{\partial v_\theta}{\partial \theta} + \frac{v_r v_\theta}{r} + v_z\frac{\partial v_\theta}{\partial z} \qquad [4.8(b)] \\ a_z &= \frac{\partial v_z}{\partial t} + v_r\frac{\partial v_z}{\partial r} + \frac{v_\theta}{r}\frac{\partial v_z}{\partial \theta} + v_z\frac{\partial v_z}{\partial z} \end{aligned}$$

where $\boldsymbol{U} = \boldsymbol{i}v_r + \boldsymbol{j}v_\theta + \boldsymbol{k}v_z$ and v_r, v_θ, and v_z are the velocity components in the r-, θ-, and z-direction of the coordinate system shown in Fig. A.12.

4.3 Acceleration in the Natural Coordinates

The *natural coordinates* of a motion are represented by the direction of the streamline, by the direction of its radius of curvature at the same point, and finally by a third direction perpendicular to the first two. It is termed *natural* because one of the coordinates represents the natural direction of motion, the streamline.

First, for simplicity, consider a steady motion of fluid along the streamline from point P to P', as shown in Fig. 4.3. At an initial time, let the fluid element considered be at the point P and moving along the streamline at a velocity $\boldsymbol{v}$. After a small increment of time, the element

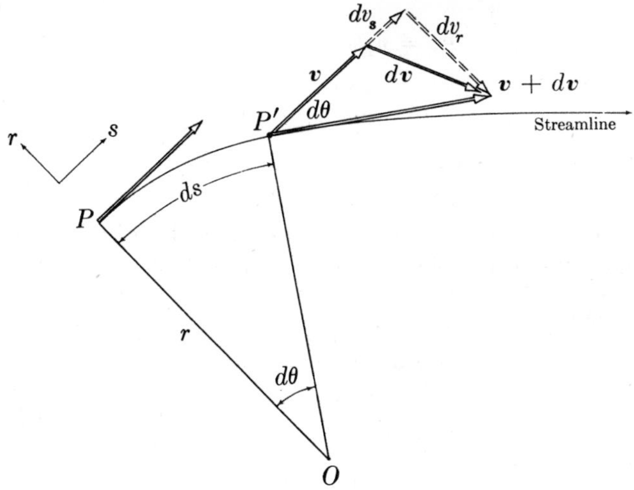

Figure 4.3
Velocity relations in natural coordinates.

travels an arc PP' equivalent in length to ds. The new velocity at P' is $\boldsymbol{v} + d\boldsymbol{v}$, where the increment $d\boldsymbol{v}$ represents the total change in the velocity from one point to the other. This change $d\boldsymbol{v}$ can be expressed in components dv_s and dv_r along the coordinates at P. The change of velocity in the s-direction from point P to P' is $(v + dv_s) - v$. This represents the change dv_s which can also be expressed as $\frac{\partial v}{\partial s}\, ds$. If this change occurs in a differential time dt, the acceleration component along the streamline at P is

$$a_s = \frac{\partial v}{\partial s}\frac{ds}{dt} = v\,\frac{\partial v}{\partial s} \tag{4.9}$$

since $\frac{ds}{dt}$ is the velocity of the fluid element moving past P. The component dv_r can be found also from

$$\begin{aligned} dv_r &= (v + dv)\sin d\theta \\ &= (v + dv)\, d\theta \end{aligned}$$

for small angles. The change $dv\, d\theta$ is small compared with $v\, d\theta$, and, as $d\theta$ approaches zero, it can be neglected. Also from the geometry, $d\theta = \frac{ds}{r}\cdot$ The radial component of the velocity change then becomes

$$dv_r = v\,d\theta$$
$$= \frac{v\,ds}{r}$$
$$\frac{dv_r}{ds} = \frac{v}{r}$$

The acceleration in the radial direction can be found by dividing this change by the time it takes the element to go from P to P'. This time for small changes will be $dt = \dfrac{ds}{v}$

$$a_r = \frac{v\,ds}{r} \Big/ \frac{ds}{v} = \frac{v^2}{r} \tag{4.10}$$

In the case of an unsteady motion, there will be an additional term, in Eqs. (4.9) and (4.10), representing the rate of change of the velocity at the point P itself:

$$a_s = \frac{\partial v}{\partial t} + v\frac{\partial v}{\partial s}$$
$$a_r = \frac{\partial v_r}{\partial t} + \frac{v^2}{r} \tag{4.11}$$

4.4 Uniformly Accelerated Fluids

A fluid with a uniform acceleration throughout behaves as if it were in static equilibrium. An interesting example is that of a liquid contained in a tank and the entire system being accelerated at an arbitrary constant acceleration $\boldsymbol{a}$. Owing to the forces set up in the fluid because of the acceleration, the liquid will change shape and ultimately will seek a fixed position relative to the tank. There will be no motion of the fluid relative to the tank.

Consider the element[3] O of fluid and its pressure p at its center under the influence of the acceleration $\boldsymbol{a}$ and that of gravity $\boldsymbol{g}$. The pressures at the various faces of the element can be found by Taylor's

[3] Instead of taking a small finite element, as was done in the preceding sections, infinitesimal volumes are considered here; in this way it will not be necessary to take the limit of the derived equations.

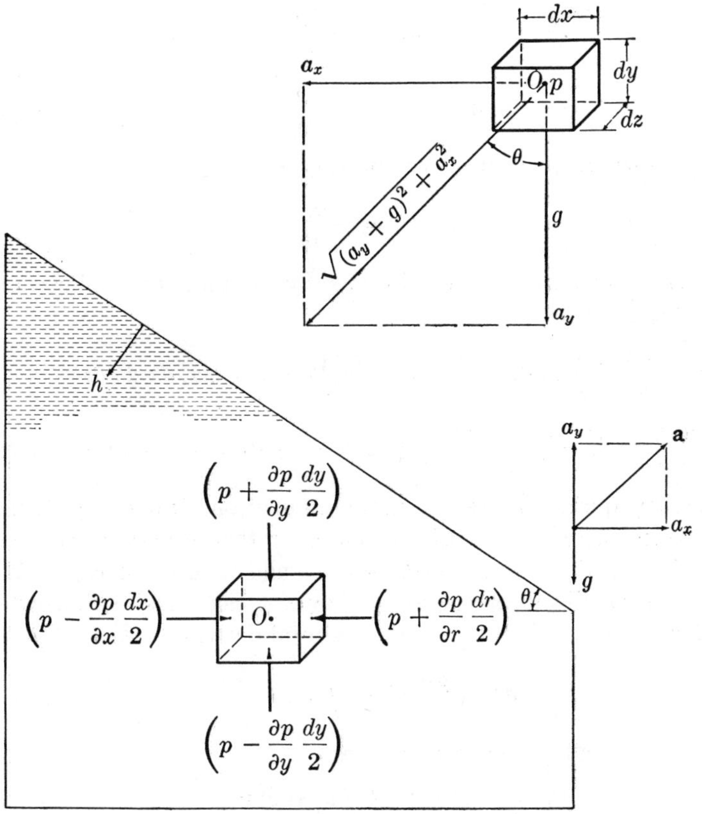

Figure 4.4
Uniformly accelerated fluid.

expansion. For equilibrium of the element, the forces contributed by these pressures must be balanced by the inertial force of the element. For simplicity, the acceleration is shown on the plane of the paper; in general, it will have three components. An extension of Sec. 2.4 can give us the summation of forces in this case. Instead of

$$\rho \boldsymbol{g} - \nabla p = 0$$

when we include the inertia force owing to $\boldsymbol{a}$, we have

$$\rho \boldsymbol{a} = \rho \boldsymbol{g} - \nabla p \tag{4.12}$$

Since $\boldsymbol{g}$ in Fig. 4.4 is in the $-y$ direction, the components of Eq. (4.12) follow:

$$\rho a_x = -\frac{\partial p}{\partial x}$$

$$\rho(a_y - g_y) = -\frac{\partial p}{\partial y} \tag{4.13}$$

Now $g_y = -g$ where g is a positive quantity.

$$\rho(a_y + g) = -\frac{\partial p}{\partial y} \tag{4.14}$$

The same results could have been obtained by summing the scalar components to begin with:

$$\left(p - \frac{\partial p}{\partial x}\frac{dx}{2}\right) dy\, dz - \left(p + \frac{\partial p}{\partial x}\frac{dx}{2}\right) dy\, dz = \rho a_x\, dx\, dy\, dz$$

$$\left(p - \frac{\partial p}{\partial y}\frac{dy}{2}\right) dx\, dz - \left(p + \frac{\partial p}{\partial y}\frac{dy}{2}\right) dx\, dz - \rho g\, dx\, dy\, dz = \rho a_y\, dx\, dy\, dz$$

The vector equation representing the summation of force, Eq. (4.12), can be integrated after it is transformed into a total ordinary differential equation. This is done by performing the scalar product of Eq. (4.12) with a differential displacement $d\mathbf{r}$ as shown in Sec. A.14. Since the pressure, here, is a function of x and y its total derivative is

$$dp = \frac{\partial p}{\partial x} dx + \frac{\partial p}{\partial y} dy$$

From Eqs. (4.13) and (4.14) this becomes

$$dp = -\rho[a_x\, dx + (a_y + g)\, dy]$$

The integration between any two points in the fluid yields

$$p_2 - p_1 = -\rho[a_x(x_2 - x_1) + (a_y + g)(y_2 - y_1)] \qquad [4.15(a)]$$

In particular, if $a_y = 0$ and $p_2 - p_1$ is evaluated along the horizontal $y_2 - y_1 = 0$, then

$$p_2 - p_1 = \rho a_x(x_2 - x_1) \tag{4.16}$$

From Eq. [4.15(*a*)], the surface of any isobar (constant pressure) can be found by taking the two points 1 and 2 on the isobar, and consequently $(p_2 - p_1) = 0$. The equation for this surface is then

$$y_2 - y_1 = -\frac{a_x}{(a_y + g)}(x_2 - x_1) \qquad [4.15(b)]$$

The surface of the liquid also has this equation, since the value of the pressure is atmospheric everywhere on it. The slope of the surface is $a_x/(a_y + g)$, and the angle, as shown, is the same as that which the resultant acceleration $\sqrt{(a_y + g)^2 + a_x^2}$ makes with the vertical. Consequently, the resultant acceleration is normal to the surface of the liquid. Since the pressure is constant on any surface normal to the resultant acceleration, this problem behaves exactly as Theorem I of Sec. 2.4 and thus can be treated as a fluid in static conditions. If h is a measure of the depth normal to the free surface, the hydrostatic equation can be written for this case as

$$p - p_0 = \rho\sqrt{(a_y + g)^2 + a_x^2}\, h$$

In particular, if $a_y = 0$, then the surface of the liquid takes the form

$$y_2 - y_1 = -\frac{a_x}{g}(x_2 - x_1) \tag{4.17}$$

Another case is that of free fall when $a_x = 0$ and $a_y = -g$. In that case $p_2 - p_1$ everywhere is zero, meaning that the pressure is the same everywhere in the fluid.

Illustrative Example 4.1

Water in a tank has the original level PLM. The tank is accelerated at $0.5g$ in a direction 30° with the horizontal. Find the level of the water surface and the increase in pressure at the corner of the tank O.

From Eq. (4.16) the tangent of the angle θ is

$$\begin{aligned}\tan\theta &= \frac{a_x}{(a_y + g)}\\ &= \frac{0.433g}{0.25g + g}\\ &= 0.3465\\ \theta &= 19°7'\end{aligned}$$

Since the volume of the fluid in the tank does not change, the water originally in the area LMN has now moved into LPQ, and the rise PQ is found from $\tan\theta = QP/LP = QP/2$. Therefore, $QP = 0.693$ ft and the height $OQ = 4.693$ ft. The normal distance $OS = OQ\cos\theta = 4.693 \times 0.9449 = 4.43$ ft. The pressure at O is then

$$p_O = p_a + g\rho\sqrt{\frac{a_x^2 + (a_y + g)^2}{g^2}}\, OS,$$

and the pressure at O before accelerating the tank was

$$p_O' = p_a + \rho g\, OP$$

Evaluation of $p_O - p_O'$ yields

$$\begin{aligned}p_O - p_O' &= 62.4(1.321\, OS - OP)\ \text{lb}_f/\text{ft}^2\\ &= 0.802\ \text{psi}\end{aligned}$$

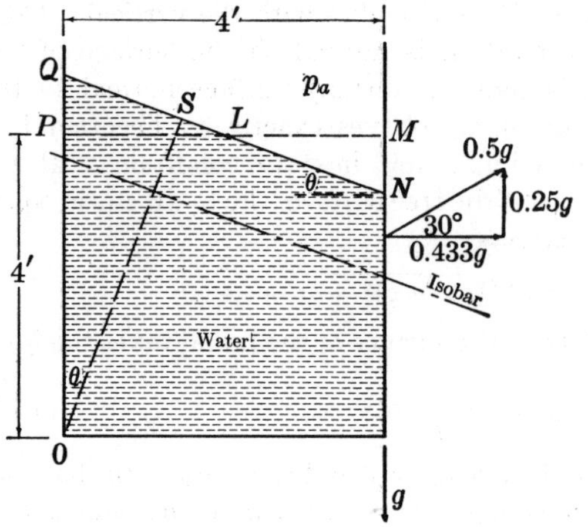

Figure 4.5
Uniformly accelerated tank containing water.

4.5 Axisymmetric Circulatory Motion

Consider a fluid moving around the z-axis according to either a rigid-body motion or a free-vortex motion, as discussed in Chap. III.

In the absence of viscous forces, Eq. (4.12) should be valid here. In cylindrical coordinates, owing to the nature of the flow, the acceleration components are given in Eq. [4.8(*b*)]. For a steady flow, the time dependence is zero. Since the flow is contained in the tank, $v_r = v_z = 0$. The gravitational force is in the $-z$-direction. Thus the r-component of Eq. (4.12) reads:

$$\rho \frac{v_\theta^2}{r} = \frac{\partial p}{\partial r} \tag{4.18}$$

This is the *radial equilibrium equation.* The θ-component of Eq. (4.12) vanishes identically because $v_z = v_r = 0$, and owing to axisymmetry, $\partial/\partial\theta$ of v_θ is zero. In the axial equation, the inertia term is zero and the hydrostatic equilibrium is obtained:

$$\frac{\partial p}{\partial z} = -\rho g \tag{4.19}$$

From Fig. 4.6, if we had performed the summation of forces in the radial and axial directions, we would have had

$$\left(p - \frac{\partial p}{\partial r}\frac{dr}{2}\right)\left(r - \frac{dr}{2}\right) d\theta\, dz + 2p\, dr\, dz \sin\frac{d\theta}{2}$$

$$- \left(p + \frac{\partial p}{\partial r}\frac{dr}{2}\right)\left(r + \frac{dr}{2}\right) d\theta\, dz + \rho\frac{v_\theta^2}{r} r\, d\theta\, dr\, dz = 0$$

and

$$\left(p - \frac{\partial p}{\partial z}\frac{dz}{2}\right) r\, d\theta\, dr - \left(p + \frac{\partial p}{\partial z}\frac{dz}{2}\right) r\, d\theta\, dr - \rho g r\, d\theta\, dr\, dz = 0$$

to yield Eqs. (4.18) and (4.19).

The pressure is considered, here, to be a function of the radius r

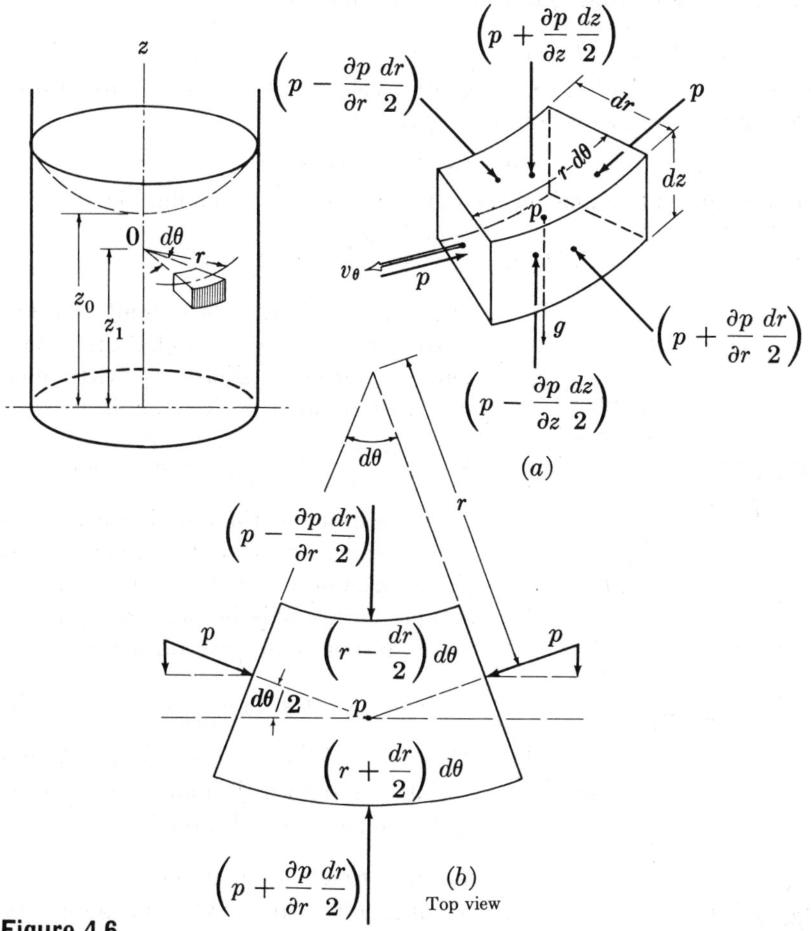

Figure 4.6
(a) and (b) Equilibrium in circulatory motion.

and the elevation z. Therefore, any total change in pressure is caused by a partial change with elevation as given by the hydrostatic equation, and a partial change in the radial direction as given by the radial-equilibrium equation. Therefore

$$\begin{aligned} dp &= \frac{\partial p}{\partial r}\,dr + \frac{\partial p}{\partial z}\,dz \\ &= \frac{\rho\, v_\theta^2}{r}\,dr - \rho g\,dz \end{aligned} \qquad (4.20)$$

If ρ and g are constants, this total differential equation can be integrated, provided that v_θ is known as a function of r.

Case I: Rigid-Body Motion

For rigid-body motion the tangential velocity is $v_\theta = \omega r$. Substitution in the differential equation for p gives

$$dp = \rho\omega^2 r\,dr - \rho g\,dz$$

The pressure difference between any two points in the fluid is

$$p_2 - p_1 = \rho\,\frac{\omega^2(r_2^2 - r_1^2)}{2} - \rho g(z_2 - z_1)$$

In particular, if the lower limit is taken at the axis z where the radial distance is zero, the pressure difference with reference to that at any elevation is

$$\frac{(p_2 - p_1)}{\rho} = \frac{\omega^2 r^2}{2} - g(z - z_1)$$

At the surface of the liquid, for any two points, the pressure is the same, that of the atmosphere. The elevation of the surface at the axis becomes $z_0 = z_1$, and the equation at the free surface reads

$$z = z_0 + \frac{\omega^2}{2g}\,r^2 \qquad (4.21)$$

This is, then, the equation of the free surface for rigid-body motion and also of a paraboloid of revolution.

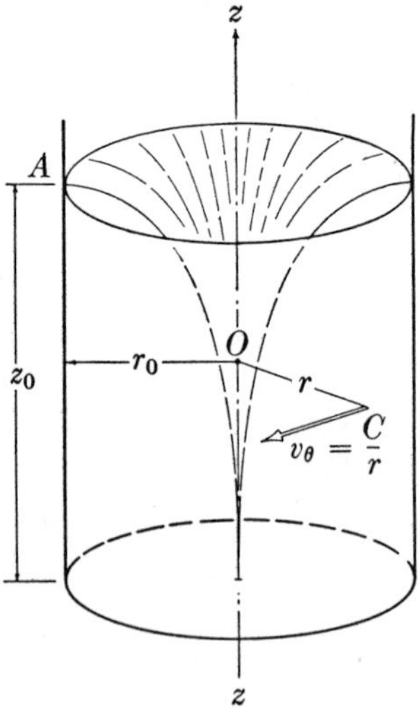

Figure 4.7
Liquid surface of a free vortex.

Case II: Free-Vortex Motion

According to Eq. (3.40), the peripheral velocity of the free vortex is $v_\theta = \dfrac{C}{r}$.

Substituting this relationship into the pressure differential equation Eq. (4.20) yields

$$dp = \rho \frac{C^2}{r^3}\, dr - \rho g\, dz$$

Between any two points in Fig. 5.6

$$p_2 - p_1 = -\frac{\rho C^2}{2}\left(\frac{1}{r_2^2} - \frac{1}{r_1^2}\right) - \rho g(z_2 - z_1)$$

If the point A is taken as a reference where $z_1 = z_0$, $r_1 = r_0$ and on the surface of the liquid where the pressure is the same at every point,

$$z = z_0 + \frac{C^2}{2g}\frac{1}{r_0^2}\left[1 - \left(\frac{r_0}{r}\right)^2\right] \tag{4.22}$$

The surface is a hyperboloid profile of the second degree. The constant C which represents the strength of the vortex can be determined experimentally by measuring the velocity at a known radius.

4.6 Hydrostatic Accelerometers

The relationship derived in Eq. (4.17) can be used to measure linear acceleration. If a U-tube, as shown in Fig. 4.8, is located on a platform that accelerates from left to right with a magnitude a_x, the level in both legs of the tube will not be the same, as already discussed in Sec. 4.4.

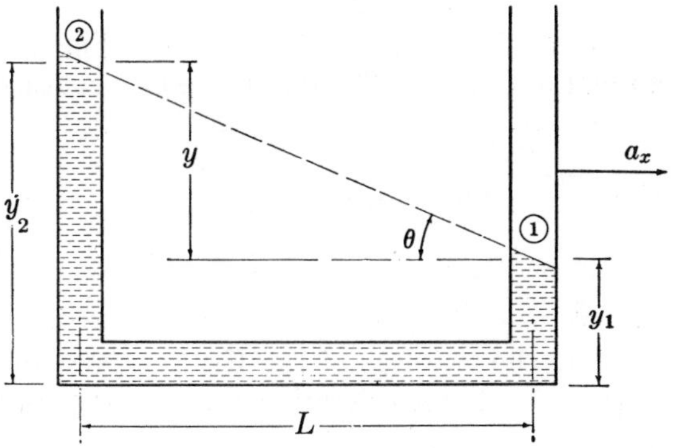

Figure 4.8
Linear accelerometer.

The difference of elevation of liquid in the two legs of the tube is given by Eq. (4.17). Since the density of the fluid does not appear in the equation, then the difference of elevation $y_2 - y_1 = y$ is independent of the kind of fluid used. If the horizontal distance between the two legs is called $L = x_2 - x_1$, the value of the acceleration is

$$a_x = \frac{g}{L} y$$

If g and L are constants, the difference of elevation can be graduated in terms of acceleration.

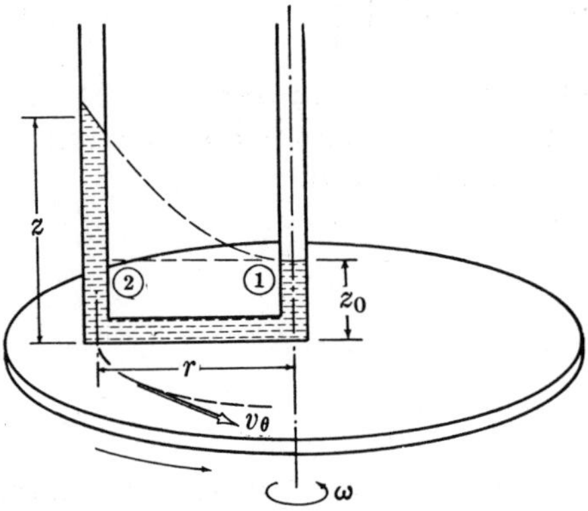

Figure 4.9
Radial accelerometer.

The radial acceleration of a rotating platform shown in Fig. 4.9 can be found with the help of Eq. (4.21). The difference of elevation between points 2 and 1 is

$$z - z_0 = \frac{\omega^2 r^2}{2g} = \omega^2 r \frac{r}{2g} = a_r \frac{r}{2g}$$
$$= \frac{v_\theta^2}{2g}$$

Knowing the distance separating the two legs of the U-tube r and the difference of the liquid levels, the radial acceleration can be computed

$$a_r = \frac{2g(z - z_0)}{r}$$

Illustrative Example 4.2

A U-tube, shown in Fig. 4.10, rotates around its axis z–z so that the peripheral velocity of the vertical legs is $v_\theta = 17.2$ ft/sec. Find the pressure difference between points B and C and the gauge pressure at B and C.

Since points B and C are at the same elevation, the difference in their pressure is

$$p_B - p_C = \frac{\rho\omega^2 r^2}{2} = \frac{\rho v_\theta^2}{2}$$

$$= \frac{62.4}{32.17}\frac{(17.2)^2}{2} = 288 \text{ lb/ft}^2$$

$$= 2.0 \text{ psi}$$

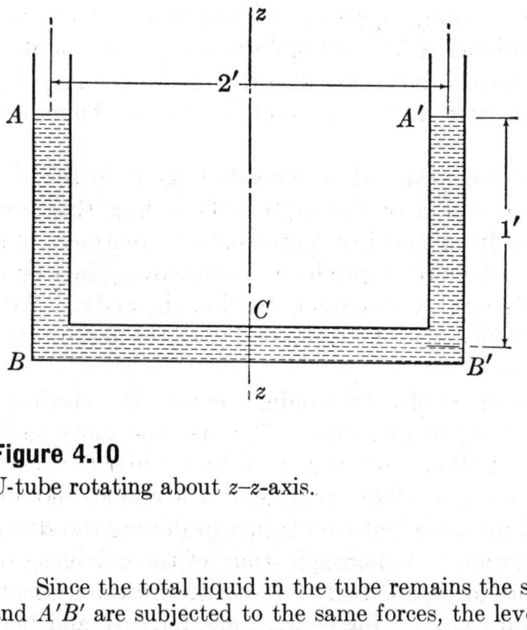

Figure 4.10
U-tube rotating about z–z-axis.

Since the total liquid in the tube remains the same, and both columns AB and $A'B'$ are subjected to the same forces, the level of the liquid must be the same before and after rotation. Consequently, the pressure at B can be evaluated for two points on the same radius

$$p_B - p_A = \rho g\,\overline{AB}$$

$$= 62.4 \text{ lb/ft}^2$$

$$p_B = 0.433 \text{ psig}$$

$$p_C = -1.567 \text{ psig}$$

4.7 Considerations on the Frictionless Motion of a Fluid

The viscosity and its effects on the motion of a fluid were qualitatively discussed in Secs. 1.10 and 1.13. A motion can be considered to be frictionless not only for the ideal case when the viscosity is zero but also for the real cases when velocity gradients are zero. This fact can be verified from Eq. (1.7). In some hydro- and aerodynamic applications, such as the flow about an airfoil or blade, the flow in short pipes and channels and the flow through turbomachines can sometimes be treated as ideal frictionless motions, provided that the regions near the solid walls, where most of the viscous effects take place, are kept out of the analysis. These viscous layers in the neighborhood of solid walls, where large friction forces are present, are called boundary layers; they were discussed very briefly in Sec. 1.12 and are treated in more detail in Chap. IX. For most engineering applications the flow outside the boundary layer may be treated, with favorable results, as frictionless motion. It must be understood, however, that the results obtained by this frictionless treatment must not be extended into the boundary layers.

The drag on moving immersed bodies depends largely on the viscous frictional effects on the skin of the body. This drag therefore cannot possibly be deduced from the ideal mathematical treatment of a frictionless motion. The wake a body produces when moving in a fluid is completely due to the viscous layers moving back of the body. Naturally, this portion of the flow cannot be estimated with the assumption of frictionless motion.

The study of the dynamics of a frictionless motion is considered advantageous for the following two reasons. The first and more basic reason is academic, in that it allows the student to be familiar first with a simple and yet possible motion. The treatment of a viscous motion appears to be complicated for a student who is just beginning the study of the dynamics of fluid motion. A thorough study of the influences of inertial force, normal surface force, and body force will allow the student, in the future, to incorporate viscous forces with greater ease and better understanding. Furthermore, the applications of momentum and energy transfer in the fluid can be easily illustrated without the use of tangential shear forces dissipating frictional heat.

The second reason for studying frictionless motions is that actually they are useful to the practical engineer and scientist. Consequently, the benefits to be derived from this treatment are both academic and practical.

4.8 Euler's Equations of Motion. Frictionless Motion

Since the motion of fluid to be analyzed is frictionless, there are no frictional tangential forces to be considered. All external forces on a fluid element must be normal to the surfaces of the element. These external normal surface forces that are partly responsible for the motion of the fluid element are the *pressure forces.* The motion is also influenced by *body forces* proportional to the mass of the element considered. In this case only the gravitational force as a body force will be discussed.

This balance of forces was already considered in Sec. 4.4 and in Eq. (4.12). Vectorially, the inertia force per unit volume $\rho \mathbf{a}$ is the balance between the gravitational body force per unit volume $\rho \mathbf{g}$ and the surface force per unit volume ∇p. As explained in Sec. 4.4, this is a logical extension of the hydrostatic equation which does not involve any motion. When the inertia force is considered then Eq. (4.12) applies.

$$\rho \mathbf{a} = \rho \mathbf{g} - \nabla p \tag{4.12}$$

This equation, representing the balance of forces in the motion of a frictionless fluid, is given the name *Euler's equation.* From Eqs. [4.8(*a*)] and (2.2) the components in Cartesian or other orthogonal coordinates can be deduced immediately. These component equations can be obtained independently by summing up the component forces.

Consider the element of fluid shown in Fig. 4.11. The essential dependent properties of the motion p, ρ, u, v, and w are defined, for convenience, at the center G. The three components of the velocity at the center point are u in the x-direction, v in the y-direction, and w in the z-direction. For the sake of following a logical convention, let the acceleration components of the fluid all be in the positive direction of the coordinate system. For this reason the component external forces must also be in the same sense of increasing coordinate. The pressures shown on the element increase, then, in the direction of increasing coordinate. The gravitational force in this case is shown acting in the z-direction.

Since the element is considered in motion, according to Newton's second law the summation of all applied forces on the element must be equal to the resultant inertial force proportional to the acceleration of the element. If the motion is considered in three directions, then this summation of forces must be applicable to all three directions. In the x-direction the summation of applied forces reads

$$\left(p - \frac{\partial p}{\partial x}\frac{dx}{2}\right) dy\, dz - \left(p + \frac{\partial p}{\partial x}\frac{dx}{2}\right) dy\, dz = \rho a_x\, dx\, dy\, dz$$

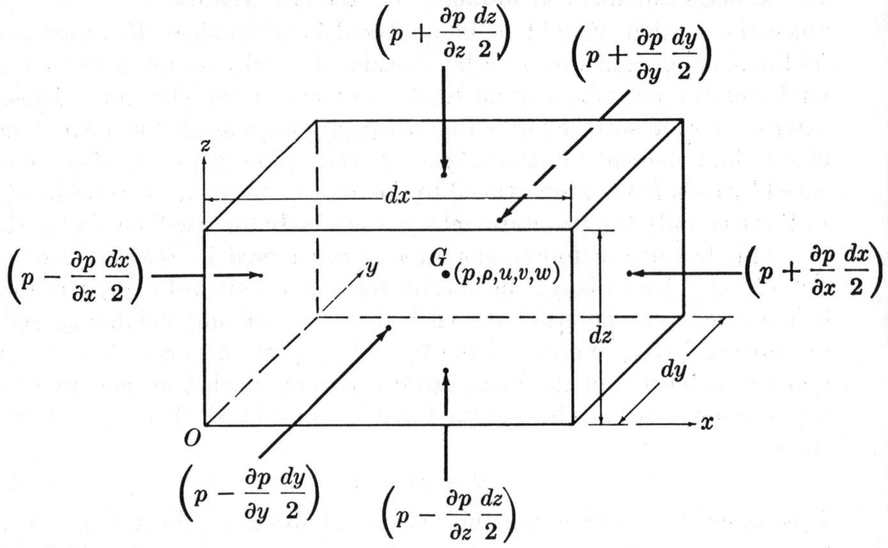

Figure 4.11
Forces on a fluid element in frictionless motion.

In Cartesian coordinates the components of the acceleration were derived in Eq. [4.8(a)]. Substitution of a_x in terms of the velocity derivatives yields the x-component of Euler's equation for a frictionless motion

$$\frac{\partial u}{\partial t} + u\,\frac{\partial u}{\partial x} + v\,\frac{\partial u}{\partial y} + w\,\frac{\partial u}{\partial z} = -\frac{1}{\rho}\frac{\partial p}{\partial x} \tag{4.23}$$

The differential equations for the motion in the other two components can be obtained in an identical fashion, except for the fact that the z-component has an additional force owing to the weight.

$$\begin{aligned} \frac{\partial v}{\partial t} + u\,\frac{\partial v}{\partial x} + v\,\frac{\partial v}{\partial y} + w\,\frac{\partial v}{\partial z} &= -\frac{1}{\rho}\frac{\partial p}{\partial y} \\ \frac{\partial w}{\partial t} + u\,\frac{\partial w}{\partial x} + v\,\frac{\partial w}{\partial y} + w\,\frac{\partial w}{\partial z} &= -g - \frac{1}{\rho}\frac{\partial p}{\partial z} \end{aligned} \tag{4.24}$$

These three partial differential equations represent the component equations of Eq. (4.12). The general solution of this problem will yield answers for the dependent variables p, ρ, u, v, and w in terms of the four independent variables x, y, z, and t. Therefore, there are five dependent unknowns to be determined; and thus far only three equations of motion [(4.23) and (4.24)] have been discussed here. For a completely determined solution there is need for five equations—as many as the number of unknowns. Besides the equations of motion being satisfied, the conservation of mass must also be satisfied, since we are concerned with physically real solutions. This general condition of mass continuity was derived in Eq. (3.16). It relates the relationship of the density and the velocity to the space and time coordinates. Since this equation is independent of the equations of motion, it brings the total number of independent equations to four.

The fifth independent relation expresses the pressure in terms of the density alone. Therefore $p = \phi(\rho)$ will complete the set of required equations for a possible solution. This last dependence of p on ρ alone can be shown, through the system equation in thermodynamics, to exist for isentropic cases as applied to any system.

$$Tds - pd\left(\frac{1}{\rho}\right) = de$$

e is the internal energy per unit mass of a steady motion of fluid inside the system. The quantity de is a total *exact* differential, and, when ds, the change of entropy, is zero (this implies an isentropic process), $pd\left(\frac{1}{\rho}\right)$ must also be an exact differential and consequently p must be a function of ρ alone. For a perfect gas this is known to be true, since for an isentropic process the pressure is given by p/ρ^γ = constant.

The dependence of the pressure on the density alone is also true for isothermal cases of *pure* substances. The definition of a pure substance is given by Eq. (1.2).

In general, if none of the above cases prevail, then the equation of state, such as Eq. (1.2), will constitute the fifth independent equation. But, since it introduces one additional variable T, then a sixth equation, namely the energy equation, must be considered also.

4.9 Integration of Euler's Equations

Having discussed the necessary five independent equations for a complete solution of the flow field, we will next consider the possibilities of performing a general integration of the equations of motion. Multiply the three component equations of motion Eqs. (4.23) and (4.24) by dx, dy, and dz, respectively.

$$\begin{aligned}
\frac{\partial u}{\partial t}\,dx + u\,\frac{\partial u}{\partial x}\,dx + v\,\frac{\partial u}{\partial y}\,dx + w\,\frac{\partial u}{\partial z}\,dx &= -\frac{1}{\rho}\frac{\partial p}{\partial x}\,dx \\
\frac{\partial v}{\partial t}\,dy + u\,\frac{\partial v}{\partial x}\,dy + v\,\frac{\partial v}{\partial y}\,dy + w\,\frac{\partial v}{\partial z}\,dy &= -\frac{1}{\rho}\frac{\partial p}{\partial y}\,dy \qquad (4.25) \\
\frac{\partial w}{\partial t}\,dz + u\,\frac{\partial w}{\partial x}\,dz + v\,\frac{\partial w}{\partial y}\,dz + w\,\frac{\partial w}{\partial z}\,dz &= -\frac{1}{\rho}\frac{\partial p}{\partial z}\,dz - g\,dz
\end{aligned}$$

Two different methods for integration of the preceding equations will be described, both giving the same result but with different consequences.

(a) Steady Flow Along a Streamline

For steady motion the first three terms of the equations of motion are not considered. In this first method the *streamline* will be used as a path for integration of Eq. (4.25). By definition of a streamline, the total velocity $U = \sqrt{u^2 + v^2 + w^2}$ has its direction always tangential to the streamline, as shown in Fig. 4.12. Although this figure is drawn in two dimensions, it will serve to illustrate the following derivable relations. Since the element of length ds of the streamline is in the same direction as the velocity U, the three angles of ds and $\boldsymbol{U}$ with the coordinates are

$$\frac{dx}{ds} = \frac{u}{U}; \qquad \frac{dy}{ds} = \frac{v}{U}; \qquad \frac{dz}{ds} = \frac{w}{U}$$

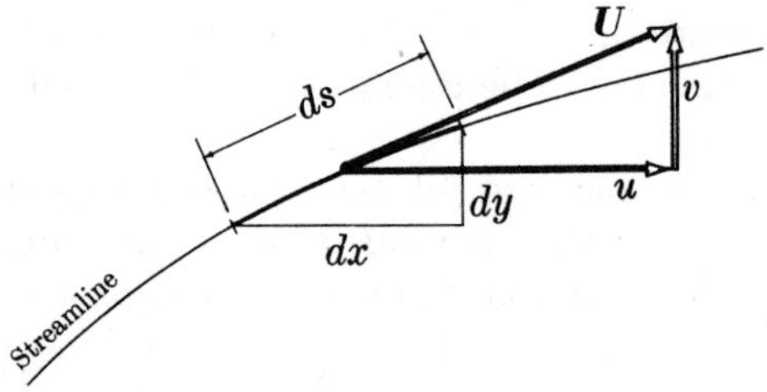

Figure 4.12
Kinematic relationship of a streamline.

Dividing these relations simultaneously, the following kinematic relationships are obtained:

$$\frac{dx}{u} = \frac{dy}{v} = \frac{dz}{w}$$

or

$$u\,dy = v\,dx; \qquad u\,dz = w\,dx; \qquad v\,dz = w\,dy$$

These relations were derived along the streamline and can be used only as such. Substitution of the preceding equations into the steady-state form of Eq. (4.25) yields

$$\begin{aligned} u\frac{\partial u}{\partial x}dx + u\frac{\partial u}{\partial y}dy + u\frac{\partial u}{\partial z}dz &= -\frac{1}{\rho}\frac{\partial p}{\partial x}dx \\ v\frac{\partial v}{\partial x}dx + v\frac{\partial v}{\partial y}dy + v\frac{\partial v}{\partial z}dz &= -\frac{1}{\rho}\frac{\partial p}{\partial y}dy \\ w\frac{\partial w}{\partial x}dx + w\frac{\partial w}{\partial y}dy + w\frac{\partial w}{\partial z}dz &= -\frac{1}{\rho}\frac{\partial p}{\partial z}dz - g\,dz \end{aligned} \tag{4.26}$$

All the acceleration terms are of the form $u\dfrac{\partial u}{\partial x}$ which can be replaced by $\frac{1}{2}\dfrac{\partial(u^2)}{\partial x}$. After this substitution the components of Eq. (4.26) are rewritten as

$$\begin{aligned} \frac{1}{2}\left[\frac{\partial(u^2)}{\partial x}dx + \frac{\partial(u^2)}{\partial y}dy + \frac{\partial(u^2)}{\partial z}dz\right] &= \tfrac{1}{2}\,d(u^2) = -\frac{1}{\rho}\frac{\partial p}{\partial x}dx \\ \frac{1}{2}\left[\frac{\partial(v^2)}{\partial x}dx + \frac{\partial(v^2)}{\partial y}dy + \frac{\partial(v^2)}{\partial z}dz\right] &= \tfrac{1}{2}\,d(v^2) = -\frac{1}{\rho}\frac{\partial p}{\partial y}dy \\ \tfrac{1}{2}\,d(w^2) &= -\frac{1}{\rho}\frac{\partial p}{\partial z}dz - g\,dz \end{aligned} \tag{4.27}$$

Remember again that the total derivative is given in terms of its partials, as follows: $dp = \dfrac{\partial p}{\partial x}dx + \dfrac{\partial p}{\partial y}dy + \dfrac{\partial p}{\partial z}dz$. After summing the three component Eqs. (4.27), a total differential equation is obtained:

$$\begin{aligned} \tfrac{1}{2}[d(u^2) + d(v^2) + d(w^2)] = \tfrac{1}{2}\,dU^2 &= -\frac{dp}{\rho} - g\,dz \\ \tfrac{1}{2}\,dU^2 + \frac{dp}{\rho} + g\,dz &= 0 \end{aligned} \tag{4.28}$$

This total differential equation, derived for a steady motion and valid along a streamline, can now be integrated along a streamline. Integrating between two points along a streamline, the important *Bernoulli*[4] *equation* is obtained.

$$\frac{U_2^2 - U_1^2}{2} + \int_1^2 \frac{dp}{\rho} + g(z_2 - z_1) = 0$$

[4] Daniel Bernoulli (1700–1782), one member of a famous family of Swiss mathematicians. The word "hydrodynamics" originated with his publication, *Hydrodynamica*, in 1738.

and at every point along the streamline

$$\tfrac{1}{2}U^2 + \int \frac{dp}{\rho} + gz = \text{constant} \tag{4.29}$$

This constant will remain the same along a streamline and, in general, will vary from streamline to streamline.

(b) Steady Irrotational Motion

If the motion of a fluid is said to be irrotational, then, according to Eqs. (3.32) and (3.33), the following relationships between derivatives are true:

$$\frac{\partial v}{\partial x} = \frac{\partial u}{\partial y}$$

$$\frac{\partial u}{\partial z} = \frac{\partial w}{\partial x}$$

$$\frac{\partial w}{\partial y} = \frac{\partial v}{\partial z}$$

These relationships can be substituted in Euler's equation for steady motion, Eq. (4.25), neglecting the time dependence.

$$u\frac{\partial u}{\partial x}dx + v\frac{\partial v}{\partial x}dx + w\frac{\partial w}{\partial x}dx = -\frac{1}{\rho}\frac{\partial p}{\partial x}dx$$

$$u\frac{\partial u}{\partial y}dy + v\frac{\partial v}{\partial y}dy + w\frac{\partial w}{\partial y}dy = -\frac{1}{\rho}\frac{\partial p}{\partial y}dy$$

$$u\frac{\partial u}{\partial z}dz + v\frac{\partial v}{\partial z}dz + w\frac{\partial w}{\partial z}dz = -\frac{1}{\rho}\frac{\partial p}{\partial z}dz - g\,dz$$

These equations are not the same as those given in Eq. (4.26), and yet, when all are added together, they give the same result as Eq. (4.28)

$$\tfrac{1}{2}dU^2 + \frac{dp}{\rho} + g\,dz = 0$$

the only difference being that, instead of restricting the integration to flow along the streamline, the integration can be performed for any two points in the fluid which is now *irrotational*. Equation (4.29),

$$\tfrac{1}{2}U^2 + \int \frac{dp}{\rho} + gz = \text{constant}$$

is valid for every point in the irrotational motion and the constant is the same everywhere.

Bernoulli's equation [Eq. (4.29)] represents a form of energy level at a point consisting of the kinetic energy per unit mass, the pressure energy per unit mass $\int \frac{dp}{\rho}$ representing the energy required to move a unit mass from one pressure to another without change of volume, and the potential energy of the fluid. The sum of these three energies has been shown to be preserved along a streamline for a rotational nonviscous motion and everywhere for an irrotational nonviscous motion. This equation should not be confused with the total energy equation including work done on the fluid, heat transferred into the fluid, and changes in internal energy. For special conditions Bernoulli's equation may become the total energy equation, but, in general, Eq. (4.29), derived entirely on dynamic principles, must be satisfied independently of the total energy equation, which will be discussed in Chap. VI.

4.10 Special Applications of Bernoulli's Equation

As discussed already, the pressure p must be a unique function of the density ρ in order to finish the integration of Eq. (4.29). For the flow of liquids and slow motions of gases without heat addition, the motion of the fluid may, in many instances, be considered incompressible. The density in that case is constant, and the incompressible form of Eq. (4.29) becomes

$$\tfrac{1}{2}U^2 + \frac{p}{\rho} + gz = \text{constant} \tag{4.30}$$

It can be observed that in the case of no motion $U = 0$, the preceding equation becomes the hydrostatic equation, Eq. (2.3). If Eq. (4.30) is divided by g, it will have the units of energy per unit weight of fluid. The term $U^2/2g$ is the energy required per unit weight to move a fluid element from rest to a velocity U. The energy per unit weight has the dimension of length, and consequently $U^2/2g$ is called the *dynamic* or *velocity head*. It is also the energy per unit weight obtainable when the fluid is brought to rest. The term z is the potential energy per unit weight necessary to raise the fluid element a distance z from a given datum line. The quantity $p/\rho g$, called *flow energy*, has the significance shown in Fig. 4.13. If a container is at a pressure p above atmosphere, the amount of work necessary to move a volume of fluid $A\,dl$ against the pressure p is $F\,dl = pA\,dl$. The energy per unit weight moved is

$$\frac{pA\,dl}{\rho gA\,dl} = \frac{p}{\rho g}$$

Since the quantity $\left(\frac{p}{\rho g} + z\right)$ is the ambient pressure head that any surface would register when moving at the velocity U of the fluid, then the quantity is often called the *static head.* According to Eq. (4.30), then, the sum of the dynamic head and the static head is a constant and is generally called the *total pressure* or *total head.*

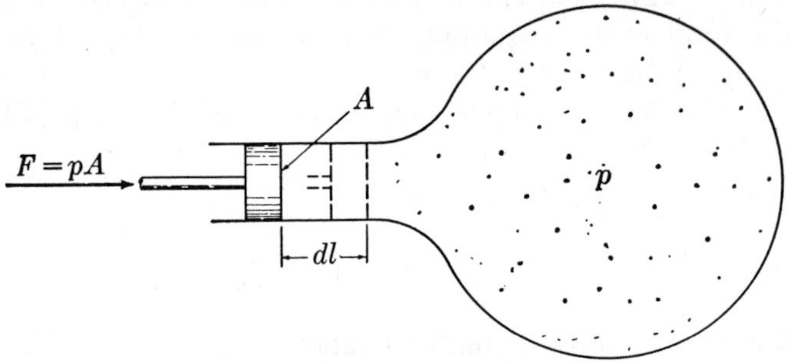

Figure 4.13
Flow work against pressure.

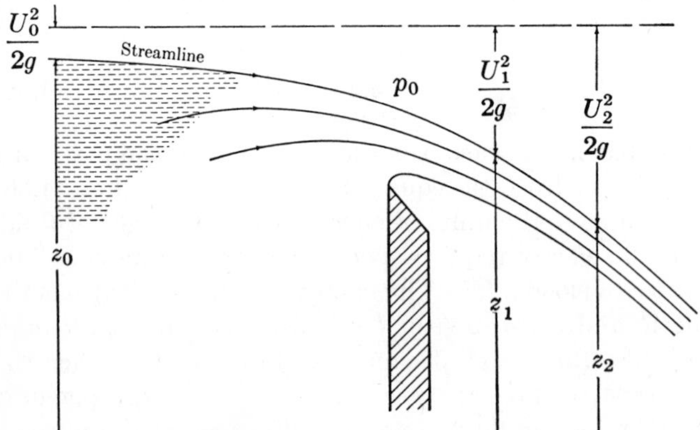

Figure 4.14
Flow of liquid over a weir.

(a) Flow of Liquid Over a Weir

If losses in the motion shown in Fig. 4.14 are neglected, and if the fluid is a liquid, the incompressible form of Bernoulli's equation, Eq. (4.30), can be used. Along the surface streamline, the pressure is atmospheric everywhere and therefore a constant.

$$\frac{U_0^2}{2g} + \frac{p_0}{\rho g} + z_0 = \frac{U_1^2}{2g} + \frac{p_0}{\rho g} + z_1 = \frac{U_2^2}{2g} + \frac{p_0}{\rho g} + z_2$$

hence

$$\frac{U^2}{2g} + z = \text{constant}$$

The total head being a constant, then the sum of the dynamic head and the elevation of the fluid surface is a constant. The datum line shown is arbitrary, since it establishes only the value of the constant.

(b) Flow of Liquid from a Large Tank

Considering the losses at the discharge of the tank shown in Fig. 4.15 to be negligible, Bernoulli's equation for the two points on the same streamline can be written as

$$\frac{U_2^2 - U_1^2}{2g} = \frac{p_1 - p_2}{\rho g} + (z_1 - z_2)$$

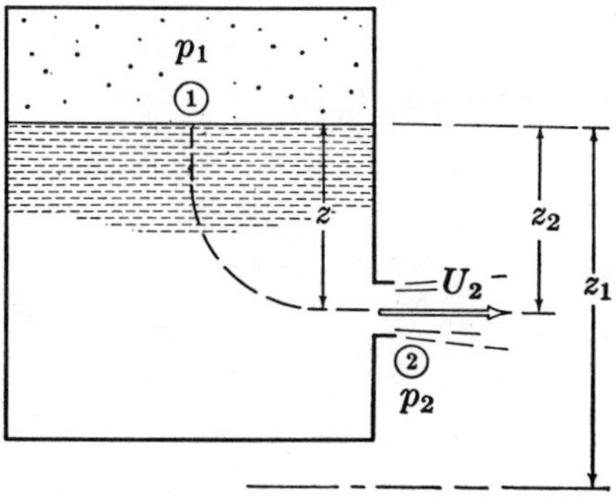

Figure 4.15
Flow from a tank.

Two special cases can be studied here, both cases with a very large tank compared with the size of the aperture at 2. The first case is considered when the tank is not pressurized and p_1 is atmospheric, as is p_2. This case, for which $U_1 \ll U_2$, yields the famous *Torricelli's law* for efflux from a container

$$U_2 = \sqrt{2gz}$$

The second case is for the condition existing when the tank is so highly pressurized that $\frac{(p_1 - p_2)}{\rho g} \gg z$; also for small z the discharge velocity takes the form

$$U_2 = \sqrt{2 \frac{(p_1 - p_2)}{\rho}} \tag{4.31}$$

Illustrative Example 4.3

Liquid is discharged at the rate of 3.86 ft³/sec from a siphon in the reservoir shown. The siphon has a diameter of 6 in. Find the elevation z and the fluid pressure at 1, the top of the siphon.

From the mass-continuity equation, the velocity of the fluid everywhere in the siphon tube is the same. If the cross section of the tank is large compared with the siphon diameter, Eq. (4.30) for the three points 0,1,2 can be written

$$\frac{U_0^2}{2g} + \frac{p_0}{\rho g} + z_0 = \frac{U_1^2}{2g} + \frac{p_1}{\rho g} + z_1 = \frac{U_2^2}{2g} + \frac{p_2}{\rho g} + z_2$$

The velocity $U_0 = 0$, and the pressures p_0 and p_2 are equal. Calling $z = z_0 - z_2$; then

$$U_2^2 = 2gz$$

also

$$U_2 = \frac{3.86}{\frac{\pi}{4}\left(\frac{1}{2}\right)^2} = 19.62 \text{ ft/sec}$$

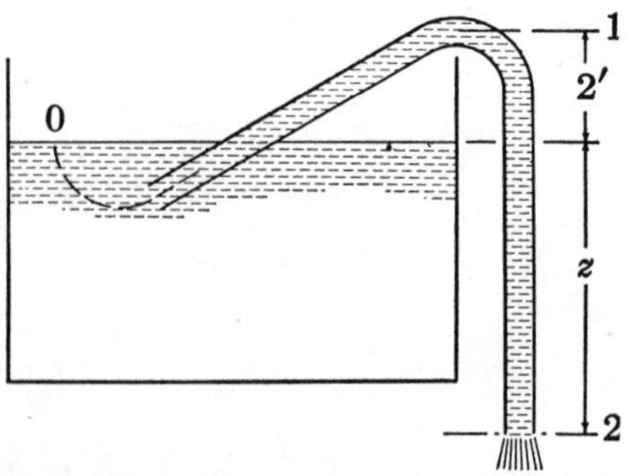

Figure 4.16
Siphon.

and

$$z = 6 \text{ ft of liquid.}$$

Since the velocity at 1 is the same as that at 2, Bernoulli's equation written between 1 and 2 or 0 and 1 gives

$$\frac{p_1}{\rho g} = -8 \text{ ft of liquid (below atmospheric pressure)}$$

(c) The Pitot-Static Tube in Incompressible Flow

A Pitot-static tube[5] is a small tube pointing in the direction of the stream so that, through the measurement of appropriate pressures, the magnitude of the velocity in that stream may be determined. The instrument is shown in Fig. 4.17 immersed in a fluid of density ρ_0. The probe of circular cross section has an opening at 1 which is the stagnation point[6] of the stagnation streamline 0–1. The pressure measured at this point is separately transmitted into the right leg of the manometer containing a liquid of density ρ_m. A series of holes are drilled along the periphery of the tube at 2. The contour of the probe is designed in such a way that point 2 is far enough back of 1 so that the

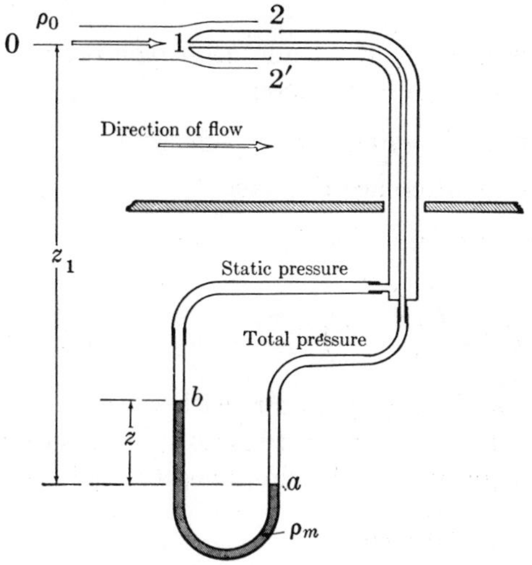

Figure 4.17
The Pitot-static tube with manometer.

[5] H. Pitot (1695–1771), a French inventor.
[6] Consult Sec. 3.12.

conditions of the fluid at 2 are identically those of the undisturbed flow at 0. The pressure measured at 2 is only the ambient pressure and consequently is not affected by the dynamic head, since the velocity there is parallel to the side of the probe. This pressure at 2 is transmitted through a separate passage into the left-hand side of the manometer. The manometer, therefore, reads the difference of pressures between those at 1 and 2 or 0.

According to Bernoulli's equation, the conditions of the fluid at the stagnation point are related to those of the undisturbed flow if losses are neglected in the motion from 0 to 1 and if the flow is incompressible:

$$\tfrac{1}{2}U_0^2 + \frac{p_0}{\rho_0} = \tfrac{1}{2}U_1^2 + \frac{p_1}{\rho_0}$$

Since at the stagnation point the velocity is zero by definition, then the undisturbed velocity U_0 may be solved.

$$p_1 - p_0 = \tfrac{1}{2}\rho_0 U_0^2 \tag{4.32}$$

$$U_0 = \sqrt{\frac{2(p_1 - p_0)}{\rho_0}} = \sqrt{\frac{2(p_1 - p_2)}{\rho_0}} \tag{4.31}$$

Considering the static equilibrium of the manometer, the pressure at a can be written for both sides of the manometer.

$$p_a = p_1 + \rho_0 g z_1 = p_2 + \rho_0 g(z_1 - z) + \rho_m g z$$

Substituting p_2 for p_0, the pressure difference becomes

$$p_1 - p_0 = gz(\rho_m - \rho_0)$$

and the velocity

$$U_0 = \sqrt{2gz\left(\frac{\rho_m}{\rho_0} - 1\right)} \tag{4.33}$$

In the case of measurements of velocity in air, with water as the manometer fluid, the ratio of the density of water to air is approximately 850, and therefore the velocity equation can be simplified to read

$$U_0 = \sqrt{2gz\rho_m/\rho_0}$$

Thus the Pitot-static tube, together with a manometer, becomes an adequate device for the measurement of fluid speed. The simplicity of this analysis depends on the following factors which were assumed to be true: First, it was mentioned that the viscous losses in the motion of the fluid from 0 to 2 are negligible. For this, the size of the probe, together with the magnitude of the velocity, must give a Reynolds number sufficiently high to make the inertial forces predominant. The probe must not be placed in fluid motions with large accelerations in the direction of motion. This condition influences the assumption that the conditions of the undisturbed flow essentially become those of station 2. The motion naturally must be steady, since the derivation of the equations was based on this assumption. The flow must also be uniform, at least within the extent of the probe cross section. In flows with curved streamlines, this conventional straight probe will not give adequate results, because the stem of the probe is not along the streamline, and consequently the pressure at the opening 2 will not be strictly the ambient static pressure; furthermore, owing to the curvature, there will exist, according to Eq. (4.18), a pressure gradient normal to the streamline in the direction 2-2′. Lastly, since Eq. (4.30) was used for the probe analysis, the fluid was considered to be incompressible. For gases at relatively high speeds, the high decelerations from 0 to 1 cause changes in the density which alter the solution already derived. This case of compressibility effects in the Pitot-static measurements will be considered next.

(d) The Pitot Static Tube in Compressible Flows

For the deceleration process between points 0 and 1 in Fig. 4.17, and for a compressible fluid, the somewhat more general Eq. (4.28) and its solution [Eq. (4.29)] apply. In most cases used in fluid-mechanics applications, the gas can be considered as a *perfect gas*. Assuming that no heat transfer takes place in the motion, then, for a frictionless motion, the density and pressure are related according to the isentropic expansion law $p = C\rho^\gamma$, where C is a constant representing the initial conditions in the expansion or compression, and $\gamma = c_p/c_v$ is the ratio of the specific heats of the gas. This law is derived in Sec. 8.2(*d*). Since there is no change in elevation between points 0 and 1 with this isentropic pressure-density relationship, Euler's equation becomes

$$dp = C\gamma\rho^{\gamma-1}\,d\rho$$

$$\tfrac{1}{2}dU^2 + C\gamma\rho^{\gamma-2}\,d\rho = 0$$

and the integration along the streamline between points 0 and 1 becomes

$$\tfrac{1}{2}(U_0^2 - U_1^2) + \frac{\gamma}{\gamma - 1}C[\rho_0^{\gamma-1} - \rho_1^{\gamma-1}] = 0 \qquad (4.34)$$

The constant $C = p_0/\rho_0^\gamma = p_1/\rho_1^\gamma$; the density is also replaced by the pressure, hence

$$p_1 = p_0 \left\{1 + \frac{\gamma - 1}{\gamma}\left[\frac{\rho_0(U_0^2 - U_1^2)}{2p_0}\right]\right\}^{\frac{\gamma}{\gamma-1}} \tag{4.35}$$

At the stagnation point 1 the velocity is zero—$U_1 = 0$. According to Sec. 3.2(*b*), the velocity of sound $a^2 = dp/d\rho$. For the isentropic law, then, $a^2 = \gamma p/\rho$. Therefore, at the undisturbed flow the speed of sound propagation can be replaced by $a_0^2 = \gamma p_0/\rho_0$. Substitution of this relationship into Eq. (4.35) gives

$$\begin{aligned} p_1 &= p_0 \left\{1 + \frac{\gamma - 1}{\gamma}\left(\frac{\gamma U_0^2}{2a_0^2}\right)\right\}^{\frac{\gamma}{\gamma-1}} \\ &= p_0\left(1 + \frac{\gamma - 1}{2}\,\mathfrak{M}_0^2\right)^{\frac{\gamma}{\gamma-1}} \end{aligned} \tag{4.36}$$

in terms of the Mach number $\mathfrak{M}_0$. This is independently derived from the energy point of view in Eq. (8.30). This expression can be expanded into a binomial series according to the binomial theorem.

$$\begin{aligned} p_1 = p_0 \bigg[1 + \frac{\gamma}{2}\,\mathfrak{M}_0^2 + \frac{\gamma}{8}\,\mathfrak{M}_0^4 + \frac{\gamma(2-\gamma)}{48}\,\mathfrak{M}_0^6 \\ + \frac{\gamma(2-\gamma)(3-2\gamma)}{384}\,\mathfrak{M}_0^8 + \cdots\bigg] \end{aligned}$$

Multiplying through by p_0 and factoring $\frac{1}{2}\rho_0 U_0^2$ gives

$$\begin{aligned} p_1 - p_0 = \tfrac{1}{2}\rho_0 U_0^2 \bigg[1 + \frac{1}{4}\,\mathfrak{M}_0^2 + \frac{(2-\gamma)}{24}\,\mathfrak{M}_0^4 \\ + \frac{(2-\gamma)(3-2\gamma)}{192}\,\mathfrak{M}_0^6 + \cdots\bigg] \end{aligned} \tag{4.37}$$

One can immediately see the difference between Eqs. (4.32) and (4.37)—one derived for the incompressible and the other for the compressible flow in the vicinity of a Pitot static tube. The first term of Eq. (4.37) is identical with that of Eq. (4.32), and this clearly shows that the solution in both cases is the same for low values of the free-stream Mach number $\mathfrak{M}_0$. For increasing speeds of fluid and consequently for large $\mathfrak{M}_0$, Eq. (4.37) will be applicable.

For the purpose of comparison, calculations are presented in Table 4.1 showing the incompressible dynamic pressure $\frac{1}{2}\rho_0 U_0^2$ for various velocities of air and the correction for compressibility as indicated by the terms in the brackets of Eq. (4.37). The case considered here is for $p_0 = 2{,}116\ \text{lb}_f/\text{ft}^2$ and $\rho_0 = 0.0023\ \text{slugs/ft}^3$ which are nearly standard

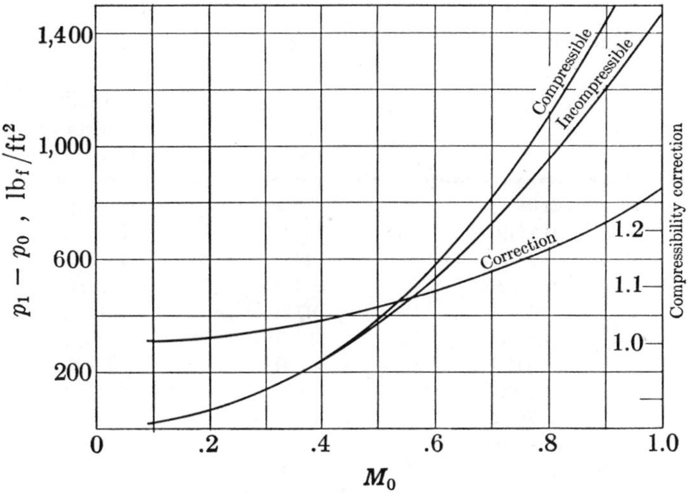

Figure 4.18
Dynamic pressure and compressibility correction at various $\mathfrak{M}_0$.

conditions. The expansion coefficient $\gamma = 1.4$, and therefore, from these data, the velocity of sound in the undisturbed stream is calculated to be $a = 1{,}133$ ft/sec.

The dynamic pressures for the incompressible and the compressible cases are plotted together in Fig. 4.18. The variation of the compressibility correction as a function of $\mathfrak{M}_0$ is also shown in the same figure. This treatment of isentropic compressibility throughout the stream is strictly valid for the condition of no shock wave forming ahead of the Pitot static tube mouth. This discussion will be continued in Chap. IX, taking into account the pressure change across the shock. Table 4.1 is then valid for $\mathfrak{M}_0 < 1$. The term in $\mathfrak{M}_0^6$ in Eq. (4.37) is very small and therefore can be neglected. For $\mathfrak{M}_0 = 1$ it contributes only an amount equal to 0.000625, which is less than 0.1 per cent.

(*e*) *Isothermal Flow in Conduits*

Again in the isothermal case of a perfect gas, the pressure can be expressed in terms of the density alone: $p = C\rho$. For two points along the streamline of a conduit, Eq. (4.28) may be integrated after substituting the density ρ for the pressure p. The result of this integration gives

$$gz_1 + \tfrac{1}{2}U_1^2 + C \ln p_1 = gz_0 + \tfrac{1}{2}U_0^2 + C \ln p_0$$

Table 4.1
Dynamic pressure and compressibility factor at various air speeds.

U_0 ft/sec	M_0	$\frac{1}{2}\rho_0 U_0^2$ lb$_f$/ft^2	Compressibility correction brackets in Eq. (4.37)
100	0.0882	11.5	1.0019
200	0.1765	46.0	1.0078
300	0.2648	103.5	1.0177
400	0.3530	184.0	1.0316
500	0.4413	287.5	1.0496
600	0.5296	414.0	1.0722
700	0.6178	564.0	1.0990
800	0.7061	736.0	1.1309
900	0.7944	932.0	1.1678
1,000	0.8826	1,150.0	1.2102
1,100	0.9709	1,391.0	1.2584
1,133	1.0000	1,476.2	1.2756

The constant C may be expressed in terms of the pressure and density at the two points considered, $C = p_1/\rho_1 = p_0/\rho_0$

$$gz_1 + \tfrac{1}{2}U_1^2 + \frac{p_1}{\rho_1}\ln p_1 = gz_0 + \tfrac{1}{2}U_0^2 + \frac{p_0}{\rho_0}\ln p_0 \qquad (4.38)$$

In addition, the condition of continuity of mass expressed by Eq. (3.10) must be satisfied also.

$$\rho_1 U_1 A_1 = \rho_0 U_0 A_0$$

$$\frac{U_0}{U_1} = \frac{\rho_1 A_1}{\rho_0 A_0} = \frac{p_1 A_1}{p_0 A_0}$$

Substitution of this relation into Eq. (4.38) gives the velocity for a horizontal convergent or divergent conduit.

$$\tfrac{1}{2}U_1^2\left[1 - \left(\frac{p_1 A_1}{p_0 A_0}\right)^2\right] = \frac{p_1}{\rho_1}\ln\frac{p_0}{p_1} = RT_1 \ln\frac{p_0}{p_1} \qquad (4.39)$$

Illustrative Example 4.4

Argon in a tank at 300°F and 2 atm is discharged to the atmosphere. If the discharge is made through a nozzle with a large contraction, find the discharge velocity (*a*) if the flow is adiabatic and (*b*) if the flow is assumed to be isothermal.

(*a*) According to Eq. (4.34), if subscript 0 denotes the discharge,

$$\tfrac{1}{2}(U_0^2 - U_1^2) + \frac{\gamma}{\gamma - 1}C(\rho_0^{\gamma-1} - \rho_1^{\gamma-1}) = 0$$

$$\tfrac{1}{2}U_0^2 = \frac{\gamma}{\gamma - 1}\left(\frac{p_1}{\rho_1} - \frac{p_0}{\rho_0}\right)$$

$$= \frac{\gamma}{\gamma - 1} R(T_1 - T_0)$$

The discharge temperature is found from the adiabatic expansion law $T_0 p_0^{\frac{1-\gamma}{\gamma}} = T_1 p_1^{\frac{1-\gamma}{\gamma}}$. Then $T_0 = T_1/1.324 = 574°\text{R}$.

$$U_0^2 = 2 \times \frac{1.68}{0.68} 32.17 \times 38.73 \times 186$$

$$= 1{,}142{,}000 \text{ ft}^2/\text{sec}^2$$

$$U_0 = 1{,}067 \text{ ft/sec}$$

The values of γ and R for argon are given in Table 1.2.

(*b*) For the isothermal case, Eq. (4.39) written for U_0 and a large contraction ratio will be

$$\tfrac{1}{2}U_0^2 = RT_0 \ln \frac{p_1}{p_0}$$

$$U_0^2 = 2 \times 32.17 \times 38.73 \times 760 \ln 2$$

$$= 1{,}310{,}000$$

$$U_0 = 1{,}145 \text{ ft/sec}$$

Computing the Mach number in both cases indicates that the flow at the discharge is slightly below sonic speed. The velocity of sound in the adiabatic case is 1,078 ft/sec and in the isothermal case 1,260 ft/sec.

4.11 Bernoulli's Equation for Nonuniform Flows in Conduits

It has already been noted, in Sec. 4.10, that the Bernoulli equation derived totally from dynamic principles also represented a particular energy balance at every point along a streamline. This particular energy balance states that the sum of the kinetic energy, potential energy, and work against the fluid pressure must be preserved along the streamline if the fluid motion is rotational, and it will be preserved everywhere if the motion is irrotational. It must be pointed out here that, in general, Bernoulli's equation is not the total energy equation. The conservation of total energy will be discussed in Chap. VI. In conclusion, it must be understood that Bernoulli's equation derived from dynamic considerations alone is, in general, completely independent

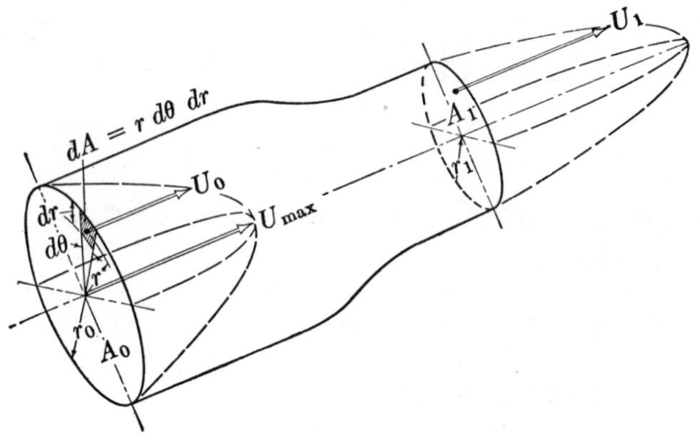

Figure 4.19
Velocity of fluid in converging pipe.

from the conservation of total energy equation. Therefore, in general, the two equations must be satisfied independently.

Often for flows in conduits, an over-all Bernoulli equation for the entire conduit is preferred to Eq. (4.30), which is valid along the streamline alone. In that case the entire conduit is considered as a big stream tube, and the summation of Eq. (4.30) at two sections A_0 and A_1 is considered.

Since the flow is still considered to be nonviscous, and since Eq. (4.30) is valid between any two points on the same streamline of Fig. 4.19, then the integration of this equation for all the fluid crossing at A_0 must be equal to that crossing A_1. The rate of infinitesimal mass flow crossing every cross section is $\rho U\,dA$, and then

$$\oint_A \left(\tfrac{1}{2}U^2 + \frac{p}{\rho} + gz\right)\rho U\,dA = 0$$

In general, the pressure and the density have negligible variations across the cross sections A through which mass and energy are transferred. In most instances the same applies to the elevation z, which can be considered constant across the cross sections. The only variation to be considered would be that of the velocity across the conduit. It follows, then, that

$$\tfrac{1}{2}\rho_0 \int_{A_0} U_0^3\,dA_0 + \rho_0\frac{p_0}{\rho_0}\int_{A_0} U_0\,dA_0 + \rho_0 g z_0 \int_{A_0} U_0\,dA_0$$
$$= \tfrac{1}{2}\rho_1 \int_{A_1} U_1^3\,dA_1 + \rho_1\frac{p_1}{\rho_1}\int_{A_1} U_1\,dA_1 + \rho_1 g z_1 \int_{A_1} U_1\,dA_1$$

From the definition of the average, the volume rate of flow $\int_{A_0} U_0\, dA_0$ must also equal the *spatial* average velocity $\overline{U}_0$ across the area A_0 times the area. The same pertains to the cross section A_1. Therefore, this summation becomes

$$\tfrac{1}{2}\rho_0 \int_{A_0} U_0^3\, dA_0 + \rho_0 \overline{U}_0 A_0 \left(\frac{p_0}{\rho_0} + gz_0\right)$$

$$= \tfrac{1}{2}\rho_1 \int_{A_1} U_1^3\, dA_1 + \rho_1 \overline{U}_1 A_1 \left(\frac{p_1}{\rho_1} + gz_1\right)$$

Since from continuity $\rho_0 A_0 \overline{U}_0 = \rho_1 A_1 \overline{U}_1$, dividing by the mass rate of flow, the preceding equation becomes finally

$$\frac{\overline{U}_0^2}{2} \frac{\overline{U_0^3}}{\overline{U}_0^3} + \frac{p_0}{\rho_0} + gz_0 = \frac{\overline{U}_1^2}{2} \frac{\overline{U_1^3}}{\overline{U}_1^3} + \frac{p_1}{\rho_1} + gz_1 \tag{4.40}$$

The quantity $\dfrac{1}{A} \displaystyle\int \left(\frac{U}{\overline{U}}\right)^3 dA$ is the departure of the average of the cube of the velocity from the cube of the average. By definition of the average, $\dfrac{1}{A} \displaystyle\int U^3\, dA = \overline{U^3}$ and the integral appearing in Eq. (4.40) is nothing but $\overline{U^3}/\overline{U}^3$. Consequently, Bernoulli's equation can be used for the over-all flow in the conduit as modified in Eq. (4.40). If the pressure, density, and elevations are functions of the area, then the integration should be performed for the other two terms as well.

Illustrative Example 4.5

Find the correction factor $\overline{U^3}/\overline{U}^3$ for the flow in Illustrative Example 3.2.

$$\overline{U_0^3} = \frac{1}{\pi r_0^2} \int_0^{2\pi} \int_0^{r_0} U_{\max}^3 \left[1 - \left(\frac{r}{r_0}\right)^2\right]^3 r\, d\theta\, dr$$

$$= \frac{2}{r_0^2} \int_0^{r_0} U_{\max}^3 \left[1 - 3\left(\frac{r}{r_0}\right)^2 + 3\left(\frac{r}{r_0}\right)^4 - \left(\frac{r}{r_0}\right)^6\right] r\, dr$$

$$= \tfrac{1}{4} U_{\max}^3$$

But the space average of the velocity was found to be one half the maximum velocity $\overline{U} = \frac{1}{2} U_{\max}$ and $\overline{U}^3 = U_{\max}^3/8$. The correction factor is then

$$\frac{\overline{U^3}}{\overline{U}^3} = 2$$

In the absence of viscosity, Bernoulli's equation for the entire tube in terms of the spatial average velocity becomes, from Eq. (4.40),

$$\overline{U}_0^2 + \frac{p_0}{\rho_0} + gz_0 - \overline{U}_1^2 + \frac{p_1}{\rho_1} + gz_1$$

4.12 Fluid Motion with Internal Losses

Thus far the discussion of Bernoulli's equation has been for motions without internal frictional forces. The study of these frictional forces is the subject of Chap. IX. The losses considered in this section are totally irreversible and consequently will only increase the internal entropy of the substance. Equation (4.28) will have to be modified so as to include a dissipation term in terms of the entropy change of the substance. If, however, work is done from the fluid or into the fluid, it must enter also in the balance of Eq. (4.28). Without specifying at this time the nature of the loss as a result of friction or of work done by the fluid on the boundary, this additional term will be called dH. The modified form of the differential Bernoulli equation becomes

$$\tfrac{1}{2}dU^2 + \frac{dp}{\rho} + g\,dz + dH = 0 \tag{4.41}$$

and, when dH is an exact differential, it may be integrated in the form

$$\tfrac{1}{2}U_1^2 + \int_1 \frac{dp}{\rho} + gz_1 = \tfrac{1}{2}U_2^2 + \int^2 \frac{dp}{\rho} + gz_2 + H \tag{4.42}$$

Since H is the loss of energy per unit mass, point 2 is downstream of point 1.

Illustrative Example 4.6

As shown in Fig. 4.20, a liquid is discharged vertically from a very large tank. If the losses at the discharge nozzle and its approach region are 20 per cent of the actual discharge-velocity head, find the discharge velocity and the actual height that the jet will reach.

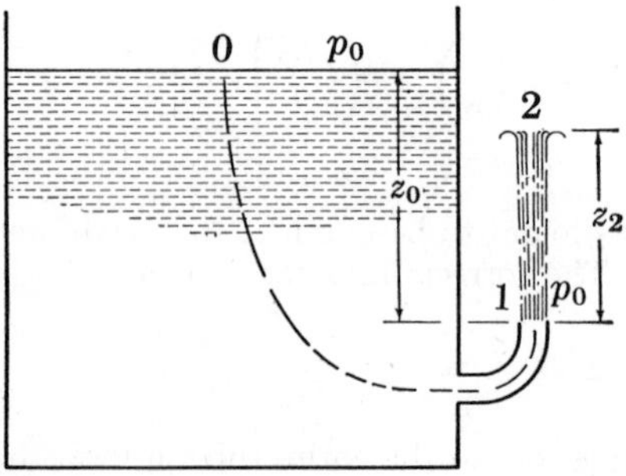

Figure 4.20
Vertical discharge from a large tank.

Consider the datum line for measuring elevations at the discharge of the jet. The pressures at the points 0, 1, and 2 are all atmospheric, and consequently Eq. (4.42), written for the incompressible case, will read:

$$\tfrac{1}{2}U_0^2 + \frac{p_0}{\rho} + gz_0 = \tfrac{1}{2}U_1^2 + \frac{p_0}{\rho} + H$$

$$0 + 0 + gz_0 = \tfrac{1}{2}U_1^2 + 0 + 0.20(\tfrac{1}{2}U_1^2)$$

$$\tfrac{1}{2}U_1^2 = \frac{gz_0}{1.2}$$

$$U_1 = \sqrt{\frac{gz_0}{0.6}}$$

The elevation of the jet at point 2 can be found by writing Bernoulli's equation between points 1 and 2. Since there are no losses between these two points,

$$\tfrac{1}{2}U_1^2 = gz_2$$

$$\frac{gz_0}{1.2} = gz_2$$

$$z_2 = \frac{z_0}{1.2}$$

4.13 Losses in Metering Systems

In Sec. 4.10(*c*) the Pitot-static tube was described as an instrument for the measurement of fluid velocity in a stream. There are three other types of instruments that are used in the measurement of over-all rates of flow in closed conduits. These are the Venturi meter, the nozzle, and the orifice plate. All these instruments are based on the principles of the modified Bernoulli equation, Eq. (4.42).

(*a*) *The Venturi Meter*

The principle behind this meter is to introduce, along a conduit of constant cross section, a gradual constriction so that it accelerates the flow and produces a variation in the static pressure of the fluid. This change of static pressure owing to the constriction can be measured with the help of a manometer and then can be interpreted in terms of the velocity through the conduit. This gradual constriction, followed by an expansion, is shown in Fig. 4.21. For an incompressible motion and for no

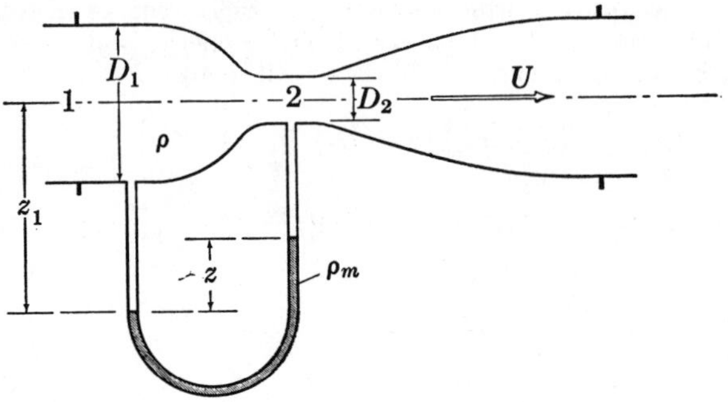

Figure 4.21
The Venturi flow-meter.

change in elevation, Eq. (4.42) can be used between sections 1 and 2 in order to analyze the flow relationships. It is always presumed that the area A_2 of the constriction is known, and the same applies to the area of the conduit A_1.

$$\tfrac{1}{2}U_1^2 + \frac{p_1}{\rho} = \tfrac{1}{2}U_2^2 + \frac{p_2}{\rho} + H$$

Another independent equation which can be used in order to reduce the number of unknowns is the equation of mass continuity for an incompressible motion which reads:

$$A_1U_1 = A_2U_2$$

$$U_1 = \frac{A_2}{A_1}U_2$$

Substitution of U_1 into the modified Bernoulli equation gives

$$U_2 = \frac{1}{\sqrt{1 - \left(\frac{A_2}{A_1}\right)^2}}\sqrt{2\left(\frac{p_1 - p_2}{\rho} - H\right)}$$

The rate of mass flow through the throat 2 is found by assuming uniform flow in that cross section. Then

$$Q_2 = \frac{\pi\rho D_2^2}{4\sqrt{1 - \left(\frac{D_2}{D_1}\right)^4}}\sqrt{2\left(\frac{p_1 - p_2}{\rho} - H\right)} \qquad (4.43)$$

It can be seen immediately that $\left(\frac{p_1 - p_2}{\rho}\right)$ is the actual static pressure head measured across the two legs of the manometer and that the entire quantity $\left(\frac{p_1 - p_2}{\rho} - H\right)$ is the pressure head that would have been recorded in the manometer at the same velocity if there were no losses. Consequently, the square root of the ratio of these two static heads represents the ratio of the actual velocity to the ideal velocity if there were no losses. Defining, then, a *velocity coefficient* C_v as

$$C_v = \sqrt{\frac{\dfrac{p_1 - p_2}{\rho} - H}{\dfrac{p_1 - p_2}{\rho}}}$$

and substituting this relation into Eq. (4.43), a final expression for the rate of flow is obtained. The ratio of the areas can be called the *contraction coefficient* $C_c = A_2/A_1$.

$$Q_2 = \frac{\pi \rho D_2^2}{4\sqrt{1 - C_c^2}} C_v \sqrt{2\frac{p_1 - p_2}{\rho}} \tag{4.44}$$

The static equilibrium of the manometer gives the following relations

$$p_1 + \rho g z_1 = p_2 + \rho g(z_1 - z) + \rho_m g z$$

$$\frac{p_1 - p_2}{\rho} = gz\left(\frac{\rho_m}{\rho} - 1\right)$$

which can be substituted into Eq. (4.44).

Since the velocity coefficient C_v is a measure of the loss during contraction, this viscous loss must be a function of the relative level of the inertia to viscous force, that is, the Reynolds number. The variation of the velocity coefficient as a function of the $\mathcal{R}$ is given in Fig. 4.22. The Reynolds number is computed at the conditions of the throat. Since the boundary layer forms on the solid walls of the passages, it is conceivable that the larger the diameter of the passage, the less the influence of the viscous layer on the entire flow. It is for this reason that one also suspects that C_v, besides being a function of $\mathcal{R}$, is a function of the diameter ratio D_2/D_1 as well. The data given in Fig. 4.22 were seen to be valid experimentally up to a diameter ratio of 0.5.

(b) The Nozzle

The nozzle in Fig. 4.23 can be considered as the contraction part of the Venturi meter. Unlike the Venturi meter, the nozzle, instead of recovering the pressure after the contraction through a smooth guided expansion, allows it to expand freely in the conduit. The static pressures

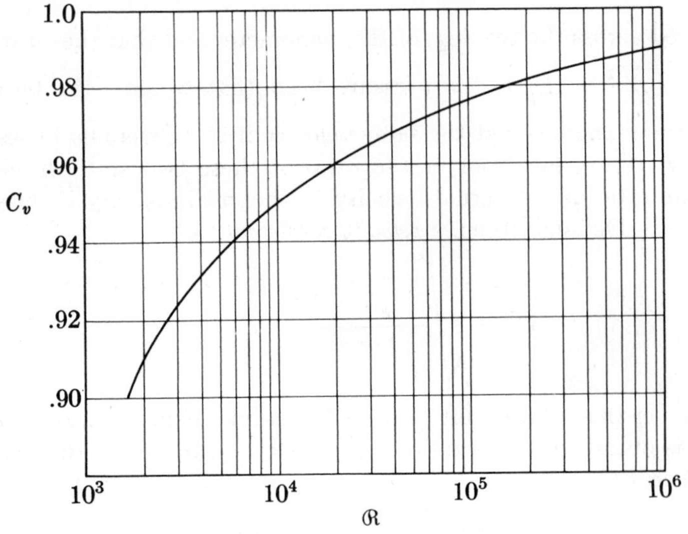

Figure 4.22
Velocity coefficient for the Venturi meter.

on the legs of the manometer are connected in a fashion similar to the Venturi meter. The same analysis performed for the Venturi meter will apply here as well. Since the pressure measured on the right-hand side of the manometer, in this case, does not necessarily represent the

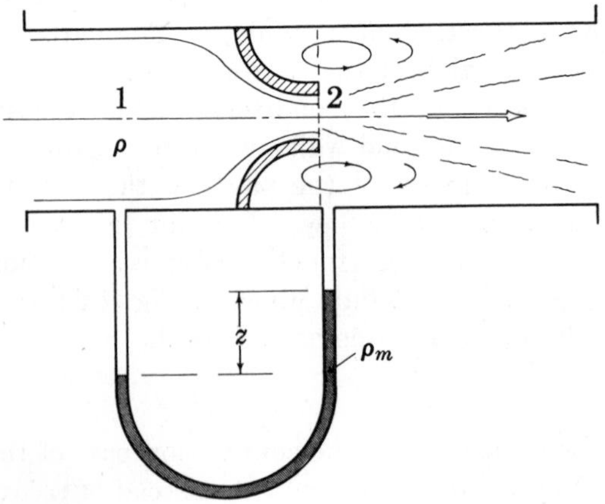

Figure 4.23
The nozzle.

pressure at mouth 2 of the nozzle, it is preferable to use Eq. (4.44) in a more condensed fashion. A *coefficient of discharge* C_d is defined here in such a manner that it contains both the velocity coefficient C_v and the contraction coefficient C_c:

$$Q = \rho A_2 C_d \sqrt{2gz\left(\frac{\rho_m}{\rho} - 1\right)} \tag{4.45}$$

Again, as in the previous case, C_d will be a function of the Reynolds number and the ratio of the contraction diameter to that of the conduit diameter. Figure 4.24 shows the variation of C_d as defined by $C_v/\sqrt{1 - C_c^2}$.

(c) The Sharp-edged Orifice

This metering device consists of a thin flat plate with a sharp edge opening at its center. The discharge from such an opening is shown in

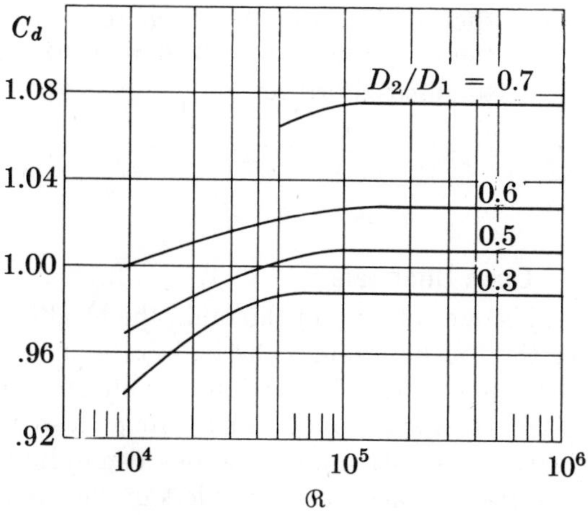

Figure 4.24
Discharge coefficient for the nozzle.

Fig. 4.25. It can be observed experimentally that the final dimension of the jet at 3 is smaller than the dimension of the orifice opening.

This reduction in area $A_3/A_2 = C_c$ is called the contraction coefficient for the orifice. In more advanced studies of nonviscous fluids and for a long sharp-edged orifice, it can be shown analytically that the area ratio $C_c = \dfrac{\pi}{\pi + 2}$, which is equal to 0.611. In practice, for

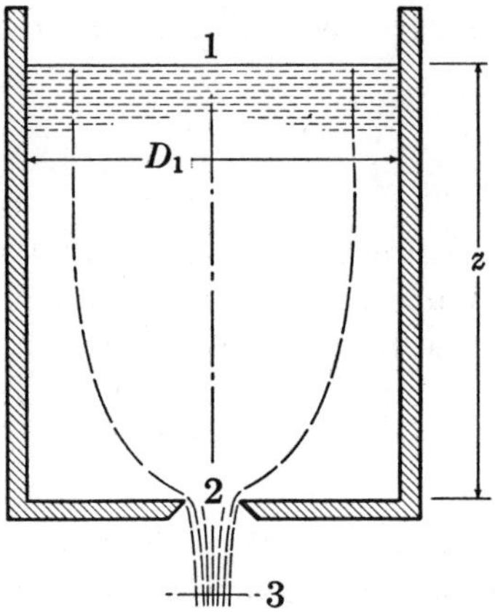

Figure 4.25
Efflux from a sharp-edged orifice.

large orifices and large pressure difference between the two sides of the orifice, this value of C_c is approached.

Again, similar to the previous analysis, the rate of flow through the orifice is

$$Q = \rho A_2 C_d \sqrt{2gz} \\ = \rho A_3 \frac{C_d}{C_c} \sqrt{2gz} \tag{4.46}$$

The ratio C_d/C_c represents the losses resulting from friction or, in other words, the velocity coefficient C_v. The value of C_v for the orifice varies from 0.96 to 0.98. Since the contraction coefficient was ideally about the same as in the actual case, the discharge coefficient C_d varies from 0.56 to 0.59 for small-sized orifices.

4.14 Flow Measurements in Open Channels

If liquid inside a large tank spills over the top of the tank, the height of the liquid crest spilling over the top determines the mass rate of flow from the tank. The analysis shown here is valid for small spilling heights. As shown in Fig. 4.26, water spills over a weir through a small height z_0. The surface of the water is a streamline and has atmospheric pressure throughout. On the free surface far to the left of the weir, the velocity of the liquid is practically zero owing to the large area of the tank as compared with that of the spilling weir. According to Bernoulli's equation written along the free surface,

$$gz_1 = \tfrac{1}{2}U_2^2 + gz_2$$

For small heights of liquid over the weir, this equation can be written for any depth of the spilling layer.

$$U_2 = \sqrt{2g(z_1 - z_2)} \\ = \sqrt{2gz}$$

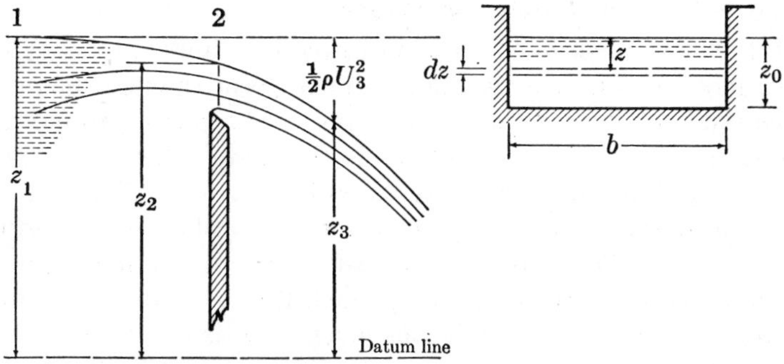

Figure 4.26
Flow over a wide rectangular weir.

The distance z is measured from the free surface to any depth in the spilling layer of the weir. Since the velocity is a function of depth, the infinitesimal mass flowing at a depth z is

$$\begin{aligned} dQ &= \rho U_2 b\, dz \\ &= \rho b\sqrt{2gz}\, dz \end{aligned}$$

If the total depth of the spilling layer is z_0, then the total integrated flow spilling from the weir is

$$\begin{aligned} Q &= \rho\sqrt{2g}b \int_0^{z_0} (z)^{1/2}\, dz \\ &= \tfrac{2}{3}\rho b\sqrt{2gz_0^3} \end{aligned}$$

In practice, it is seen that the rate of mass flow varies with $z_0^{3/2}$, but the coefficient is found to be less than predicted by the previous equation. Owing to the losses and because of the effects of the contraction of liquid at the weir, this problem must be treated in a fashion similar to those previously treated with losses and non-uniformities in the flow. A discharge coefficient can be introduced here to take care of the losses of discharge as well as the contraction effects of the liquid.

$$\begin{aligned} Q &= \tfrac{2}{3}C_d\rho b(2g)^{1/2}(z_0)^{3/2} \\ &= 3.33\rho b(z_0)^{3/2} \end{aligned} \tag{4.47}$$

The value of C_d is about 0.6.

4.15 Similarity in Ideal Nonviscous Motion

In Chap. III it was mentioned that, in order for similarity to exist between two motions, first the geometric similarity of the fluid boundaries is essential and second the ratio of the corresponding forces at corresponding points in the two motions is the same. Let these two fields of flow around an airfoil be represented in Fig. 4.27. The differential equations governing this nonviscous motion free of surface-tension forces were derived in Eq. (4.12) on the basis of a unit volume. Since geometric similarity has already been assumed, then, for complete similarity, the dynamic similarity conditions must be satisfied; that is, the ratio of corresponding forces at corresponding points must be the same for both flows. The three different types of forces described in Eq. (4.23) are the inertial force per unit volume $\frac{\partial u}{\partial t}$, $u\frac{\partial u}{\partial x}$, or any of the terms on the

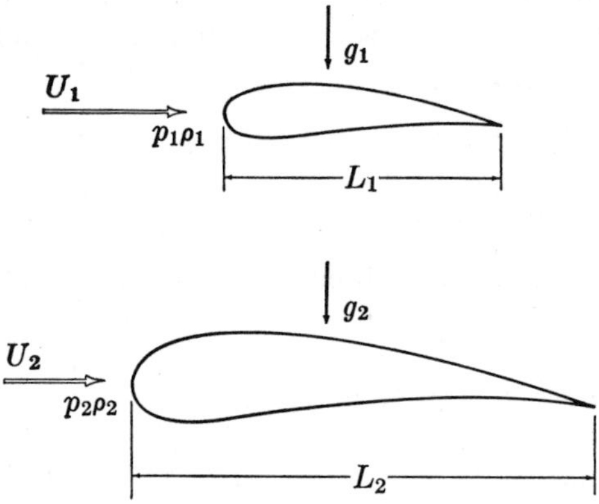

Figure 4.27
Flow over two geometrically similar objects.

left-hand side of the equations, the pressure surface force per unit volume such as $\frac{1}{\rho}\frac{\partial p}{\partial x}$, and g the gravitational body force per unit volume.

To establish the dynamic similarity, let any characteristic length in the first flow L_1 be a constant ratio b to that in the second flow L_2; that is, $L_1 = bL_2$. Also let a characteristic time t_1 in the first flow be equal to a constant c times that in the second flow $t_1 = ct_2$. In this fashion all corresponding times in both flow fields will have the same ratio c.

From these two ratios of length and time, the ratio of the corresponding velocities can be deduced:

$$U_1 = \frac{L_1}{t_1} = \frac{b}{c} \cdot \frac{L_2}{t_2} = \frac{b}{c} U_2 \tag{4.48}$$

In the same fashion the acceleration term, say $\frac{\partial u}{\partial t}$, will have the following ratio:

$$\frac{\partial u_1}{\partial t_1} = \frac{b}{c^2} \frac{\partial u_2}{\partial t_2} \tag{4.49}$$

If the pressures, the densities, and the gravitational fields in both fluid motions are also arbitrarily scaled so that

$$\rho_1 = d\rho_2, \qquad p_1 = ep_2, \quad \text{and} \quad g_1 = fg_2$$

Then the ratio of the pressure forces per unit area will have the correspondence

$$\frac{1}{\rho_1} \frac{\partial p_1}{\partial x_1} = \frac{e}{db} \frac{1}{\rho_2} \frac{\partial p_2}{\partial x_2} \tag{4.50}$$

The ratio of the gravitational forces per unit volume has already been expressed as

$$g_1 = fg_2 \tag{4.51}$$

Consulting the equations of motion again, for the same differential equation Eq. (4.23) to be valid in both cases, the coefficients in Eqs. (4.49), (4.50) and (4.51) must be the same. Therefore, solving the two equations,

$$\frac{b}{c^2} = f$$

$$\frac{b}{c^2} = \frac{e}{db},$$

yields the following facts. The first equation gives

$$\frac{L_1}{L_2} \frac{t_2^2}{t_1^2} = \frac{g_1}{g_2} = \frac{U_1^2 L_2}{U_2^2 L_1}$$

$$\frac{U_1^2}{L_1 g_1} = \frac{U_2^2}{L_2 g_2}$$

This implies that the *Froude number*, $\mathfrak{F}r$, in both flows must be the same. The second coefficient equation gives

$$\frac{b^2}{c^2} = \frac{e}{d}$$

$$\frac{L_1^2}{L_2^2}\frac{t_2^2}{t_1^2} = \frac{p_1\rho_2}{p_2\rho_1}$$

$$\frac{p_1}{\rho_1 U_1^2} = \frac{p_2}{\rho_2 U_2^2}$$

This condition specifies that the pressure coefficients in both cases must be the same. For a compressible flow it can be derived from the relations in Sec. 3.2(*b*), as shown in Sec. 4.10(*d*), that the velocity of sound in the fluid which is isentropic is $a^2 = \gamma p/\rho$; and therefore, $p_1/\rho_1 = a_1^2/\gamma$; and $p_2/\rho_2 = a_2^2/\gamma$. Substitution of these new relations in the previous equation gives the already-known expression

$$\left(\frac{a_1}{U_1}\right)^2 = \left(\frac{a_2}{U_2}\right)^2$$

The Mach number $\mathfrak{M}$ in both flows must be the same. It must be emphasized here that the Reynolds number cannot possibly be derived from the equations of a nonviscous fluid, since the viscous terms are not considered. For complete similarity of two nonviscous motions free of surface tension, the geometry of the boundaries of the fluid must be similar; the Froude number and the Mach number must satisfy the same relationship in both cases.

Problems

4.1 From Eq. (4.7) expand the operator $(\boldsymbol{U} \times \nabla)$ in Cartesian and cylindrical coordinates. Expand the rest of the equation and compare with Eqs. [4.8(*a*)] and [4.8(*b*)].

4.2 If the rate of change of temperature T was sought of a fluid particle moving with the stream, what would be its expression in Eulerian and time coordinates?

4.3 In the previous problem, for a steady flow field with temperature variations only normal to the streamlines, would one expect any time rate of change of the temperature following the particle? Explain.

4.4 Making use of Eq. (4.7), transform the continuity equation, Eq. (3.15), to reflect the total rate of change of the density with respect to time. With this result on hand, make the distinction between the continuity equations: (*a*) for a steady flow in Eulerian sense, and (*b*) for a steady flow in Lagrangian sense.

4.5 The motion on a plane normal to the gravitational field of force is considered. In the natural coordinates, show that Euler's equations in the coordinates s, r, and z are

$$v_s \frac{\partial v_s}{\partial s} + \frac{\partial v_s}{\partial t} = -\frac{1}{\rho}\frac{\partial p}{\partial s}$$

$$\frac{v_s^2}{r} + \frac{\partial v_r}{\partial t} = -\frac{1}{\rho}\frac{\partial p}{\partial r}$$

$$g = -\frac{1}{\rho}\frac{\partial p}{\partial z}$$

In the natural coordinate system, s is the streamline direction.

4.6 Incompressible, steady flow is considered along a converging conical stream tube. Show that the acceleration varies inversely to the fifth power of the tube diameter. Find the relationship with the area of the tube.

4.7 As in Prob. 4.6, evaluate the area relationship to the acceleration in a linearly converging, two-dimensional channel. The convergence in the two-dimensional channel is in only one dimension of the cross section.

4.8 Consider Eq. (4.12), in which the acceleration $\boldsymbol{a}$ is a constant vector. Consider also that the fluid in the tank of Fig. 4.4 is a liquid. The gravitational acceleration $\boldsymbol{g}$ can be written in terms of the gradient of the potential energy $\Omega = gz$ where z is the elevation from the earth's surface. Thus, Eq. (4.12) can be written as

$$-\nabla(p + \rho\Omega) = \rho\boldsymbol{a}$$

In order to integrate this equation, one must transform it into an ordinary differential equation through Eq. (A.37). Multiplying by $d\boldsymbol{r}$, show immediately that Eqs. (4.13), [4.15(*a*)], and (4.16) follow.

4.9 A horizontal 12-ft-long tube of water, sealed at both ends, is accelerated horizontally in such a manner that the pressure difference at both ends is 2 psi. Find the acceleration to produce this pressure difference.

4.10 A 1-ft-long tube, filled with mercury, is used in a car for an accelerometer. The tube rests horizontally along its axis. If a pressure gauge is connected at both ends of the tube and is calibrated in pounds-force per square foot, what is the calibration constant to change pounds-force per square foot into feet per second per second acceleration?

4.11 Show that the slope of the free surface of a liquid contained in an accelerated tank is independent of the density of the liquid.

4.12 In Illustrative Example 4.5, find the variation of pressure along the bottom of the tank.

4.13 A U-tube, as shown in the figure, is accelerated horizontally $a_x = 18.52\ \text{ft/sec}^2$. If both ends of the tube are opened, find the angle the line of liquid levels makes with the horizontal and the column of liquid that has spilled out of one leg of the U-tube.

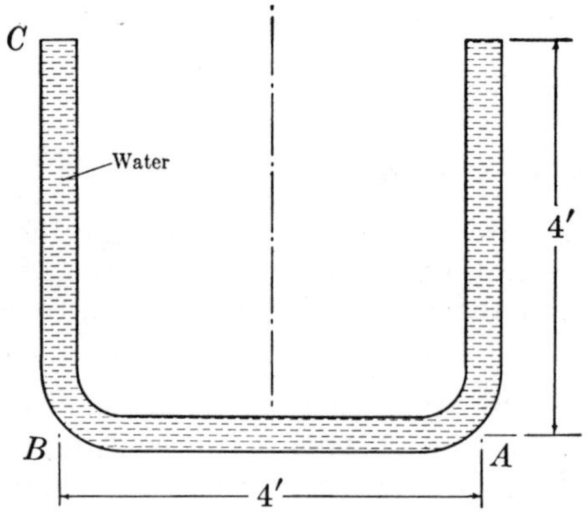

4.14 In Prob. 4.13, if the left-hand leg of the U-tube is sealed and the U-tube is accelerated horizontally to the right at the same value $a_x = 18.52\ \text{ft/sec}^2$, find the pressures at A, B, and C. The liquid in the U-tube is water.

4.15 A tank contains 4 ft of water in depth and is allowed to drop vertically at an acceleration $g/2$. Find the pressure of the water in the bottom of the tank. Find the acceleration if the pressure in the bottom is required to be atmospheric.

4.16 From Eq. (4.12), show that for an integration on a plane normal to $\mathbf{g}$, the gravitational force does not play a role. Then, obtain Eq. (4.18) with the appropriate assumptions from the resulting equation.

4.17 A river makes a 90° turn, as shown in the figure at top of p. 197. The cross section of the river bed is rectangular. The inner bank turns with a radius of 500 ft and the outer bank with one of 1,000 ft. Assume a free-vortex motion and the velocity not a function of depth. The velocity at the inner bank is 10 ft/sec. Find the difference in elevation of the water level at the two banks.

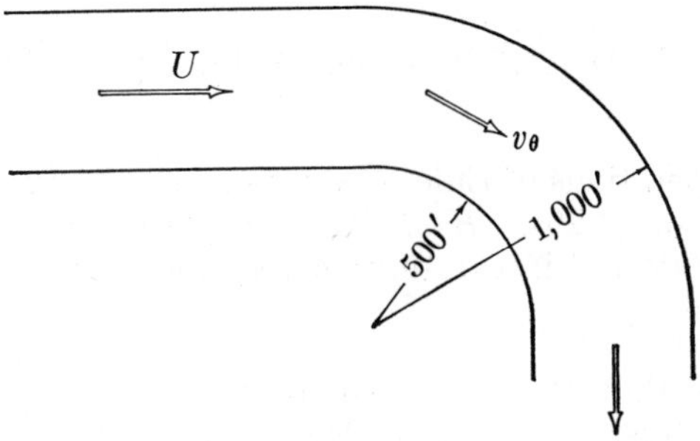

4.18 Consider again the river in Prob. 4.17. If a velocity $U = 10$ ft/sec, uniform across the cross section, enters the bend and if, again, the motion in the bend is irrotational (free-vortex), find the velocities at the two banks of the river.

4.19 The U-tube in Prob. 4.13 is rotated around an axis halfway between A and B at an angular speed of 600 rpm. Find the pressure in the tube halfway between A and B if the liquid in the tube is water.

4.20 When the U-tube in Prob. 4.17 is rotated around A with an angular velocity of 2 radians/sec, find the column of water spilled out at C. What is the pressure at A?

4.21 The level of the liquid inside a cylindrical tank is h below the level of the liquid outside the tank. Consider the liquid outside the tank to have an infinite extent. If the tank is rotated about its axis with an

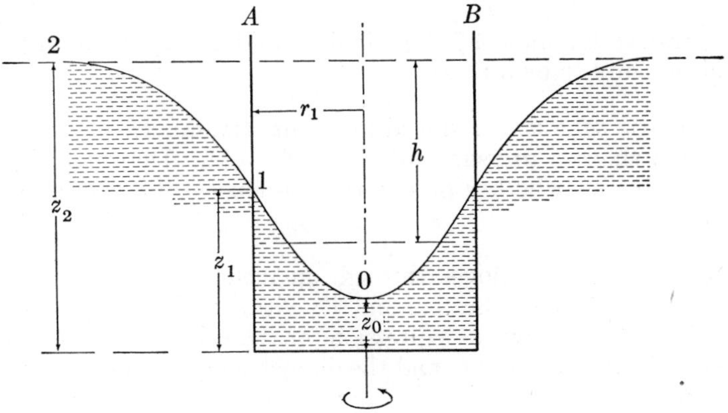

angular velocity ω, find this angular velocity such that the interior and exterior surface levels will be the same at the walls of the tank as shown at 1. Show that the interior and exterior curves have continuous derivatives at 1.

4.22 Obtain Eqs. (4.23) and (4.24) by introducing in Eq. (4.12) the components of the vectors.

4.23 Carrying out vectorial operations of Euler's equation, Eq. (4.12), obtain Bernoulli's equation, Eq. (4.29). *Hint:* Assume $\boldsymbol{g}$ to have a potential, multiply through by $d\boldsymbol{r}$ and integrate, remembering that the density is a variable with space.

4.24 In the static case, show that Bernoulli's equation [Eq. (4.29)] reduces to the conventional hydrostatic equation [Eq. (2.2)].

4.25 An airfoil moves in still air at a velocity of 100 mph. The air pressure is standard at 50°F. Calculate the stagnation pressure of the air on the airfoil. At this low speed, assume the air to be incompressible.

4.26 Water at ordinary temperature flows through a 3-in. pipeline at the rate of 400 gpm. What is the total head of the fluid referred to a datum 5 ft below the pipe? The pressure in the pipe is 10 psig.

4.27 If a small solid particle were to move with the fluid in Prob. 4.26, what would be the pressure on its exterior surface? If the tiny particle were to stop suddenly, what would be the pressure experienced at its stagnation point?

4.28 If the ideal efflux of water from the tank in Fig. 4.18 has a velocity of 15 ft/sec, what is the height of the water in the tank at that instant? The pressure of the liquid surface in the tank is atmospheric.

4.29 In Illustrative Example 4.7, how high should point 1 be in order for the liquid pressure to be 5 psia?

4.30 A Pitot static tube is introduced in an air stream at 50°F. The water manometer shows a pressure difference of 1.0 in. Determine the velocity of the air and whether or not the motion can be considered incompressible.

4.31 A fluid of density ρ_f moves through an inclined contraction as shown below. The fluid in the manometer with density ρ_m shows a level differential of h. Derive an expression for the velocity at 2, U_2, in terms of the densities ρ_f, ρ_m, and h, and the diameter ratio. The motion is incompressible.

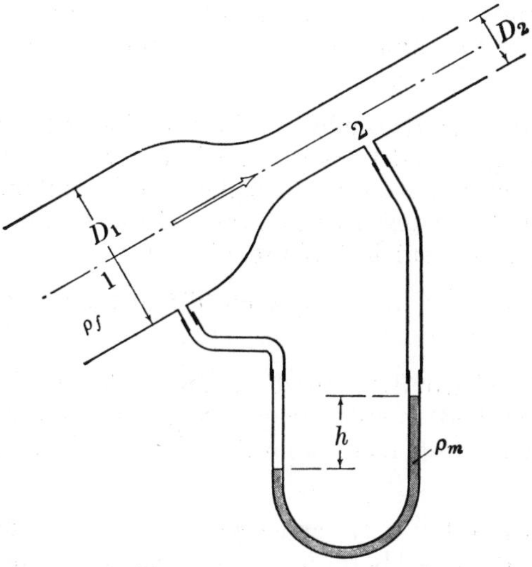

4.32 For comparison, solve Prob. 4.31 for an ideal isothermal flow in terms of p_1, p_2, ρ_m, ρ_f, h, and the diameter ratio.

4.33 Solve Prob. 4.31 for the case of isentropic motion in terms of p_1, p_2, ρ_m, ρ_f, h, and the diameter ratio.

4.34 A water manometer registers 10 in. of water differential when connected across the two leads of a Pitot static probe. The probe is located in an air stream at 100°F. Show whether the motion of the air can be treated as incompressible or compressible. What is the velocity of the air? What is the compressibility correction?

4.35 A projectile moves in helium at 2 atm and 80°F. What is its absolute stagnation pressure if the projectile moves at a speed of 1,000 mph?

4.36 Find the adiabatic compressibility correction and the speed of sound for hydrogen moving at the speed of 2,000 mph. The temperature of the hydrogen is 80°F.

4.37 If the velocity distribution in a two-dimensional channel, as given in Prob. 4.6, is parabolic, then determine the Bernoulli equation correction factor for nonuniform flow $\overline{U^3}/\bar{U}^3$. Compare the result with the solution of Illustrative Example 4.5.

4.38 The velocity distribution at a given cross section in a pipe in the turbulent-flow case is often described as $\dfrac{U}{U_{\max}} = \left(\dfrac{r}{r_0}\right)^{1/7}$. The dimension r_0 is the radius of the pipe, and the velocity at the center is U_{max}. Determine the correction factor for the kinetic energy in the Bernoulli equation.

4.39 If, in the siphon of Illustrative Example 4.7, there are losses to be considered and the same discharge of 3.86 ft^3/sec occurs but for $z = 12$ ft, and since the losses occur at the entrance into the siphon, in the siphon, and in its discharge, they could be represented as a ratio of the dynamic head $KU_2^2/2g$. Calculate the loss coefficient K for this case.

4.40 In Illustrative Example 4.11, if the velocity coefficient C_v is 0.98, find the relationship between z_2 and z_0.

4.41 Consider the efflux of fluid from the nozzle in Fig. 4.30. If the discharge coefficient C_d is given, find an analytic expression for the time required t for the fluid level to drop from a level z_0 to an arbitrary level z.

4.42 The Venturi meter shown in Fig. 4.27 carries water at 50°F. The manometer differential marks 10 in. of Hg for a Venturi diameter reduction of 0.5. Estimate the velocity coefficient C_v and determine the velocity of the water at the throat.

4.43 The overflow of a weir in the form of an isosceles triangular notch of angle θ is shown. Derive an expression for the mass rate of flow through the notch in terms of θ and z_0.

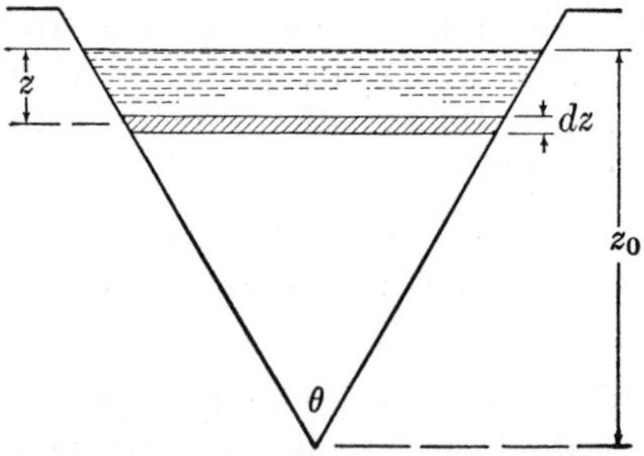

Momentum Considerations in Fluid Dynamics

chapter V

5.1 Introduction

The analysis presented in Chap. IV has shown that the problem of frictionless flow of a fluid is completely determined, subject, of course, to simple boundary conditions and the availability of methods of integrating Euler's equations. If the solution for all types of flows, frictionless and frictional, with all types of boundary conditions were available, then treating fluid-dynamics problems from the momentum point of view would be superfluous.

The use of a momentum approach becomes useful when the overall forces acting on a *finite* fluid *system* or *control volume*[1] are to be determined instead of the forces on an infinitesimal fluid particle as given by Euler's equations. It must be understood that, in the end, both of these methods should give the same information if applied to the same volume, since they are both based on Newton's equations of motion. If Euler's equations are used to determine the forces on a

[1] For definition, read Sec. 1.2.

finite volume, the external forces on the volume are established by integrating Euler's equations along the streamline through the volume and thus summing the calculated forces throughout the surface of the volume at the bounds of the volume.

In order to establish the external forces on an arbitrary fluid system, the momentum approach sums up the net momentum changes of the system, and, according to Newton's second law, the total rate of change of the momentum in the system is the resultant external force on the system. It will be seen that, subject to a modification of Newton's second law for the control volume, the same treatment will apply to a control volume.

For instance, information about the external forces exerted by a fluid on geometrically complicated control volumes such as an airfoil, the row of blades of a turbomachine, the fluid emanating from a jet, the fluid passing through the airplane or helicopter blades, etc., can be obtained from momentum considerations applied to the boundaries of the particular control volume to be analyzed. For steady flow the knowledge of the state of the fluid inside the control volume is not necessary; just the conditions at the boundaries are sufficient to determine the resultant force on the stationary or moving control volume.

The condition of steady motion in the application of the momentum equations will make the treatment considerably simpler.

5.2 Mass and Momentum Equations Applied to a Finite Control Volume

In many respects, the treatment for momentum exchange across the boundaries of an arbitrary control volume is similar to the treatment of mass exchange across the boundaries of the same volume, as discussed in Sec. 3.9. It follows, from Newton's second law of motion, that the mass within an arbitrary volume $\mathcal{V}$ undergoes a change of momentum only when external forces are applied to the mass within the volume.

Consider the arbitrary *control volume* $\mathcal{V}_c$ shown in Fig. 5.1 and bounded by $AMBM'A$. The velocity vector $\boldsymbol{U}$ of the fluid is defined everywhere in the volume through which the fluid is moving in the direction of the streamlines shown. The fluid enters through the surface S_c of the control volume at the left of the volume, and leaves at the right-hand side. The vector $\boldsymbol{n}$ is the outer normal drawn on the surface.

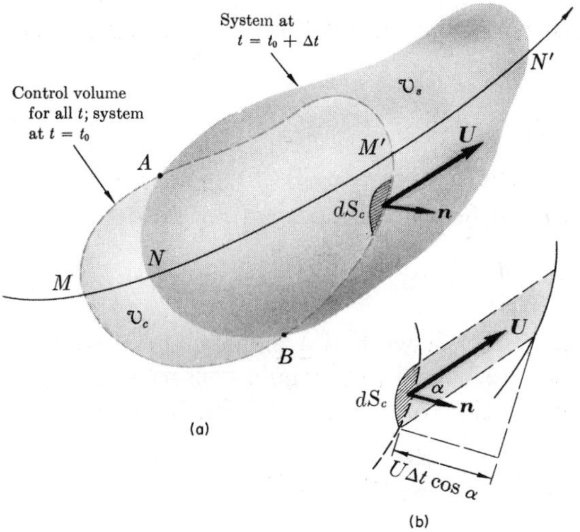

Figure 5.1
Fluid motion through an arbitrary control volume $\mathcal{V}_c$.

During this motion of the fluid through the arbitrary control volume, the momentum of the fluid within the volume may change with respect to time, for two reasons: First, because the density and the velocity within the volume may change with time, that is, unsteady motion; second, when the momentum entering the volume is not the same as that leaving the control volume, causing an accumulation or depletion of momentum in the volume.

At an arbitrary time $t = t_0$ let us consider the mass occupied by $\mathcal{V}_c$, and let us follow it in a small time Δt. At the end of this time the volume occupied by this mass will be in the volume $\mathcal{V}_s$ bounded by the surface S_s ($ANBN'A$). Since the volume $\mathcal{V}_s$ contains the same mass during the motion, it is a *system*, by definition. In general, the volume $\mathcal{V}_s$ is unequal to $\mathcal{V}_c$ except at time $t = t_0$ and by definition.

$$t = t_0; \qquad S_s = S_c \quad \text{and} \quad \mathcal{V}_s = \mathcal{V}_c,$$

also the masses and momenta $\boldsymbol{M}$ are equal

$$m_s(t_0) = m_c(t_0) \quad \text{and} \quad \boldsymbol{M}_s(t_0) = \boldsymbol{M}_c(t_0)$$

The mass in the system is given at any time by

$$m_s = \int_{\mathcal{V}_s} \rho d\mathcal{V}_s$$

Both ρ and $\mathcal{V}_s$ may change in time but, by definition, m_s is not allowed to change. Thus, the mass conservation equation in an integral form and applied to a system is

$$\frac{d}{dt}\int_{\mathcal{V}_s} \rho d\mathcal{V}_s = 0 \tag{5.1}$$

Newton enunciated his second law for a system. Thus if $\boldsymbol{F}$ is the resultant external force on $\mathcal{V}_s$ and S_s, then the second law reads:

$$\boldsymbol{F} = \frac{d}{dt}\int_{\mathcal{V}_s} \rho \boldsymbol{U} d\mathcal{V}_s = \frac{d\boldsymbol{M}_s}{dt} \tag{5.2}$$

This is very similar to Eq. (5.1). If we had a momentum conserving motion with $\boldsymbol{F} = 0$, then Eqs. (5.1) and (5.2) would conserve mass and momentum. With the help of Eq. (5.1), Eq. (5.2) can be modified to

$$\boldsymbol{F} = \int_{\mathcal{V}_s} \rho \frac{d\boldsymbol{U}}{dt} d\mathcal{V}_s$$

$$= \int_{\mathcal{V}_s} \rho \boldsymbol{a} d\mathcal{V}_s \tag{5.3}$$

We shall proceed, now, to write both Eqs. (5.1) and (5.2) in terms of the *control volume* and its motion properties. At time $t_0 + \Delta t$ shown in Fig. 5.1 the mass in the control volume $AMBM'A$ is equal to that in the system $ANBN'A$ plus the mass $AMBNA$ and less the mass $AN'BN'A$. The same argument is true for the difference in momenta. The mass in the volume $AM'BN'A$ is the amount per unit time that crossed the surface $AM'B$ in time[2] Δt. In Fig. 5.1(*b*) an infinitesimal of this volume is shown to be $(U \cos \alpha)\, dS_c\, \Delta t$. In vector notation the infinitesimal mass is $\rho(\boldsymbol{n}\cdot\boldsymbol{U})\, dS_c\, \Delta t$. The infinitesimal mass in $AMBNA$ is written in the same way except that $(\boldsymbol{n}\cdot\boldsymbol{U})$ has a negative sign, since $\boldsymbol{n}$ and $\boldsymbol{U}$ form an obtuse angle. We can evaluate the mass and the momentum in the control volume at the instant of time $t_0 + \Delta t$ shown in Fig. 5.1.

$$\begin{aligned} m_c(t_0 + \Delta t) &= m_s(t_0 + \Delta t) - m(AM'BN'A) + m(AMBNA) \\ &= m_s(t_0 + \Delta t) - [m(AM'BN'A) - m(AMBNA)] \\ &= m_s(t_0 + \Delta t) - \Delta t \oint_{S_c} \rho(\boldsymbol{n}\cdot\boldsymbol{U})\, dS_c \end{aligned} \tag{5.4}$$

The integral is taken in the entire surface S_c in a counterclockwise direction and it represents the mass difference in the bracket according to Eqs. (3.6) and (3.9). It is the net mass that crossed the control surface in time Δt.

[2] This time is shown to be small and finite in Fig. 5.1. Later in the argument, it will be made to approach zero.

By definition of a system

$$m_s(t_0 + \Delta t) = m_s(t_0)$$
$$= m_c(t_0)$$

The equality of $m_s(t_0)$ and $m_c(t_0)$ was already discussed. Thus Eq. (5.4) becomes

$$m_c(t_0 + \Delta t) = m_c(t_0) - \Delta t \oint_{S_c} \rho(\boldsymbol{n} \cdot \boldsymbol{U})\, dS_c$$

Dividing by Δt and taking the limit as $\Delta t \rightarrow 0$

$$\lim_{\Delta t \rightarrow 0} \frac{m_c(t_0 + \Delta t) - m_c(t_0)}{\Delta t} + \oint_{S_c} \rho(\boldsymbol{n} \cdot \boldsymbol{U})\, dS_c = 0,$$

or, according to the definition of differentiation with time,

$$\frac{\partial m_c}{\partial t} + \oint_{S_c} \rho(\boldsymbol{n} \cdot \boldsymbol{U})\, dS_c = 0;$$

and, since

$$m_c = \int_{\mathcal{V}_c} \rho d\mathcal{V}_c,$$

the mass conservation equation [Eq. (5.1)] written in terms of the *control volume* is

$$\frac{d}{dt} \int_{\mathcal{V}_s} \rho d\mathcal{V}_s = \frac{\partial}{\partial t} \int_{\mathcal{V}_c} \rho d\mathcal{V}_c + \oint_{S_c} \rho(\boldsymbol{n} \cdot \boldsymbol{U})\, dS_c = 0 \qquad (5.5)$$

The physical significance of this equation follows immediately. The left hand term represents the time increase or decrease of mass with time inside the control volume $\mathcal{V}_c$. According to Eq. (5.5), this term is non-zero if the second term representing the *flux of mass across* S_c is non-zero. Putting it simply, if the mass rate leaving the control volume (positive, since $\boldsymbol{n}$ is in the same direction) is larger than the mass rate entering, then according to Eq. (5.5) and for $\mathcal{V}_c$ constant, $\partial \rho / \partial t < 0$ indicating a reduction of mass and density with time. The converse argument is also true. In a steady motion where the density cannot be a function of time,

$$\oint_{S_c} \rho(\boldsymbol{n} \cdot \boldsymbol{U})\, dS_c = 0 \qquad (5.6)$$

This equation was already discussed in Sec. 3.9.

The argument in Eq. (5.5) is identical[3] for the balance of linear

[3] The student should try to repeat the identical reasoning for linear momentum. Since the infinitesimal flux of mass is $\rho(\boldsymbol{n} \cdot \boldsymbol{U})dS_c$ the flux of momentum is $\rho(\boldsymbol{n} \cdot \boldsymbol{U})\boldsymbol{U}dS_c$.

momentum in a control volume. At time t_0, where the system and control volume coincide in Fig. 5.1,

$$\boldsymbol{F} = \frac{d}{dt}\int_{\mathcal{V}_s} \rho \boldsymbol{U} d\mathcal{V}_s = \frac{\partial}{\partial t}\int_{\mathcal{V}_c} \rho \boldsymbol{U} d\mathcal{V}_c + \oint_{S_c} \rho(\boldsymbol{n}\cdot\boldsymbol{U})\ \boldsymbol{U} dS_c \tag{5.7}$$

For a steady flow

$$\boldsymbol{F} = \oint_{S_c} \rho(\boldsymbol{n}\cdot\boldsymbol{U})\ \boldsymbol{U} dS_c \tag{5.8}$$

The need for the transformation of Eq. (5.2) into Eq. (5.7) is apparent. It was stated in the introductory sections of this chapter and Chap. IV that, insofar as fluid motion is concerned, it is not practical to identify systems in the laboratory or in practical problems. Pipes, boilers, compressors, rockets, etc. are control volumes, and Eq. (5.7) or Eq. (5.8), as the case may be, will determine the external forces on the control volume.

The angle between $\boldsymbol{n}$ and $\boldsymbol{U}$ is α. In component form, Eq. (5.8) can be written:

$$\begin{aligned} F_x &= \frac{dM_x}{dt} = \oint_S (\rho U \cos\alpha) u\ dS \\ F_y &= \frac{dM_y}{dt} = \oint_S (\rho U \cos\alpha) v\ dS \\ F_z &= \frac{dM_z}{dt} = \oint_S (\rho U \cos\alpha) w\ dS \end{aligned} \tag{5.9}$$

The quantity $\rho U \cos\alpha\ dS$ represents the elemental mass flux crossing the boundary of the control volume, and u, v, and w represent the velocity components in the x-, y-, and z-directions, respectively.

Since momentum is a vector quantity, a change in momentum will occur when either its magnitude or its direction changes or when both change. In some engineering applications, such as the flow in large converging or diverging pipes or channels, large pipe bends, etc., the control volume can be chosen as the boundary of a section of pipe or channel. According to Fig. 5.2, for instance, the bounds of the control volume are the surface of the conduit across which there is no exchange of mass or momentum, and the two conduit cross sections at 1 and 2 across which mass and momentum are transferred. For a short conduit of large cross section, if the viscous effects near the walls are small compared with the over-all flow, then the fluid properties at each cross section may be considered uniform so that ρ and U are not functions of the surface area A. Furthermore, since $\alpha = 0$, the integration of Eq.

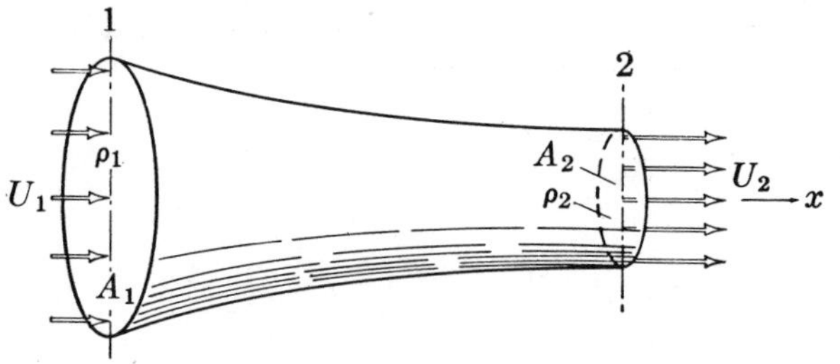

Figure 5.2
Simple converging control volume with uniform properties.

(5.9) is simplified, because the integrand is not a function of S or A_1 and A_2 in this case.

$$F_x = (\rho_2 U_2 A_2) U_2 - (\rho_1 U_1 A_1) U_1$$

and from mass continuity, since $\rho_1 U_1 A_1 = \rho_2 U_2 A_2 = Q$, then

$$F_x = Q(U_2 - U_1) \tag{5.10}$$

In flow of Fig. 3.10, this simplified relationship cannot hold, since the velocities at inlet and discharge are not uniform at each cross section. The total momentum must be obtained from integration.

Illustrative Example 5.1

In Illustrative Example 3.2, evaluate the change in momentum between outlet and inlet and find the driving force on the fluid volume passing through the control volume.

If the density is considered constant throughout, then Eq. (5.9) applied to the control volume on Fig. 3.10 will give the momentum transferred across its surfaces. Since the surface of the pipe does not exchange any mass or momentum, its contribution in the integration will be zero. Therefore, the net rate of momentum transported along the axis is

$$F_x = \rho \left(\int_{A_1} U_1^2 \, dA_1 - \int_{A_0} U_0^2 \, dA_0 \right)$$

The velocities U_1 and U_0 are parabolic functions of the radius.

$$F_x = \int_0^{r_1} \int_0^{2\pi} \rho U_{1\max}^2 \left(1 - \frac{2r^2}{r_1^2} + \frac{r^4}{r_1^4}\right) r \, dr \, d\theta - \int_0^{r_0} \int_0^{2\pi} \rho U_{0\max}^2 \left(1 - \frac{2r^2}{r_0^2} + \frac{r^4}{r_0^4}\right) r \, dr \, d\theta$$

$$= 2\pi\rho U_{1\max}^2 \left[\frac{r^2}{2} - \frac{2r^4}{4r_1^2} + \frac{r^6}{6r_1^4}\right]_0^{r_1} - 2\pi\rho U_{0\max}^2 \left[\frac{r^2}{2} - \frac{2r^4}{4r_0^2} + \frac{r^6}{6r_0^4}\right]_0^{r_0}$$

$$= \frac{\pi\rho}{3} (U_{1\max}^2 r_1^2 - U_{0\max}^2 r_0^2)$$

From the mass-continuity relation of an incompressible steady motion, it can be shown, by integrating the mass flow alone, that the ratio of the velocities is

$$\frac{U_{0_{\max}}}{U_{1_{\max}}} = \frac{r_1^2}{r_0^2}$$

Then

$$F_x = \frac{\pi r_1^2 \rho}{3} U_{1_{\max}}^2 \left[1 - \left(\frac{U_{0_{\max}}}{U_{1_{\max}}}\right)^2 \left(\frac{r_0}{r_1}\right)^2\right]$$

$$F_x = \frac{\pi \rho r_1^2}{3} U_{1_{\max}}^2 \left[1 - \left(\frac{r_1}{r_0}\right)^2\right]$$

If Q is the mass rate of flow $\rho A_1 U_{1_{av}} = \rho A_0 U_{0_{av}}$ and for the parabolic pipe flow since $U_{av} = \frac{1}{2} U_{\max}$, then

$$F_x = \frac{2QU_{1_{\max}}}{3} \left[1 - \left(\frac{r_1}{r_0}\right)^2\right]$$

5.3 Derivation of Steady-Flow Momentum Equation by Integration Through a Stream Filament in an Arbitrary Control Volume

The steady-flow momentum equations given in Eq. (5.9) can also be derived by integrating Newton's second law along a stream tube through

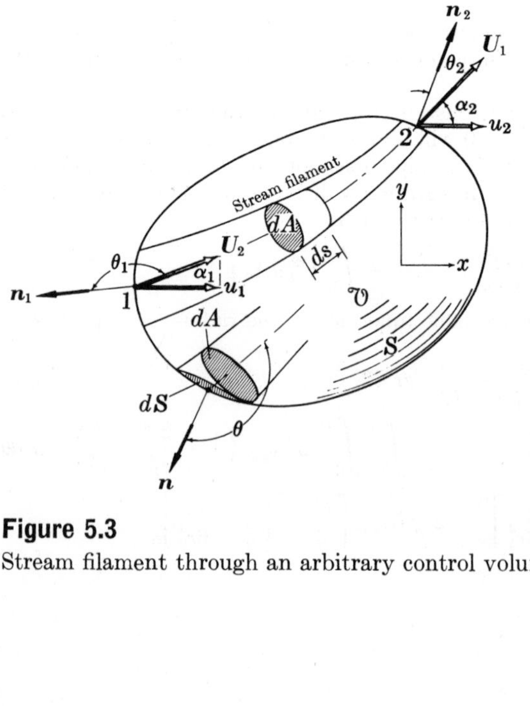

Figure 5.3
Stream filament through an arbitrary control volume.

an arbitrary control volume. In Fig. 5.3 let a stream filament of cross section dA pierce the arbitrary control volume at points 1 and 2. The elementary length of the filament is ds. The velocity of the fluid entering the control volume at 1 is U_1 and that leaving at 2 is U_2. These velocities make an angle θ with the normal $\boldsymbol{n}$ drawn outward on the surface S of the control volume. Furthermore, these velocities make angles α with the horizontal coordinate, giving $u_1 = U_1 \cos \alpha_1$ and $u_2 = U_2 \cos \alpha_2$.

The acceleration of the fluid in the stream filament along the direction of the axis of the filament is given as $a_s = U \dfrac{dU}{ds}$ for steady flow in Eq. (4.11). The x-component of this acceleration is $a_s \cos \alpha = U \dfrac{dU}{ds} \cos \alpha = U \dfrac{d}{ds} (U \cos \alpha) = U \dfrac{du}{ds}$. If a small element of fluid is considered of dimensions dA and ds, the force acting on this accelerating element in the x-direction is

$$dF'_x = \rho \, ds \, dA \, U \frac{du}{ds}$$

$$= (\rho U \, dA) \frac{du}{ds} \, ds$$

Since U is perpendicular to dA, the quantity $\rho U \, dA = dQ$, the total rate of flow through the stream filament. Therefore, the elemental force on the fluid element $dA \, ds$ is

$$dF'_x = dQ \frac{du}{ds} \, ds$$

The total force on the entire stream filament is obtained by summing all these forces along the axis of the stream filament.

$$dF_x = \int_1^2 dF'_x = \int_1^2 dQ \frac{du}{ds} \, ds$$

$$= dQ \, (u_2 - u_1) \tag{5.11}$$

This is the same as Eq. (5.10), since the flow in the stream filament is uniform at every cross section.

The mass rate of flow dQ can be expressed from continuity relations in the form

$$dQ = \rho_1 U_1 \, dA_1 = \rho_2 U_2 \, dA_2$$

On the surface of the control volume, the relationship between the cross section of the filament and the surface of the control volume is $dA = dS \cos \theta$. Therefore, Eq. (5.11) becomes

$$dF_x = (\rho_2 U_2 \cos \theta_2) u_2 \, dS_2 + (\rho_1 U_1 \cos \theta_1) u_1 \, dS_1 \tag{5.12}$$

The plus sign comes from the fact that at the entrance of the stream filament the angle $\theta > \frac{\pi}{2}$.

The entire control volume is made up of an infinite number of such stream filaments. In order to determine the force component F_x on the entire control volume, Eq. (5.12) must be integrated for the entire surface S, and therefore

$$F_x = \int_{\mathcal{V}} \rho a_x \, dA \, ds = \oint_S (\rho U \cos \theta) u \, dS \tag{5.13}$$

This is the same equation as Eq. (5.9). This equation represents the application of Newton's second law of motion to a control volume $\mathcal{V}$ through which a fluid is moving. The net external force F_x on the fluid inside the control volume is found by evaluating the net flux of momentum in the x-direction crossing the boundaries S of the volume $\mathcal{V}$.

5.4 The Stream Tube as a Control Volume

In a great number of engineering applications, the control volume across which momentum transport is considered in a stream tube, as shown in Fig. 5.4. This stream tube may be represented by the flow of fluid in a pipe or channel with curved walls and varying cross section. Since the control volume is a stream tube, mass and momentum transfer across the stream tube occurs at its inlet and exit cross sections, and consequently the integration of Eq. (5.13) is confined to the inlet and exit surfaces. Furthermore, in this stream tube the entering and leaving velocity vectors are perpendicular to the inlet and exit areas, and thus the angle θ in Eq. (5.13) is zero.

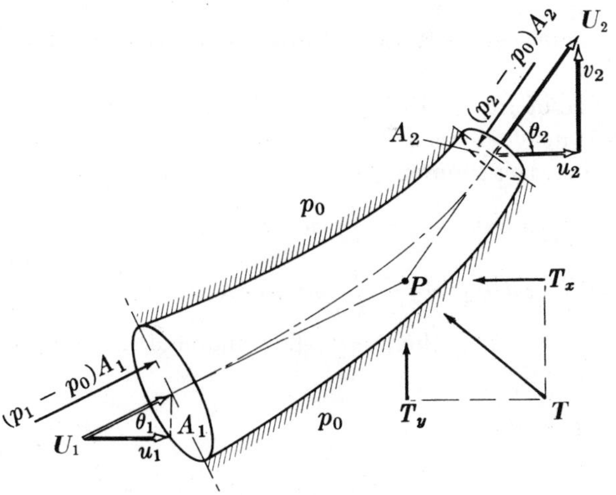

Figure 5.4
The stream tube as a control volume.

The forces represented in Fig. 5.4 are those of a free-body diagram that maintain the control volume in the stationary position in which it is analyzed. Because the stream tube is curved and of unequal cross section, the pressure distribution on the upper part of the stream surface is not the same as on the lower surface. As a result of this, and as a result of the momentum difference at 1 and 2, there will be a net action force $-\boldsymbol{T}$ exerted from the fluid into the walls of the conduit and a reaction force $\boldsymbol{T}$, as shown. Considering the gravity g in a direction normal to the paper, then the total external force on the fluid in the stream tube is composed of the pressure forces at inlet and exit and the summation of surface forces T on the entire curved stream surface. These surface forces, in general, will include tangential frictional forces as well.

Applying Eq. (5.13) to the stream tube, it follows that the external forces F_x and F_y are

$$\begin{aligned} F_x &= \int_{A_1} (p_1 - p_0)\, dA_1 \cos\theta_1 - T_x - \int_{A_2} (p_2 - p_0)\, dA_2 \cos\theta_2 \\ F_y &= \int_{A_1} (p_1 - p_0)\, dA_1 \sin\theta_1 + T_y - \int_{A_2} (p_2 - p_0)\, dA_2 \sin\theta_2 \end{aligned} \tag{5.14}$$

Here the atmospheric pressure p_0 is taken as a reference level because it is assumed that the ambient pressure all around the stream tube is atmospheric.[4]

The right-hand side of Eq. (5.13) applies only to the areas A_1 and A_2, since there is no transfer of mass or momentum across the stream surface itself. Therefore, this momentum surface integral becomes

$$F_x = \int_{A_2} \rho_2 U_2 u_2 \, dA_2 - \int_{A_1} \rho_1 U_1 u_1 \, dA_1$$
$$F_y = \int_{A_2} \rho_2 U_2 v_2 \, dA_2 - \int_{A_1} \rho_1 U_1 v_1 \, dA_1 \tag{5.15}$$

Equating Eqs. (5.14) and (5.15), the steady-flow momentum equation for the stream tube is obtained:

$$\int_{A_2} \rho_2 U_2 u_2 \, dA_2 - \int_{A_1} \rho_1 U_1 u_1 \, dA_1 = \int_{A_1} (p_1 - p_0) \, dA_1 \cos \theta_1 - T_x - \int_{A_2} (p_2 - p_0) \, dA_2 \cos \theta_2$$
$$\int_{A_2} \rho_2 U_2 v_2 dA_2 - \int_{A_1} \rho_1 U_1 v_1 \, dA_1 = \int_{A_1} (p_1 - p_0) \, dA_1 \sin \theta_1 + T_y - \int_{A_2} (p_2 - p_0) \, dA_2 \sin \theta_2 \tag{5.16}$$

[4] To illustrate the need of atmospheric pressure reference consider the channel section with no flow in the figure.

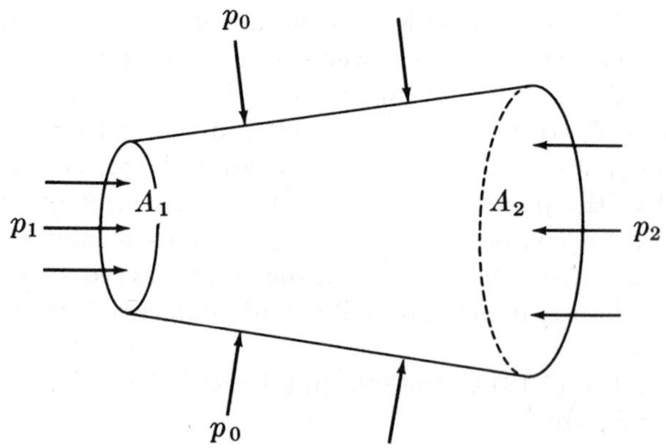

$$p_1A_1 - p_2A_2 + p_0(A_2 - A_1) = A_1(p_1 - p_0) - A_2(p_2 - p_0) = 0$$

If p_1 is the pressure at the inlet, p_2 that at the outlet, and p_0 that on the outside surface, then

$$p_1A_1 - p_2A_2 + p_0(A_2 - A_1) = 0$$

or

$$A_1(p_1 - p_0) - A_2(p_2 - p_0) = 0$$

Knowing the distribution of velocities, densities, and pressures across the inlet and discharge, the reaction forces T_x and T_y can be evaluated.

In the case of uniform flow across each section A_1 and A_2, the integrals in Eq. (5.16) are easily evaluated, since ρ, U, and p are not functions of A. Furthermore, from the equation of mass continuity Eq. (3.10), $Q = \rho_2 U_2 A_2 = \rho_1 U_1 A_1$ can be factored:

$$\begin{aligned} Q(u_2 - u_1) &= (p_1 - p_0)A_1 \cos\theta_1 - T_x - (p_2 - p_0)A_2 \cos\theta_2 \\ Q(v_2 - v_1) &= (p_1 - p_0)A_1 \sin\theta_1 + T_y - (p_2 - p_0)A_2 \sin\theta_2 \end{aligned} \tag{5.17}$$

This equation illustrates the fact that, through the momentum equations, the force system on the stream tube is found without any knowledge of the pressure and velocity distributions inside the stream tube.

The number of unknowns in Eq. (5.17) can be reduced if the pressures and the velocities at the inlet and discharge are related through Bernoulli's equation for the ideal case [Eq. (4.29)] or the modified Bernoulli equation including losses, as in Eq. (4.42).

$$p_2 = p_1 - \frac{\rho}{2}(U_2^2 - U_1^2) - \rho H$$

and

$$U_2 = \frac{U_1 A_1}{A_2}$$

for an incompressible flow. Substitution of p_2 and U_2 in Eq. (5.17) reduces them in terms of the conditions at the inlet. It must be remembered, in this case shown in Fig. 5.4, that both the velocity components u_1 and u_2 are positive. If they were negative, the sign of Eq. (5.17) would have been negative in the momentum term.

$$\begin{aligned} Q(U_2 \cos\theta_2 - U_1 \cos\theta_1) &= (p_1 - p_0)A_1 \cos\theta_1 - T_x \\ &\quad - \left\{p_1 - \frac{\rho U_1^2}{2}\left[\left(\frac{A_1}{A_2}\right)^2 - 1\right] - \rho H - p_0\right\} A_2 \cos\theta \end{aligned}$$

$$\frac{QU_1}{2}\left[\left(\frac{A_1}{A_2} + \frac{A_2}{A_1}\right)\cos\theta_2 - 2\cos\theta_1\right] = (p_1 - p_0)(A_1\cos\theta_1 - A_2\cos\theta_2) - T_x + \rho H A_2 \cos\theta_2 \tag{5.18}$$

In the same fashion the y-component equation gives

$$\frac{QU_1}{2}\left[\left(\frac{A_1}{A_2} + \frac{A_2}{A_1}\right)\sin\theta_2 - 2\sin\theta_1\right] = (p_1 - p_0)(A_1\sin\theta_1 - A_2\sin\theta_2) + T_y + \rho H A_2 \sin\theta_2 \tag{5.19}$$

Knowing the geometry of the stream tube, the conditions at the entrance, and the losses, the reaction force T on the walls of the stream tube can be evaluated from the two equations Eqs. (5.18) and (5.19). There are three forces constituting the external forces on the stream tube—the two pressure forces at the inlet and the exit and the reaction force T. In order for the free body to be in equilibrium, these three forces must be concurrent. Therefore, the point P, the intersection of U_1 and U_2 at the axis, must also be the point of application of T.

5.5 Applications of the Momentum Equation

(a) Conservation of Momentum

According to Eq. (5.8), if the fluid in a control volume does not experience any external force $\boldsymbol{F}$, then the net flux of momentum crossing the surface area S of the control volume is zero; that is, the rate of momentum entering the volume must be identically equal to that leaving the volume. In this case the momentum is said to be preserved. The free flow of a straight jet into a stationary ambient medium has the property that, in the absence of external force, the momentum of the jet at all positions downstream is preserved. This implies that it takes an external force to deflect the jet and therefore change its momentum.

A simple illustration of this situation can be considered. When two masses of fluid m_1 and m_2 move freely along the same line at different velocities U_1 and U_2. If $U_1 > U_2$, there will come a time when mass m_1 will catch up with mass m_2, and the two will become a single mass $m_1 + m_2 = m$. Just before impact, the total momentum in both masses was $m_1U_1 + m_2U_2$. At collision, there will be a force F between the two masses. This force will vary with time as the impact proceeds. During the time Δt when there is a force between the two masses, the momentum of both masses is being changed. The momentum of mass m_1 is being reduced to a value $m_1U_1 - F\,\Delta t$, and that of mass m_2 is being increased to $m_2U_2 + F\,\Delta t$, meaning that the sum of the momenta is the same. Consequently, the new mass m, moving at a new velocity U, will have the same momentum as the sum of the momenta of the previous individual masses:

$$mU = m_1U_1 + m_2U_2 \tag{5.20}$$

Naturally, since the mass and the momentum are conserved, in general, the kinetic energy of the combined system of mass m will show a loss over the sum of the original kinetic energies. This loss of energy occurs at the impact of the two masses m_1 and m_2.

Illustrative Example 5.2

A mass of fluid $m_1 = 1$ lb$_m$ moves along a straight line at the velocity of 10 ft/sec. Another mass of fluid $m_2 = 2$ lb$_m$ follows along the same line of motion at the velocity of 25 ft/sec. After impact, if the two masses combine into one, find the velocity of the combined mass and the kinetic energy loss in the process.

According to Eq. (5.20), the conservation of momentum will read:

$$10 \times 1 + 25 \times 2 = 3U$$
$$U = 20 \text{ ft/sec}$$

$$\tfrac{1}{2} m U^2 + \tfrac{1}{2} m U^2 =$$

The initial kinetic energies of the separate masses were

$$\left(\frac{1}{2} \times \frac{1}{32.17} \times 100 + \frac{1}{2} \times \frac{2}{32.17} \times 625 \right) \text{ft} \times \text{lb}_f$$

The kinetic energy of the combined system is

$$\left(\frac{1}{2} \times \frac{3}{32.17} \times 400 \right) \text{ft} \times \text{lb}_f$$

The net loss of kinetic energy in the combination process is

$$\frac{75}{32.17} = 2.33 \text{ ft} \times \text{lb}_f$$

(b) *Momentum Change Owing to Change in Direction*

Since momentum is a vector quantity, changes of momentum occur across a control volume not only when the magnitude of the directed momentum occurs but also when its direction changes without changing the magnitude. This is illustrated in Fig. 5.5 when a uniform stream

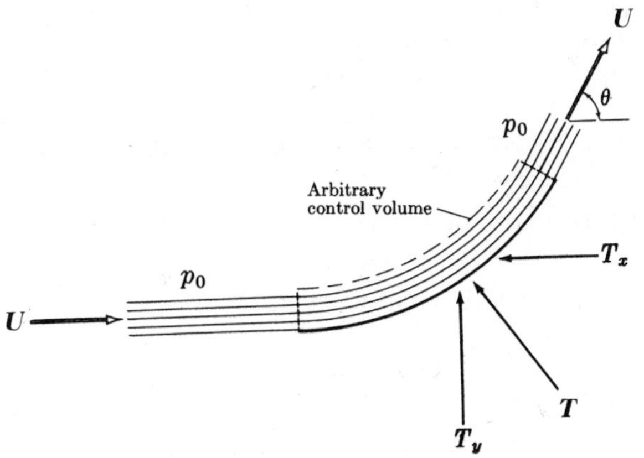

Figure 5.5
Forces owing to deflection of a stream.

of fluid, moving at the velocity U, is deflected by an angle θ, while its velocity remains the same. Because of the deflection, it is apparent that there is a change in the x-momentum from QU to $QU \cos \theta$. This net change must, according to our past analysis, balance the external forces in that direction—in this case $-T_x$. The pressure force at the inlet and exit of the arbitrary control volume is taken to be the same at both ends and equal to the ambient pressure p_0, and therefore their contribution will be zero. The same thinking applies to the y-momentum, and therefore the equations will read:

$$\begin{aligned} QU(\cos \theta - 1) &= -T_x \\ QU \sin \theta &= T_y \end{aligned} \tag{5.21}$$

These equations can also be obtained by reducing the more general forms of Eqs. (5.18) and (5.19). In those equations $A_1 = A_2$, $\theta_1 = 0$, $p_1 = p_0$, and the head loss H is neglected. The quantity $Q = \rho UA$ is the mass rate of flow. The vectorial sum of the two components T_x and T_y gives the magnitude of the total reaction force from the curved vane to the fluid:

$$T = QU\sqrt{2(1 - \cos \theta)}$$

The location of the point of application of this force was already discussed at the end of Sec. 5.4.

(c) *The Moving Vane*

If the vane just considered moves to the right with a velocity V, then, considering the same arbitrary control volume, the mass rate of fluid going through the control volume is different, since the velocity of the fluid relative to the vane is now $(U - V)$ for that single vane. Consequently, the rate of mass flow entering the control volume around the vane is $Q = \rho A(U - V)$. With this new relative velocity of the fluid with respect to the vane, the x-momentum can be computed again on the basis of this relative velocity

$$\begin{aligned} \rho A(U - V)[(U - V) \cos \theta - (U - V)] &= -T_x \\ \rho A(U - V)^2 \sin \theta &= T_y \\ \rho A(U - V)^2(1 - \cos \theta) &= T_x \end{aligned}$$

or

$$\begin{aligned} Q(U - V) \sin \theta &= T_y \\ Q(U - V)(1 - \cos \theta) &= T_x \end{aligned} \tag{5.22}$$

Since the vane is moving at the velocity V in the direction of T_x, then the work done per unit time by the fluid on the single vane is

$$\text{Power} = T_x V = QV(U - V)(1 - \cos \theta) \tag{5.23}$$

In the case of the single vane, the amount of flow whose momentum is being converted is $Q = \rho A(U - V)$, while the total flow emanating from a jet impinging on the vane is larger, $Q = \rho AU$. Now, instead of a single vane, if a number of vanes on the periphery of a rotating wheel, as on a turbine disk, are acted on by the same jet, then in time all of the flow ρAU emanating from the jet will have its momentum changed, as given in Eq. (5.22). The total momentum changed and the power must then be computed on the basis of the total jet flow ρAU passing in time through all vanes.

Illustrative Example 5.3

The curve on a single vane in Fig. 5.6 is 120°, and it has a speed in the x-direction of 40 ft/sec. A jet of water impinges on the vane at the leading edge

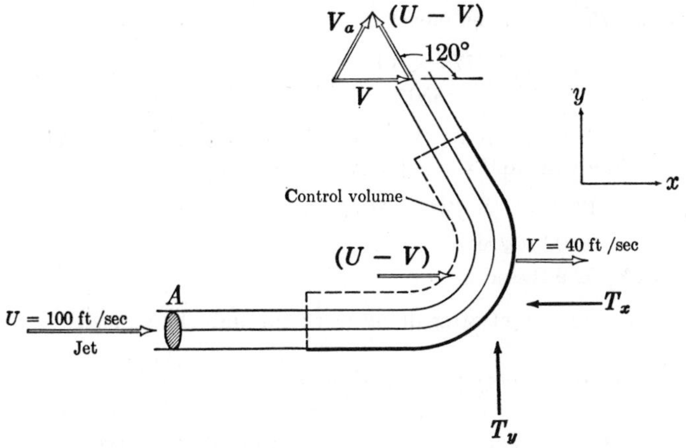

Figure 5.6
Velocity and forces on the moving vane.

through a cross section of 1.44 sq in. The jet velocity is 100 ft/sec. Find the two components of the force T_x and T_y, the reactions of the vane on the water, and the power on the vane.

(*a*) The fluid whose momentum is being changed through the vane flows at the rate of $Q = \rho A(U - V)$

$$Q = \frac{62.4}{32.17} \times \frac{1.44}{144} \times 60 = 1.165 \text{ slugs/sec}$$

According to Eq. (5.22), the forces on the vanes will be

$$T_x = 1.165 \times 60(1 + 0.5)$$
$$= 105 \text{ lb}_f$$
$$T_y = 1.165 \times 60 \times 0.866$$
$$= 60.6 \text{ lb}_f$$

The power is found by multiplying T_x by the velocity of the vane V:

$$\text{Power} = \frac{105 \times 40}{550} = 7.64 \text{ hp}$$

(*b*) If, instead of a single vane, a series of vanes were considered, the total flow whose momentum is being changed by the vanes would be that of the jet $Q = \rho AU$:

$$Q = \frac{62.4}{32.17} \times \frac{1.44}{144} \times 100$$

$$= 1.94 \text{ slugs/sec}$$

The force T_x is now 175 lb_f and the power is

$$\text{Power} = \frac{175 \times 40}{550} = 12.7 \text{ hp}$$

The absolute velocity V_a leaving the vane is the resultant of the velocity $(U - V)$ relative to the vane and the velocity of the vane V

$$V_a^2 = V^2 + (U - V)^2 + 2V(U - V) \cos 120°$$
$$= 2{,}800 \text{ ft}^2/\text{sec}^2$$
$$V_a = 52.9 \text{ ft/sec}$$

The kinetic energy left in the jet after doing work through the vanes is

$$\text{Remaining kinetic energy per unit time} = 1.94 \times \frac{(52.9)^2}{2}$$

$$= 2{,}715 \text{ ft} \times \text{lb}_f/\text{sec}$$

$$\text{Kinetic energy in the jet per unit time} = 1.94 \times \frac{(100)^2}{2}$$

$$= 9{,}715 \text{ ft} \times \text{lb}_f/\text{sec}$$

The remaining energy per unit time, 7,000 ft $\times$ lb_f/sec, is what the water has transmitted to the vanes, which is identically equal to $T_xV = 175 \times 40 = 7{,}000$ ft $\times$ lb_f/sec.

(*d*) *The Reaction from a Jet*

Another common application of the momentum-exchange principle is the jet in Fig. 5.7 emanating from a nozzle and moving from an area A_1 to a discharge area A_0. In this process there is a pressure reduc-

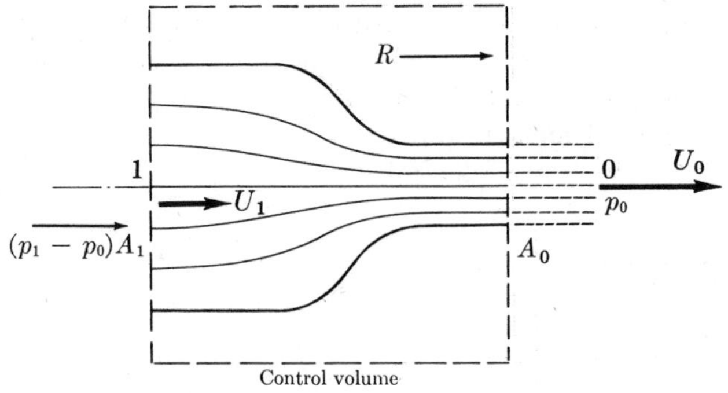

Figure 5.7
The jet from a nozzle.

tion from 1 to 0, and the momentum increases. Since the fluid is accelerating from 1 to 0, there is a force imparted by the fluid on the nozzle from right to left, and consequently to keep the control volume stationary an equal and opposite reaction force T must be applied as shown.

The sum of external forces on the control volume considered will be the reaction force T and the pressure forces at the inlet and discharge of the nozzle. According to Eq. (5.10), these external forces must be balanced by the change in momentum of the fluid. Considering an incompressible liquid,

$$\begin{aligned}(p_1 - p_0)A_1 + T &= Q(U_0 - U_1)\\ &= \rho A_0 U_0^2 - \rho A_1 U_1^2\end{aligned}$$

Furthermore, for a nonviscous fluid, the relationship between the pressures and the velocities can be established through the Bernoulli equation,

$$\frac{2(p_1 - p_0)}{\rho} = U_0^2 - U_1^2$$

Substitution of U_1^2 into the momentum equation yields

$$T = A_1(p_1 - p_0) + \rho U_0^2(A_0 - A_1) \qquad (5.24)$$

or, using the continuity equation,

$$T = \rho U_0^2\left[A_0 - \frac{A_0^2}{A_1}\right] - (p_1 - p_0)A_1 \qquad (5.25)$$

Next let us study a jet of fluid emanating from a small aperture at a depth z on the side of a tank. Considering the arbitrary control volume of Fig. 5.8, momentum leaves its surface with the magnitude of $\rho A U_0^2$, the pressures being the same all around the control surface. The reaction T, necessary to hold the control volume from moving, must be equal to this exit of momentum:

$$T = \rho A U_0^2$$

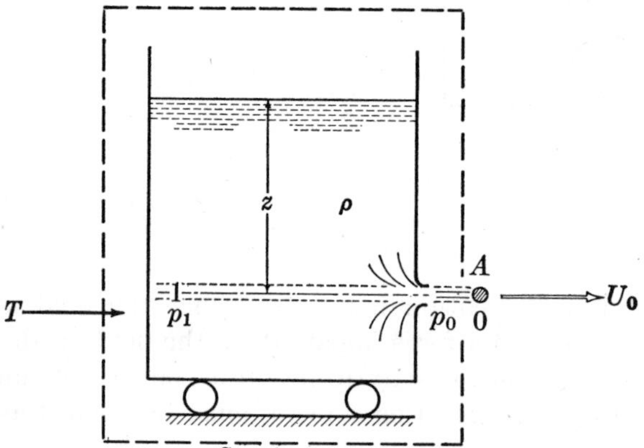

Figure 5.8
The jet emanating from an open tank.

For a nonviscous fluid the velocity of exit is related to the height and to the pressure at the depth z as follows:

$$\tfrac{1}{2}U_0^2 = gz = \frac{p_1 - p_0}{\rho}$$

Thus the reaction T is found in terms of the pressure force:

$$T = 2A(p_1 - p_0) \tag{5.26}$$

Looking at the long dotted tube of cross section A represented in Fig. 5.8, the pressure force on this tube is $(p_1 - p_0)A$. This indicates that the reaction force T is twice as large as the force on that long tube. In conclusion it must, therefore, be stated that the force on the long tube is only part of the force imparted on the tank owing to the reaction of the jet. The other half of the force comes from the fact that around the aperture the fluid is accelerating, and consequently the pressure on the wall near the aperture is less than that predicted by the elevation of the fluid. The pressure on the wall opposite to the aperture, however, will be given by gz. Therefore, this pressure-force difference on the two opposite walls must be computed for a larger area than that of the jet, and consequently Eq. (5.26) will be found to be correct.

In order to account for the reaction force T in terms of the pressure-force difference in the extended liquid tube, an inset mouth of cross section area A_1, called a *Borda mouth,* is used, in Fig. 5.9, instead of

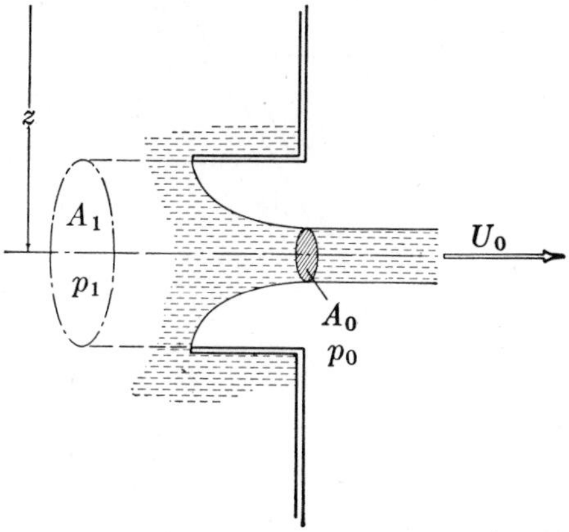

Figure 5.9
The Borda mouth.

the one in Fig. 5.8. As in the case of orifices, the cross section of the liquid jet will reduce to A_0, giving a contraction coefficient of A_0/A_1. In order for $(p_1 - p_0)A_1$ to balance exactly $T = \rho A_0 U_0^2$, then, according to Eq. (5.26), the contraction coefficient must be equal to 0.5, or, in other words, $A_1 = 2A_0$.

(e) A Jet Impinging on a Flat Plate

Consider first the case of a jet in Fig. 5.10(a) impinging at 90° on a flat plate. For a stationary plate the direction of the jet is deflected, and consequently, applying the momentum relations to the control surface, the fluid will experience a change of momentum in the x-direction and a reaction force $\boldsymbol{T}$ from the plate to the fluid. If this experiment is conducted in a free atmosphere, the static pressure p_0 at the entrance of the control surface will be the same as that at the two discharge ends. If the gravitational force is normal to the plane of the paper, then, through Bernoulli's equation, it is established that the velocities $\boldsymbol{U}$ at inlet and discharge of the control surface are the same.

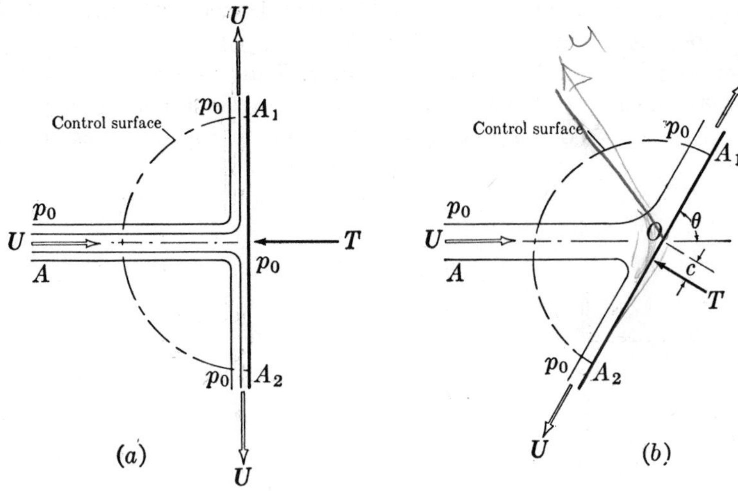

Figure 5.10
Jet impinging on a flat plate.

Because of the symmetry of the flow, the reaction $\boldsymbol{T}$ will be normal to the plate, and any components of forces along the plate will be canceled. Since the velocity at the two exits is the same, this implies that the fluid areas A_1 and A_2 are the same.

Since the pressure force is atmospheric all around, the reaction $\boldsymbol{T}$ must be equal to the exchange of momentum in the incident jet direction.

$$\begin{aligned} -T &= [0 - (\rho A U)U] \\ T &= \rho A U^2 \end{aligned} \tag{5.27}$$

As shown in Fig. 5.10(*b*), consider the plate inclined to an angle θ from the incident direction of jet flow. Assuming again that the experiment is performed in a free atmosphere with a pressure p_0 all around, and that there are no losses of kinetic energy in the deflection, then again from Bernoulli's equation, it follows that the deflected velocities on both sides of the plate are the same as the incident velocity $\boldsymbol{U}$.

The direction of the reaction force $\boldsymbol{T}$ in this case is also normal to the plate. This follows from the fact that, if the fluid is considered ideal, there are no tangential forces along the plate between the fluid and the plate, and therefore there is no momentum change in that direction. Even in the case of friction, if the velocities on both sides of the plate can still be considered equal, the shear forces on the plate are equal and opposite, and, therefore, again, no net momentum is exchanged in that direction.

Writing the momentum equation in the direction normal to the plate,

$$T = \rho A U^2 \sin \theta \tag{5.28}$$

Since there is no net force along the plate, then the momentum equation reads:

$$(\rho A_1 U^2 - \rho A_2 U^2) - \rho A U^2 \cos \theta = 0$$

and therefore, for the incompressible case,

$$A_1 - A_2 = A \cos \theta$$
$$Q_1 - Q_2 = Q \cos \theta$$

From continuity of mass relation the areas and the rates of mass flow have the following relationship:

$$Q_1 + Q_2 = Q$$
$$A_1 + A_2 = A$$

The solution of these two equations in A or Q gives the following result:

$$\begin{aligned} A_1 &= \frac{A}{2}(1 + \cos \theta); \qquad Q_1 = \frac{Q}{2}(1 + \cos \theta) \\ A_2 &= \frac{A}{2}(1 - \cos \theta); \qquad Q_2 = \frac{Q}{2}(1 - \cos \theta) \end{aligned} \tag{5.29}$$

The location of the reaction $\boldsymbol{T}$ is obtained when the moment of the momentum equation is taken around any point in the control volume, say at O. Then, if the jet is two-dimensional so that all areas A are a width b times a depth h in the direction normal to the paper, and when the momentum at every cross section is located at its centroid, the resultant moment of the momentum equation reads:

$$\rho b_1 h U^2 \frac{b_1}{2} - \rho b_2 h U^2 \frac{b_2}{2} = Tc$$

The magnitude of $\boldsymbol{T}$ can be replaced for the value in Eq. (5.28):

$$T = \rho b h U^2 \sin \theta$$

Then, dividing through by $\rho h U^2$,

$$\frac{b_1^2}{2} - \frac{b_2^2}{2} = bc \sin \theta$$

whence the distance c is determined:

$$c = \frac{1}{\sin \theta} \frac{b_1^2 - b_2^2}{2b} \tag{5.30}$$

From the two relationships for the areas $(A_1 + A_2)$ and $(A_1 - A_2)$, the following difference of the squares can be evaluated:

$$\frac{A_1^2 - A_2^2}{A_2} = \frac{b_1^2 - b_2^2}{b^2} = \cos\theta$$

and finally the location of the reaction force $\boldsymbol{T}$ is at

$$c = \frac{b}{2}\cot\theta \tag{5.31}$$

(f) The Propeller

Another application in aerodynamics where momentum principles are used to solve the over-all thrust on a stream of air is the flow across a rotating propeller. The purpose of the propeller is to produce a thrust by changing the momentum of the fluid around it. Essentially, it achieves the same purpose as does the jet in a rocket, the difference being that the propeller moves larger masses of air through smaller changes of velocity, whereas the jet may achieve the same thrust by forcing relatively smaller fluid masses to undergo larger changes of velocity.

Considering ideal flow through the propeller, the flow pattern will be as shown in Fig. 5.11. If the propeller is moving in an undisturbed stream at the velocity U_0, then, with reference to the propeller, the entire stream to the left of the propeller moves toward it at the velocity U_0, as shown in the figure. Because of the suction pressure created on the upstream side of the propeller, the fluid will accelerate toward it, increasing its velocity to U_p. The velocity U_p does not change across the propeller; only the pressure increases across it for the amount Δp. The velocity continues to increase and levels off again to a value of U_1 downstream of the propeller where the pressure assumes its atmospheric condition. Because of the acceleration of the fluid through the propeller, the stream tube, carrying the same amount of sucked-in flow, narrows as it proceeds downstream. The tubular surface of this stream tube is called the *slipstream surface,* since ideally there is a jump in the velocity across the boundary.

If the stream tube is considered as a control volume, the thrust T imparted by the propeller on the fluid must be equal to the change of momentum of the fluid from 0 to 1. Therefore,

$$\begin{aligned} T &= \rho A U_p(U_1 - U_0) \\ &= Q(U_1 - U_0) \end{aligned} \tag{5.32}$$

Here A is the cross-sectional area of the propeller. This force T must

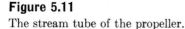

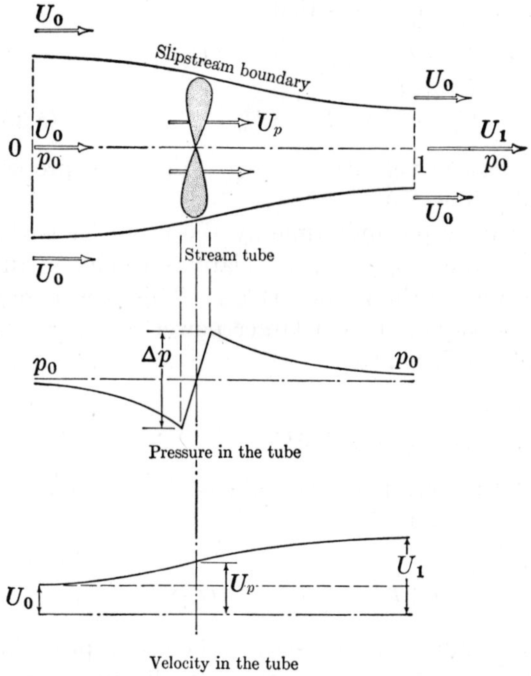

Figure 5.11
The stream tube of the propeller.

also be equal to the pressure difference between the two sides of the propeller times its area.

$$\Delta p = \rho U_p(U_1 - U_0) \tag{5.33}$$

The Bernoulli equation for this case of an ideal motion can be applicable to the conditions upstream and separately to the conditions downstream of the propeller, but not through it, since work has been added.

$$p_0 + \tfrac{1}{2}\rho U_0^2 = (p_0 - \tfrac{1}{2}\,\Delta p) + \tfrac{1}{2}\rho U_p^2$$

and downstream

$$(p_0 + \tfrac{1}{2}\,\Delta p) + \tfrac{1}{2}\rho U_p^2 = p_0 + \tfrac{1}{2}\rho U_1^2$$

Combining these two Bernoulli equations, the pressure rise across the propeller may be obtained independently from Eq. (5.33).

$$\Delta p = \tfrac{1}{2}\rho(U_1^2 - U_0^2) \tag{5.34}$$

Equating Eqs. (5.33) and (5.34), it follows that

$$\begin{aligned} \tfrac{1}{2}\rho(U_1 + U_0)(U_1 - U_0) &= \rho U_p(U_1 - U_0) \\ U_1 + U_0 &= 2U_p \\ U_p - U_0 &= U_1 - U_p \end{aligned} \tag{5.35}$$

This indicates that the increase of velocity $(U_p - U_0)$ up to the propeller is only half of the total $(U_1 - U_0)$.

The ideal useful work done per unit time by the propeller is the thrust T times the speed of the propeller (the relative velocity of the undisturbed fluid with respect to the propeller) U_0. This power may be considered as the *power output,* since a larger power was actually given to the stream, as will be shown soon.

$$\begin{aligned} \text{Useful power of propeller} &= TU_0 \\ &= Q(U_1 - U_0)U_0 \end{aligned}$$

The total energy per unit time given to the fluid is the difference in kinetic energies from state 1 to state 0.

$$\begin{aligned} \text{Available power} &= \tfrac{1}{2}Q(U_1^2 - U_0^2) \\ &= Q(U_1 - U_0)U_0 + \tfrac{1}{2}Q(U_1 - U_0)^2 \end{aligned}$$

The available power is then made up of two parts—the useful propeller power $Q(U_1 - U_0)U_0$ and the kinetic energy left in the slipstream tube $\tfrac{1}{2}Q(U_1 - U_0)^2$.

The theoretical propeller efficiency is then the ratio of the useful to the available power:

$$\begin{aligned} \eta &= \frac{(U_1 - U_0)U_0}{\tfrac{1}{2}(U_1^2 - U_0^2)} \\ &= \frac{2U_0}{U_1 + U_0} \\ &= \frac{U_0}{U_p} \end{aligned} \tag{5.36}$$

Actually, a real flow approaches this efficiency but never quite equals it. This is because dissipative viscous forces in the propeller neighborhood and between the slipstream and the outside free stream have not been taken into account. Furthermore, as can be seen from Fig. 4.18, the compressibility effects begin to take place at speeds in excess of 400 ft/sec for air. An increase of drag on the propeller system begins to demonstrate itself at compressible speeds, and consequently the efficiency of the propeller drops rapidly.

Illustrative Example 5.4

A propeller produces a thrust of 2,000 lb_f and flies at a speed of 180 mph. Consider the diameter of the propeller as 10 ft and the atmospheric conditions as those at sea level and 50°F dry air. (*a*) Determine the velocity of the ideal flow through the propeller and the velocity in the final wake. (*b*) Determine the pressure rise across the propeller.

(*a*) From Eq. (5.32) the thrust is

$$T = \rho A U_p (U_1 - U_0)$$

Also from Eq. (5.35) $2U_p = U_1 + U_0$, and therefore:

$$2T = \rho A (U_1^2 - U_0^2)$$

$$U_1^2 = \frac{2T}{\rho A} + U_0^2$$

The density is 0.0785/32.2 = 0.00244 slug/ft³, and the propeller velocity is 264 ft/sec. Substitution of these values in the previous relation yields:

$$U_1^2 = \frac{4{,}000 \times 4}{0.00244 \times \pi \times 100} + (264)^2$$

$$U_1 = 301 \text{ ft/sec}$$

This is the velocity in the final wake of the propeller. The velocity through the propeller is halfway between this value and that of the propeller

$$U_p = 282.5 \text{ ft/sec}$$

(*b*) The pressure rise across the propeller is the thrust divided by the area of the propeller

$$\Delta p = \frac{2{,}000 \times 4}{\pi \times 100}$$

$$= 25.5 \text{ lb}_f/\text{ft}^2$$

(*g*) *Cascade of Vanes*

The wing of an airplane is a kind of a vane that deflects the stream of fluid passing over it, producing a change in the direction of the momentum of the fluid and consequently a lift and drag resulting from this change. A similar phenomenon occurs around the set of blades in the periphery of a turbine disk, giving rise to a torque on the shaft and a thrust along the shaft.

Consider a row of a large number of these blades, all equally spaced and identical, as shown in Fig. 5.12. The spacing between vanes is b, and let their height in the direction normal to the paper be unity. In order to study the reaction forces F_x and F_y on the blades or vanes, it becomes essential that the stationary control volume $ABCD$ be considered and that the summation of external forces be equated to the net

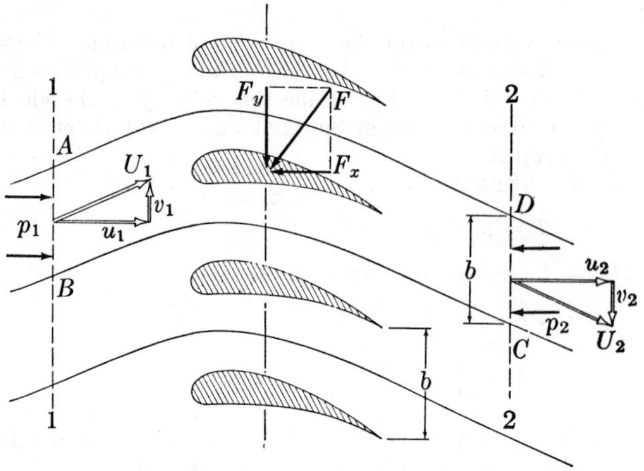

Figure 5.12
A cascade of vanes deflecting a fluid stream.

change of momentum across the volume. Since it was assumed that the number of vanes is infinite in extent, for uniform entering flow, the conditions of the fluid along the surface AD will be identical with those of BC. Since these surfaces are streamlines, there will be no exchange of mass or momentum, and the pressure forces summed along AD will be identically equal and opposite to those summed along BC.

Along AB and CD momentum enters and leaves, and the pressure at 1 is not necessarily the same as that at 2. From a continuity equation of a steady and incompressible flow,

$$\rho u_1 b = \rho u_2 b,$$

meaning that the x-components of the velocities are equal. It must follow also that the net x-momentum exchanged is zero. The summation of forces in the x-direction then becomes

$$F_x = b(p_1 - p_2) \tag{5.37}$$

Because the properties along AD and BC are the same, there is no net pressure force in the y-direction. The only external force is $-F_y$, which must be balanced by the change of momentum in that direction.

$$\begin{aligned} -F_y &= \rho b u_1(-v_2 - v_1) \\ F_y &= \rho b u_1(v_1 + v_2) \end{aligned} \tag{5.38}$$

In this equation the sign of the velocities was taken into account when evaluating the momentum.

Thus far the motion has been considered to be ideal, since viscous forces were not taken into account; therefore the Bernoulli equation is applicable to the flow between 1 and 2:

$$\frac{p_1}{\rho} + \frac{U_1^2}{2} = \frac{p_2}{\rho} + \frac{U_2^2}{2}$$

Since $u_1 = u_2$, then

$$\frac{p_1 - p_2}{\rho} = \frac{v_2^2 - v_1^2}{2}$$

From Eq. (5.37) the drag F_x then becomes

$$F_x = \frac{b\rho}{2}(v_2^2 - v_1^2) \tag{5.39}$$

According to the definition of the circulation as given in Eq. (3.44), the circulation on the vane around the path $ABCD$ becomes the summation of the velocity component along the path times the length of the path. Whatever the velocity along AD, it must be the same along BC; and, in the counterclockwise integration, the contribution along these two paths will cancel. The other two pieces of the complete closed contour are AB and CD.

$$\begin{aligned}\Gamma &= -bv_1 - bv_2 \\ &= -b(v_2 + v_1)\end{aligned}$$

Substitution of Γ into Eqs. (5.38)–(5.39) gives

$$F_y = -\rho u_1 \Gamma \tag{5.40}$$

and

$$F_x = \frac{\rho}{2}\Gamma(v_1 - v_2)$$

calling $\frac{1}{2}(v_1 - v_2) = \bar{v}$, then

$$F_x = \rho\Gamma\bar{v} \tag{5.41}$$

5.6 Moment of Momentum or Angular Momentum

From principles of general mechanics it can be concluded that when a solid body is submerged in a steady flow, the body in general is acted upon by a set of forces in such a manner that in order for the body to be kept at rest it must be balanced by an opposing resultant force and a resultant opposing moment. The resultant force on the submerged body has already been developed through the momentum considerations of the fluid streaming around the body. What needs to be treated now is the resultant moment that may develop from the actual position of the forces on the body. Since the resultant force has been found to be equal to the change of momentum across a control volume including the body, the net moment, if any, that may result from this force will then be equal to the *moment of the momentum* or the *angular momentum.*

In Sec. 5.2, a balance of moment of momentum could have been performed instead of a balance of moments. Then Eq. (5.7) would have given the torque due to external forces.

$$\begin{aligned} \boldsymbol{T} &= \boldsymbol{r} \times \boldsymbol{F} \\ &= \frac{\partial}{\partial t} \int_{\mathcal{V}_c} \rho \boldsymbol{r} \times \boldsymbol{U} d\mathcal{V}_c + \oint_{S_c} \rho(\boldsymbol{r} \times \boldsymbol{U})(\boldsymbol{n} \cdot \boldsymbol{U})\, dS_c \end{aligned} \tag{5.42}$$

This is the law of moments and together with Newton's second law gives the condition of equilibrium. Equation (5.42) is in terms of a control volume. The comparable equation for a system is

$$\boldsymbol{T} = \int_{\mathcal{V}_s} \boldsymbol{r} \times \left(\rho \frac{d\boldsymbol{U}}{dt}\right) d\mathcal{V}_s \tag{5.43}$$

In steady state,

$$\boldsymbol{T} = \oint_{S_c} \rho(\boldsymbol{r} \times \boldsymbol{U})(\boldsymbol{n} \cdot \boldsymbol{U})\, dS_c \tag{5.44}$$

If the angle that $\boldsymbol{U}$ forms with $\boldsymbol{n}$ on the surface of Fig. 5.1 is α, then, according to the vector product rule $\boldsymbol{r} \times \boldsymbol{U}$, the components of Eq. (5.45) will read:

$$\begin{aligned} T_x &= \oint_{S_c} \rho U(yw - zv) \cos \alpha \, dS_c \\ T_y &= \oint_{S_c} \rho U(zu - xw) \cos \theta \, dS_c \\ T_z &= \oint_{S_c} \rho U(xv - yu) \cos \theta \, dS_c \end{aligned} \tag{5.45}$$

In a simple scalar analysis this can be shown easily.

Consider an element of fluid inside a control volume like that shown in Fig. 5.3. Let this element be shown in its Cartesian coordinates in Fig. 5.13. The velocity of the fluid element U is in the direction of the streamline s, and the components of the velocity vector are u, v, and w in the x-, y-, and z-directions, respectively. The elemental unit mass

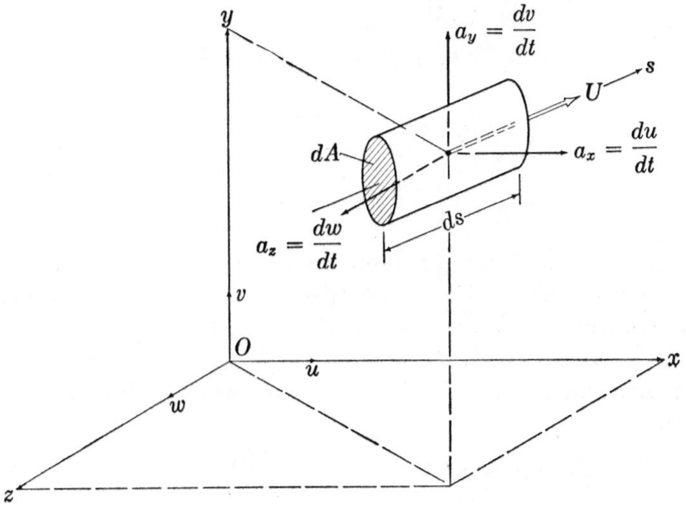

Figure 5.13
Coordinate representation of elemental volume $dA\ ds$ and its acceleration components.

of the elemental fluid volume $dA\ ds$ is $\rho\ dA\ ds$, and, according to Newton's law, the force components on the element are

$$dF'_x = \rho\ dA\ ds\ \frac{du}{dt}$$

$$dF'_y = \rho\ dA\ ds\ \frac{dv}{dt}$$

$$dF'_z = \rho\ dA\ ds\ \frac{dw}{dt}$$

Since $ds/dt = U$, the total velocity, then the preceding inertial equations can be transformed in the following form:

$$\begin{aligned} dF'_x &= (\rho U\ dA)\ du = (\rho U\ dA)\ \frac{du}{ds}\ ds \\ dF'_y &= (\rho U\ dA)\ \frac{dv}{ds}\ ds \\ dF'_z &= (\rho U\ dA)\ \frac{dw}{ds}\ ds \end{aligned} \tag{5.46}$$

Since moment is a vector quantity, the moment components of the forces on the element are

$$dT'_x = dQ\left(y\frac{dw}{ds} - z\frac{dv}{ds}\right)ds$$

$$dT'_y = dQ\left(z\frac{du}{ds} - x\frac{dw}{ds}\right)ds$$

$$dT'_z = dQ\left(x\frac{dv}{ds} - y\frac{du}{ds}\right)ds$$

Here the (′) refers to the forces or moments of the elementary volume $dA\,ds$. The quantity $dQ = \rho U\,dA$, the rate of mass flow going through the elemental control stream filament, as shown in Fig. 5.3.

The terms in the parentheses of Eq. (5.47) can be changed into the following form illustrated for the first component. The following equality is true:

$$\frac{d}{ds}(yw - zv) = \left(y\frac{dw}{ds} - z\frac{dv}{ds}\right) \tag{5.48}$$

This is so because the left-hand side can be expanded to the form

$$\frac{d}{ds}(yw - zv) = \left(y\frac{dw}{ds} - z\frac{dv}{ds}\right) + \left(w\frac{dy}{ds} - v\frac{dz}{ds}\right)$$

From the streamline geometry, $dy/ds = v/U$ and $dz/ds = w/U$. Relations similar to these were obtained in Sec. 4.9(a). The second parenthesis in the right-hand side of the preceding equation is zero after substitution of these results. Therefore, Eq. (5.48) stands proved.

Similar relations for the parentheses in the last two equations of Eq. (5.47) can be derived

$$\frac{d}{ds}(zu - xw) = \left(z\frac{du}{ds} - x\frac{dw}{ds}\right) \tag{5.49}$$

$$\frac{d}{ds}(xv - yu) = \left(x\frac{dv}{ds} - y\frac{du}{ds}\right) \tag{5.50}$$

Therefore, the moment of the external forces on the fluid element $dA\,ds$ is equal to the *moment of the momentum change* occurring through the elementary control volume $dA\,ds$. This is seen to be so when Eqs. (5.48), (5.49), (5.50) are substituted into Eq. (5.47).

$$\begin{aligned} dT'_x &= dQ\frac{d}{ds}(yw - zv)\,ds \\ dT'_y &= dQ\frac{d}{ds}(zu - xw)\,ds \\ dT'_z &= dQ\frac{d}{ds}(xv - yu)\,ds \end{aligned} \tag{5.51}$$

These relations can be integrated along the length s of the stream filament in Fig. 5.3, from points 1 to 2 on the control surface:

$$dT_x = \int_1^2 dT'_x = \int_1^2 dQ \frac{d}{ds}(yw - zv)\, ds$$

The rate of mass flow is a constant in the integration, since it is a constant throughout the stream filament. Because the integrand is an exact total differential, then

$$\begin{aligned} dT_x &= dQ[(yw - zv)]_1^2 \\ dT_y &= dQ[(zu - xw)]_1^2 \\ dT_z &= dQ[(xv - yu)]_1^2 \end{aligned} \tag{5.52}$$

These quantities are called the rate of change of *angular momentum*, or *moment of momentum* through the control surface represented by that of the stream filament, and it is equal to the moment or *torque* in the fluid volume in the stream filament.

In order to obtain the total moment on the entire control volume $\mathcal{V}$ of Fig. 5.3, Eq. (5.52) must be integrated once more, this time for all stream filaments in the volume. The mass rate of flow leaving the stream filament at the surface S of the control volume is $dQ = \rho U\, dA = \rho U \cos\theta\, dS$. Then, for instance,

$$T_z = \oint_S \rho U(xv - yu) \cos\theta\, dS \tag{5.53}$$

This is the same as the z-component of Eq. (5.45). The other components are obtained in the same fashion. This is, then, the equation for the summation of external moments on the control volume $\mathcal{V}$ which, for a steady state, is equal to the net flux of moment of momentum across the surface of the volume. Equation (5.53) is a similar form of Eq. (5.13), already derived for the summation of external forces.

These equations of angular momentum are applied a great deal to flows through turbines and compressors. Such flows undergo a change of angular momentum because, in the case of the turbine, the blades derive a torque from the flow, and, in the case of a fan or compressor, the torque is imposed on the blades and the fluid thus must increase its angular momentum.

Because of the geometry of turbines and compressors, it is often desirable and more convenient to write Eq. (5.53) in cylindrical components. It is understood that in such machines the torque is only in one direction, say the z-direction; consequently, only Eq. (5.53) is used. From Fig. 5.14, when projected on the x–y-plane, U can also be resolved into the peripheral velocity v_θ and the radial component v_r. The dis-

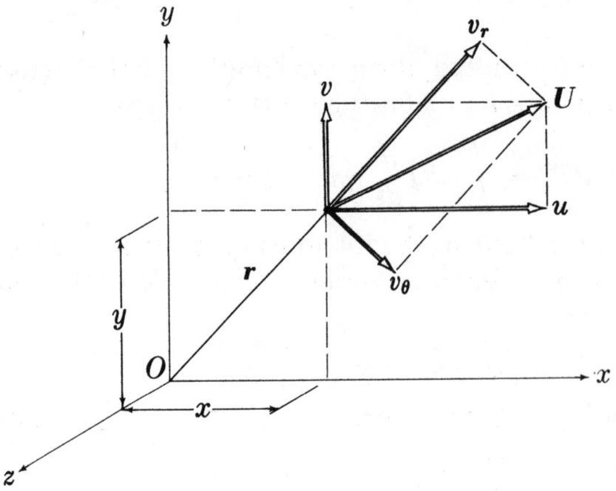

Figure 5.14
Cartesian and cylindrical components of the velocity U projected to the x–y-plane.

tance r must be taken as the shorter radial distance from the z-axis to the element and not the radial distance from the origin to the element. Figure 5.14, being two dimensional, is drawn in such a manner that the shortest radial distance goes through the origin. Here $u^2 + v^2 = v_\theta^2 + v_r^2$. Since the same velocity is resolved into two different sets of components, the moment of one set of the components must be equal to the moment of the other set with respect to the z-axis. The component v_r being along r does not contribute to the moment, therefore

$$(xv - yu) = v_\theta r$$

Substitution of this expression into Eq. (5.53) gives

$$T_z = \oint_S \rho U v_\theta r \cos\theta \, dS \tag{5.54}$$

It must be remembered that this last expression for the torque on the matter momentarily occupying the volume $\mathcal{V}$ was derived on the assumption that the flow was steady. Thus it was found that the torque equaled the net flux of moment of momentum crossing the surface of the control volume. If the flow is not steady, velocities will vary within the volume with time, and an additional term of rate of change of angular momentum with time must be added to the right-hand side of Eq. (5.54). The resultant equation will then be similar to the form of Eq. (5.7) for the momentum.

In some engineering applications, the density, the velocity U, and the angle θ that the flow makes with the surface of the chosen control volume are uniform across the inlet and across the discharge, therefore they can be removed outside the integral sign in Eqs. (5.53) and (5.54). It is not possible to maintain the same uniform relation for $v_\theta r$, since v_θ, r, and consequently the product are functions of position when the flow is rotational. In any event, a representative velocity moment at the inlet and outlet can be defined as the mean value across it.

$$\overline{(v_\theta r)}_i = \frac{1}{S_i}\int_{S_i} v_\theta r\, dS$$

$$\overline{(v_\theta r)}_o = \frac{1}{S_o}\int_{S_o} v_\theta r\, dS$$

The subscripts (i) and (o) refer to inlet and discharge conditions. Remembering the condition of uniformity of ρ, U, and θ and the spatial average conditions defined lastly, the integration of Eq. (5.54) becomes

$$T_z = \rho_o U_o \cos\theta_o S_o \overline{(v_\theta r)}_o - \rho_i U_i \cos\theta_i S_i \overline{(v_\theta r)}_i$$

From continuity of mass, the rate of mass flow is

$$Q = \rho_o U_o S_o \cos\theta_o = \rho_i U_i S_i \cos\theta_i$$

and therefore the moment or torque equation finally becomes

$$T_z = Q[\overline{(v_\theta r)}_o - \overline{(v_\theta r)}_i] \tag{5.55}$$

Illustrative Example 5.5

The impeller in Fig. 5.15 rotates counterclockwise at 1,800 rpm and draws air at 50°F from a center pipe of radius $r_0 = 4$ in. The measured spatial mean velocity in the pipe is 100 ft/sec. The blades' passage in the impeller is 2 in. wide and 1 in. high, and at the discharge end the direction of the passage makes an angle of 60° with the tangent to the circle $r = 8$ in. Find the power necessary to drive the impeller, assuming the absolute velocity to be radial at the vane inlet.

The rate of flow through the central pipe is

$$Q = \frac{0.0785 \times \pi \times 16 \times 100}{144}$$

$$= 2.74 \text{ lb}_\text{m}/\text{sec}$$

$$= 0.085 \text{ slug/sec}$$

The velocity in the vane is found by distributing the total volume flow into six vanes

$$U_i = \frac{\pi \times 16 \times 100}{6 \times 2 \times 1}$$

$$= 41.9 \text{ ft/sec}$$

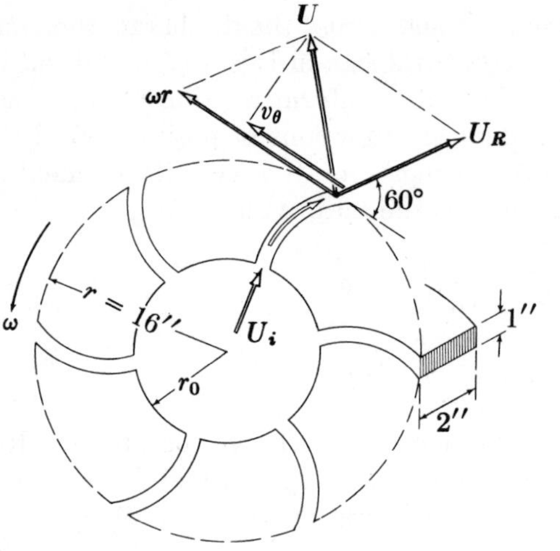

Figure 5.15
Impeller discharging air into atmosphere.

From a continuity standpoint of an incompressible flow, the velocity of the fluid leaving the vane and relative to the vane is the same, $U_R = 41.9$ ft/sec. The peripheral velocity of the impeller at the discharge is

$$\omega r = \frac{2 \times \pi \times 1{,}800 \times 8}{60 \times 12}$$

$$= 125.6 \text{ ft/sec}$$

The absolute velocity $\boldsymbol{U}$ is the vectorial resultant of U_R and ωr, and the peripheral component of this absolute velocity $\boldsymbol{U}$ is

$$v_\theta = 125.6 - \tfrac{1}{2}(41.9)$$
$$= 104.65 \text{ ft/sec}$$

From Eq. (5.55) the torque on the impeller is

$$T_z = \frac{0.085 \times 104.65 \times 8}{12}$$

$$= 5.93 \text{ ft} \times \text{lb}_f$$

The inlet angular momentum is zero, since the inlet velocity is radial.

The power required will be

$$\text{Power} = \frac{5.93 \times 2 \times \pi \times 30}{550}$$

$$= 2.03 \text{ hp}$$

5.7 Application of Angular Momentum to Turbomachines

Since Eq. (5.55) represents the equation for the torque on a volume through which the moment of momentum is changing, and if the control volume is a machine such as a turbine or a compressor rotating at an angular velocity ω, then the work put into the control volume or taken out of it can be easily computed by multiplying the torque by the angular velocity.

To illustrate this application, consider the impeller of a compressor or a pump as shown in Fig. (5.16). The rotation of the impeller is

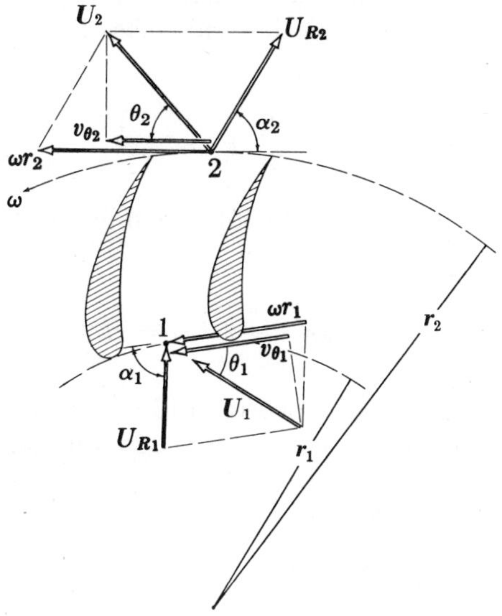

Figure 5.16
Velocity vector diagram for the flow through a compressor impeller.

counterclockwise, and, for the arrangement of the impeller blades shown, the flow moves from 1 to 2. At the designed angular velocity of the machine, for efficient compression with minimum losses, the velocity of the fluid relative to the blades U_R follows the direction of the blades. The absolute velocity $\boldsymbol{U}$ of the fluid, with reference, of course, to the stationary axis of the machine, is obtained by adding vectorially the relative velocity vector U_R to the peripheral velocity ωr at the point. The tangential component v_θ of the fluid velocity is then the peripheral component of the absolute velocity $\boldsymbol{U}$.

These velocities $\boldsymbol{U}$, U_R, ωr, and v_θ are shown for the inlet and discharge of the fluid through the blade system. According to Eq. (5.55), the torque and work done on the fluid per unit mass are

$$\frac{T_z}{Q} = v_{\theta_2} r_2 - v_{\theta_1} r_1$$

$$\frac{\text{Work}}{\text{Unit mass}} = \frac{T_z \omega}{Q} = v_{\theta_2} r_2 \omega - v_{\theta_1} r_1 \omega \tag{5.56}$$

Bernoulli's equation can be written for the absolute conditions with a modification similar to Eq. (4.42), taking into account the energy loss per unit mass H and the work done on the fluid per unit mass W. In the incompressible and steady case,

$$\frac{p_1}{\rho} + \frac{U_1^2}{2} + gz_1 + W - H = \frac{p_2}{\rho} + \frac{U_2^2}{2} + gz_2$$

Since the work per unit mass was derived in Eq. (5.56), it can be substituted in the last equation:

$$\frac{p_1 - p_2}{\rho} + \frac{U_1^2 - U_2^2}{2} + g(z_1 - z_2) + v_{\theta_2} r_2 \omega - v_{\theta_1} r_1 \omega = H$$

From the geometry of the vector diagram of Fig. 5.16, the following relations can be obtained and substituted into the previous equation:

$$U_1^2 = \omega^2 r_1^2 + U_{R_1}^2 - 2\omega r_1 U_{R_1} \cos \alpha_1$$

$$U_2^2 = \omega^2 r_2^2 + U_{R_2}^2 - 2\omega r_2 U_{R_2} \cos \alpha_2$$

$$v_{\theta_1} = \omega r_1 - U_{R_1} \cos \alpha_1$$

$$v_{\theta_1} = \omega r_1 - U_{R_2} \cos \alpha_1$$

Substituting these trigonometric expressions into the modified form of Bernoulli's equation, it will follow that

$$\frac{p_1 - p_2}{\rho} + \frac{U_{R_1}^2 - U_{R_2}^2}{2} + g(z_1 - z_2) = \frac{\omega^2(r_1^2 - r_2^2)}{2} + H \tag{5.57}$$

This equation is a modified form of Bernoulli's equation in terms of the relative kinetic energy U_R^2. The additional terms that appear here $\omega^2(r_1^2 - r_2^2)/2$ are called the *centrifugal head*.

It can be verified without difficulty that, in the case of no losses, and solid body motion for which $U_R = 0$, Eq. (5.57) reduces to the form already derived in Sec. 4.5, Case I.

$$\frac{p_1 - p_2}{\rho} + g(z_1 - z_2) = \frac{\omega^2(r_1^2 - r_2^2)}{2} \tag{5.58}$$

Problems

5.1 Explain the following concepts from Eq. (5.8). Consider some form of a machine whose entire surface S_c is made up of an inlet A_i, an outlet A_o and the remaining of a rigid surface, Σ.

(a) Insofar as the fluid moving through this machine is concerned, if the momentum entering the machine was in the same direction but larger than the momentum leaving, what is the direction of the force *on the fluid.* How do you explain this result?

(b) What is the force on the machine in case (a)? By what principle do you explain this?

(c) In the same problem, what is the contribution of the exchange of momentum on Σ? Explain your answer.

(d) If the machine was a stream tube, what would be the contribution of Eq. (5.8) on the stream surface?

5.2 Using the principles of Chap. IV dealing with differential equations instead of integral equations and the integration of flow properties along a streamline, how would you solve a problem as in Prob. 5.1 to determine the total force on a machine? Take a simple case when A_i and A_o are in the same direction, while U_i and U_o are normal to A_i and A_o respectively.

5.3 Two identical masses of fluid move along the same line but in opposite directions. The mass moving to the right has a speed $U_1 = 20$ ft/sec, and its speed is twice that moving to the left. Find the final velocity of the fluid after the two masses meet and move together at one speed.

5.4 In Prob. 5.3, what would be the final velocity if the two masses moved originally in the same direction and at the same speeds as above?

5.5 For Probs. 5.3 and 5.4, compute the loss in kinetic energy per unit total mass after impact. The loss in kinetic energy is the difference between the total kinetic energy before impact and that after impact.

5.6 An incompressible fluid of density ρ flows through a tube shown below with two 90° bends. The bends are in two different planes. For static equilibrium of the tube, find the force F to prevent the tube from rotating around the pivot axis z–z and the magnitude and direction of the reaction force at the pivot.

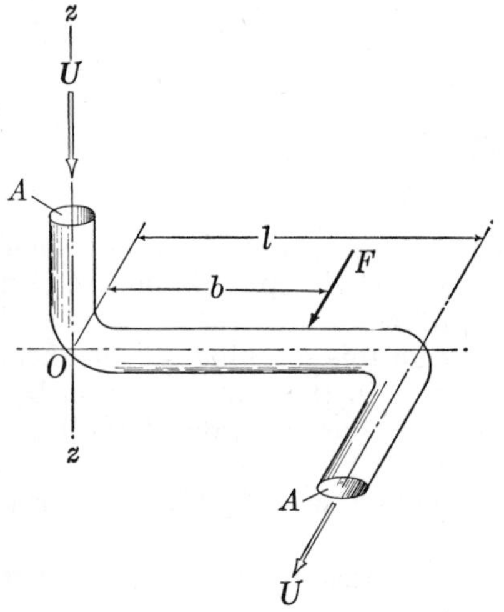

5.7 A jet of radius $r = 1.35$ in. discharges water at the rate of 2 ft^3/sec into a curved vane which deflects the jet 135°. What are the forces on the vane along the jet and normal to it such that the vane will be stationary? Find the total force.

5.8 Water flows through an expanding pipe elbow that turns the liquid 120°. The rate of flow is 1.000 gpm, the diameter of the inlet is 4 in., and that of the discharge is 5 in. Determine the force to keep the elbow in equilibrium. Repeat the problem if the direction of the flow is reversed. In both cases assume the absence of friction.

5.9 Oil of specific gravity 0.75 flows through a 135° bend. The conditions at the inlet are $r_i = 2.5$ in., $U_i = 25$ ft/sec, and $p_i = 20$ psia. The conditions at the outlet are $r_o = 5$ in., and the head loss through the bend is 10 ft $\times$ lb$_f$/lb$_m$. If the atmospheric pressure is 15 psia, find the reaction force on the bend.

5.10 An atmospheric jet impinges on a stationary vane as shown in the figure on p. 241. The total rate of flow of air at 50°F is 1,000 cfm at a velocity of 100 ft/sec. Find the force components along U and normal to U if the motion is considered frictionless and if the flow is equally divided by the vane.

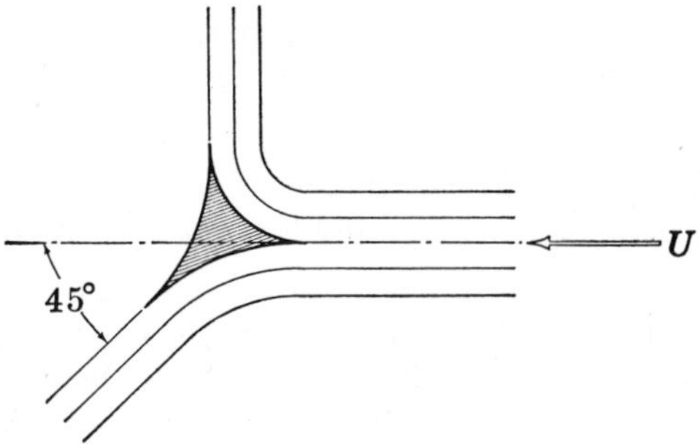

5.11 A flat plate moves perpendicularly toward a discharging jet at the rate of 5 ft/sec. The jet discharges water at the rate of 2 cfs and a speed of 30 ft/sec. Find the force on the plate and compare it with that if the plate were stationary.

5.12 Oil of specific gravity 0.75 leaves a jet 2 in. in diameter and strikes a vane at the speed of 50 ft/sec. The vane moves in the direction of the jet at a velocity 30 ft/sec. If the horsepower obtained by the vane is 0.40, what should be the angle of the vane and the reaction forces on it?

5.13 Water impinges on a set of vanes curved through an arc of 135°. The vanes move at a tangential velocity of 40 ft/sec, and the water is discharged from a nozzle at the rate of 4 cfs and at a speed of 100 ft/sec. Find the force components on the vane and the power that can be developed if friction is neglected.

5.14 A jet of fluid of specific gravity 0.80 impinges downward into a tank of liquid at the rate of 4 cfs and 50 ft/sec. What is the force exerted by the jet on the liquid tank?

5.15 A 1-in.-diameter nozzle is connected at its larger end into a pipe 3 in. in diameter. The water in the pipe is at 75 psig. If gravity and losses are neglected, find the action of the nozzle on the stationary pipe.

5.16 The level of the water in a tank is 5 ft above a $\frac{1}{2}$-in. nozzle on the side of the tank. If the water in the tank is 10 ft^3 in volume, determine the reaction forces on the tank.

5.17 In Prob. 5.16, if the nozzle is replaced by a simple 1-in. hole in the tank with a contraction coefficient of 0.6, find the forces on the tank for ideal flow.

5.18 A 3-in.-wide, two-dimensional jet impinges at the velocity of 50 ft/sec on a stationary inclined plate. The inclination of the plate with the direction of the jet is 30°. If the fluid is water and flows ideally, find the velocities and widths of the streams at both ends of the plate after the fluid has been deflected. Find the forces on the plate and the point of application.

5.19 In Prob. 5.18, if the plate moves in the direction of flow at the velocity of 20 ft/sec, find the force on the plate and the point of application.

5.20 An airplane propeller 10 ft in diameter and moving at a speed of 220 mph produces a thrust of 3,110 lb_f. Find the diameter of the slipstream far upstream and far downstream of the propeller. Use air at sea level and 50°F.

5.21 In Prob. 5.20, find the theoretical propeller efficiency.

5.22 Assume the theoretical efficiency of a ship's propeller to be 65 per cent and its radius 2 ft. If the ship moves at 20 mph, find the thrust and the theoretical horsepower.

5.23 Two horizontal jets strike a flat plate at right angles. The distance between the jets is 12 in., and they strike on opposite sides of the plate. The rate of discharge of both jets is the same, and the conditions in the smaller-area jet are $A = 4$ in.^{2}, $U = 50$ fps, $\rho = 62.4$ lb_m/ft^3. The area of the larger jet is $A = 6$ in.^{2}. Find the force necessary to keep the plate in equilibrium and find its location on the plate relative to either jet.

5.24 The ideal flow of water passes through a cascade of blades 1 in. apart, as shown in Fig. 6.12. $U_1 = 80$ ft/sec and is inclined 30° with the horizontal. $U_2 = U_1$, and the angle is the negative value of that of U_1. Find the forces that keep the cascade stationary. What is the circulation around a blade?

5.25 Compare and discuss the analogy of Eqs. (5.5), (5.7), and (5.42).

Energy Considerations in Fluid Dynamics

chapter VI

6.1 Introduction

The first law of thermodynamics is an energy-conservation law. Like the equation of mass continuity, which specifies that all the mass entering the boundaries of an arbitrary control volume must be accounted for as leaving the same boundaries and in unsteady cases altering the mass content within the volume, the energy equation must account for the energy transfer through the boundaries of the same control volume in the same manner. If continuity of mass implies the accounting for and preservation of mass, the energy equation implies accounting for and preservation of energy. The laws of preservation of mass and energy must be satisfied in all real physical problems.

Since energy can be transferred across the boundaries of any volume with or without mass transfer, it becomes essential to distinguish the difference between a system and a control volume. A volume across whose boundaries there is no mass transfer is called a *system.* For a moving fluid, the system must move with the fluid. Conversely, if mass is transferred across the boundaries of an arbitrary volume, then it is called a *control volume.* The *system* is, then, a volume where the interior fluid is in the mean stationary with respect to its boundaries. This type of reference volume was not considered previously when we dealt with the mass-continuity relation and the momentum relation, since it actually behaves like a solid body across which neither mass nor momentum is transferred. Since energy can be transferred without the help of mass, the system must be examined first.

6.2 Energy Transfer Within a System

For any substance within a system, the first law of thermodynamics states that the difference between the heat transferred across the boundaries and the work done must finally appear as a change in the *internal energy* of the substance within the volume.

$$đq - \frac{1}{J} đW = de \tag{6.1}$$

For the process of energy interchanged, $đq$ represents an infinitesimal amount of heat flow per unit mass between the confining volume and the surroundings. In general, the amount of heat flow for a finite process, obtained by integrating Eq. (6.1) is a function of the type of process as well as the end states. This implies that, in general, $đq$ is not an exact differential. The same pertains to the external work $\frac{1}{J} đW$. To obtain the total work for the finite process, it is necessary to include in the integration information about the type of process followed. The state of a fluid is determined by the value of its properties; since q and W are not unique functions of the end states in the integration but are a function of the process as well, they are not properties of the fluid. The heat flow q is positive when added from the surroundings to the system. The work W is positive when it is done by the fluid on the surroundings of the system. The constant J is the mechanical equivalent of heat equal to 778.16 ft $\times$ lb_f/Btu.

The balance between the heat transferred and the external work per unit mass is what changes the energy stored internally per unit mass e. In contrast to the work and heat, the *internal energy* e depends entirely on the state of the system and therefore does not depend on how the particular state was reached. Therefore, de is mathematically an exact differential whose integral $e_2 - e_1$ is evaluated between the two end states 1 and 2, regardless of the process joining these two states.

Illustrative Example 6.1

To illustrate the difference between the integration of a differential that is exact and one that is not exact, consider the infinitesimal reversible work done on a closed arbitrary volume of fluid

$$đW = pd\left(\frac{1}{\rho}\right) \tag{6.2}$$

To find the exact amount of work involved between two end states, the exact type of process joining these two states must be known. In other words, unless $p = f(\rho)$ is known, the integration of Eq. (6.2) cannot be performed. The relationship between p and ρ establishes the process equation. For instance, if a perfect gas is considered, let the process be isentropic so that

$$p = C\rho^{\gamma} \tag{6.3}$$

where $C = \dfrac{p_1}{\rho_1^{\gamma}} = \dfrac{p_2}{\rho_2^{\gamma}}$. Equation (6.2) can be integrated now if the process Eq. (6.3) is introduced.

$$\begin{aligned}
\int_1^2 đW &= \int_1^2 pd\left(\frac{1}{\rho}\right) = C\int_1^2 \rho^{\gamma} d\left(\frac{1}{\rho}\right) \\
&= \frac{C}{1-\gamma}\,\rho^{\gamma-1}\Big]_1^2 \\
&= \frac{C}{1-\gamma}\,(\rho_2^{\gamma-1} - \rho_1^{\gamma-1}) \\
&= \frac{1}{1-\gamma}\left(\frac{p_2}{\rho_2} - \frac{p_1}{\rho_1}\right)
\end{aligned} \tag{6.4}$$

The result of this integration for the work done would be different if an isothermal process $p = C\rho$ were assumed between the same two states. The work done is represented by the area 1′122′ in Fig. 6.1. The same reasoning holds true for the integral:

$$\begin{aligned}
\int_2^1 đI &= \int_2^1 \frac{1}{\rho}\,dp = C\gamma \int_2^1 \rho^{\gamma-2}\,d\rho \\
&= \frac{C\gamma}{\gamma-1}\,\rho^{\gamma-1}\Big]_2^1 \\
&= \frac{C\gamma}{\gamma-1}\,(\rho_1^{\gamma-1} - \rho_2^{\gamma-1}) \\
&= \frac{\gamma}{\gamma-1}\left(\frac{p_1}{\rho_1} - \frac{p_2}{\rho_2}\right)
\end{aligned} \tag{6.5}$$

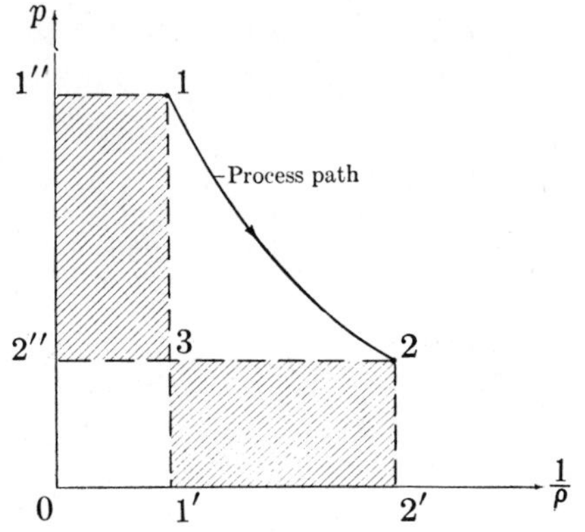

Figure 6.1
Adiabatic expansion.

This integral is again a function of the process and is represented by the positive area 2''211'' in Fig. 6.1. Although each of these integrals is a function of the process, their difference is not, since

$$\int_1^2 đW - đI = \int_1^2 pd\left(\frac{1}{\rho}\right) - \int_2^1 \frac{1}{\rho}\,dp$$

$$= \int_1^2 pd\left(\frac{1}{\rho}\right) + \frac{1}{\rho}\,dp$$

$$= \int_1^2 d\left(\frac{p}{\rho}\right)$$

It follows, then, that the integral of the exact differential $d\left(\frac{p}{\rho}\right)$ is

$$\left(\frac{p_2}{\rho_2} - \frac{p_1}{\rho_1}\right)$$

In Fig. 6.1, since the area 123 is common to both integrals W and I, it cancels in the difference. What remains from the difference is the area 1'2'23 less the area 2''1''13, or

$$p_1\left(\frac{1}{\rho_2} - \frac{1}{\rho_1}\right) - \frac{1}{\rho_1}(p_1 - p_2) = \left(\frac{p_2}{\rho_2} - \frac{p_1}{\rho_1}\right)$$

This, of course, is the result already found. Now, graphically, it can be seen that $\int_1^2 đW$ is a function of the process connecting the end states 1 and 2. The same is true for $\int_1^2 đI$. But, since $\int_1^2 đW - đI$ is represented by the difference between the rectangular areas 1′2′23 and 2″1″13, regardless of what process connnects the two points these areas will be unchanged as long as the end states remain fixed. As a conclusion: $pd\left(\frac{1}{\rho}\right)$ is not a differential property of any fluid system, and neither is $\frac{1}{\rho}\,dp$. However, $pd\left(\frac{1}{\rho}\right) + \frac{1}{\rho}\,dp = d\left(\frac{p}{\rho}\right)$, is a differential property of any fluid system.

6.3 The Mechanical Power Equation

An equation expressing the rate of energy transfer by mechanical means can be obtained by multiplying Newton's second law by the velocity of the motion. This equation is independent of the first law of thermodynamics.

Consider a frictionless flow where Euler's Equation, Eq. (4.12), applies. Multiplying this summation of force by $\boldsymbol{U}$ we obtain a mechanical power equation per unit volume:

$$\frac{\rho}{2}\frac{dU^2}{dt} = -\rho(\boldsymbol{U}\cdot\boldsymbol{\nabla})\Omega - (\boldsymbol{U}\cdot\boldsymbol{\nabla})p \tag{6.6}$$

Here, the body force is assumed to be conservative $\boldsymbol{g} = -\boldsymbol{\nabla}\Omega$ where Ω is the potential energy. Usually, the body force does not vary with time and thus, $\partial\Omega/\partial t = 0$. According to the time rate of change discussed in Section 4.2,

$$\frac{d\Omega}{dt} = \frac{\partial\Omega}{\partial t} + (\boldsymbol{U}\cdot\boldsymbol{\nabla})\Omega$$

Then, for a steady body force,

$$\frac{d\Omega}{dt} = (\boldsymbol{U}\cdot\boldsymbol{\nabla})\Omega;$$

and Eq. (6.6) becomes

$$\rho\frac{d}{dt}\left(\tfrac{1}{2}U^2 + \Omega\right) = -(\boldsymbol{U}\cdot\boldsymbol{\nabla})p \tag{6.7}$$

Since this result originated from Newton's second law, it applies to every moving, fluid particle. If we take a finite number of these particles in a finite system given by the volume $\mathcal{V}_s$ and the bounding surface S_s, and integrate Eq. (6.7), we have

$$\int_{\mathcal{V}_s} \rho\frac{d}{dt}\left(\tfrac{1}{2}U^2 + \Omega\right) d\mathcal{V}_s = -\int_{\mathcal{V}_s} (\boldsymbol{U}\cdot\boldsymbol{\nabla})p\, d\mathcal{V}_s \tag{6.8}$$

For this system the mass conservation equation,

$$\frac{d}{dt}\int_{\mathcal{V}_s} \rho \, d\mathcal{V}_s = 0$$

can be combined with Eq. (6.8) and we have

$$\frac{d}{dt}\int_{\mathcal{V}_s} \rho(\tfrac{1}{2}U^2 + \Omega) \, d\mathcal{V}_s = -\int_{\mathcal{V}_s} \nabla\cdot(p\boldsymbol{U}) \, d\mathcal{V}_s + \int_{\mathcal{V}_s} p\nabla\cdot\boldsymbol{U} \, d\mathcal{V}_s$$

Finally, using Gauss' Theorem, Eq. (A.62), for the volume integral containing the divergence, it follows that

$$\frac{d}{dt}\int_{\mathcal{V}_s} \rho(\tfrac{1}{2}U^2 + \Omega) \, d\mathcal{V}_s = -\oint_{S_s} (\boldsymbol{n}\cdot\boldsymbol{U})p \, dS_s + \int_{\mathcal{V}_s} p(\nabla\cdot\boldsymbol{U}) \, d\mathcal{V}_s \qquad (6.9)$$

The integral on the left hand is the net time change of kinetic and potential energies[1] in the system. The first term on the right is the *flow energy* the system exchanges with the surroundings because of its motion against the pressure of the surrounding. The second integral to the left is the work of compression. When the density varies, $\nabla\cdot\boldsymbol{U} \neq 0$.

6.4 Total Energy Transfer Within a Control Volume

Often, Eq. (6.1) is used to represent the energy balance for a stationary arbitrary control volume as well. Caution must be taken, however, in order to give the proper interpretation to the terms in the energy equation for the control-volume case where the fluid moves across the boundaries.

If Eq. (6.1) is used for the control volume, the heat transferred and the internal energy represent the same energies as for the case of the system. The total work done, however, for the control-volume case is different from that for the system. In the case of any system of fluid, the work done is that which is mechanically performed on the boundaries of the system. This work may be done by the system or received into the system. This work is also known as the *shaft work*. In the control volume, since the fluid is flowing across the boundaries in a manner relative to the stationary system of reference, there is additional *kinetic*

[1] The term "energy" is used, here, to mean power. This usage will be repeated often in this text. Power is the rate of change of energy; however, certain power relations are erroneously but commonly known as energy relations.

work involved. Also, if the fluid moves from one elevation to another, *gravitational work* or *potential work* is also involved. A fourth type of work also is apparent in this case. This is the work necessary for the fluid to move against a pressure head. This is called the *flow work* or *displacement work*. In the absence of surface tension and magnetic and electrical forces, the fluid through a control volume will experience the four types of work mentioned. Therefore, the quantity W for a fluid occupying the bounds of a control volume stands for more than the external shaft work it represents in the fluid occupied within the system. All this will become clearer shortly. As we proceeded in the case of mass and momentum conservation in Sec. 5.2, we shall use the same approach for energy.

Consider at time t_0 the system in Fig. 6.2 with volume $\mathcal{V}_s$ and surface S_s and the total energy transferred with its surroundings. This transfer of energy is given by Eq. (6.1) multiplied by the mass. In most cases, the heat transferred with the surroundings is done through *conduction* owing to the gradient of temperature at the surface S_s. According to Fourier's law of conduction,

$$\begin{aligned} dQ &= m_s\, dq \\ &= k\boldsymbol{n}\cdot\nabla T\, dS_s \end{aligned}$$

and

$$Q = \oint_s k\boldsymbol{n}\cdot\nabla T\, dS_s \tag{6.10}$$

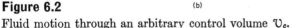

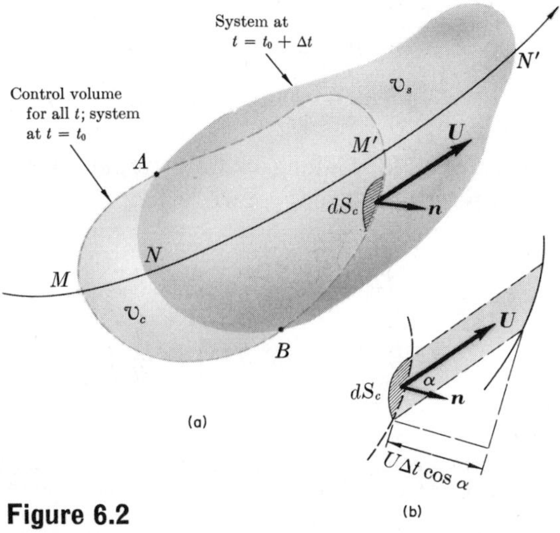

Figure 6.2
Fluid motion through an arbitrary control volume $\mathcal{V}_c$.

Where m_s is the mass of the system. In the case of radiation or chemical heat generation, they should be added to Eq. (6.10).

The inertia force moving at a velocity $\boldsymbol{U}$ of the system represents a certain *kinetic power*. This can be evaluated for the entire volume as follows:

$$W_k = \int_{\mathcal{V}_s} \rho \boldsymbol{U} \cdot \frac{d\boldsymbol{U}}{dt} \, d\mathcal{V}_s$$

Using the mass conservation for a system, Eq. (5.1), the kinetic power becomes

$$W_k = \tfrac{1}{2} \frac{d}{dt} \int_{\mathcal{V}_s} \rho U^2 \, d\mathcal{V}_s \tag{6.11}$$

The body force, such as the gravitational pull of the earth, represents a certain potential energy when the system is moved. It can be computed as follows:[2]

$$W_b = -\int_{\mathcal{V}_s} \rho \boldsymbol{U} \cdot \boldsymbol{g} \, d\mathcal{V}_s \tag{6.12}$$

Finally, the surface forces moving at a velocity $\boldsymbol{U}$ will require a *flow power*. Assuming frictionless motion, the surface forces are normal to S_s and taking the pressure p as the force per unit area pointing inward, the flow power is

$$W_f = -\oint_{S_s} (-\boldsymbol{n}p) \cdot \boldsymbol{U} \, dS_s \tag{6.13}$$

The total work per unit time is

$$W = \tfrac{1}{2} \frac{d}{dt} \int_{\mathcal{V}_s} \rho U^2 \, d\mathcal{V}_s - \int_{\mathcal{V}_s} \rho \boldsymbol{U} \cdot \boldsymbol{g} \, d\mathcal{V}_s - \oint_{S_s} \boldsymbol{U} \cdot (-\boldsymbol{n}p) \, dS_s \tag{6.14}$$

Now we are ready to apply Eq. (6.1). Calling e the internal energy per unit mass then making it a power equation, we write

$$\oint_{S_s} k\boldsymbol{n} \cdot \nabla T \, dS_s - \left[\tfrac{1}{2} \frac{d}{dt} \int_{\mathcal{V}_s} \rho U^2 \, d\mathcal{V}_s + \int_{\mathcal{V}_s} \rho \boldsymbol{U} \cdot \boldsymbol{g} \, d\mathcal{V}_s + \oint_{S_s} \boldsymbol{U} \cdot (-\boldsymbol{n}p) \, dS_s \right] = \frac{d}{dt} \int_{\mathcal{V}_s} \rho e \, d\mathcal{V}_s$$

Rearranging,

[2] The negative sign on the following two equations comes from the force balance: The inertia force minus the body and surface forces equal zero. The total power is precisely the mechanical power.

$$\frac{d}{dt}\int_{\mathcal{V}_s} \rho(e + \frac{1}{2}U^2)\, d\mathcal{V}_s = \int_{\mathcal{V}_s} \rho \boldsymbol{U}\cdot\boldsymbol{g}\, d\mathcal{V}_s - \oint_{S_s} \boldsymbol{U}\cdot\boldsymbol{n}p\, dS_s + \oint_{S_s} k\boldsymbol{n}\cdot\boldsymbol{\nabla}T\, dS_s \qquad (6.15)$$

Now, in going to a control volume, the only term that will be affected is the first one, since it has a time rate of change. According to Eq. (5.5) for a control volume Eq. (6.15) becomes

$$\frac{\partial}{\partial t}\int_{\mathcal{V}_c} \rho(e + \frac{1}{2}U^2)\, d\mathcal{V}_c = -\oint_{S_c} [\rho(\boldsymbol{U}\cdot\boldsymbol{n})(e + \frac{1}{2}U^2) + \boldsymbol{U}\cdot\boldsymbol{n}p - k\boldsymbol{n}\cdot\boldsymbol{\nabla}T]\, dS_c + \int_{\mathcal{V}_c} \rho\boldsymbol{U}\cdot\boldsymbol{g}\, d\mathcal{V}_c \qquad (6.16)$$

This is the power equation applied to a control volume. No consideration was given to *shaft work* in Eq. (6.16). This type of work is brought in externally, not through the fluid, but through a shaft. If it were present, it would have appeared in the equation as $\dot{W}_s$.

The surface integral in Eq. (6.16) can be changed into a volume integral through Eq. A.62

$$\int_{\mathcal{V}_c} \left\{\frac{\partial}{\partial t}\rho(e + \frac{1}{2}U^2) + \boldsymbol{\nabla}\cdot\left[\rho\boldsymbol{U}\left(e + \tfrac{1}{2}U^2 + \frac{p}{\rho}\right) - k\boldsymbol{\nabla}T\right] - \rho\boldsymbol{U}\cdot\boldsymbol{g}\right\} d\mathcal{V}_c = 0 \qquad (6.17)$$

Since $\mathcal{V}_c$ is arbitrary and if the integral is zero for all $\mathcal{V}_c$, then the integrand is concluded to be zero. The quantity $e + p/\rho = h$ is called the *enthalpy* and the stagnation enthalpy $h^\circ = h + \frac{1}{2}U^2$. For a steady flow, Eq. (6.17) becomes

$$\boldsymbol{\nabla}\cdot(k\boldsymbol{\nabla}T) = \boldsymbol{\nabla}\cdot(\rho\boldsymbol{U}h^\circ) - \rho\boldsymbol{U}\cdot\boldsymbol{g} \qquad (6.18)$$

The first term to the right of the equality sign can be written as

$$\boldsymbol{\nabla}\cdot(\rho h^\circ\boldsymbol{U}) = h^\circ\boldsymbol{\nabla}\cdot\rho\boldsymbol{U} + \rho\boldsymbol{U}\cdot\boldsymbol{\nabla}(h^\circ)$$

because of steady flow, from [Eq. (3.15)], $\boldsymbol{\nabla}\cdot\rho U = 0$ and thus Eq. (6.18) becomes

$$\boldsymbol{\nabla}\cdot(k\boldsymbol{\nabla}T) = \rho\boldsymbol{U}\cdot(\boldsymbol{\nabla}h^\circ - \boldsymbol{g}) = \rho\boldsymbol{U}\cdot[\boldsymbol{\nabla}(h^\circ + \Omega)] \qquad (6.19)$$

where Ω is the potential of the body force. Because of conservation of mass, again,

$$\nabla \cdot (k\nabla T) = \nabla \cdot [\rho \boldsymbol{U}(h^\circ + \Omega)]$$

or

$$\nabla \cdot [\rho \boldsymbol{U}(h^\circ + \Omega) - k\nabla T] = 0 \tag{6.20}$$

If $\Omega = gz$, then

$$\nabla \cdot [\rho \boldsymbol{U}(h^\circ + gz) - k\nabla T] = 0 \tag{6.21}$$

This is a form of conservation law for the energy similar to the differential form of the mass conservation equation given in Eq. [3.16(*b*)].

If we call the rate of heat transfer per unit mass $\dot{q} = \frac{1}{\rho}\nabla \cdot (k\nabla T)$, Eq. (6.19) becomes

$$\frac{dq}{dt} = \boldsymbol{U} \cdot \nabla (h^\circ + \Omega)$$

Substituting $\boldsymbol{U} = d\boldsymbol{r}/dt$ and eliminating dt,

$$dq = [d\boldsymbol{r} \cdot \nabla (h^\circ + \Omega)]$$

We have seen in Sec. A.14 that the right hand side becomes the total derivative of $(h^\circ + \Omega)$. Thus,

$$dq = d(h^\circ + \Omega)$$

Then the differential equation expressing the heat transfer per unit mass, better known as *the first law for a control volume,* becomes

$$dq = d(h^\circ + \Omega) \tag{6.22}$$

or

$$dq = d\left(e + \frac{p}{\rho} + \frac{1}{2}U^2 + gz\right) \tag{6.23}$$

In case there is a shaft work dW introduced from outside the boundaries, Eq. (6.23) becomes the first law for a control volume.

$$dq - dW = de + d\left(\frac{p}{\rho} + \frac{1}{2}\,dU^2 + g\,dz\right) \tag{6.24}$$

The difference between this equation and Eq. (6.1) is the additional terms $d(p/\rho) + dU^2 + g\,dz$, which is the work against the external forces.

Illustrative Example 6.2

Derive the differential form of the first law of thermodynamics for the fluid moving in an expanding tube shown in Fig. 6.3.

(*a*) *External or Shaft Power*

As the fluid moves into the tube it exerts forces on the solid boundaries which guide the motion. If these forces expand or contract these boundaries, work is involved, and such external work can be useful work if a moving shaft is attached to the solid boundaries of the tube. This type of work was discussed in Illustrative Example 6.1. Naturally, to determine this work, the way in which the pressure varies with the change of volume must be known. This is the work per unit mass.

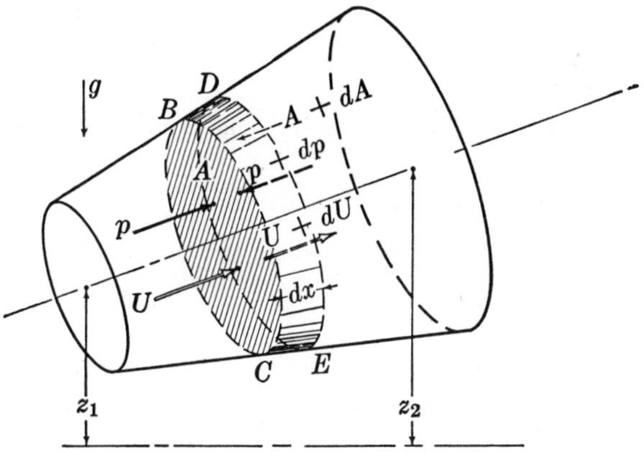

Figure 6.3
Displacement of a fluid element against pressure.

If the boundaries move continuously like the walls of a balloon at Q slugs of fluid flow per unit time, then the total power transferred in this external movement of the solid boundaries is

$$Q\,\text{đ}W$$

(b) Kinetic Power

If a unit volume of the fluid, as shown in Fig. 6.3, is accelerated or decelerated, according to Newton's second law of inertia a force is involved. Since the force moves at the velocity of the fluid, it takes power to achieve this result.

In a time dt, if the element changes its velocity from U to $U + dU$, it has accelerated by an amount dU/dt. If the density of the fluid is ρ, then the mass of the element of fluid shown is $\rho \dfrac{(A + dA) + A}{2}\,dx$. Neglecting, in the following analysis, all second- and third-order terms, such as $dA\,dx$, the mass of the element reduces to $\rho A\,dx$. Since the acceleration is dU/dt, the inertial force acting on the element is

$$\begin{aligned} dF_k &= \rho A\,dx\,\frac{dU}{dt} \\ &= \rho A\,\frac{dx}{dt}\,dU \end{aligned}$$

$$dF_k = \rho AU\,dU$$
$$= Q\,dU$$

Since this force moves along at the velocity U, the power which results is called the *kinetic power* and is equal to

$$dP_k = QU\,dU$$
$$= Q\,d(\tfrac{1}{2}U^2) \tag{6.25}$$

(*c*) *Gravitational Power*

As the fluid element in Fig. 6.3 moves along the tube, it changes its elevation. The weight of the element is

$$dF_g = \rho gA\,dx$$

This force is along z, and while the element moves along the tube it changes, in a unit time dt, its elevation from z to $z + dz$. The potential work involved for the element considered is

$$dW_g = \rho gA\,dx\,dz$$

But, since $dx = U\,dt$, the potential work becomes

$$dW_g = \rho gAU\,dz\,dt$$
$$= Qg\,dz\,dt$$

and the gravitational power becomes

$$dP_g = Qy\,dz \tag{6.26}$$

(*d*) *Flow Power*

It has been mentioned that flow work is the work required by the fluid to move against the pressure. In Fig. 6.3 the element *BDCE* will be pushed on the left-hand side by the pressure p. This indicates that the left-hand-side surroundings will do work on the elemental volume. The velocity at the face *BC* is U, and, in time dt, the face will move a distance $U\,dt$. Therefore, the work done by the left-hand-side surroundings on the face *BC* is

$$pAU\,dt$$

In order for the element to move on the right-hand side, it must, in turn, do work on the right-hand-side surroundings. The pressure there is $p + dp$, the cross-sectional area is changed to $A + dA$, and the velocity is $U + dU$. The work done by the element *BDCE* on the right-hand-side surroundings is

$$(p + dp)(A + dA)(U + dU)\,dt$$

The net flow work is then

$$dW_f = (p + dp)(A + dA)(U + dU)\,dt - pAU\,dt$$

If one neglects again the second- and third-order terms such as $p\,dA\,dU$ and $dp\,dA\,dU$, the work becomes

$$dW_f = [pA\,dU + AU\,dp + pU\,dA]\,dt$$
$$= d(pAU)\,dt$$
$$= d\left(p\frac{Q}{\rho}\right)dt$$

The flow power is consequently equal to

$$dP_f = d\left(p\frac{Q}{\rho}\right)$$

and for a steady state, as was assumed initially,

$$dP_f = Q\,d\left(\frac{p}{\rho}\right) \tag{6.27}$$

The power equation for the steady motion of an infinitesimal fluid element can now be written in differential form from the various terms already obtained. It is assumed here that other forces owing to surface tension, magnetism, and electricity are not present and therefore do not contribute to the power balance.

The total work per unit mass, as represented in Eq. (6.1), is the sum of all the powers derived divided by Q. Then the differential form of the energy equation for a control volume becomes

$$đq - \frac{1}{J}\left[đW + d(\tfrac{1}{2}U^2) + g\,dz + d\left(\frac{p}{\rho}\right)\right] = de$$

After rearranging, this equation takes the conventional form:

$$đq - \frac{1}{J}đW = de + \frac{1}{J}d\left(\frac{p}{\rho}\right) + \frac{1}{J}d(\tfrac{1}{2}U^2) + \frac{g}{J}dz \tag{6.28}$$

The last three terms are those that distinguish flow through a control volume from the energy balance of the fluid contained in a system.

By definition, the sum of the internal energy and the flow energy is called the *enthalpy*, which is identified by the letter h. Then

$$h = e + \frac{1}{J}\frac{p}{\rho} \tag{6.29}$$

In terms of the enthalpy, the energy equation per unit mass becomes

$$đq - \frac{1}{J}đW = dh + \frac{1}{2J}dU^2 + \frac{g}{J}dz \tag{6.30}$$

As the fluid moves and a thermodynamic process takes place from one location to another, Eq. (6.30) can be integrated between the two locations 1 and 2, and it will represent the energy interchanged by the fluid per unit mass.

$$\int_1^2 đq - \frac{1}{J}\int_1^2 đW = (h_2 - h_1) + \frac{1}{2J}(U_2^2 - U_1^2) + \frac{g}{J}(z_2 - z_1) \tag{6.31}$$

The first two integrals on the left-hand side cannot be integrated unless the type of process followed is clearly defined.

By definition, let the *stagnation enthalpy* be the sum of the three terms:

$$h^{\circ} = h + \frac{1}{J2} U^2 + \frac{g}{J} z \tag{6.32}$$

Then the energy equation for a control volume becomes

$$\int_1^2 đq - \frac{1}{J} \int_1^2 đW = h_2^{\circ} - h_1^{\circ} \tag{6.33}$$

6.5 Comparison Between Bernoulli's Equation and the Energy Equation

The differential form of the modified Bernoulli equation [Eq. (4.41)] can be obtained from the energy equation after making the following modifications. In the absence of external work W, Eq. (6.28) becomes

$$J\, đq = J\, de + d\left(\frac{p}{\rho}\right) + d(\tfrac{1}{2}U^2) + g\, dz \tag{6.34}$$

It can be shown without great difficulty[3] that the system equation

$$JT\, ds - p\, d\left(\frac{1}{\rho}\right) = J\, de \tag{6.35}$$

made of properties alone applies both to reversible or irreversible processes and to systems or control volumes. This is because all terms in Eq.(6.35)are properties and consequently are not affected by the presence of motion. The temperature in the system equation is T (absolute), and the change of entropy is identified with ds. Substitution of de into the energy equation [Eq. (6.34)] yields

$$J\, đq = JT\, ds - p\, d\left(\frac{1}{\rho}\right) + d\left(\frac{p}{\rho}\right) + U\, dU + g\, dz$$

$$= JT\, ds + \frac{dp}{\rho} + U\, dU + g\, dz \tag{6.36}$$

The change of entropy in this relationship can occur, according to the second law of thermodynamics, through the external heat exchanged q

[3] E. F. Obert, *Thermodynamics*, McGraw-Hill Book Company, Inc., New York, 1948, pp. 138–139.

and through irreversibilities in the flow process. Assuming the flow to be adiabatic, then $đq = 0$, and the change of entropy owing to the heat transfer is zero. This still leaves, however, a possible change of entropy within the system caused by irreversible losses such as friction. If this entropy change is designated by ds_i, then Eq. (6.36) becomes

$$U\,dU + \frac{dp}{\rho} + g\,dz + JT\,ds_i = 0 \tag{6.37}$$

This equation is identical with that already derived in Chap. IV, Eq. (4.41). The internal loss dH is clearly seen here to be $JT\,ds_i$, which is an energy dissipated into some form of internal heat that raises the level of the internal entropy of the fluid. In the absence of external work and external heat, and for a steady flow, the modified differential Bernoulli equation is then the energy equation. In the steady-flow case the thermodynamic process occurs along the motion of the fluid; consequently, as a fluid system follows a streamline, it undergoes changes in its thermodynamic properties. The end states of the thermodynamic process correspond to two different positions on a streamline.

In the case of an isentropic flow, Eq. (6.37) is simplified and can be integrated to

$$\tfrac{1}{2}(U_2^2 - U_1^2) + \int_1^2 \frac{dp}{\rho} + g(z_2 - z_1) = 0$$

Problems

6.1 The internal energy per pound-mass within a system containing air can be described as $e = e_0 + 0.172\,T$, where e_0 is the internal energy at 0°F and T is the temperature in degrees Fahrenheit. If the properties of the system change with time, find the net heat and the mechanical power crossing the boundaries as a function of the rate of change of temperature.

6.2 Discuss if frictional work is involved in Eqs. (6.6) and (6.16).

6.3 In Eq. (6.6) identify the three terms in the mechanical power equation. Which is kinetic, potential and flow power?

6.4 In Sec. 6.4, what other sources of heat transfer Q could have been considered?

6.5 Does Eq. (6.16) contain work due to friction? Where would it have appeared from?

6.6 Show the analogy between Eq. (6.16) and Eqs. (5.5) and (5.7).

6.7 A system receives 150 Btu of heat from the surroundings while it delivers 200 Btu of work to the same surroundings. (*a*) Is this situation possible? (*b*) If so, explain why.

6.8 A system containing 1 lb_m of carbon monoxide undergoes a constant pressure expansion with the temperature changing 100°F. The system does work on the surroundings. (*a*) What is the maximum work obtainable under constant-pressure conditions? (*b*) Does the temperature increase or decrease after the expansion?

6.9 If the system in Prob. 6.8 is maintained at constant temperature $T = 1000°R$ and the gas is expanded with a pressure ratio of 5, what is the maximum work obtainable from this expansion?

6.10 In order to gain familiarity with orders of magnitude of velocity and elevation changes: (*a*) Compute the velocity increase in feet per second, starting from rest, for a kinetic-energy transfer of 1 Btu/lb_m. (*b*) For the same amount of energy transfer, compute the corresponding elevation change in feet.

6.11 If, in Prob. 6.1, the pressure-density relation is given by $p = 53.36\,\rho\,(T + 460)$, find the expression for the enthalpy in Btu per pound-mass in terms of the temperature.

6.12 The enthalpy, the velocity, and the elevation at the entrance of a control volume are, respectively, 500 Btu/lb_m, 100 ft/sec, and 50 ft. The same properties at the exit are 450 Btu/lb_m, 10 ft/sec, and zero elevation. Find the external rate of work done, in horsepower, by or on the control volume if there is a heat loss from the boundaries equal to 10 Btu/sec. The rate of fluid flow is 1 lb_m/sec.

6.13 In Prob. 6.12, evaluate the stagnation enthalpy at the inlet and outlet of the control volume.

6.14 A pipeline, carrying water between two points 100 ft of elevation apart, registers a pressure drop between these two points of 7 $lb_f/in.^2$. If the flow is adiabatic, find the amount of frictional heat in Btu per pound-mass that is dissipated to the surroundings. The cross section of the pipe is constant.

6.15 A pipeline carries water at constant temperature. At a point (1) in the pipeline, the diameter of the pipe is 5 in. and the pressure is 20 psi. At another point (2) 20 ft above (1), the diameter is 10 in. and the pressure is 13 psi. If the rate of flow is 1 ft^3/sec, what is the direction of flow?

The Motion of a Two-Dimensional Perfect Fluid

chapter VII

7.1 Introduction

This chapter will deal with the mechanics of the motion of a perfect fluid. Simple elementary motions will be considered as well as the motion around some bodies with simple geometries. The fact that the motion to be studied is that of a perfect fluid implies that the fluid does not possess any viscosity and that its density remains constant. This type of fluid was discussed in detail in Sec. 1.12. It was pointed out that when a perfect fluid flows over a solid boundary which is stationary with respect to the fluid, the fluid in the vicinity of the solid boundary is not influenced by any frictional effects between the boundary and the fluid. This condition, although not real, helps to determine certain aspects of the flow that are not affected by frictional resistance. Therefore, in this case the flow is said to slip over the boundary, and consequently no viscous drag is expected from this analysis. The purpose of the solid boundary is of geometrical importance; that is, it serves the purpose of guiding the flow according to its geometry.

This study deals with two-dimensional flows alone. It implies that the flow takes place only in two coordinate dimensions. In Cartesian coordinates it will be referred to as a motion on a plane with no variations in the third direction. The same two-dimensional motion in cylindrical and polar coordinates implies that there exists complete symmetry with respect to one axis. In other words, the conditions of the flows are the same all around a circle normal to the *axis of symmetry* and with the center on the axis of symmetry. This condition is often referred to as the *condition of axisymmetry.*

7.2 The Stream Function

For steady motion the stream function $\psi'(x,y)$ or $\psi'(r,\theta)$ is a mathematical function representing the geometry of the stream surfaces. In Sec. 3.11, through the equation of continuity, the stream function was related to the velocity of the flow field in the following manner:

$$\boldsymbol{b} \times \nabla\psi' = \rho\boldsymbol{U}, \tag{7.1}$$

meaning that $\boldsymbol{U}$, $\nabla\psi'$ and $\boldsymbol{b}$ form an orthogonal set of vectors. If the motion is on a plane normal to the unit vector $\boldsymbol{b}$, then $\boldsymbol{U}$ is normal to $\nabla\psi'$ or in other words that $\boldsymbol{U}$ is tangent to the surface $\psi' =$ constant.

In Cartesian coordinates, let $\boldsymbol{b}$ represent the z-direction, or, in other words, let $\boldsymbol{b} = \boldsymbol{k}$:

$$\boldsymbol{k} \times \left(\boldsymbol{i}\frac{\partial}{\partial x} + \boldsymbol{j}\frac{\partial}{\partial y} + \boldsymbol{k}\frac{\partial}{\partial z}\right)\psi' = \rho(\boldsymbol{i}u + \boldsymbol{j}v + \boldsymbol{k}w)$$

Then,

$$\boldsymbol{j}\frac{\partial\psi'}{\partial x} - \boldsymbol{i}\frac{\partial\psi'}{\partial y} = \boldsymbol{i}\rho u + \boldsymbol{j}\rho v$$

From this we deduce that

$$\begin{aligned} \rho u &= -\frac{\partial\psi'}{\partial y} \\ v &= \frac{\partial\psi'}{\partial x} \end{aligned} \tag{7.2}$$

From Eq. (7.1) it is apparent that the units of ψ' are lb_m per second and per unit length. Since this chapter is considering the motion of a perfect fluid which has a constant density, we can define a stream function $\psi(x,y)$ or $\psi(r,\theta)$ as

$$\psi = \frac{\psi'}{\rho}$$

Then,

$$u = -\frac{\partial \psi}{\partial y}$$
$$v = \frac{\partial \psi}{\partial x} \tag{7.3}$$

In cylindrical coordinates for two-dimensional motion, the velocity component along the axis of the cylinder is zero, and the other two components have been shown to be

$$v_r = -\frac{1}{r}\frac{\partial \psi}{\partial \theta}$$
$$v_\theta = \frac{\partial \psi}{\partial r} \tag{7.4}$$

The velocity components for the spherical coordinates will be derived in terms of the stream function in the discussion on the point source.

It was deduced in Sec. 3.11 that the stream function, if it existed, was a property of the fluid such that its differential $d\psi$ was exact, meaning, from calculus, that

$$\frac{\partial}{\partial x}\left(\frac{\partial \psi}{\partial y}\right) = \frac{\partial}{\partial y}\left(\frac{\partial \psi}{\partial x}\right)$$

Substitution of Eq. (7.3) then yields

$$\frac{\partial u}{\partial x} + \frac{\partial v}{\partial y} = 0$$

which is the mass-continuity equation for a steady two-dimensional and incompressible flow [Eq. (3.19)]. This implies that, for a stream function to exist as a property of the fluid motion, the equation of continuity must be satisfied. This is not much of a restriction on any flow, since for real solutions the mass must always be accounted for.

It was also mentioned that since the stream function was a mathematical expression describing the stream surfaces, the expression

$$\psi(x,y) = \text{constant} \tag{7.5}$$

is a description of the geometry of that surface. Since only two-dimensional cases are being discussed here, every constant value of ψ will describe the contour of the streamline on the x–y-plane. It has already been shown that the difference between two stream functions $\Delta\psi = \psi_2 - \psi_1 = C_2 - C_1$ represents the volume rate of flow per unit depth flowing between these two streamlines. Here C_2 and C_1 are the two constant values describing the particular streamline, as given by Eq. (7.5).

Furthermore, it was shown that, in the case of irrotational motion in the x–y-plane, the vorticity $\zeta_z = 0$ and

$$\frac{\partial v}{\partial x} - \frac{\partial u}{\partial y} = 0$$

When applying the relations of the velocities in terms of the stream function as given by Eq. (7.3), the above vorticity equation becomes

$$\frac{\partial}{\partial x}\left(\frac{-\partial\psi}{\partial x}\right) - \frac{\partial}{\partial y}\left(\frac{\partial\psi}{\partial y}\right) = 0$$
$$\frac{\partial^2\psi}{\partial x^2} + \frac{\partial^2\psi}{\partial y^2} = 0 \tag{7.6}$$

This equation has already been derived in Sec. 3.16. It represents the differential equation for the motion of a steady two-dimensional irrotational perfect fluid in terms of the stream function ψ. The equation is called *Laplace's equation* for the stream function. Together with the boundary conditions of the flow, it will provide a solution for the conditions imposed. From knowledge of the stream function, the velocities u and v can be determined through Eq. (7.3), and from Bernoulli's equation the pressure field is obtained. Thus a solution of $\psi(x,y)$ implies a knowledge of the velocity and pressure fields of the flow.

7.3 The Velocity Potential

In Sec. 3.14 the vorticity was defined as

$$\boldsymbol{\zeta} = \nabla \times \boldsymbol{U}$$

Since vorticity is a measure of the rotation in the fluid, an irrotational flow is one in which $\boldsymbol{\zeta} = 0$. Then it follows that the velocity vector $\boldsymbol{U}$ in an irrotational flow is very special. In fact, its curl is zero.

$$\nabla \times \boldsymbol{U} = 0$$

We shall see in Sec. A.22 that if the curl of a vector is zero then the vector can be expressed in terms of the gradient of a scalar function.

This scalar function is called the *potential*. Thus, for an irrotational flow

$$\boldsymbol{U} = -\nabla\phi \tag{7.7}$$

In Cartesian coordinates where $\phi(x,y,z)$ represents the velocity potential, the components of $\boldsymbol{U}$ are given by

$$u = -\frac{\partial\phi}{\partial x}$$

$$v = -\frac{\partial\phi}{\partial y} \tag{7.8}$$

$$w = -\frac{\partial\phi}{\partial z}$$

In cylindrical coordinates,

$$vr = -\frac{\partial\phi}{\partial r}$$

$$v_\theta = -\frac{1}{r}\frac{\partial\phi}{\partial\theta} \tag{7.9}$$

$$v_z = -\frac{\partial\phi}{\partial z}$$

It is seen from Eqs. (7.3) and (7.9) that complete information about the velocity is contained in the potential and stream functions. If a solution of ψ or ϕ is known, then the velocity field is also known.

7.4 The Geometrical Relationship Between the Stream Function and the Velocity Potential

In Sec. 3.11 and according to Fig. 3.13(b), the stream-function increment between two points A and C in the fluid was defined as the volume rate of flow per unit depth crossing the element AC. Consequently,

$$d\psi_{AC} = U\cos\theta\, ds \qquad [7.10(a)]$$

Since $\theta = [90° - (\alpha - \beta)]$, as shown in Fig. 7.1, then $\cos\theta = \sin(\alpha - \beta)$; and

$$d\psi_{AC} = U\sin(\alpha - \beta)\, ds \qquad [7.10(b)]$$

Noting that the following trigonometric relations are true,

$$\sin(\alpha - \beta) = \sin\alpha\cos\beta - \cos\alpha\sin\beta$$

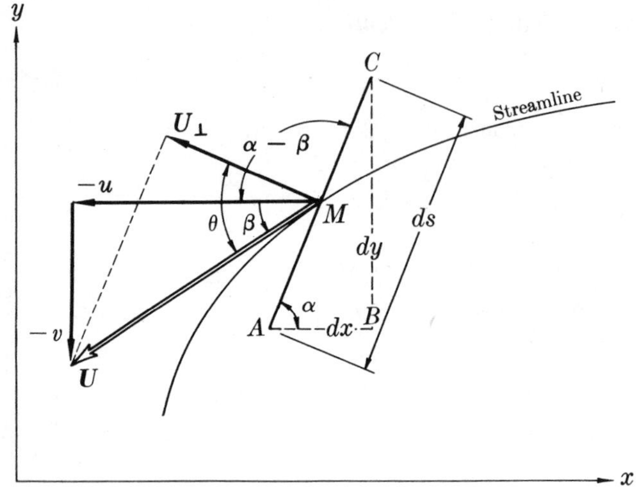

Figure 7.1
Two-dimensional motion.

and also that

$$\sin\alpha = dy/ds; \qquad \cos\alpha = dx/ds$$
$$\sin\beta = -v/U; \qquad \cos\beta = -u/U$$

then the differential equation for the stream function becomes

$$d\psi_{AC} = U\left[\frac{v}{U}\frac{dx}{ds} - \frac{u}{U}\frac{dy}{ds}\right]$$
$$= v\,dx - u\,dy \tag{7.11}$$

This is Eq. (3.29) already derived by a different approach through the continuity relations.

If we define the function ϕ such that, similar to Eq. (7.9), its differential is given by the value of the velocity U along ds times the length ds. Accordingly, this definition can be written as

$$d\phi_{AC} = U\sin\theta\,ds$$
$$= U\cos(\alpha - \beta)\,ds \tag{7.12}$$

The cosine of the difference of two angles is

$$\cos(\alpha - \beta) = \cos\alpha\cos\beta + \sin\alpha\sin\beta$$

and then Eq. (7.12) becomes

$$d\phi_{AC} = -U\left(\frac{dx}{ds}\frac{u}{U} + \frac{dy}{ds}\frac{v}{U}\right) ds$$

$$= -u\,dx - v\,dy \tag{7.13}$$

Like the stream function, since $\phi = f(x,y)$, then its differential is also

$$d\phi = \frac{\partial \phi}{\partial x}\,dx + \frac{\partial \phi}{\partial y}\,dy \tag{7.14}$$

Equating the coefficients of Eqs. (7.13) and (7.14), the velocity components can be expressed as

$$u = -\frac{\partial \phi}{\partial x}$$

$$v = -\frac{\partial \phi}{\partial y} \tag{7.15}$$

These relations for the velocity u and v are very similar to those obtained in terms of the stream function as given in Eq. (7.3). For the condition for ϕ to exist and for it to be expressed in the exact differential form as given in Eq. (7.14), the following calculus relation must be true:

$$\frac{\partial}{\partial y}\left(\frac{\partial \phi}{\partial x}\right) = \frac{\partial}{\partial x}\left(\frac{\partial \phi}{\partial y}\right)$$

After substitution of relations given in Eq. (7.15), this condition becomes

$$\frac{\partial u}{\partial y} = \frac{\partial v}{\partial x}$$

which is the condition of irrotationality, ($\zeta = 0$), as given when Eq. (3.33) is equated to zero. Therefore, in order for the velocity components u and v to be expressed as Eq. (7.15), the conditions of irrotationality must exist; that is, the flow must be free of rotation. Then and only then it is said that the velocity U can be expressed in terms of a *velocity potential* ϕ. The motion is called a *potential motion.*

Carrying this discussion just a bit further one can see that, if the continuity conditions are also satisfied according to Eq. (3.19), then

$$\frac{\partial u}{\partial x} + \frac{\partial v}{\partial y} = 0$$

and for u and v, using the relations of Eq. (7.15) in terms of the velocity potential ϕ, the continuity equation becomes

$$\frac{\partial}{\partial x}\left(\frac{\partial \phi}{\partial x}\right) + \frac{\partial}{\partial y}\left(\frac{\partial \phi}{\partial y}\right) = 0$$
$$\frac{\partial^2 \phi}{\partial x^2} + \frac{\partial^2 \phi}{\partial y^2} = 0 \qquad (7.16)$$

This indicates that the velocity potential ϕ also obeys the same Laplace differential equation as the stream function ψ as given by Eq. (7.6).

The geometrical properties of the stream surface $\psi(x,y) = C_1$ and the potential surface $\phi(x,y) = C_2$ are such that the two surfaces are orthogonal at the point P where they cross each other. Since these surfaces are two-dimensional, $\psi(x,y) = C_1$ and $\phi(x,y) = C_2$ represent, in general, two curved lines intersecting at the point P. This is shown in Fig. 7.2 where, at the same point, the tangents to each curved line

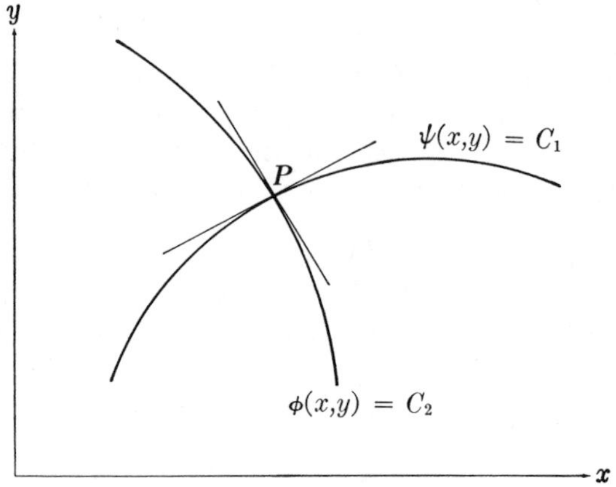

Figure 7.2
Orthogonal properties of ψ and ϕ.

are also drawn. The constants C represent the family of such lines, and each constant represents one member of the entire family.

By definition of orthogonality of ϕ and ψ, the tangents at the point P must be orthogonal or, in other words, the product of the slopes at the point P must be equal to -1.

$$\left(\frac{dy}{dx}\right)_{\phi=C_2}\left(\frac{dy}{dx}\right)_{\psi=C_1} = -1 \qquad (7.17)$$

The subscripts to the derivatives refer to the curve along which the slope has been evaluated. The total changes of ϕ and ψ can also be evaluated from

$$d\phi = \frac{\partial \phi}{\partial x}\,dx + \frac{\partial \phi}{\partial y}\,dy$$

and

$$d\psi = \frac{\partial \psi}{\partial x}\,dx + \frac{\partial \psi}{\partial y}\,dy$$

but along C_1 and C_2 these total changes are zero, since ψ and ϕ are constants, and then the slopes are thus evaluated:

$$\left(\frac{dy}{dx}\right)_{\phi=C_2} = -\frac{\partial \phi/\partial x}{\partial \phi/\partial y}$$

$$\left(\frac{dy}{dx}\right)_{\psi=C_1} = -\frac{\partial \psi/\partial x}{\partial \psi/\partial y}$$

Substitution of these slopes in Eq. (7.17) yields

$$\frac{\dfrac{\partial \phi}{\partial x}\dfrac{\partial \psi}{\partial x}}{\dfrac{\partial \phi}{\partial y}\dfrac{\partial \psi}{\partial y}} = -1$$

This equality is verified when the relations of Eqs. (7.3) and (7.15) are used. Therefore, the proof of the orthogonality is completed.

7.5 The Point Source

The flow of fluid emanating from a point and flowing radially in equal amounts in all three directions is called the *point-source flow*. A *point sink* is the reverse flow of a point source, the flow going radially inward toward a point. Since this flow is spherical in nature, it is convenient to express the velocity component in spherical coordinates. It was said that the point source has only a radial component of the velocity, but, for a more general case of two-dimensional motion, let us first consider a flow with two velocity components v_r and v_θ. Since two-dimensional motions are considered, let the third component of velocity v_α be zero and let no variations of properties with the coordinate α be allowed.

Consider the origin O in Fig. 7.3 and a point A a distance r away from O at an angle θ from the x-axis and at an angle α on the circle with diameter ADA'. These three coordinates r, θ, and α establish the

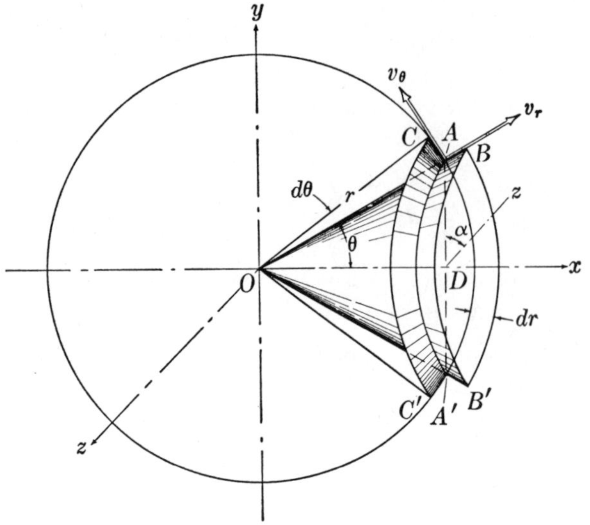

Figure 7.3
Spherical representation of two-dimensional flow.

spherical location of any point A from O. Let there be two velocity components at A, as shown. The elemental surface $CAA'C'$ is a strip on the sphere with radius r contained between the two cones, one with angle θ and the other with angle $\theta + d\theta$. The elemental surface $ABB'A'$ is an extension of the conical surface with angle θ, but it extends between r and $r + dr$.

For two-dimensional flow it has been assumed that there are no variations of v_r and v_θ with α. The volume rate of flow emanating from the surface $ACC'A$, and for positive ψ defined for a flow from right to left as in Fig. 7.1,

$$\begin{aligned} -2\pi\, d\psi &= 2\pi(AD)(r\, d\theta)v_r \\ &= 2\pi(r \sin\theta)(r\, d\theta)v_r \end{aligned}$$

and

$$v_r = -\frac{1}{r^2 \sin\theta}\frac{\partial\psi}{\partial\theta} \tag{7.18}$$

In the same fashion the volume rate of flow emanating from the surface $ABB'A'$ is

$$\begin{aligned} 2\pi\, d\psi &= 2\pi(AD)(dr)v_\theta \\ &= 2\pi(r \sin\theta)(dr)v_\theta \end{aligned}$$

and

$$v_\theta = \frac{1}{r \sin\theta} \frac{\partial \psi}{\partial r} \tag{7.19}$$

The same velocity components in terms of the potential function can easily be shown to be related as follows:

$$v_r = -\frac{\partial \phi}{\partial r} \quad \text{and} \quad v_\theta = -\frac{\partial \phi}{r\,\partial \theta} \tag{7.20}$$

In the case of a point source, $v_\theta = 0$, and, if the total volume flow emanating from the point source is k, then, at any radius r this volume rate of flow will be

$$k = 4\pi r^2 v_r$$

or

$$v_r = \frac{k}{4\pi} \frac{1}{r^2} \tag{7.21}$$

The quantity $k/4\pi$ is called the strength of the source, and the radial velocity varies inversely as the radial distance squared.

Since v_r is now known and $v_\theta = 0$ then Eq. (7.20) can be integrated and the velocity potential for the point source can be found. The component $v_\theta = 0$ implies that ϕ is not a function of θ, and therefore

$$\frac{\partial \phi}{\partial r} = \frac{d\phi}{dr} = -\frac{k}{4\pi} \frac{1}{r^2}$$

Integration of this equation yields

$$\phi = \frac{k}{4\pi} \frac{1}{r} + \text{constant}$$

The constant is an arbitrary level which can be set to be zero if $\phi = 0$ when $r = \infty$, so that the new value of

$$\phi = \frac{k}{4\pi} \frac{1}{r} \tag{7.22}$$

measures the potential function from the value at $r = \infty$. Equation (7.22) implies that when $r = constant$ then $\phi = constant$. The surface represented by $r = constant$ is a spherical shell; thus the potential surfaces $\phi = constant$ are spherical shells.

The stream function is obtained in the same fashion if Eq. (7.21) is equated to Eq. (7.18). Remember again that since $v_\theta = 0$, ψ is not a function of r.

$$-\frac{k}{4\pi}\frac{1}{r^2} = \frac{1}{r^2 \sin\theta}\frac{d\psi}{d\theta}$$

$$d\psi = -\frac{k}{4\pi}\sin\theta\, d\theta$$

and, upon integration,

$$\psi = \frac{k}{4\pi}\cos\theta + \text{constant}$$

If arbitrarily $\psi = 0$ when $\theta = \pi/2$, then the constant can be eliminated, since all new ψ are measured with reference to that at $\theta = \pi/2$. Then

$$\psi = \frac{k}{4\pi}\cos\theta \tag{7.23}$$

Since it was shown that these stream surfaces must be orthogonal to the potential surfaces, which for the point source are spherical shells, the stream surface is found for ψ = *constant*, implying that θ = *constant*. These are the conical surfaces shown in Fig. 7.4. Therefore,

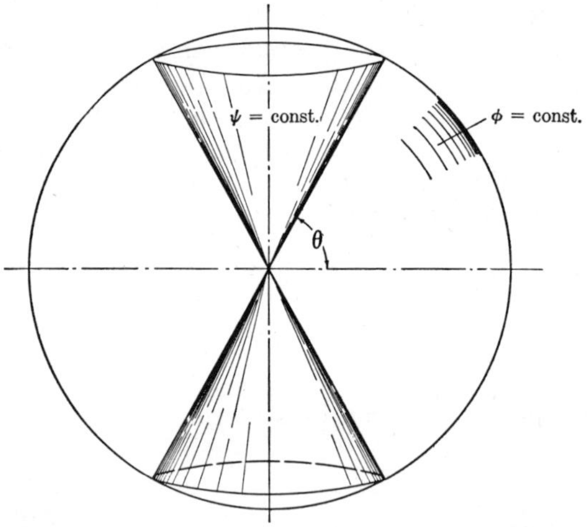

Figure 7.4
Potential and stream surfaces for a point source.

shells of various radii will constitute the family of potential surfaces, whereas conical surfaces of constant θ will make up the family of stream surfaces. The solution for a point sink is identical to Eqs. (7.22) and (7.23), except that the signs will be positive owing to the fact that the velocity is toward the center instead of outward. In other words, it is possible to say that the strength of a source is $k/4\pi$ while that of a sink is $-k/4\pi$.

Illustrative Example 7.1

A point sink draws 6 ft³/sec from an infinite fluid. What are the values of the potential and of the radial velocity at $r = 6$ in.?

$$\phi = -\frac{k}{4\pi}\frac{1}{r}$$

$$= -\frac{6}{4\pi} \times \frac{1}{0.5}$$

$$= -0.956 \text{ ft}^2/\text{sec}$$

The velocity can be obtained from the potential function or from the stream function

$$v_r = -\frac{d\phi}{dr} = \frac{1}{r^2 \sin\theta}\frac{d\psi}{d\theta}$$

$$= \frac{k}{4\pi}\frac{1}{r^2}$$

$$= -1.91 \text{ ft/sec}$$

7.6 Superposition of Point Sources on a Finite Line Segment

Since the stream function and the potential function obey a set of linear differential equations as given by Eqs. (7.6) and (7.16), the solution of any combined perfect fluid and irrotational flow fields is equal to the sum of the individual solutions. The resultant solution for point sources superimposed on a line segment will be the algebraic sum of the individual solutions for each point source.

As shown in Fig. 7.5, let an infinite number of sources be placed an infinitesimal distance apart along a finite line of length L. In order for the total strength of the line to remain finite, let $k(\xi)$ be the strength of the line per unit length at the position ξ along L. In other words, ξ is the coordinate along x of a particular source element $d\xi$. Since the sources are strung along the x-axis, the entire flow field will show symmetry with respect to that axis; that is, on a plane perpendicular to x and at the same radial distance from x, the properties of the flow

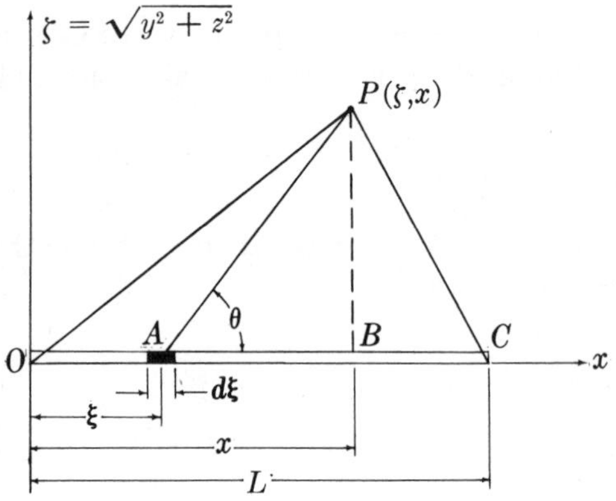

Figure 7.5
Geometry of the superimposed field.

field will be constant. Referring to the coordinate system in Fig. 7.3, this implies that the flow field is not a function of α, and consequently, along a circle of radius $\zeta = \sqrt{y^2 + z^2}$ on a plane normal to x, the properties of the flow will be constant.

Consider a point $P(\zeta,x)$ in the flow field where the properties of the motion are to be determined. The conditions of the flow will be the same at every point on the circle with radius PB and on a plane normal to x. Let θ be the angle of AP from the x-axis. It must be remembered here that there exist two independent variables along the x-axis. The variable ξ represents the location of the elementary source, and the x-coordinate represents the location of the point P where the flow field is to be evaluated. These two variables must be kept independent of each other. According to Eq. (7.23), the elementary value of the stream function at the point P owing to the elementary source at A of strength $k(\xi)\, d\xi$ is

$$d\psi = \frac{k(\xi)\, d\xi}{4\pi} \cos\theta$$

Since there are an infinite number of such sources from O to C along L, the total value of the stream function at P will be the integral of the preceding expression:

$$\psi = \int_O^L \frac{k(\xi)\cos\theta}{4\pi}\, d\xi \tag{7.24}$$

From the geometry in Fig. 7.5, $\cos\theta = \dfrac{(x - \xi)}{\sqrt{\zeta^2 + (x - \xi)^2}}$. Letting

$(x - \xi) = \chi$ and thus $d\xi = -d\chi$, and also assuming that the strength $k(\xi)$ of the sources is a constant with ξ, Eq. (7.24) becomes

$$\begin{aligned}\psi &= \frac{k}{4\pi}\int_{x-L}^{x} \frac{\chi\, d\chi}{\sqrt{\zeta^2 + \chi^2}} \\ &= -\frac{k}{4\pi}\left[\sqrt{\zeta^2 + (x - L)^2} - \sqrt{\zeta^2 + x^2}\right] \qquad (7.25) \\ &= \frac{k}{4\pi}(\overline{PO} - \overline{PC})\end{aligned}$$

The location of the stream surface $\psi = 0$, according to Eq. (7.25) occurs at the symmetry plane $x = L/2$.

The potential function can be obtained starting from Eq. (7.22) and applying to the point P:

$$d\phi = \frac{k(\xi)\, d\xi}{4\pi} \frac{1}{\sqrt{\zeta^2 + (x - \xi)^2}}$$

Upon substitution of the change in variables performed in the determination of ψ, the value of the potential function at P becomes

$$\begin{aligned}\phi &= -\frac{k}{4\pi}\int_{x}^{x-L} \frac{d\chi}{\sqrt{\zeta^2 + \chi^2}} \\ &= -\frac{k}{4\pi}\ln\left[\frac{\sqrt{\zeta^2 + (x - L)^2} + (x - L)}{x + \sqrt{\zeta^2 + x^2}}\right] \qquad (7.26)\end{aligned}$$

Solutions of the stream function and the potential function are plotted in Fig. 7.6. Changing the coordinate axis from $x = 0$ to $x = L/2 = a$, then, in terms of the new location of O, the new coordinate $x' = x - a$. The two solutions of Eqs. (7.25) and (7.26) in terms of x' become

$$\begin{aligned}\psi &= \frac{k}{4\pi}\left[\sqrt{\zeta^2 + (x' + a)^2} - \sqrt{\zeta^2 + (x' - a)^2}\right] \\ \phi &= -\frac{k}{4\pi}\ln\frac{(x' - a) + \sqrt{\zeta^2 + (x' - a)^2}}{(x' + a) + \sqrt{\zeta^2 + (x' + a)^2}}\end{aligned} \qquad (7.27)$$

If Eq. (7.25) is multiplied and divided by L, the stream function becomes

$$\psi = \frac{Lk}{4\pi}\left\{\sqrt{\left(\frac{\zeta}{L}\right)^2 + \left(\frac{x}{L}\right)^2} - \sqrt{\left(\frac{\zeta}{L}\right)^2 + \left(\frac{x}{L} - 1\right)^2}\right.$$

Now, if the limit of this equation is taken when $L \to \infty$, the stream function will approach infinity if k remains finite. But instead, if

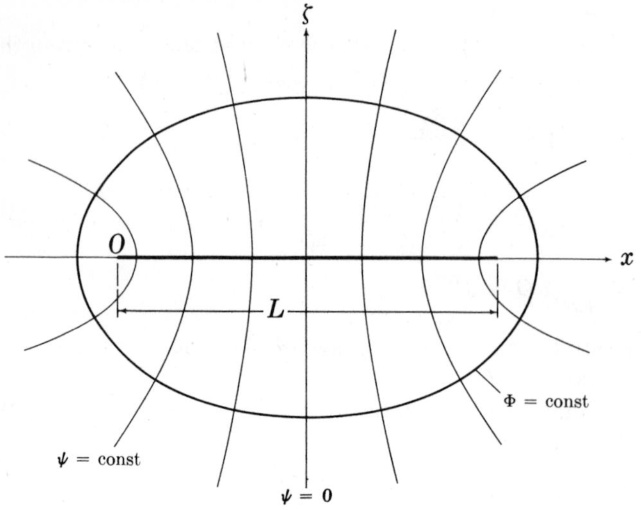

Figure 7.6
Flow field for the finite line source.

$k \to 0$ so that the product $\dfrac{kL}{4\pi} = K$, the total strength of the line remains finite; then, as L goes to infinity, $\psi \to K$. The flow field becomes that of an infinite line source with cylindrical ϕ = constant surfaces and radial planes for ψ = constant, as shown in Fig. 7.7. On the x–y-plane $\psi = K$ for a complete turn of α. For a *two-dimensional rectilinear*

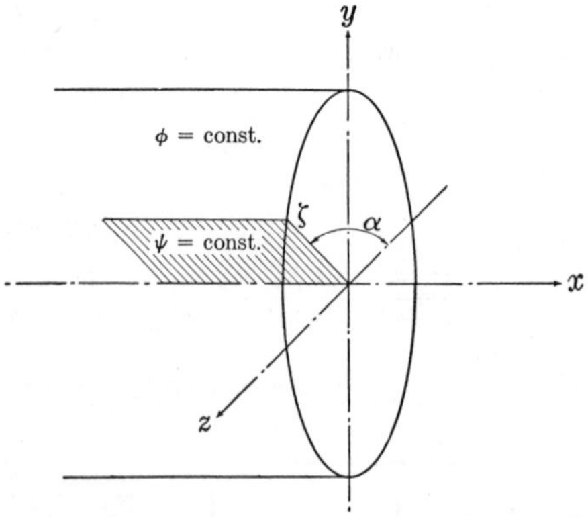

Figure 7.7
Geometry on a plane perpendicular to x.

source and for any arc α, the stream function will have the value of

$$\psi = \frac{K}{2\pi}\alpha \tag{7.28}$$

Illustrative Example 7.2

Show that the intersection of an x = constant plane and the stream and potential surfaces in Fig. 7.6 make circles. This actually indicates axisymmetry.

Take, for instance, the plane $x = 0$. Then the solution of Eq. (7.25) for this value of x becomes

$$\psi = \frac{k}{4\pi}(\sqrt{\zeta^2} - \sqrt{\zeta^2 + L^2})$$

$$-\frac{4\pi\psi}{k} + \zeta = \sqrt{\zeta^2 + L^2}$$

$$\zeta = \frac{2\pi\psi}{k} - \frac{kL^2}{8\pi\psi}$$

$$= \frac{2\pi\psi}{k} - \frac{ka^2}{2\pi\psi}$$

This indicates that for a given ψ = constant surface ζ = constant, which is a circle.

The same applies to the potential function sliced with a plane $x = 0$. Letting x vanish in Eq. (7.26) the result is

$$\phi = -\frac{k}{4\pi}\ln\left[\frac{\sqrt{\zeta^2 + L^2} - L}{\zeta}\right]$$

$$e^{\frac{4\pi\phi}{k}} = \frac{\sqrt{\zeta^2 + L^2} - L}{\zeta}$$

Solving for ζ,

$$\zeta = \frac{Le^{-4\pi\phi/k}}{1 - e^{-8\pi\phi/k}}$$

This indicates again that the intersecting line is a circle with ζ = constant for any given ϕ.

7.7 The Two-Dimensional Rectilinear Source. The Line Source

The stream function for the infinite line source was developed in the preceding section. It can also be developed from a knowledge of the radial velocity. According to Fig. 7.8, if K is the output of the source

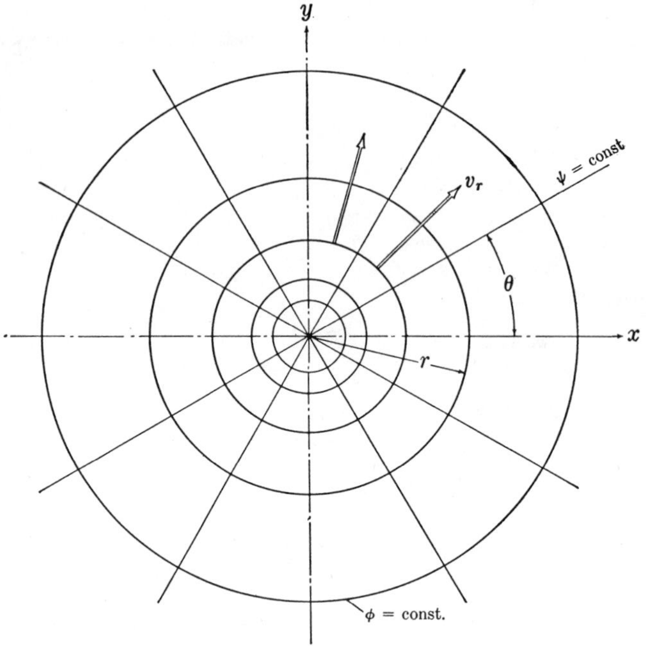

Figure 7.8
A cross section of the line source.

in cubic feet per second per foot deep, then at any r this rate of flow will equal

$$2\pi r v_r = K$$

$$v_r = \frac{K}{2\pi}\frac{1}{r} \tag{7.29}$$

Equation (7.4) related the velocity components in cylindrical coordinates in terms of the stream function, and Eq. (7.9) did the same in terms of the velocity potential. But, since $v_\theta = 0$,

$$v_r = -\frac{1}{r}\frac{d\psi}{d\theta} = -\frac{d\phi}{dr} = \frac{K}{2\pi}\frac{1}{r}$$

and, upon integration,

$$\psi = -\frac{K}{2\pi}\theta + \text{constant}$$

$$\phi = -\frac{K}{2\pi}\ln r + \text{constant}$$

The two constants can be dissolved if, arbitrarily, ψ is set to zero at $\theta = 0$ and likewise if $\phi = 0$ when r is unity. Then the two equations become

$$\psi = -\frac{K}{2\pi}\,\theta$$
$$\phi = -\frac{K}{2\pi}\ln r \tag{7.30}$$

For the line sink the value of K must be replaced by $-K$.

Figure 7.8 is a diagram of the cross section of a line source. According to Eq. (7.30), the stream surfaces are radial planes with equal increments of ψ for equal increments in angle θ. Arbitrarily, $\psi = 0$ is the positive x-axis, and it increases in the conventional sense in which θ increases. The potential function is constant for constant r, and consequently they are represented by concentric circles. These potential circles are not equally spaced for equal increments in the ϕ values; for equal $\Delta\phi$ the spacing between them varies as $1/r$.

7.8 Flow from Two Line Sources

Two line sources of equal strength K are placed at a distance $2a$ apart along the x-axis, as shown in Fig. 7.9. The solution of this combined flow field is that of the sum of the individual solutions for each source. Let the value of the stream and potential function be evaluated at an arbitrary point $P(x,y)$. For this, the contribution of each source to the point P is added as follows:

$$\psi = -\frac{K}{2\pi}(\theta_1 + \theta_2)$$
$$\phi = -\frac{K}{2\pi}(\ln r_1 + \ln r_2) \tag{7.31}$$
$$= -\frac{K}{2\pi}\ln r_1 r_2$$

These equations can be easily transformed into Cartesian notation if the following trigonometric relations are considered:

$$\tan\theta_1 = -\frac{y}{a - x}; \qquad \tan\theta_2 = \frac{y}{a + x}$$
$$\tan(\theta_1 + \theta_2) = \frac{\tan\theta_1 + \tan\theta_2}{1 - \tan\theta_1\tan\theta_2}$$

Upon substitution,

$$\theta_1 + \theta_2 = \tan^{-1} \frac{2yx}{x^2 - y^2 - a^2}$$

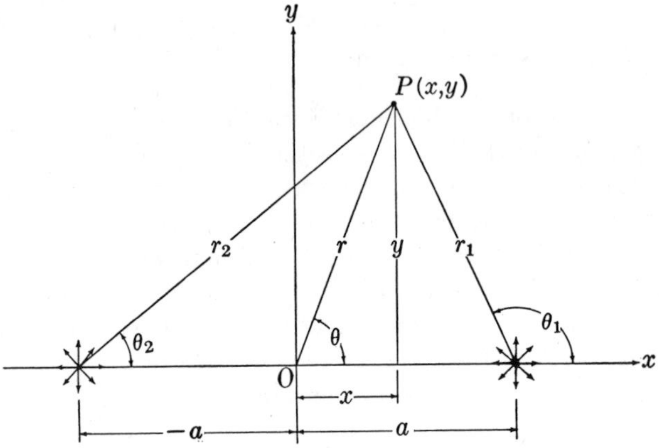

Figure 7.9
Geometry of the two-line-source system.

These angles are now substituted in the expression for the stream function, and the result will be

$$\psi = -\frac{K}{2\pi} \tan^{-1} \frac{2yx}{x^2 - y^2 - a^2} \tag{7.32}$$

The geometrical form of these streamlines is determined by solving this preceding equation.

$$\tan \frac{2\pi\psi}{K} = \frac{2yx}{x^2 - y^2 - a^2}$$

If $\cot \frac{2\pi\psi}{K} = m$ is introduced, then the streamline contour equation reads:

$$x^2 - y^2 - 2mxy = a^2$$

This is the equation of a hyperbola with its axes rotated an angle equivalent to $\frac{1}{2} \tan^{-1} (-m)$. The value of m is constant for a given streamline ψ = constant.

The contour of the potential lines is determined by replacing

$r_1 = \sqrt{y^2 + (a - x)^2}$ and $r_2 = \sqrt{y^2 + (a + x)^2}$ in the expression for ϕ in Eq. (7.31). Introducing $e^{\frac{4\pi\phi}{K}} = n$, the contour equation becomes

$$(y^2 + x^2) + 2a^2(y^2 - x^2) + a^4 = n$$

Every value of n determines one potential line, and the preceding equation determines its contour.

This flow field is shown in Fig. 7.10, which was constructed graphically. The graphic solution was carried out in the following manner: Arbitrarily, the flow of each source was divided into 24 streamlines labeled from 0 to 12 on the upper half of the plane in a counterclockwise direction. At the point of intersection of two streamlines or two potential lines, the value of the new stream function and potential function for the combined flow is the sum of the intersecting values. The streamline of the combined field was drawn by connecting equal-valued intersections. For instance, the streamline of symmetry yy' has the value of 12, since it joins the intersection of streamlines adding up to 12.

7.9 A Line Source Near a Wall

The solution of the flow from a line source situated near a wall at a distance a is the same as that in the previous section. It can be seen in Fig. 7.10 that the axis yy' represents a streamline across which fluid is not permitted to flow, and consequently, since the flow is nonviscous, the streamline can be replaced by a solid wall. The problem now reduces to a source at a distance a from the wall which, together with its reflection, gives the modified flow field.

As shown in Fig. 7.11, let a source O situated at a distance a from the wall be considered. The value of the streamline at a point P will be the value of the streamline at the angle θ_1 plus the value of the streamline OA reflected from the wall into AP. The streamline OP has the value of $K\theta_1/2\pi$, and the reflected streamline AP has the value of $K(180° - \theta_2)/2\pi$. So

$$\psi_P = \frac{K}{2\pi}(\theta_1 + 180° - \theta_2)$$

Graphically, if OP has the value of 8, the streamline OA will have

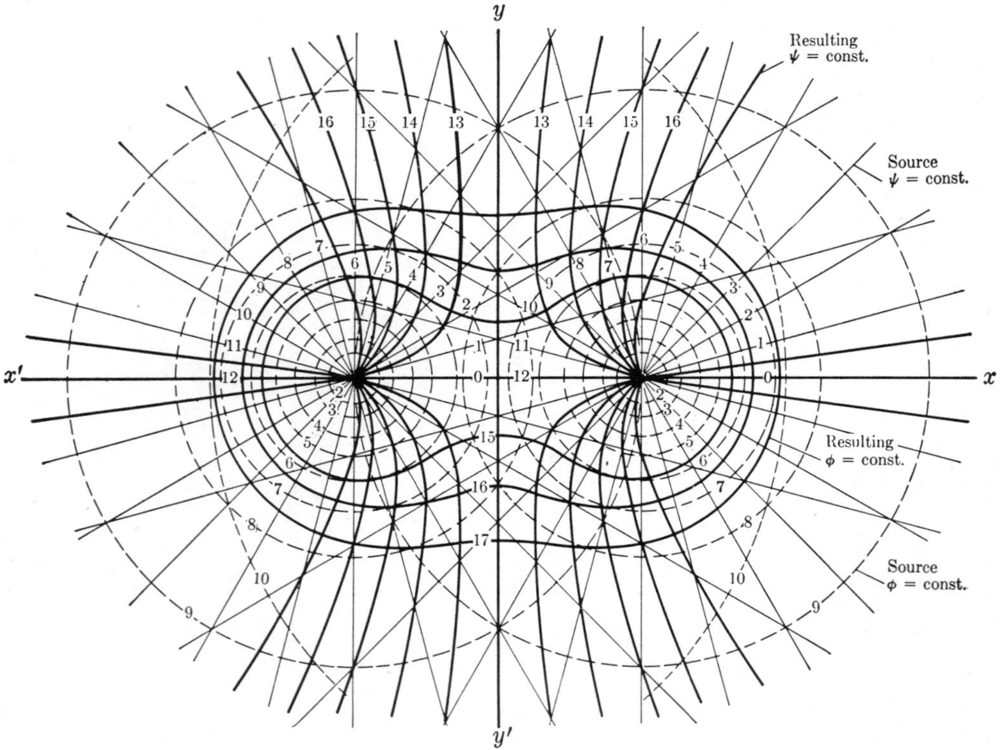

Figure 7.10
Streamlines and potential lines for a pair of sources of equal strength.

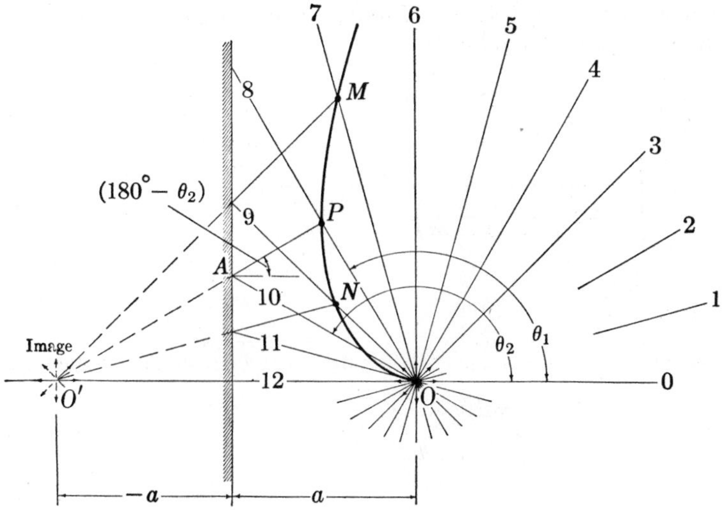

Figure 7.11
Graphic solution of flow for source near a wall.

the value of 10, and the reflected streamline AP having the angle of $(180° - \theta_2)$ will have the value of $12 - 10 = 2$. Therefore

$$\psi_P = 8 + 2$$
$$= 10$$

The points M and N will have the same value and will belong to the same streamline.

The same treatment can be applied to a source situated in front of a corner wall. The student should try the solution of the flow of a line source in a $\pi/2$ corner.

Illustrative Example 7.3

A line source of strength K is located on the x-axis at a distance $x = a$, and the y-axis is a rigid wall. Determine the velocity distribution along the wall and find the position where it reaches a maximum.

The solution of the flow from a line source at a distance a from a wall was found to be the same as that of two sources placed a distance $2a$ apart. According to Eq. (7.32), this solution for the stream function is

$$\psi = -\frac{K}{2\pi} \tan^{-1} \frac{2yx}{x^2 - y^2 - a^2}$$

The only component of the velocity at the wall is v which, according to Eq. (7.3), can be deduced from the stream function.

$$v = \left.\frac{\partial \psi}{\partial x}\right]_{x=0}$$

$$= -\frac{K}{2\pi}\left[\frac{1}{1+\left(\dfrac{2yx}{x^2-y^2-a^2}\right)^2}\,\frac{(x^2-y^2-a^2)2y-4yx^2}{(x^2-y^2-a^2)^2}\right]_{x=0}$$

$$= \frac{K}{2\pi}\frac{2y}{y^2+a^2}$$

and in dimensionless form the velocity distribution can be rewritten in the form

$$\frac{\pi a v}{K} = \frac{y/a}{(y/a)^2+1}$$

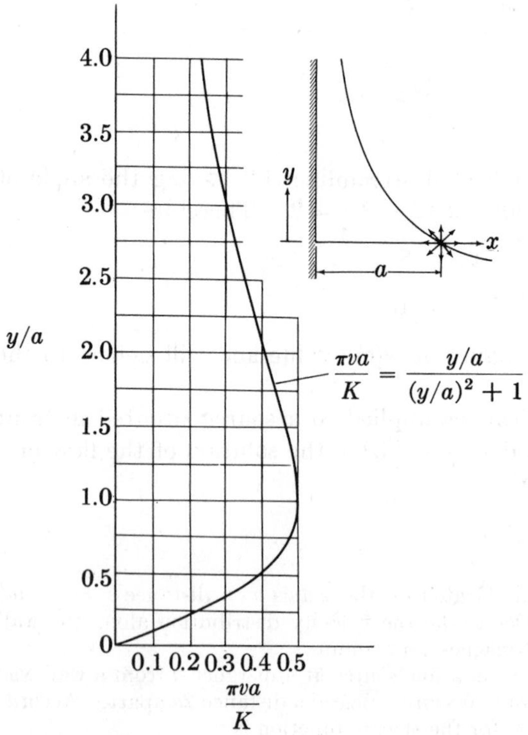

Figure 7.12
Velocity distribution at the wall.

This equation is plotted in Fig. 7.12. The maximum value can be obtained by differentiating v with respect to y and setting the result equal to zero.

$$\frac{dv}{dy} = \frac{(y^2 + a^2) - 2y^2}{(y^2 + a^2)^2}\frac{K}{\pi} = 0$$

For the numerator to equal zero, the solution is

$$y = \pm a$$

If the pressure back of the wall, on the other side of the source, is that of the fluid far away from the source, there will be a pressure difference from the two sides at every point on the wall. The pressure on the wall, on the source side, can be computed from Bernoulli's equation written between that point and a point far away from the source where the pressure is p_∞ and the velocity is zero. Since, on the wall, the x-component of the velocity is zero, then

$$p + \tfrac{1}{2}\rho v^2 = p_\infty + 0$$

$$p_\infty - p = \tfrac{1}{2}\rho v^2$$

and the total force per unit depth of wall attracting the wall toward the source is the integration of this pressure force for the entire plate:

$$F = \int_{-\infty}^{+\infty} (p_\infty - p)\, dy = \tfrac{1}{2}\rho \int_{-\infty}^{+\infty} v^2\, dy$$

The velocity along the wall has already been found, and thus, the net force on the plate is

$$\begin{aligned} F &= \frac{K^2\rho}{8\pi^2}\int_{-\infty}^{+\infty} \frac{4y^2}{(y^2 + a^2)^2}\, dy \\ &= \frac{K^2\rho}{2\pi^2}\left[\frac{1}{2a}\tan^{-1}\frac{y}{a} - \frac{y}{2(a^2 + y^2)}\right]_{-\infty}^{+\infty} \\ &= \frac{K^2\rho}{2\pi^2}\frac{1}{2a}\left(\frac{\pi}{2} + \frac{\pi}{2}\right) \\ &= \frac{K^2\rho}{4a\pi} \end{aligned}$$

This is also equal to the strength of the source K times the induced velocity at the position of the source from its own image.

7.10 A Line Source and a Line Sink Placed at a Finite Distance Apart

In Fig. 7.9, if a line sink is placed at the left of O at the distance $x = -a$, then the equations for the stream function and the potential function are

$$\psi = -\frac{K}{2\pi}(\theta_1 - \theta_2)$$

$$\phi = -\frac{K}{2\pi}(\ln r_1 - \ln r_2) \tag{7.33}$$

$$= \frac{K}{2\pi}\ln\frac{r_2}{r_1}$$

If the same trigonometric relations used in Sec. 7.8 for the tangents of angles θ_1 and θ_2 are used here, and remembering this time that

$$\tan(\theta_1 - \theta_2) = \frac{\tan\theta_1 - \tan\theta_2}{1 + \tan\theta_1\tan\theta_2}$$

then the stream function becomes

$$\psi = -\frac{K}{2\pi}\tan^{-1}\frac{2ya}{x^2 + y^2 - a^2}$$

$$\phi = \frac{K}{2\pi}\ln\frac{\sqrt{y^2 + (a + x)^2}}{\sqrt{y^2 + (a - x)^2}} \tag{7.34}$$

Again letting $m = \cot\frac{2\pi\psi}{K}$ and $n = e^{\frac{4\pi\phi}{K}}$, the preceding equations take the form

$$x^2 + (y - ma)^2 = a^2(1 + m^2)$$

$$y^2 + \left(x + \frac{n+1}{n-1}a\right)^2 = \left[a\frac{2\sqrt{n}}{n-1}\right]^2 \tag{7.35}$$

The first equation for ψ and m constants represents the family of streamlines. These streamlines are circles with centers on the y–y-axis a distance ma from the origin and with a radius equal to $a\sqrt{1 + m^2}$. These circles all pass through the source and the sink. The potential lines are represented by the second part of Eq. (7.35) and they are also circles with centers along the x–x-axis a distance $\frac{n+1}{n-1}a$ from the origin and with radius $a\frac{2\sqrt{n}}{n-1}$. The value of the parameter n depends on the value of the potential line considered. This flow field is shown in Fig. 7.13.

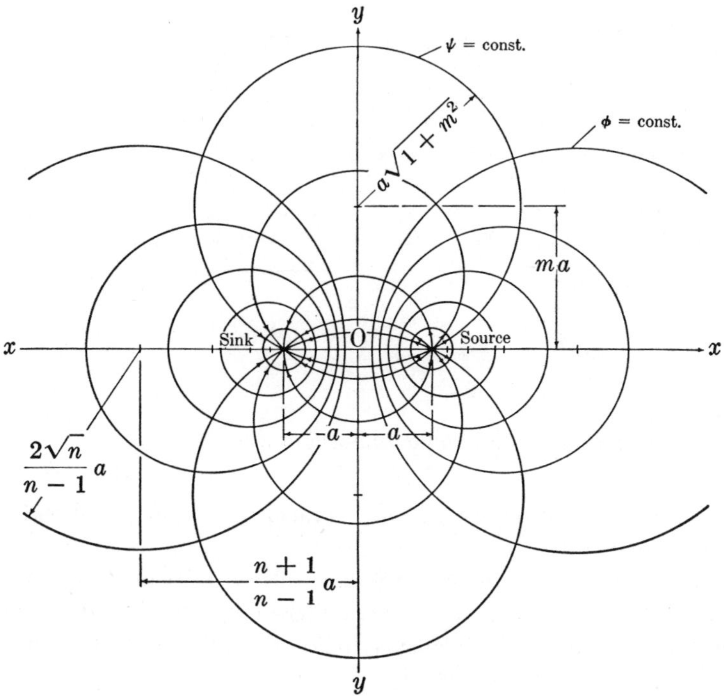

Figure 7.13
Streamline and potential-line pattern for a source and sink placed $2a$ apart.

7.11 The Uniform Stream

The superposition of sources and sinks by themselves has very limited usage in fluid dynamics. When a uniform parallel flow is also superimposed on source and sink flows, the resultant flow field, as will be shown, can be very useful.

In two-dimensional plane flow the stream and potential function of a uniform stream can be obtained from Eqs. (7.3) and (7.15). For a uniform flow along the x-axis, $v = 0$ and

$$u = U_0 = -\frac{d\psi}{dy} = -\frac{d\phi}{dx}$$

Therefore,

$$\begin{aligned} \psi &= -U_0 y \\ \phi &= -U_0 x \end{aligned} \tag{7.36}$$

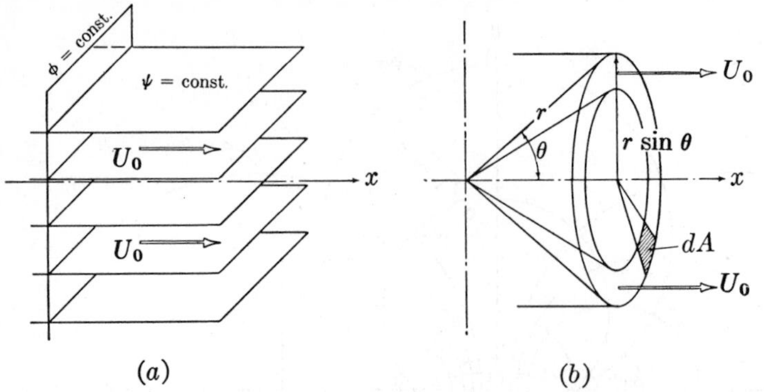

Figure 7.14
Cartesian and spherical representation of uniform flow.

The constants of integration are zero if ψ is measured from $y = 0$ and ϕ is measured from $x = 0$.

When dealing with nonplanar problems but with axial symmetry, the uniform stream is often more conveniently represented in terms of polar coordinates. Referring to Fig. 7.14(b), the rate of volume flow across the infinitesimal area dA is

$$-2\pi\, d\psi = 2\pi(U_0 r \sin\theta)\, d(r\sin\theta)$$

$$\psi = -\tfrac{1}{2}U_0 r^2 \sin^2\theta \qquad (7.37)$$

and the potential function will be represented by planes perpendicular to the x-axis

$$-\frac{d\phi}{dx} = U_0$$

$$\phi = -U_0 x = -U_0 r\cos\theta \qquad (7.38)$$

Equations (7.36), (7.37), and (7.38) represent the same uniform stream, but the results are in terms of different coordinate systems.

7.12 A Line Source in a Uniform Stream

When a line source located at O in Fig. 7.15 is superimposed on a uniform flow with a velocity U_0 moving from right to left, the combined flow field is derived from the summation of the individual stream and potential functions:

$$\psi_{\text{source}} = -\frac{K}{2\pi}\theta \quad \text{and} \quad \psi_{\substack{\text{uniform}\\\text{stream}}} = U_0 y$$

$$\psi = -\frac{K}{2\pi}\theta + U_0 y \tag{7.39}$$

$$= -\frac{K}{2\pi}\theta + U_0 r \sin\theta$$

This problem was treated without details in Sec. 3.12, and the preceding equation is identical with Eq. (3.30). For a given strength of source and a given velocity U_0, the streamline $\psi = C$ can be plotted from the resulting r, θ relationship in Eq. (7.39). From physical reasoning it can be seen, in Fig. 7.15, that along OA, where $\psi = 0$ for both the source flow and the uniform stream, there will be a point S such that the velocity of the source will be equal in magnitude but opposite in direction to the free stream velocity U_0. At that point S the velocity of the combined flow will be zero; consequently, by definition, the point S will be the stagnation point, and the streamline AS will be the *approach stagnation streamline.*

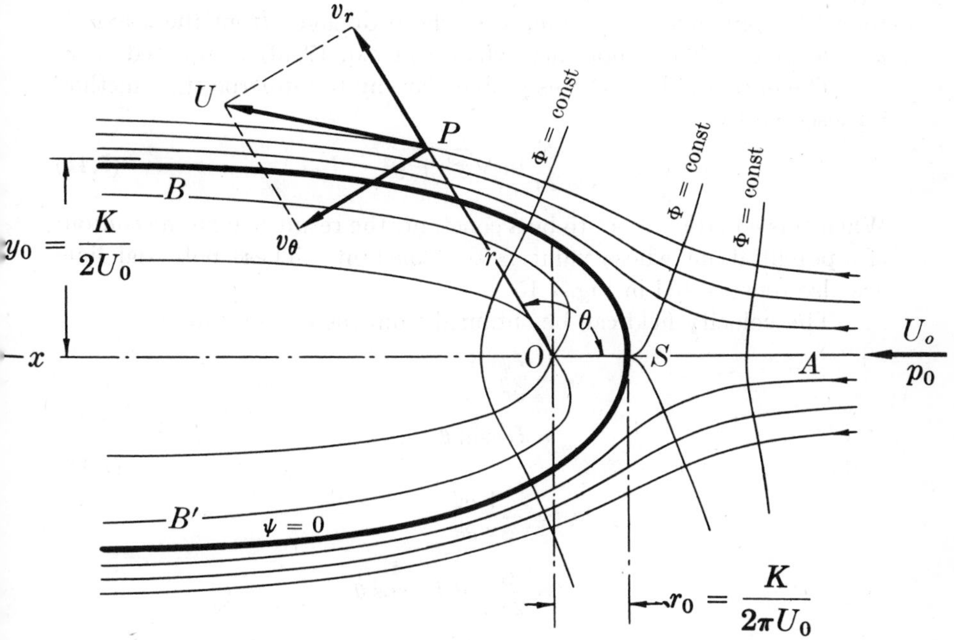

Figure 7.15
The plane half-body.

The streamline AS, whose value is zero, does not end at S but continues to SB on one side and SB' on the other. The equation of this contour is given when Eq. (7.39) is set to zero.

$$r = \frac{K}{2\pi U_0} \frac{\theta}{\sin\theta},$$

or (7.40)

$$y = r \sin\theta = \frac{K}{2\pi U_0} \theta$$

The distance of the stagnation point S from O, the location of the source, is found by evaluating r when $\theta = 0$. The limiting process of Eq. (7.40) as $\theta \to 0$ is $r = r_0 = K/2\pi U_0$. Physically, what has happened is that all the source flow has confined itself inside the stagnation streamline contour BSB', and the uniform stream spills over it. The contour BSB' is called the *plane half-body* or the *plane Rankine*[1] *body*. Since the flow is nonviscous, if the source flow inside the contour is ignored and is replaced by a solid body with the same geometry, the external flow will be the same. Since the internal flow has no engineering applications, the external flow alone is of interest here. The contour SB approaches an asymptote whose distance from the x-axis is $y = K/2U_0$. This is obtained when θ in Eq. (7.40) is equated to π.

The potential lines in this problem are by the superposition method represented by

$$\phi = -\frac{K}{2\pi} \ln \sqrt{x^2 + y^2} - U_0 x \tag{7.41}$$

When this equation is set to be a constant, the result will be the contour of a potential line whose value is the constant. These potential lines are also represented in Fig. 7.15.

The velocity field can be obtained from the stream function.

$$v_\theta = \frac{\partial \psi}{\partial r}$$

$$= U_0 \sin\theta$$

and (7.42)

$$v_r = -\frac{1}{r}\frac{\partial \psi}{\partial \theta}$$

$$= \frac{K}{2\pi r} - U_0 \cos\theta$$

[1] William John Rankine, born in 1820, was a successful Scottish physicist and engineer whose works in mechanics and thermodynamics are major contributions to science. He died in 1872.

The stagnation point can be obtained here again when $v_\theta = 0$ for $\theta = 0$ and when $v_r = 0$ for $r = r_0 = K/2\pi U_0$. The velocity components u and v in the x- and y-directions can be derived easily:

$$u = \frac{K}{2\pi}\frac{x}{x^2 + y^2} - U_0$$

$$v = \frac{K}{2\pi}\frac{y}{x^2 + y^2}$$

and the total velocity

$$V^2 = v_\theta^2 + v_r^2 = u^2 + v^2$$

On the surface of the contour BSB' on which r can be substituted in terms of θ according to Eq. (7.40) the value of the total velocity becomes

$$V^2 = U_0^2\left[\left(\frac{\sin\theta}{\theta}\right)^2 - \frac{\sin 2\theta}{\theta} + 1\right] \tag{7.43}$$

On the approach streamline AS the velocity is radial only, and $\theta = 0$. Therefore, along AS

$$v_r = \frac{K}{2\pi r} - U_0$$

or (7.44)

$$\frac{v_r}{U_0} = \frac{r_0}{r} - 1$$

This velocity starts far away from the body as $-U_0$ and decelerates hyperbolically to zero at the stagnation point S. The velocity along the stagnation streamline from A to B' is plotted in Fig. 7.16. According to Eq. (7.43), the fluid starts accelerating from S along the surface of the half-body. It reaches the value of U_0 at approximately 67°, and it accelerates further to a value of about $V = 1.25U_0$ at 117° (point D'). From point D' to B' the fluid decelerates to its original value of U_0.

The *pressure coefficient* is defined as the rise in pressure above that at the undisturbed flow at A divided by the dynamic pressure of the undisturbed flow. If p is the static pressure anywhere and p_0 and U_0 the pressure and velocity of the undisturbed flow at A, then the pressure coefficient is

$$C_p = \frac{p - p_0}{\frac{1}{2}\rho U_0^2} \tag{7.45}$$

But, from Bernoulli's equation,

$$p + \tfrac{1}{2}\rho V^2 = p_0 + \tfrac{1}{2}\rho U_0^2$$

$$C_p = 1 - \frac{V^2}{U_0^2} \tag{7.46}$$

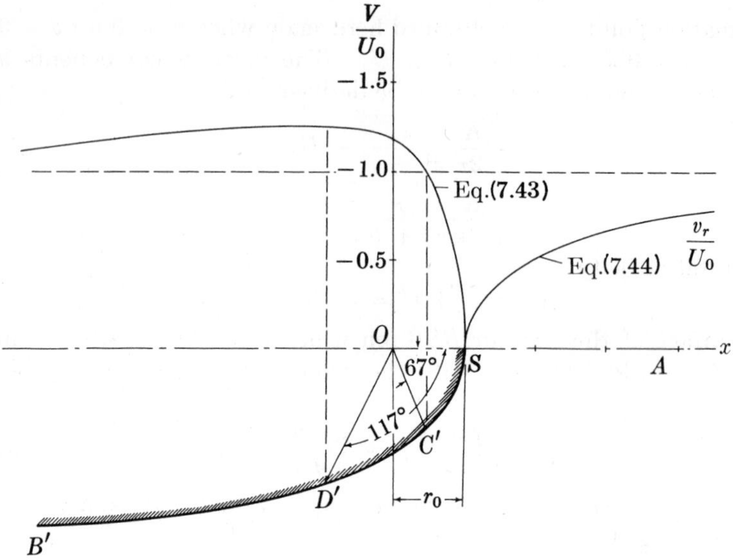

Figure 7.16
Velocity along stagnation streamline $ASC'D'B'$ of plane half-body.

Since $V = v_r$ along the approach stagnation streamline, then the pressure coefficient along AS is, from Eqs. (7.44) and (7.46),

$$C_p = \frac{2r_0}{r} - \left(\frac{r_0}{r}\right)^2 \tag{7.47}$$

When Eq. (7.43) is substituted into Eq. (7.46), the pressure coefficient along the surface of the half-body is

$$C_p = \frac{\sin 2\theta}{\theta} - \left(\frac{\sin \theta}{\theta}\right)^2 \tag{7.48}$$

The pressure coefficient C_p is plotted in Fig. 7.17 along the stagnation streamline $ASC'D'B'$. Since the velocity $V = 0$ at the stagnation point, then, from Eq. (7.46) it is seen that $C_p = 1.0$ at S. Furthermore, since the velocity at C' is $V = U_0$, again from Eq. (7.46), it follows that $C_p = 0$. The minimum value of C_p is found at D' where the velocity is the maximum. At D' where $\theta = 117°$, the value of $C_p = -0.58$ approximately. Since the velocity beyond B' approaches that of the undisturbed flow U_0, the pressure coefficient far at the left of the body approaches the value of zero.

A two-dimensional body of this shape can be used in a two-

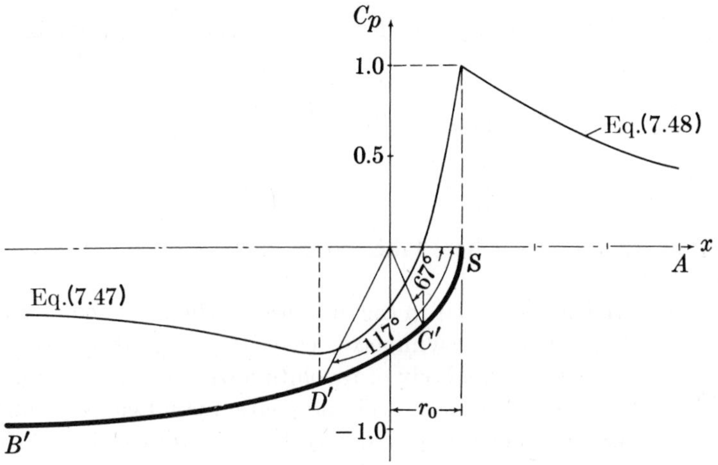

Figure 7.17
Pressure coefficient along stagnation streamline of plane half-body.

dimensional plane flow for a Pitot static tube that will measure the dynamic pressure of the undisturbed flow. If a tiny hole is drilled at the stagnation point S and this hole is connected with a manometer, the pressure measured will be the total pressure any place on the stagnation streamline

$$p_t = p + \tfrac{1}{2}\rho V^2 = p_0 + \tfrac{1}{2}\rho U_0^2$$

Another hole at the point C' will measure the undisturbed static pressure p_0, as can be deduced from Figs. 7.16 and 7.17. The difference in pressure between these two holes will give the dynamic pressure $\tfrac{1}{2}\rho U_0^2$, and from this the undisturbed velocity can be calculated. The location of C' for a viscous fluid will move on the body a few degrees farther downstream on account of the viscous layer that grows from S to C'.

7.13 The Point Source in a Uniform Stream

Equations (7.22) and (7.23) represent the potential and stream functions for the point source in spherical coordinates. In Sec. 7.11 and Eqs. (7.37) and (7.38) the same functions were established for the uniform stream in terms of spherical coordinates. If the two flows are now combined, the resultant potential and stream functions for the combination will be

$$\begin{aligned} \phi &= \frac{k}{4\pi}\frac{1}{r} + U_0 r \cos\theta \\ \psi &= \frac{k}{4\pi}\cos\theta + \tfrac{1}{2}U_0 r^2 \sin^2\theta \end{aligned} \tag{7.49}$$

The uniform stream flow is here taken to go in the negative direction, from right to left.

The flow here will be similar to the case previously discussed. This being a three-dimensional axisymmetric case, the stagnation stream surface will have the form of a body of revolution with a contour similar to the half-body already described. The stagnation point can be found, for instance, where the velocities v_r and v_θ go to zero. From Eq. (7.20) the spherical components of the velocity are

$$\begin{aligned} v_r &= -\frac{\partial\phi}{\partial r} = \frac{k}{4\pi}\frac{1}{r^2} - U_0\cos\theta \\ v_\theta &= -\frac{\partial\phi}{r\,\partial\theta} = U_0\sin\theta \end{aligned} \tag{7.50}$$

As in the previous case, the stagnation point is at $\theta = 0$ and $v_r = v_\theta = 0$. Solving Eq. (7.50), the distance r_0 from the location of the source to the stagnation point is

$$r_0 = \sqrt{\frac{k}{4\pi U_0}}$$

The contour equation for the three-dimensional Rankine body can be found if the value of the stream surface is known at the stagnation point. For $\theta = 0$ the value of the stream function is $-k/4\pi$, since this will be the value of the stream surface passing through the stagnation point. This contour is shown in Fig. 7.18. Substituting it in Eq. (7.49), the equation for the stagnation stream surface is obtained:

$$\begin{aligned} \frac{k}{4\pi} &= \frac{k}{4\pi}\cos\theta + \tfrac{1}{2}U_0 r^2 \sin^2\theta \\ 1 &= \cos\theta + \frac{2\pi U_0}{k} r^2 \sin^2\theta \end{aligned} \tag{7.51}$$

This half-body of revolution also has an asymptote which it approaches at the far left-hand side. This can be evaluated by letting, in Eq. (7.51), $\zeta = r\sin\theta$ for $\theta = \pi$. Then

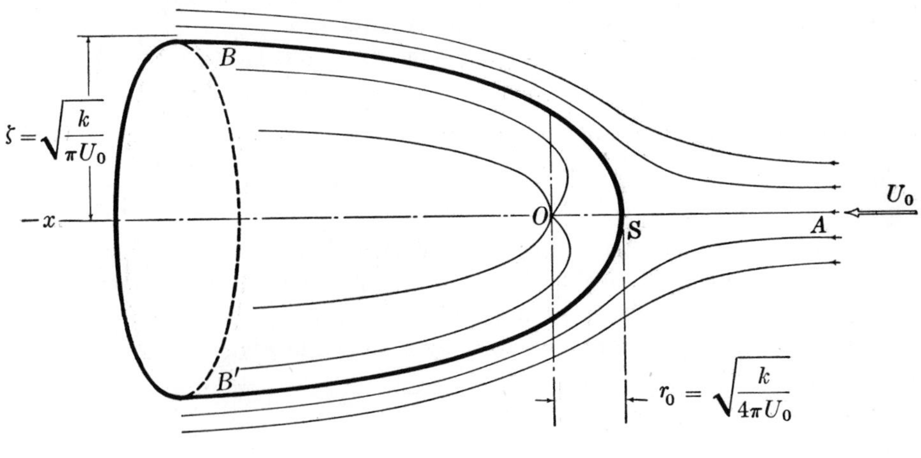

Figure 7.18
Three-dimensional Rankine half-body.

$$1 = -1 + \frac{2\pi U_0}{k} \zeta^2$$
$$\zeta = \sqrt{\frac{k}{\pi U_0}} \tag{7.52}$$

This same result is found by the following different reasoning: Since the source flow starting at O is confined inside the surface BSB', then the total source flow k must come out at the left of the cross section BB' at the velocity U_0. Therefore,

$$\pi \zeta^2 U_0 = k$$
$$\zeta = \sqrt{\frac{k}{\pi U_0}}$$

The total velocity at any point in the flow field can be found from Eq. (7.50):

$$V^2 = v_r^2 + v_\theta^2$$
$$= U_0^2 + \left(\frac{k}{4\pi}\right)^2 \frac{1}{r^4} - \frac{kU_0}{2\pi} \frac{1}{r^2} \cos\theta$$

On the surface of the half-body whose contour is given by Eq. (7.51) the value of r can be substituted in the total velocity just found. The result will give the velocity on the body contour,

$$V^2 = U_0^2\left[1 + \frac{\sin^4\theta}{4(1-\cos\theta)^2} - \frac{\sin^2\theta\cos\theta}{1-\cos\theta}\right] \tag{7.53}$$

The pressure coefficient on the surface of the half-body is then

$$C_p = \frac{\sin^2\theta\cos\theta}{1-\cos\theta} - \frac{\sin^4\theta}{4(1-\cos\theta)^2} \tag{7.54}$$

The angle at which the pressure coefficient is zero, or, in other words, where the velocity on the surface is that of the undisturbed flow, is approximately $\theta = 70.5°$. The variation of pressure with angle on the three-dimensional Rankine half-body is shown in Fig. 7.19.

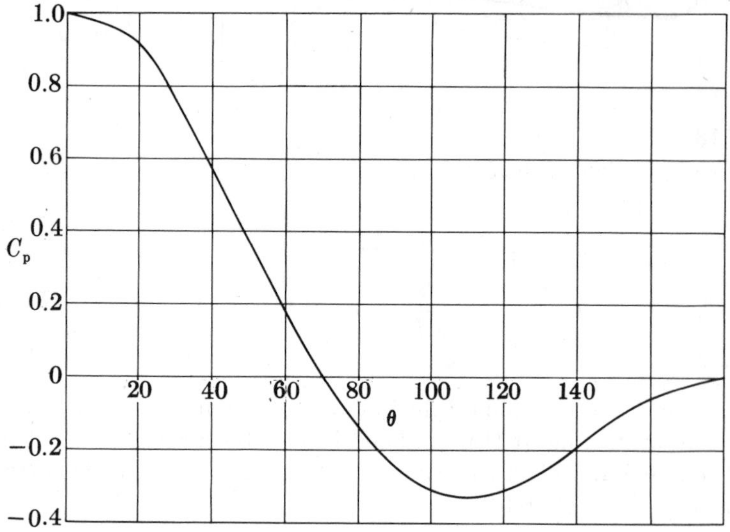

Figure 7.19
Variation of pressure coefficient with angle on the three-dimensional Rankine half-body.

Illustrative Example 7.4
Determine the velocity and the pressure coefficient along the approach stagnation streamline.

Along the approach stagnation streamline $v_\theta = 0$ and $\theta = 0$, and, from Eq. (7.50)

$$v_r = \frac{k}{4\pi r^2} - U_0$$

$$\frac{v_r}{U_0} = \left(\frac{r_0}{r}\right)^2 - 1$$

The pressure coefficient is

$$
\begin{aligned}
C_p &= \frac{p - p_0}{\frac{1}{2}\rho U_0^2} \\
&= 1 - \left(\frac{v_r}{U_0}\right)^2 \\
&= 1 - \left(\frac{r_0}{r}\right)^4 + 2\left(\frac{r_0}{r}\right)^2 - 1 \\
&= 2\left(\frac{r_0}{r}\right)^2 - \left(\frac{r_0}{r}\right)^4
\end{aligned}
$$

7.14 Line Source and Line Sink in a Uniform Stream

In Sec. 7.10, the solution of the line source and a line sink placed at a distance $2a$ apart was given. If parallel uniform flow of velocity $-U_0$ moving from right to left is superimposed on the source and sink flow, the stream and potential functions for the combined flow will be

$$
\begin{aligned}
\psi &= -\frac{K}{2\pi} \tan^{-1} \frac{2ya}{x^2 + y^2 - a^2} + U_0 y \\
\phi &= \frac{K}{2\pi} \ln \frac{\sqrt{y^2 + (a + x)^2}}{\sqrt{y^2 + (a - x)^2}} + U_0 x
\end{aligned}
\tag{7.55}
$$

It must be understood in this case that the strength of the source and sink is the same. The stream and potential lines of this flow field are also determined by setting ψ and ϕ to various constants and solving the equations for x and y.

Judging from Fig. 7.20, the resultant motion is divided into two separate flows. The flow outside the contour $SBS'B'$ is that of the uniform stream deflected by the presence of the contour. The flow inside the contour is self-preserved, since the source has the same strength as the sink, and all the flow emanating from the source is absorbed by the sink. If, now, the contour $SBS'B'$ is replaced by a solid contour of the same profile, then the exterior flow will remain the same for the inviscid case considered. As usual, the distances from the stagnation points (two in this case) to the origin O are of importance. The velocities u and v, from differentiation of Eq. (7.55) are

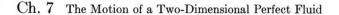

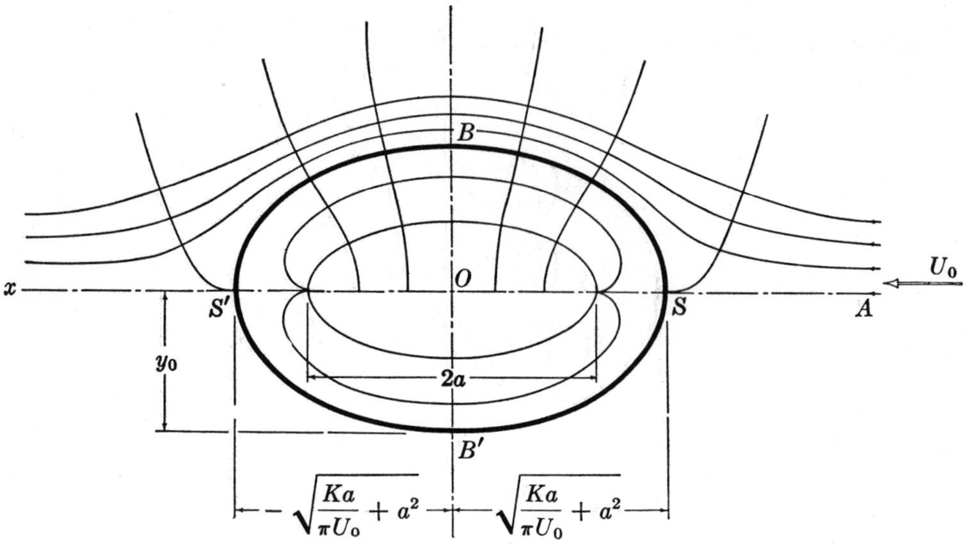

Figure 7.20
Flow around a closed body formed by the superposition of a source, sink, and uniform stream.

$$u = \frac{Ka}{\pi} \frac{x^2 - y^2 - a^2}{(x^2 + y^2 - a^2)^2 + 4y^2a^2} - U_0$$
$$v = \frac{Ka}{\pi} \frac{2xy}{(x^2 + y^2 - a^2)^2 + 4y^2a^2} \tag{7.56}$$

On the approach stagnation streamline the velocity $v = 0$ and the coordinate $y = 0$; therefore, the velocity u is

$$u = \frac{Ka}{\pi} \frac{1}{x^2 - a^2} - U_0$$

Since at the stagnation points S and S' the velocity u is also zero, the solution of the previous equation yields

$$x^2 - a^2 = \frac{Ka}{\pi U_0}$$

$$x_0 = \pm\sqrt{a^2 + \frac{Ka}{U_0}}$$

The maximum ordinate y_0 of the oval in Fig. 7.20 can be obtained more simply by considering Fig. 7.9 and writing the stream function of the source, sink, and uniform stream in terms of the angles

$$\psi = -\frac{K}{2\pi}(\theta_1 - \theta_2) + U_0 y = 0$$

This stream function is equal to zero on the contour of the oval $SBS'B'$. Then, when the top of the oval B is considered, $\theta_1 = 180° - \theta_2$ and $y = y_0$:

$$y_0 = \frac{K}{2\pi U_0}(180° - 2\theta_2)$$

$$= \frac{K}{\pi U_0}(90° - \theta_2)$$

According to Fig. 7.9, the angle $(90° - \theta_2) = \tan^{-1}\frac{y_0}{a}$; then,

$$y_0 = \frac{K}{\pi U_0}\tan^{-1}\frac{y_0}{a}$$

The value of y_0 is also contained in the argument of the arctangent; the solution of this equation can be obtained by trial and error or by a graphic method.

Illustrative Example 7.5

Show that the flow around the oval $SBS'B'$ in the preceding section is irrotational and satisfies continuity.

The velocity components u and v are given in Eq. (7.56). To show that the flow is irrotational everywhere, Eq. (3.32) must be shown to equal zero. Since the two components of the velocity have the same denominator, it will be referred to as such.

$$\frac{\partial v}{\partial x} = \frac{[(x^2 + y^2 - a^2)^2 + 4y^2a^2]2y - 8x^2y(x^2 + y^2 - a^2)}{(\text{denominator})^2}\frac{Ka}{\pi}$$

$$\frac{\partial u}{\partial y} = \frac{[(x^2 + y^2 - a^2)^2 + 4y^2a^2](-2y) - (x^2 - y^2 - a^2)[4y(x^2 + y^2 - a^2) + 8ya^2]}{(\text{denominator})^2}\frac{Ka}{\pi}$$

$$\frac{\partial u}{\partial x} = \frac{[(x^2 + y^2 - a^2)^2 + 4y^2a^2]2x - 4x(x^2 - y^2 - a^2)(x^2 + y^2 - a^2)}{(\text{denominator})^2}\frac{Ka}{\pi}$$

$$\frac{\partial v}{\partial y} = \frac{[(x^2 + y^2 - a^2)^2 + 4y^2a^2]2x - 2xy[4y(x^2 + y^2 - a^2) + 8ya^2]}{(\text{denominator})^2}\frac{Ka}{\pi}$$

From this result it can easily be shown that Eqs. (3.32) and (3.33) are satisfied

$$\frac{\partial v}{\partial x} - \frac{\partial u}{\partial y} = 0$$

$$\frac{\partial u}{\partial x} + \frac{\partial v}{\partial y} = 0$$

and therefore both conditions of irrotationality and of continuity are satisfied for the flow around the oval. Since this chapter deals with potential flows, for every example discussed both the equation of continuity and that of irrotationality will be automatically satisfied.

7.15 The Point Source and the Point Sink in a Uniform Stream

The solution to this problem is carried out in the same fashion as the previous one. Again, with the uniform stream flowing from right to left in the direction of $-x$, and, according to Eqs. (7.22), (7.23), (7.37) and (7.38) the stream and potential functions for this three-dimensional axisymmetric flow are:

$$\psi = \frac{k}{4\pi}(\cos\theta_1 - \cos\theta_2) + \tfrac{1}{2}U_0 r^2 \sin^2\theta$$

$$\phi = \frac{k}{4\pi}\left(\frac{1}{r_1} - \frac{1}{r_2}\right) + U_0 r\cos\theta \qquad (7.57)$$

If, from Fig. 7.21, the following geometrical relations are introduced, the stream and the potential functions become

$$r_1^2 = (x - a)^2 + \zeta^2$$
$$r_2^2 = (x + a)^2 + \zeta^2$$
$$\zeta = r\sin\theta;$$

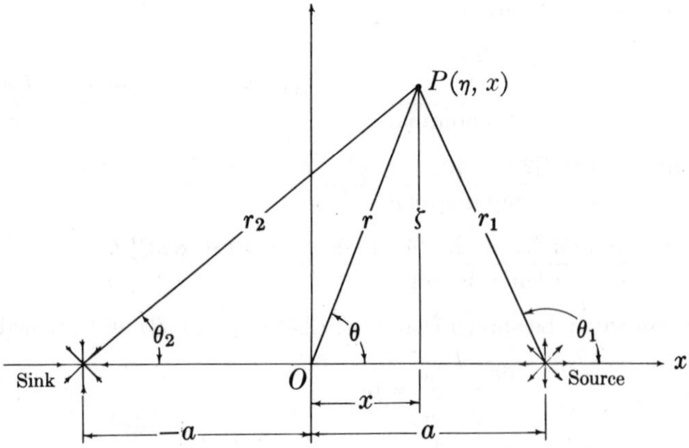

Figure 7.21
Geometry of point source and point sink at a distance $2a$ apart.

and then

$$\psi = \tfrac{1}{2}U_0\zeta^2 + \frac{k}{4\pi}(\cos\theta_1 - \cos\theta_2)$$

$$\phi = U_0x + \frac{k}{4\pi}\left(\frac{1}{\sqrt{(x-a)^2+\zeta^2}} - \frac{1}{\sqrt{(x+a)^2+\zeta^2}}\right)$$

According to Fig. 7.22, the internal flow in the oval constitutes the flow emanating from the source and being swallowed by the sink of the same

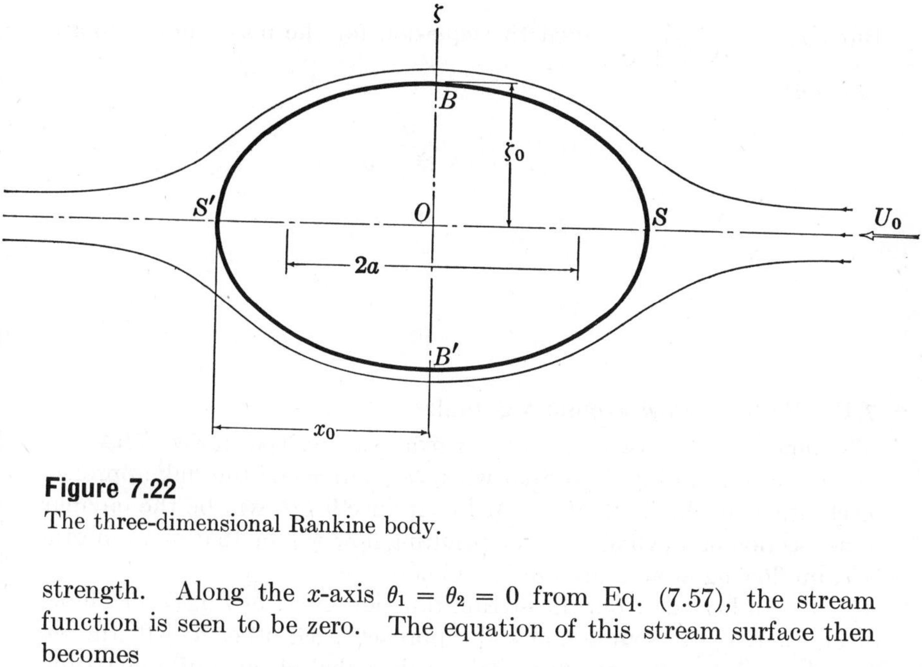

Figure 7.22
The three-dimensional Rankine body.

strength. Along the x-axis $\theta_1 = \theta_2 = 0$ from Eq. (7.57), the stream function is seen to be zero. The equation of this stream surface then becomes

$$\zeta^2 + \frac{k}{2\pi U_0}(\cos\theta_1 - \cos\theta_2) = 0 \tag{7.58}$$

Along the x-axis the potential function is equal to

$$\phi = U_0x + \frac{k}{4\pi}\left(\frac{1}{x-a} - \frac{1}{x+a}\right);$$

and along this same x-axis the velocities will be zero at the stagnation points S and S'

$$u = -\frac{\partial\phi}{\partial x} = \frac{k}{4\pi}\left[\frac{1}{(x-a)^2} - \frac{1}{(x+a)^2}\right] - U_0 = 0$$

$$\frac{\pi U_0}{ak} = \frac{x_0}{(x_0^2 - a^2)^2}$$

Here x_0 is the particular value of x measured from O where the stagnation points are located. This last equation must be solved to determine the location of S and S'.

To find the maximum ordinate ζ_0 which is located on the stagnation stream surface Eq. (7.58) let $\theta_1 = 180° - \theta_2$, and, thus, $\cos\theta_1 = -\cos\theta_2$ and

$$\zeta_0^2 - \frac{k}{2\pi U_0} 2\cos\theta_2 = 0$$

But $\cos\theta_2 = \dfrac{a}{\sqrt{\zeta_0^2 + a^2}}$; then the equation for the maximum ordinate becomes

$$\zeta_0^2 = \frac{k}{\pi U_0} \frac{a}{\sqrt{\zeta_0^2 + a^2}}$$

7.16 Uniform Flow Around a Cylinder

The flow around a two-dimensional oval was derived in Sec. 7.14. It can be seen, from Fig. 7.20, that when the source and the sink approach each other, in the limit, the closed contour $SBS'B'$ will be the circular cross section of a cylinder. The resulting flow will be that of a uniform stream flowing around an infinite cylinder.

It can be seen from the stream function given in Eq. (7.55), however, that as the source and sink approach each other $a \to 0$, the remaining value of the stream function is just that of the uniform stream. This means that as the source approaches the sink, the region of influence surrounding the source and the sink diminishes. In the limit, for a finite strength of source and sink as the source and the sink are together at a point, the output of the source is immediately swallowed by the sink without any region of influence. With the source and sink approaching each other, in order for the influence to be felt in the surroundings, the strength of the source and sink can be increased to infinity as $a \to 0$. This implies that, in order to get a finite influence from the source and the sink, their strength must be pumped up as the distance between them decreases. For that let $K' = 2Ka$, and therefore Eq. (7.55) becomes

$$\psi = -\frac{K'}{4\pi a} \tan^{-1} \frac{2ya}{x^2 + y^2 - a^2} + U_0 y$$
$$\phi = \frac{K'}{4\pi a} \ln \frac{\sqrt{y^2 + (a + x)^2}}{\sqrt{y^2 + (a - x)^2}} + U_0 x \tag{7.59}$$

Now if the limit is taken of the stream function as $a \to 0$, the $\tan^{-1}$ approaches the angle itself, and therefore,

$$\lim_{a\to 0} \psi = -\frac{K'}{4\pi a} \frac{2ya}{x^2 + y^2 - a^2} + U_0 y$$
$$= -\frac{K'}{2\pi} \frac{y}{x^2 + y^2} + U_0 y \tag{7.60}$$

A direct substitution of $a = 0$ in the potential function yields an indeterminate quotient 0/0. To evaluate the quotient, the derivative of the numerator containing the logarithm is performed with respect to a, and the same is done for the denominator $4\pi a$. Then, for this result, substitute $a = 0$ and it follows that

$$\lim_{a\to 0} \phi = \frac{K'}{2\pi} \frac{x}{x^2 + y^2} + U_0 x \tag{7.61}$$

In polar notation $r^2 = x^2 + y^2$, $y = r \sin \theta$, and $x = r \cos \theta$; then

$$\psi = -\frac{K'}{2\pi} \frac{\sin \theta}{r} + U_0 r \sin \theta$$
$$= rU_0 \left[\left(\frac{a_0}{r} \right)^2 - 1 \right] \sin \theta \tag{7.62}$$

where the value $a_0^2 = K'/2\pi U_0$.

The potential function can be written in cylindrical coordinates also:

$$\phi = \frac{K'}{2\pi} \frac{\cos \theta}{r} + U_0 r \cos \theta$$
$$= rU_0 \left[\left(\frac{a_0}{r} \right)^2 + 1 \right] \cos \theta \tag{7.63}$$

It can be seen from Eq. (7.62) that, on the contour stagnation streamline where $\psi = 0$, for any U_0 and all θ, the radius r must equal to $a_0 =$ constant. This is the radius of the cylinder around which the fluid is flowing.

From Eq. (7.4), the velocity field can be obtained by differentiating the stream function

$$v_r = -\frac{1}{r}\frac{\partial\psi}{\partial\theta} = U_0\left[\left(\frac{a_0}{r}\right)^2 - 1\right]\cos\theta$$
$$v_\theta = \frac{\partial\psi}{\partial r} = U_0\left[\left(\frac{a_0}{r}\right)^2 + 1\right]\sin\theta \tag{7.64}$$

and the total velocity at any point in the flow field is

$$V^2 = v_r^2 + v_\theta^2 = U_0^2\left(1 - \frac{2a_0}{r^2}\cos 2\theta + \frac{a_0^4}{r^4}\right)$$

In particular, the velocity along the approach stagnation streamline is v_r, and for $\theta = 0$,

$$V = -v_r = U_0\left(1 - \frac{a_0^2}{r^2}\right) \tag{7.65}$$

and along the surface of the cylinder where $v_r = 0$ and $r = a_0$

$$V = v_\theta = 2U_0 \sin\theta \tag{7.66}$$

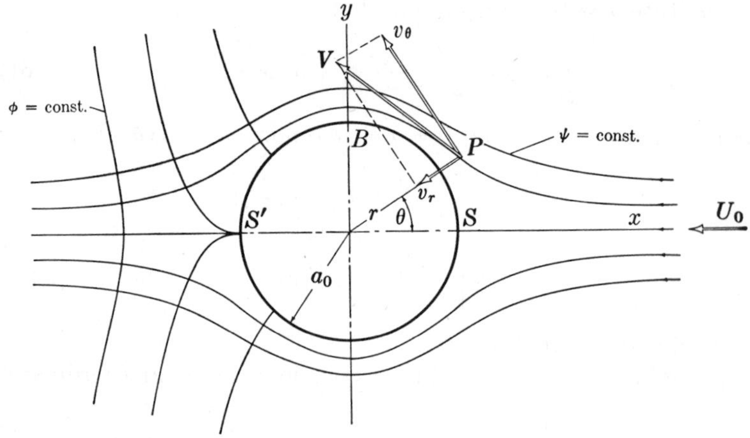

Figure 7.23
Flow around an infinitely long cylinder.

Using Bernoulli's equation for the points along the approach streamline and the cylinder surface, the pressure coefficient along the approach streamline is

$$C_p = \frac{p - p_0}{\frac{1}{2}\rho U_0^2} = \left(\frac{a_0}{r}\right)^2\left[2 - \left(\frac{a_0}{r}\right)^2\right] \tag{7.67}$$

and the pressure coefficient along the surface of the cylinder is

$$C_p = 1 - 4\sin^2\theta \tag{7.68}$$

Figure 7.24 shows the velocity distribution of an ideal fluid along the stagnation streamline of the cylinder. It also shows a comparison of the pressure coefficient for an ideal flow and an actual flow along the same stagnation streamline.

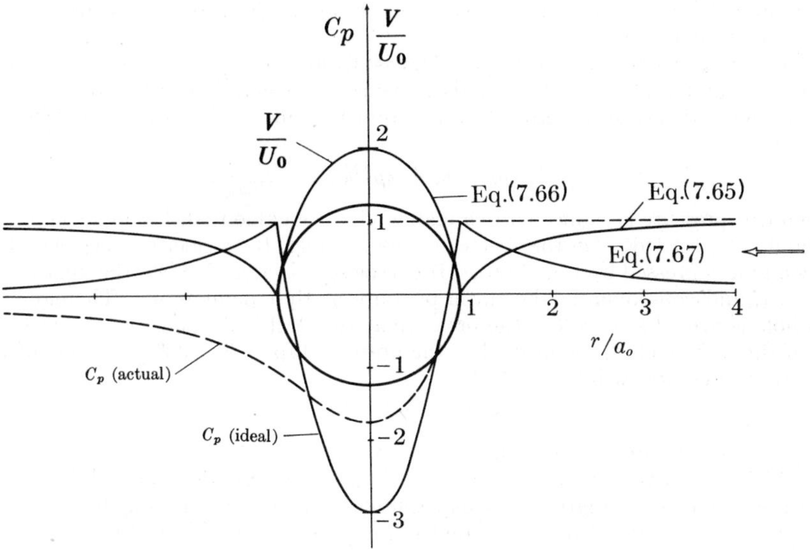

Figure 7.24
Velocity and pressure coefficient along stagnation streamline of flow around cylinder.

Illustrative Example 7.6
Determine the velocity and pressure variation with radial distance along By for the flow in Fig. 7.23.

The velocity along the ordinate By is only v_θ, since v_r there is zero. Equation 7.64 gives this relation, and for $\theta = 90°$ it becomes

$$v_\theta = U_0\left[\left(\frac{a_0}{r}\right)^2 + 1\right]$$

This implies that the peripheral velocity along By varies inversely as the square of the radial distance until v_θ reaches U_0 when r reaches infinity. The pressure can be obtained from Bernoulli's equation which, for this case of irrotational motion, is valid everywhere in the fluid [see Sec. 4.9(*b*)].

$$p_0 + \tfrac{1}{2}\rho U_0^2 = p + \tfrac{1}{2}\rho v_\theta^2$$

$$p_0 - p = \tfrac{1}{2}\rho(v_\theta^2 - U_0^2)$$

$$= \tfrac{1}{2}\rho U_0^2\left[\left(\frac{a_0}{r}\right)^4 + 2\left(\frac{a_0}{r}\right)^2\right]$$

This relation also shows that when the radial distance becomes infinite the pressure there becomes p_0.

Illustrative Example 7.7

A cylinder is to be used as a Pitot static tube for the measurement of the total static and dynamic pressure of a stream. Find the location of the pressure holes on the cylinder.

The stagnation point S in Fig. 7.23 is always the location for the total pressure (stagnation pressure). This pressure for a nonviscous motion is the sum of the static pressure p_0 and of the dynamic pressure $\frac{1}{2}\rho U_0^2$ of the undisturbed flow.

$$p_t = p_0 + \tfrac{1}{2}\rho U_0^2$$

When this pressure is connected to a manometer, its value in inches of a column of liquid is recorded. On the surface of the cylinder, the velocity is peripheral only and is expressed by Eq. (7.66). It can be seen that at $\theta = 30°$ the velocity $v_\theta = U_0$, and consequently the static pressure at that point is p_0. Therefore, if a hole is drilled at $\theta = 30°$, the pressure at the wall will be p_0. If the other leg of the manometer is connected to the pressure tap at $\theta = 30°$, then the difference in pressures will be

$$p_t - p_0 = \tfrac{1}{2}\rho U_0^2$$

the dynamic pressure of the undisturbed stream.

With a viscous motion, however, the point on the cylinder where the static pressure is p_0 is moved farther downstream on the cylinder. This is due to the boundary layer formed on the cylinder, and the amount that this point is moved downstream is a function of the Reynolds number of the flow.

7.17 Flow Around a Sphere

The solution for the three-dimensional oval was found in Sec. 7.15. Now, in a fashion similar to the flow for the cylinder, if the distance a between the source and the sink of finite strength is made to approach zero, then again the flow of the source will be swallowed by that of the sink at a point and leaving the parallel flow in Eq. (7.57). As was done in the preceding section, let $k/4\pi = k'/2a$ and then take the limit of ψ as $a \to 0$. Replace by using Fig. 7.21 as a guide $\cos\theta_1 = -(a - x)/\sqrt{(a - x)^2 + \zeta^2}$ and $\cos\theta_2 = (a + x)/\sqrt{(a + x)^2 + \zeta^2}$. After all these substitutions Eq. (7.57) becomes

$$\psi = -\frac{k'}{2a}\left(\frac{a + x}{\sqrt{(a + x)^2 + \zeta^2}} + \frac{a - x}{\sqrt{(a - x)^2 + \zeta^2}}\right) + \tfrac{1}{2}U_0 r^2 \sin^2\theta$$

To take the limit, take the derivative of the parenthesis with respect to a and the derivative of the denominator $2a$ with respect to a and substitute then the value of $a = 0$. This limiting process yields

$$\begin{aligned}\psi &= -\frac{k'\zeta^2}{(x^2+\zeta^2)^{3/2}} + \tfrac{1}{2}U_0 r^2 \sin^2\theta \\ &= -\frac{k' r^2 \sin^2\theta}{r^3} + \tfrac{1}{2}U_0 r^2 \sin^2\theta \\ &= -\frac{k' \sin^2\theta}{r} + \tfrac{1}{2}U_0 r^2 \sin^2\theta \end{aligned} \tag{7.69}$$

The same limiting steps, when repeated for the potential function, give

$$\phi = \frac{k'}{r^2}\cos\theta + U_0 r\cos\theta \tag{7.70}$$

This flow field is shown in Fig. 7.25.

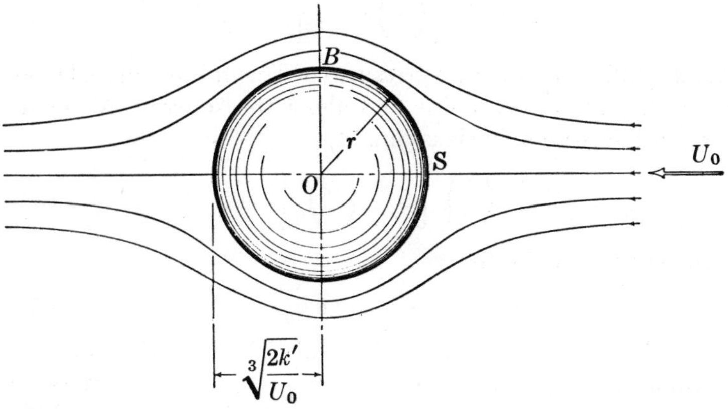

Figure 7.25
Flow around a sphere.

From Eq. (7.20) the two components of the velocity are

$$\begin{aligned} v_r &= -\frac{\partial\phi}{\partial r} = \frac{2k'}{r^3}\cos\theta - U_0\cos\theta \\ v_\theta &= -\frac{1}{r}\frac{\partial\phi}{\partial\theta} = \frac{k'}{r^3}\sin\theta + U_0\sin\theta \end{aligned} \tag{7.71}$$

The radius of the sphere is found by letting $v_r = 0$ at the stagnation point S where $\theta = 0$. This yields $r_0 = \sqrt[3]{\dfrac{2k'}{U_0}}$. Substitution of the value for the radius in the velocity relations gives

$$v_r = U_0\left[\left(\frac{r_0}{r}\right)^3 - 1\right]\cos\theta$$
$$v_\theta = U_0\left[\frac{1}{2}\left(\frac{r_0}{r}\right)^3 + 1\right]\sin\theta \tag{7.72}$$

The velocity distribution on the surface of the sphere is found when $r = r_0$. Thus $v_r = 0$ and

$$v_\theta = \tfrac{3}{2}U_0 \sin\theta \tag{7.73}$$

This result is different from Eq. (7.66), the value of the velocity on the surface of the cylinder, because of the three-dimensional nature of the spherical flow. The velocity along the approach streamline is obtained when θ is made to equal zero. Then $v_\theta = 0$, and

$$v_r = U_0\left[\left(\frac{r_0}{r}\right)^3 - 1\right] \tag{7.74}$$

From Bernoulli's equation the pressure coefficient is evaluated along the approach stagnation streamline and along the sphere. Along the approach stagnation streamline it is equal to

$$C_p = \left(\frac{r_0}{r}\right)^3\left[2 - \left(\frac{r_0}{r}\right)^3\right] \tag{7.75}$$

and along the surface of the sphere

$$C_p = 1 - \tfrac{9}{4}\sin^2\theta \tag{7.76}$$

The results of the velocity in Eqs. (7.73) and (7.74) together with the pressure coefficient along the same stagnation streamline as given by Eqs. (7.75) and (7.76), are plotted in Fig. 7.26. This figure should be compared with the corresponding one for the cylinder in Fig. 7.24.

Illustrative Example 7.8

For the flow around the cylinder evaluated in Sec. 7.16, show that the vorticity anywhere in the flow is zero and that the circulation around any closed path concentric to the cylinder is also zero.

In Chap. III, the axial vorticity in polar coordinates was given in Eq. (3.36) as

$$\zeta_z = \frac{\partial v_\theta}{\partial r} + \frac{v_\theta}{r} - \frac{1}{r}\frac{\partial v_r}{\partial \theta}$$

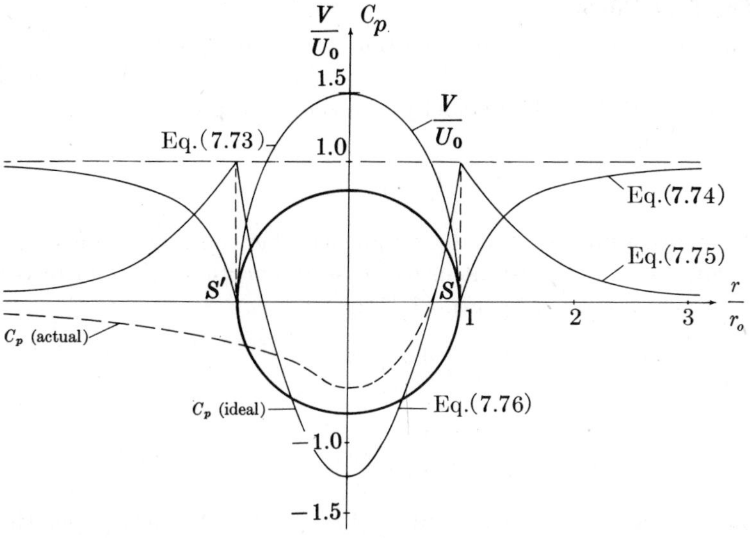

Figure 7.26
Velocity and pressure coefficient along the stagnation streamline of the flow around a sphere.

The peripheral and radial velocities for the cylinder flow are given in Eq. (7.64). Application of the vorticity equation gives

$$\zeta_z = -2U_0\left(\frac{a_0^2}{r^3}\right)\sin\theta + U_0\left(\frac{a_0^2}{r^3} + \frac{1}{r}\right)\sin\theta + U_0\left(\frac{a_0^2}{r^3} - \frac{1}{r}\right)\sin\theta = 0 \text{ everywhere}$$

This result is not surprising, since this chapter deals with flow fields that are irrotational. According to Eq. (3.45), the circulation around a closed path concentric to the cylinder is also zero, since the circulation is the integration of the vorticity inside the area of the concentric path and the vorticity is zero everywhere inside.

If the integration path, for instance, is chosen as the surface of the cylinder then, according to Eq. (3.43), the circulation is

$$\Gamma = \int v_\theta\, ds = \int_0^{2\pi} v_\theta a_0\, d\theta$$

$$= 2U_0 a_0 \int_0^{2\pi} \sin\theta\, d\theta = 0$$

7.18 The Free Vortex

The free vortex is a peripheral motion whose peripheral velocity v_θ varies inversely as the radial distance. This flow was derived and discussed in Sec. 3.16. The velocity variation was given as

$$v_\theta = \frac{C}{r}$$

It becomes of interest first to examine whether this flow is rotational or not. Since v_r is not existent in this case the vorticity normal to the plane of the flow is given by Eq. (3.37):

$$\zeta_z = \frac{\partial v_\theta}{\partial r} + \frac{v_\theta}{r}$$

$$= \frac{1}{r}\frac{\partial}{\partial r}(v_\theta r)$$

Since the product $v_\theta r$ is a constant everywhere in the flow, then the vorticity is zero everywhere in the flow except at the origin where $r = 0$ where an indeterminate value for the vorticity is obtained. This vorticity value is easily evaluated at $r = 0$ if the circulation is evaluated. According to Eq. (3.45),

$$\Gamma = \int_0^{2\pi} \frac{C}{r} r \, d\theta$$

$$= 2\pi C$$

So the circulation is a constant no matter which concentric path is considered, and yet it was just found that the vorticity is zero everywhere except at the origin. According to the second relation in Eq. (3.45), for the circulation to be finite the vorticity cannot be zero at the origin too. Since at the origin the area of the integration contour approaches zero as $r \to 0$, then the vorticity must be infinity so as to give a finite circulation. The constant C has just been evaluated in terms of the circulation which is a constant for any contour; the peripheral velocity of the free vortex is then

$$v_\theta = \frac{\Gamma}{2\pi}\frac{1}{r} \tag{7.77}$$

Since there is no radial component of the velocity, the stream function and the potential function are obtained by integration:

$$v_\theta = \frac{d\psi}{dr} = -\frac{1}{r}\frac{d\phi}{d\theta}$$

$$\psi = \frac{\Gamma}{2\pi} \ln r \tag{7.78}$$

$$\phi = -\frac{\Gamma}{2\pi}\theta$$

Since the free-vortex flow was found to be irrotational everywhere except at $r = 0$, the usual definitions of the potential and stream functions apply to this flow as well, except, of course, at the singularity point $r = 0$. The constants in the preceding integrations again have to be omitted if ψ is defined as zero at a unit radius and ϕ is zero at $\theta = 0$.

It must be noted from the set of solutions in Eq. (7.78) that they resemble those for the source in Eq. (7.30). The difference is that the stream function for the source corresponds to the potential function for the vortex, and vice versa.

7.19 Flow Around the Cylinder with Circulation

Except for the free-vortex flow, all the other flows discussed in this chapter are free of circulation, because the vorticity was zero everywhere. In the case of the flow around a cylinder, this fact was demonstrated in Illustrative Example 7.8.

To introduce circulation into the flow without introducing vorticity so that the potential theory used in this chapter can still be applicable, the method to be used is to add to the flows discussed a free-vortex motion. Since the vorticity in that case will be concentrated into the origin, this origin can easily be omitted from the region of interest. For instance, if a free-vortex motion is superimposed at the origin of the flow around a cylinder described in Sec. 7.16, the only point having vorticity will be inside the cylinder, which is not of any engineering interest.

The stream and potential functions for this flow are obtained by Eqs. (7.62), (7.63), and (7.78). The velocities are also found by addition:

$$v_r = U_0\left[\left(\frac{a_0}{r}\right)^2 - 1\right]\cos\theta$$
$$v_\theta = U_0\left[\left(\frac{a_0}{r}\right)^2 + 1\right]\sin\theta + \frac{\Gamma}{2\pi r} \tag{7.79}$$

Now the fluid velocity at the surface of the cylinder will be for $r = a_0$.

$$v_\theta = 2U_0 \sin\theta + \frac{\Gamma}{2\pi a_0} \tag{7.80}$$

Since positive Γ is in the counterclockwise direction, the positive v_θ contribution from the vortex is also counterclockwise in the direction of increasing θ. Therefore, the flow at the top surface of the cylinder will have a higher speed than the flow at the bottom, since at the bottom of the cylinder $\sin\theta < 0$. On account of the high velocity, the streamlines at the top will come closer together and those at the bottom will spread apart. This effect, called the *Magnus effect,* is shown in Fig. 7.27. Because of the circulation, the stagnation points of the flow will

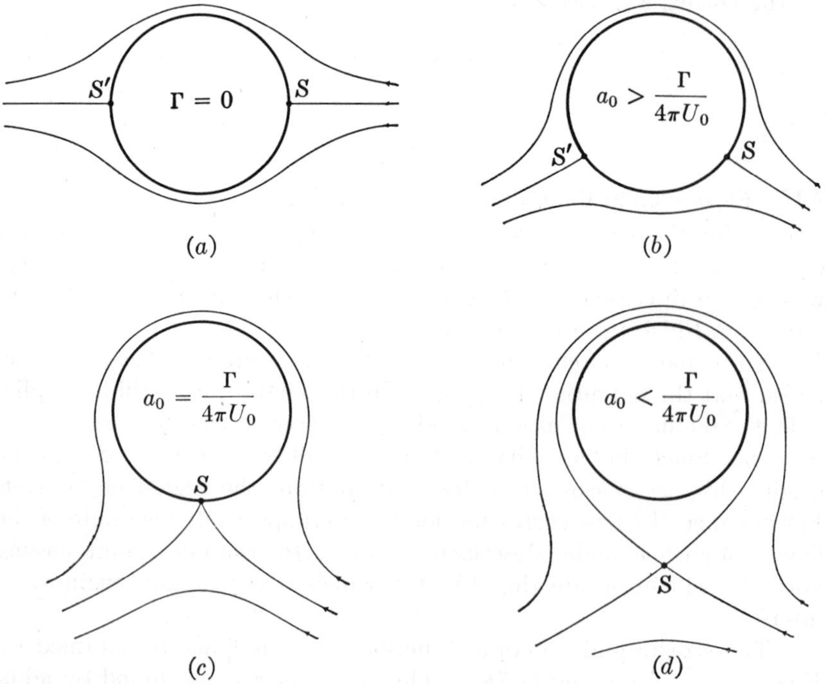

Figure 7.27
Cylinder flow with circulation.

change position also. This new position can be evaluated by letting Eq. (7.80) take the value of zero. This gives

$$y_0 = a_0 \sin\theta = -\frac{\Gamma}{4\pi U_0}$$

This is the vertical location of the stagnation point on the cylinder. The horizontal location of this stagnation point is

$$x_0 = \sqrt{a_0^2 - \left(\frac{\Gamma}{4\pi U_0}\right)^2}$$

These dimensions are indicated in Fig. 7.28. It is seen now when $\Gamma = 0$ the values of x_0 and y_0 correspond to the symmetrical flow without circulation. If, however, in the value of x_0 the term a_0 is factored out,

$$x_0 = a_0\sqrt{1 - \left(\frac{\Gamma}{4\pi U_0 a_0}\right)^2}$$

Now it can be seen that, if $\frac{\Gamma}{4\pi U_0 a_0} < 1.0$, there are two stagnation points with a distance $x_0 < a_0$. When $\frac{\Gamma}{4\pi U_0 a_0} = 1.0$, there is only one stagnation point; and it is located at the bottom of the cylinder where $x_0 = 0$. For larger values of $\frac{\Gamma}{4\pi U_0 a_0} > 1.0$, the stagnation point will be not on the cylinder but in the stream. These conditions are shown in Fig. 7.27.

7.20 The Lift on the Cylinder. Kutta-Joukowski's Theorem

This theorem states that the total force per unit length of cylinder acting on an infinitely long cylinder placed in a uniform stream of velocity U_0 is equal to the product of the density of the fluid, the circulation around the cylinder, and U_0. The sense of the force is normal to U_0 and to the axis of the cylinder. Its direction is such that the three vectors—the free stream velocity, the vorticity, and the lift force—form a right-handed coordinate system. In the preceding section, circulation was introduced around a cylinder by superimposing a free vortex at the origin. For a cylinder, actually, this can be done by spinning the cylinder. In any other submerged body such as an airfoil, unequal viscosity effects on the upper and lower parts of the airfoil produce circulation. For a positive rotation, the vorticity vector pierces the plane of the paper toward the reader. In Fig. 7.28, this is the direction of vortex rotation

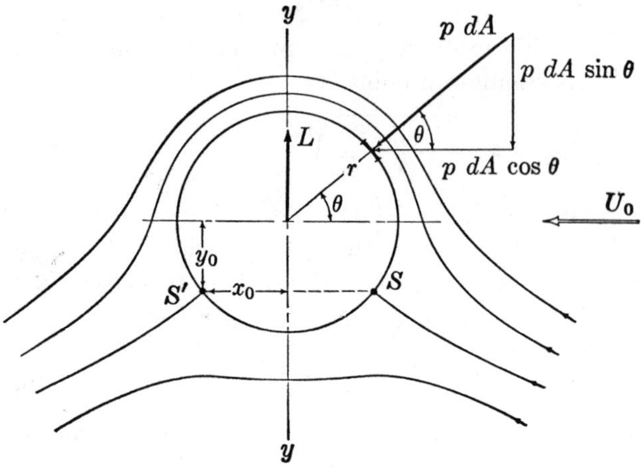

Figure 7.28
Pressure on the cylinder.

that was adopted; since the undisturbed flow velocity U_0 flows from right to left, the lift L must be upward in the direction of positive y.

The proof of this theorem will be carried out for a cylinder with circular cross section; however, the results can be generalized to hold for any cross section.

Following the details in Fig. 7.28, the horizontal and vertical force components on the cylinder are

$$F_x = \int_0^{2\pi} p \cos \theta \, dA$$

$$F_y = -\int_0^{2\pi} p \sin \theta \, dA$$

The area dA per unit length of the cylinder is $a_0 \, d\theta$, and, when this is substituted into the force integral, the result will be per unit length of cylinder. The pressure on the surface of the cylinder can be obtained from Bernoulli's equation,

$$p = (p_0 + \tfrac{1}{2}\rho U_0^2) - \tfrac{1}{2}\rho v_\theta^2$$
$$= \text{constant} - \tfrac{1}{2}\rho v_\theta^2$$

The term in the parenthesis is the total pressure, which is a constant. Substitution of the pressure in the force integral gives

$$F_x = \int_2^{2\pi} \left[\text{constant} - \tfrac{1}{2}\rho \left(2U_0 \sin\theta + \frac{\Gamma}{2\pi a_0} \right)^2 \right] a_0 \cos\theta \, d\theta$$

$$F_y = \int_0^{2\pi} \left[\tfrac{1}{2}\rho \left(2U_0 \sin\theta + \frac{\Gamma}{2\pi a_0} \right)^2 - \text{constant} \right] a_0 \sin\theta \, d\theta$$

Because of the symmetry of the flow with respect to the y-axis, the integral F_x or the drag will be zero, and its integration will not be carried through. The integrand of F_y is expanded:

$$F_y =$$

$$\int_0^{2\pi} \left(2\rho U_0^2 a_0 \sin^3\theta + \frac{\rho U_0 \Gamma}{\pi} \sin^2\theta + \frac{\Gamma^2 \rho}{8\pi^2 a_0} \sin\theta - \text{constant } a_0 \sin\theta \right) d\theta$$

All the integrals with odd powers of $\sin\theta$ vanish when integrated from 0 to 2π. The only term which is nonzero is

$$F_y = \frac{\rho U_0 \Gamma}{\pi} \int_0^{2\pi} \sin^2\theta \, d\theta$$

$$= \rho U_0 \Gamma \tag{7.81}$$

This is the proof of the theorem. This result has already been derived on the momentum basis for a cascade of vanes in Sec. 5.5(g); therefore, this proof must be valid for more general cases.

A second conclusion which must be extended from this theorem is that in a nonviscous potential fluid there will never be a component of force along the direction of the main stream U_0. This indicates that the drag of all bodies submerged in a perfect fluid will always be equal to zero.[2] With this, one may conclude that the perfect-fluid theory is completely inadequate for determining the drag of submerged bodies. The lift, on the other hand, when evaluated with this theory, gives good accuracy.

Illustrative Example 7.9

A boat has a cylindrical vertical drum for a sail. The radius of the drum is 2 ft and its height is 10 ft. It spins at 600 rpm in a wind stream of 20 mph. Find the thrust on the boat normal to the direction of the wind.

With the cylinder spinning at 600 rpm, without the wind, the air around it

[2] This is called d'Alembert's paradox. The fact that no drag could be obtained when bodies were submerged in perfect fluids, puzzled scientists up to the eighteenth century.

will be entrained at a peripheral velocity of $v_\theta = \omega a_0 = \dfrac{2\pi \times 600}{60} \times 2 = 125.6$ ft/sec. The corresponding circulation produced by the spin is

$$
\begin{aligned}
&= 2\pi a_0 v_\theta \\
&= 2 \times 3.14 \times 2 \times 125.6 \\
&= 1{,}580 \text{ ft}^2/\text{sec}
\end{aligned}
$$

Assuming the density of the air to be 0.00227 slug/ft^3, the thrust force becomes, from Eq. (7.81),

$$
\begin{aligned}
L &= 0.00227 \times 20 \times 1.46 \times 1{,}580 \times 10 \\
&= 1{,}045 \text{ lb}_f
\end{aligned}
$$

The thrust here has been multiplied by the height of 10 ft, since Eq. (7.79) represents the thrust per unit length of cylinder.

7.21 The Apparent or Virtual Mass

When a body is set in steady motion with respect to the infinite medium at rest, the medium surrounding the body will be set in motion as well. Consequently, the energy required to bring an immersed body to a constant translatory velocity is the sum of the kinetic energy of the body plus the kinetic energy of the fluid particles set in motion. Energy losses owing to the viscous effects are not taken into account in this discussion.

The *apparent mass* of a body moving at a velocity U_0 is then a virtual mass moving at the same velocity U_0, which will account for the kinetic energy of the actual body and the kinetic energy of the displaced fluid. The apparent mass is then the total kinetic energy of the body and the stream divided by one half the velocity squared of the body relative to the stationary stream far away from the body.

When the body in Fig. 7.29 moves at a constant velocity U_0, the total kinetic energy involved to set the body in motion is the kinetic energy of the body plus the kinetic energy of the fluid surrounding the body.

$$
\begin{aligned}
E_{\text{total}} &= E_{\text{body}} + E_{\text{fluid}} \\
&= \tfrac{1}{2} M U_0^2 + \tfrac{1}{2} \iiint \rho (u^2 + v^2 + w^2)\, dx\, dy\, dz \qquad (7.82)
\end{aligned}
$$

Here M is the mass of the body, U_0 is its steady velocity relative to the undisturbed fluid, and u, v, and w are the velocity components of

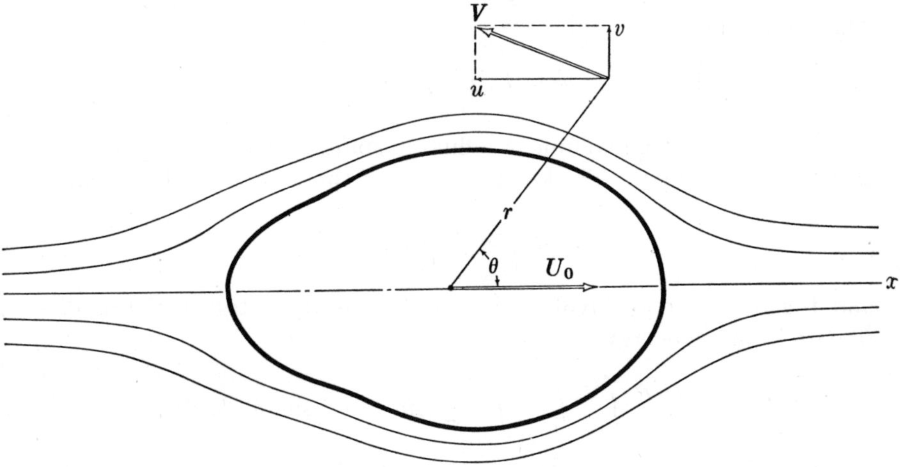

Figure 7.29
Solid body moving in a stationary fluid.

the fluid surrounding the body owing to the motion of the body. The density ρ is that of the fluid.

When a simple flow field such as that of a sphere moving in an infinite medium is considered, the velocity of the fluid is known at all points if the fluid is inviscid and irrotational. Then the kinetic energy involved in the fluid motion can be evaluated. Equation (7.71) represented the velocity components of the fluid around a sphere when the sphere was stationary and the infinite stream moved around the sphere. To obtain the flow of the fluid surrounding a sphere when a sphere moves in a stationary medium, the terms containing U_0 in Eq. (7.71) must be removed, since they represent the contribution of the moving stream. Thus,

$$\begin{aligned} v_r &= \frac{2k'}{r^3} \cos \theta \\ v_\theta &= \frac{k'}{r^3} \sin \theta \end{aligned} \tag{7.83}$$

If the radius of the sphere which was found to be $r_0 = \sqrt[3]{2k'/U_0}$ is introduced in the velocity equations, they take the form

$$\begin{aligned} v_r &= U_0 \left(\frac{r_0}{r}\right)^3 \cos \theta \\ v_\theta &= \frac{U_0}{2} \left(\frac{r_0}{r}\right)^3 \sin \theta \end{aligned} \tag{7.84}$$

The total velocity is

$$V^2 = v_r^2 + v_\theta^2 = U_0^2 \left(\frac{r_0}{r}\right)^6 (\cos^2 \theta + \tfrac{1}{4} \sin^2 \theta)$$

The infinitesimal volume of a fluid in spherical coordinates is $d\mathcal{V} = (r\, d\theta)(r \sin \theta\, d\alpha)(dr)$. The kinetic energy of the infinitesimal element is

$$dE_f = \frac{\rho}{2} V^2\, d\mathcal{V};$$

and the total energy involved in the fluid is the integral of this differential kinetic energy:

$$E_f = \frac{2\rho U_0^2 r_0^6}{2} \int_0^{2\pi} \int_0^{\pi/2} \int_{r_0}^{\infty} \frac{1}{r^4} (\sin \theta - \tfrac{3}{4} \sin^3 \theta)\, d\alpha\, d\theta\, dr$$

The limits of α are from 0 to 2π, and, since the velocities are not functions of α, the integration is treated as that of a constant. The integration of θ actually goes from 0 to π, but, since $\sin \theta$ is an odd function, the

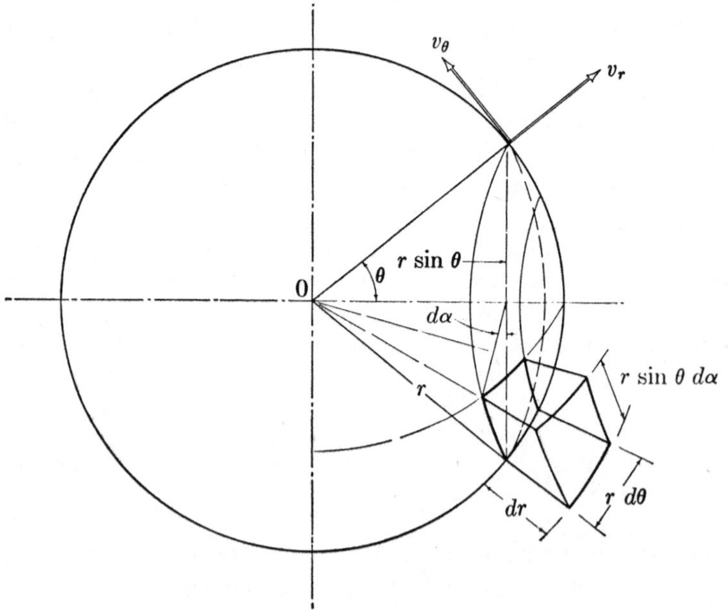

Figure 7.30
Spherical geometry.

contribution of the integration is twice that from 0 to $\pi/2$. The integration yields

$$E_f = \tfrac{1}{2}(\tfrac{2}{3}\pi\rho r_0^3)U_0^2$$

Since the volume of the sphere is $\tfrac{4}{3}\pi r_0^3$ and if its density is ρ_b, the total kinetic energy of the sphere and of the fluid is

$$E_t = \tfrac{1}{2}(\tfrac{4}{3}\pi\rho_b r_0^3 + \tfrac{2}{3}\pi\rho r_0^3)U_0^2$$

$$= \frac{\mathcal{V}}{2}(\rho_b + \tfrac{1}{2}\rho)U_0^2 \tag{7.85}$$

Here $\mathcal{V}$ is the volume of the sphere, ρ_b is the density of the body, and ρ is the density of the fluid. The apparent mass is then the total energy divided by one half the velocity U_0 squared.

$$M_a = \mathcal{V}(\rho_b + \tfrac{1}{2}\rho) \tag{7.86}$$

This apparent mass is that of a sphere; each body will have its own apparent mass, since the fluid displaced by all immersed and moving bodies is not the same.

Problems

7.1 Derive the velocity components v_r and v_θ in cylindrical coordinates in terms of the derivatives of the stream function. In other words, show a formal proof for the expressions given in Eq. (7.4).

7.2 Follow the same procedure as in Prob. 7.1, but derive the velocity components in cylindrical coordinates in terms of the derivatives of the potential function, a proof of Eq. (7.17).

7.3 Verify that the point-source flow satisfies the equation of continuity by changing the velocity of the source into Cartesian coordinates and using Eq. (3.19).

7.4 For a point source, if the pressure at any point is p and that at infinity is p_0, find an expression of the pressure difference $(p_0 - p)$ in terms of the radial distance from the center of the source.

7.5 A point source is situated in a 90° corner at a location x_0, ζ_0. If a point $P(x,\zeta)$ is considered, write the stream and potential functions at the point P in terms of the coordinates x and ζ.

7.6 In Illustrative Example 7.2, show that the plane $x = L$ intersects the stream and potential surfaces in the form of circles whose radii are functions of the particular stream and potential surface they intersect.

7.7 From the cylindrical form of the equation of continuity [Eq. (3.18)], show that the flow from a line source satisfies it.

7.8 In Sec. 7.8, for two line sources placed $2a$ apart, find the expression for the velocity along the line joining the two sources. Find the pressure distribution along that streamline. Take the pressure at infinity to be p_0.

7.9 Consider the flow from a line source and a line sink placed a distance $2a$ apart. Derive expressions for the velocity and the pressure along the ordinate halfway between the source and the sink. Show the particular value of the velocity and pressure at the origin halfway between the source and the sink.

7.10 A line source is placed in a 90° corner at the position x_0, y_0. Determine the stream and potential functions for a point $P(x,y)$ located anywhere in the flow field.

7.11 Find the radial distance on a plane half-body where the velocity on the surface is equal to that of the undisturbed flow.

7.12 Draw the contour of a half-body for $r_0 = 1$. Also draw the streamline for which $\psi/U_0 = -\frac{1}{2}$.

7.13 In Prob. 7.12, determine a relationship for v_θ/U_0 and v_r/U_0 in terms of the angle θ alone for the streamline $\psi/U_0 = -\frac{1}{2}$.

7.14 In Prob. 7.13, derive an expression for the pressure coefficient in terms of the angle θ along the same streamline.

7.15 In the three-dimensional Rankine body, if $r_0 = 1$, plot the contour of the body and compare it with the result of Prob. 7.12.

7.16 In a three-dimensional Rankine-body flow, find the deceleration of the fluid along the approach stagnation streamline at a distance r_0 from the stagnation point. The answer is to be given in U_0 and r_0.

7.17 Establish how the velocity of the flow past a cylinder varies as a function of r in a vertical direction from the top of the cylinder.

7.18 As in Prob. 7.16, find the deceleration of the flow past a cylinder at a point on the approach stagnation streamline a_0 away from the stagnation point. The answer is to be given in terms of U_0 and a_0.

7.19 Find the relationship of the spacing of the streamlines at the top of a cylinder as compared with that at the undisturbed flow.

7.20 Two static pressure holes are drilled on a cylinder at $\pm 30°$ from an arbitrary axis of its cross section, as shown in the figure. If α is the angle of this axis to the undisturbed flow direction U_0, find an expression for the pressure difference $p_2 - p_1$ as a function of the angle α. Plot the dimensionless pressure difference $(p_2 - p_1)/2\rho U_0^2$ as a function of α and discuss the possibilities of using this probe as a directional probe for determining the direction of flow of a stream.

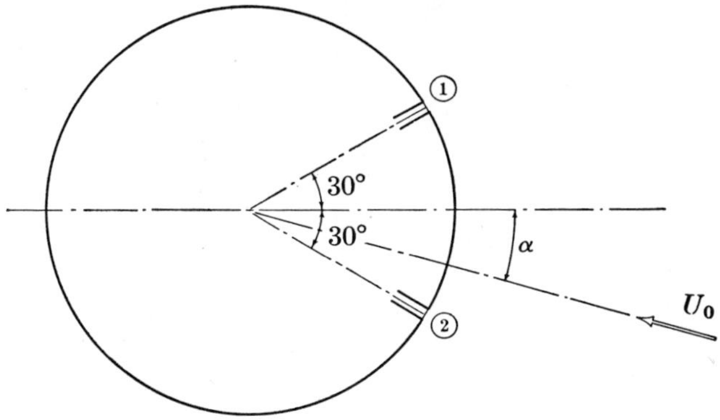

7.21 Determine the angle θ where the pressure coefficient is zero on the surface of a sphere.

7.22 What is the radius of a circle on the sphere along which the velocity of the fluid is equal to the absolute value of that of the undisturbed flow?

7.23 If the pressure of the undisturbed flow for a free vortex is p_0, determine the pressure at any other radial distance.

7.24 A cylinder 1 ft in diameter is moving at the speed of 10 ft/sec in a stationary fluid. If the stagnation points are located 30° off the axis of the motion, what should be the circulation imposed on the cylinder? If the cylinder produces the circulation by spinning in the fluid, what is the peripheral velocity of the cylinder?

7.25 Calculate Prob. 7.24 for the strength of the circulation when the two stagnation points meet at 90° from the direction of motion, and show the direction of the circulation as compared with the direction of movement of the stagnation points for a given translational direction of the velocity of the cylinder.

7.26 In Probs. 7.24 and 7.25, evaluate the lift per unit length on the cylinder if the fluid is water with a density of 62.4 lb_m/ft^3.

7.27 Find the apparent mass of a cylinder moving in a stationary fluid.

Essentials of Compressible Flow

chapter VIII

8.1 Introduction

In Sec. 4.10(*d*), in the compressible-flow example it was learned that, when the relative velocity of the fluid with respect to the immersed body became high, the results of the analysis for the pressure coefficient began to depart from the conventional treatment of incompressible motion. In the example cited it was shown that, as the speed of the fluid relative to the immersed body approached the speed of sound in the flowing medium, owing to the compressibility of the fluid, additional terms as a function of the Mach number influenced the incompressible solution. According to Table 4.1, the compressibility influence became of the order of 1.21 as the Mach number reached the value of 0.88 and the influence became larger as the Mach number increased.

The fact that the flow is compressible indicates that the density of the flowing medium is a sensitive function of the pressure. The introduction of this new variable ρ into the equations of motion will necessitate the study of its relationship to the other properties of the medium. This need then invokes the principles of thermodynamics which represent a separate and independent approach from the dynamic equations of motion. Since a new variable ρ has been added, this independent approach is necessary for the solution of the problem. So the concepts of thermodynamics will play an important role in the theory of compressible fluids.

A great number of engineering problems, associated with compressible motion, can be studied adequately with the assumption of one-dimensional motion. According to Sec. 3.7, this implies that variations of fluid properties occur in one direction—the direction of motion. This direction of motion does not have to be a straight-line motion. It can be the motion along the curved axis of a stream filament, but, in order for the properties at each cross section of the filament to be constant, the curvature of the filament should not be too large.

8.2 Basic Thermodynamic Concepts in Compressible Flows

Some of the concepts that will be described here have appeared in various sections of this book. They are again brought together here for the purpose of extending the analysis and for gathering pertinent material to be used for the solution of new problems. Reference to other sections in this book will be made when a concept appears again, and the student should attempt to correlate these concepts with those already discussed at some length.

(a) *The Energy Equation*

The general energy equation was thoroughly discussed in Chap. VI. In a great number of engineering applications of compressible flows, such as those in conduits and flows past solid bodies, however, there is no transfer of external shaft work or external heat into the fluid. The thermodynamic processes occur in the absence of shaft work and in an adiabatic fashion. The lack of shaft work for a flow through a control volume does not imply a constant-density process as in a system. Here the flow work is always present, and the density variations are represented by it.

For most applications, the potential energy change owing to altitude changes in the fluid is so small that it can be neglected. Therefore, the energy equation derived in Chap. VI as Eq. (6.27) or (6.29) can be simplified in the form

$$J\,de + d\left(\frac{p}{\rho}\right) + U\,dU = 0$$
$$J\,dh + U\,dU = 0 \tag{8.1}$$

In thermodynamics it is shown that, for a pure substance whose state is defined by two independent thermodynamic properties only (Sec. 1.7), the internal energy e for a constant-volume process can be represented in terms of the specific heat at constant volume c_v.

$$de = c_v\,dT \tag{8.2}$$

In a perfect gas, however, since the internal energy is a function of the temperature only, this expression of the internal energy is valid for any process. In general, c_v is a function of the temperature, but, as for most finite processes, it varies little; thus it is considered a constant. Integration of Eq. (8.2) yields

$$e = c_v \int_{T_0}^{T} dT$$
$$= c_v(T - T_0)$$

If T_0 is the absolute base temperature at which point $T_0 = 0$, then the internal energy can be written simply:

$$e = c_v T \tag{8.3}$$

A similar treatment is true for the enthalpy change at constant pressure. It is equivalent to the heat added at constant pressure, which can be represented in terms of the specific heat at constant pressure and the change of temperature produced.

$$dh = c_p\,dT \tag{8.4}$$

For a perfect gas this relationship is valid for all processes—not only that of a constant pressure. Integration of Eq. (8.4) between absolute zero and any other temperature gives

$$h = c_p T \tag{8.5}$$

c_p is the specific heat at constant pressure, which is also considered constant for most finite processes. With this new relation for the enthalpy, the energy equation, Eq. (8.1) readily becomes

$$Jc_p\,dT + U\,dU = 0 \tag{8.6}$$

In this equation, no use was made of the reversibility of the process, and, since Eq. (8.4) is a property equation, it is thus valid for a reversible or irreversible adiabatic process. This implies that Eq. (8.4) is just as valid for frictional motion as it is for frictionless motion. The integration of Eq. (8.4) yields

$$Jc_pT + \tfrac{1}{2}U^2 = \text{constant} \tag{8.7}$$

In steady motion the thermodynamic process of the moving fluid takes place along its motion trajectories or along the streamlines. Equation (8.7) holds then along the streamlines. It must be remembered that the basis for the derivation of Eq. (8.7) is that no shaft work or external heat is transferred. If stream filaments are considered as the infinitesimal control volumes, there must be no *net* work or heat transferred from one filament to the other. For one-dimensional motion, since the properties of the fluid are constant on a plane perpendicular to the direction of motion, then Eq. (8.7) becomes valid for any point in the flow.

It was defined in Chap. VII and Eq. (8.7) that

$$h = e + \frac{1}{J}\frac{p}{\rho}$$

Furthermore, for a perfect gas the following relations are true:

$$h = c_pT$$

$$e = c_vT$$

$$p/\rho = RT$$

The value of R can be obtained in terms of the specific heats if the expressions above can be substituted into Eq. (6.28). Therefore,

$$c_pT = c_vT + \frac{RT}{J}$$

$$R = J(c_p - c_v) \tag{8.8}$$

By definition, the ratio of the specific heats is called

$$\gamma = c_p/c_v \tag{8.9}$$

When a system goes from a temperature T_1 to a temperature T_2 at constant pressure, the heat added to achieve this result is always larger than that required to go from the same two temperature levels in a constant-volume process.[1] Thus the ratio of the specific heats $\gamma > 1$.

(b) The Equation of Motion

It was mentioned in the introduction that, for the most part, the treatment of compressible flows will be considered for one-dimensional

[1] The student can show this from the system equation, Eq. (6.34), by comparing magnitudes of ds for the constant-pressure and constant-volume processes.

motion. When the motion is also steady and inviscid, and again neglecting differences of elevation, Euler's equation, Eq. (4.28) becomes

$$U\,dU + \frac{dp}{\rho} = 0 \tag{8.10}$$

This equation is often identified as the momentum equation for the motion of the fluid. If Eq. (8.10) were multiplied by the density and the area of the stream filament, it would represent the infinitesimal rate of change of momentum between two points along the stream filament. This is why it is often called the momentum equation.

(*c*) *The Equation of Continuity of Mass*

Consider the one-dimensional motion, shown in Fig. 8.1, flowing through a stream tube from a section A toward C. Let the properties of the fluid be defined at the center B of the stream tube section AC. Since the flow is one-dimensional, there are only variations of properties with the streamline dimension S. For a time-dependent flow, the mass flux entering the stream tube at A per unit time is not equal to that leaving at C; the difference of the rates of mass flow, if positive in the sequence mentioned, means that there is an increase in mass with time within the stream tube, therefore increasing the density of the fluid.

The mass flux entering at A is called $(\rho AU)_S$ at the coordinate S, and the flux leaving at B is $(\rho AU)_{S+dS}$. The instantaneous mass of the fluid within the stream tube is $\rho A\,dS$, and its change with time is $\frac{\partial}{\partial t}(\rho A\,dS)$. The mass-rate balance is then

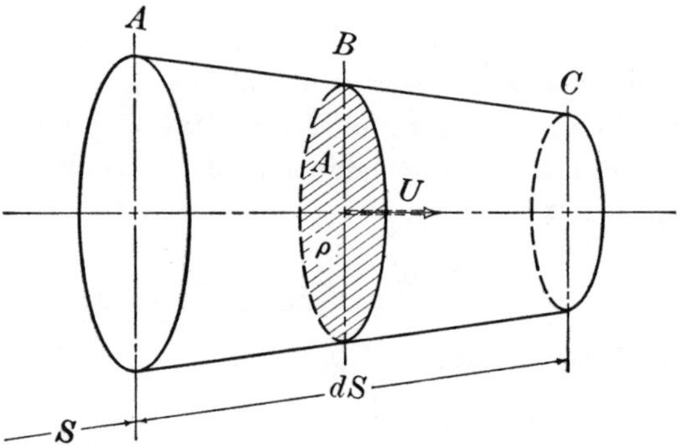

Figure 8.1
Flow through a stream tube.

$$(\rho AU)_S - (\rho AU)_{S+dS} = \frac{\partial}{\partial t}(\rho A\,dS) \tag{8.11}$$

The quantity $(\rho AU)_{S+dS}$ can be expanded in a Taylor series in terms of the value at S and its changes at S

$$(\rho AU)_{S+dS} = (\rho AU)_S + \frac{\partial}{\partial S}(\rho AU)_S\,dS + \ldots$$

Substituting this expansion into Eq. (8.11), the condition of mass continuity becomes

$$(\rho AU)_S - (\rho AU)_S - \frac{\partial}{\partial S}(\rho AU)_S\,dS = \frac{\partial}{\partial t}(\rho A\,dS)$$

But the arbitrary control volume of the stream tube $A\,dS$ does not change with time; only the density within it changes. Dividing by dS, the equation of continuity becomes

$$-\frac{\partial}{\partial S}(\rho AU) = A\frac{\partial \rho}{\partial t} \tag{8.12}$$

This is the one-dimensional form of the continuity of mass along the direction of flow S. Naturally, in a steady state $\partial\rho/\partial t = 0$, and Eq. (8.12) integrates into the form which was already derived in Eq. (3.10) by a different method.

$$\rho AU = \text{constant} \tag{8.13}$$

The differential form of this equation is

$$\rho A\,dU + \rho U\,dA + AU\,d\rho = 0$$

Dividing by Eq. (8.13), it is found that

$$\frac{dU}{U} + \frac{dA}{A} + \frac{d\rho}{\rho} = 0 \tag{8.14}$$

(d) *Isentropic Expansion-Compression Law for a Perfect Gas*

The system's equation derived from the first and second laws of thermodynamics was given in Eq. (6.33). If the definition of the enthalpy is substituted into this equation, it becomes

$$T\,ds + \frac{1}{J}\frac{dp}{\rho} = dh$$

and for a perfect gas it can be written as

$$T\,ds + \frac{1}{J}\frac{dp}{\rho} = c_p\,dT$$

In this equation ds is the change of entropy, and, since the equation is in terms of properties of the fluid, it is therefore valid for a reversible or an irreversible process. Only if the process is reversible, the quantity $T\,ds$ can be identified as the heat transferred into the fluid system. If both sides of the equation are divided by T, and $p = \rho RT$ is used,

$$ds = c_p \frac{dT}{T} - \frac{R}{J}\frac{dp}{p}$$

Using Eq. (8.9), the change-of-entropy equation can be rewritten in the form:

$$\begin{aligned} ds &= c_p \frac{dT}{T} - (c_p - c_v)\frac{dp}{p} \\ &= c_p \left(\frac{dT}{T} - \frac{dp}{p}\right) + c_v \frac{dp}{p} \end{aligned}$$

But, from the perfect-gas law,

$$\frac{dp}{p} = \frac{d\rho}{\rho} + \frac{dT}{T}$$

$$\frac{dp}{p} - \frac{dT}{T} = \frac{d\rho}{\rho}$$

The change of entropy then can be written in the form:

$$ds = -c_p \frac{d\rho}{\rho} + c_v \frac{dp}{p} \tag{8.15}$$

Now for the isentropic flow, $ds = 0$, and then

$$\frac{dp}{p} = \frac{c_p}{c_v}\frac{d\rho}{\rho}$$

The integration of this equation gives the well-known expansion-compression relation for a perfect gas undergoing an isentropic change:

$$\begin{aligned} \ln p &= \gamma \ln \rho + \text{constant} \\ p &= \text{constant}\, \rho^{\gamma} \end{aligned} \tag{8.16}$$

(e) The Change of Entropy for a Perfect Gas

In Eq. (8.15), the change of entropy for a perfect gas was expressed as

$$\begin{aligned} ds &= c_v \frac{dp}{p} - c_p \frac{d\rho}{\rho} \\ &= c_v \left(\frac{dp}{p} - \gamma \frac{d\rho}{\rho}\right) \end{aligned}$$

The integration of this equation yields

$$\begin{aligned} s &= c_v(\ln p - \gamma \ln \rho) + \text{constant} \\ &= c_v \ln \frac{p}{\rho^\gamma} + \text{constant} \end{aligned} \tag{8.17}$$

From this equation the difference of entropy between two states can be evaluated:

$$s - s_0 = c_v \ln \frac{p}{p_0} \left(\frac{\rho_0}{\rho}\right)^\gamma \tag{8.18}$$

8.3 The Sound Wave. Mach Number

In the passage shown in Fig. 8.2, consider a steady flow moving at A with an undisturbed velocity U at a pressure p and a density ρ. Let,

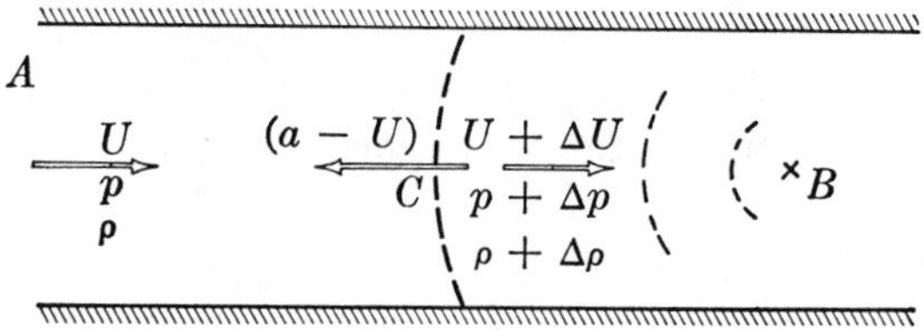

Figure 8.2
Properties of a flow upstream and downstream of a pressure wave.

for some reason, a sudden disturbance, such as the introduction of a solid body into the flow, be produced at point B. For instance, if B is the stagnation point of the body, this sudden change of pressure will propagate into the incoming fluid and change its properties when this *compression wave* has reacted with the fluid. In the region already affected by the compression wave, the new properties of the fluid will be, say, $U + \Delta U$, $p + \Delta p$, and $\rho + \Delta\rho$. As the wave travels away from B, it influences more and more fluid regions. The wave grows in size but becomes weaker and weaker per unit area, since the action area is constantly increasing. The pressure front C, shown in Fig. 8.2, moves at a speed a relative to the fluid or a speed $(a - U)$ relative to the stationary point B. In other words, the pressure wave propagates in the fluid at a velocity a.

In order to examine what takes place across the wave front C, the momentum equation can be used on a control volume which is stationary relative to the wave front C. To achieve this picture, all velocities in the fluid can be made relative to C by adding them vectorially to the wave velocity $(a - U)$ relative to B. Figure 8.3 is an outcome of this

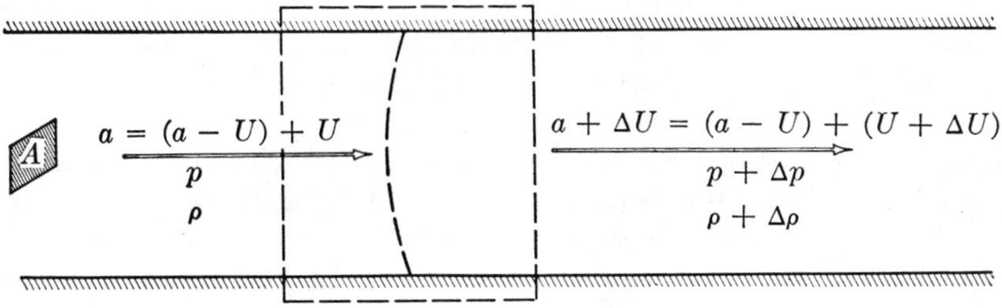

Figure 8.3
Stationary wave front with flow across it.

transformation of reference from B to C. In the absence of shear forces, the momentum relation for the flow past the wave front will read:

$$pA - (p + \Delta p)A = (\rho + \Delta\rho)(a + \Delta U)^2 A - \rho A a^2$$

Dividing through by A and neglecting second- and third-order terms such as ΔU^2, $\Delta\rho\,\Delta U$, and $\Delta U^2\,\Delta\rho$, the momentum equation becomes

$$-\Delta p = 2a\rho\,\Delta U + a^2\,\Delta\rho \tag{8.19}$$

The equation of mass continuity for the fluid crossing the area A reads:

$$\rho a A = (\rho + \Delta\rho)(a + \Delta U)A$$

This equation, after dividing by A and neglecting second-order term $\Delta\rho\,\Delta U$, becomes

$$-\rho\,\Delta U = a\,\Delta\rho$$

$$\frac{\Delta\rho}{\rho} = -\frac{\Delta U}{a} \tag{8.20}$$

The combination of this equation and Eq. (8.15) gives

$$-\Delta p = -2a^2\,\Delta\rho + a^2\,\Delta\rho$$
$$= -a^2\,\Delta\rho,$$

or

$$a^2 = \frac{\Delta p}{\Delta\rho} \tag{8.21}$$

In the limit when the disturbance is very weak, the speed of the wave is that of sound in the medium, and the property changes take place isentropically

$$a = \sqrt{\left(\frac{dp}{d\rho}\right)_s} \tag{8.22}$$

This relation was informally derived in Sec. 3.5(*b*) where $dp/d\rho$ was also related to the modulus of elasticity of the substance. The speed of propagation of small disturbances, that is, the speed of sound, has just been derived. It can be deduced from this relation that the change of pressure and density across the wave must be of the same sign so as to give a real value for the speed of sound. The change in velocity goes in the direction opposite to that of the density and pressure. This is observed from the equation of mass continuity, Eq. (8.20). A compression wave will create, after the wave, conditions of pressure and density such that dp and $d\rho$ through the wave are positive while the change in the velocity dU is negative. In other words, for the compression wave the change in the velocity dU is in the direction of wave propagation. The opposite takes place for an *expansion wave.* The pressure and density changes across the wave are negative, and consequently the velocity change is positive, meaning that it occurs in a direction opposite to that of the propagation of the wave.

There is satisfactory experimental evidence that weak sound waves take place without any changes of entropy occurring across them. For a perfect gas and an isentropic flow,

$$\begin{aligned} p &= \text{constant } \rho^\gamma \\ dp &= \text{constant } \gamma\rho^{\gamma-1}\, d\rho \\ \frac{dp}{d\rho} &= \text{constant } \gamma\rho^{\gamma-1} \\ &= \gamma\,\frac{p}{\rho} \end{aligned} \tag{8.16}$$

The speed of sound, then, for this isentropic weak-wave propagation, is

$$\begin{aligned} a &= \sqrt{\frac{\gamma p}{\rho}} \\ &= \sqrt{\gamma RT} \end{aligned} \tag{8.23}$$

As shown in Table 1.2, the units of R in the preceding equations must be on the basis of slugs and not on pound-mass.

The *Mach number* has already been defined as the ratio of the fluid velocity at a point to the velocity of sound in the moving fluid at the same point:

$$\mathfrak{M} = \frac{U}{a} \tag{8.24}$$

Illustrative Example 8.1

Compare the speed of sound in air, a diatomic gas, and in helium, a monatomic gas, at the same temperature.

The quantities γ and R in Eq. (8.23) are constants for a given gas. These constants are tabulated in Table 1.2. The quantity γ is dimensionless, but the quantity R is given in $\text{lb}_f \times \text{ft/slug} \times {}^\circ\text{R}$ or $\text{ft}^2/\text{sec}^2\,{}^\circ\text{R}$.

For air the velocity of sound at the temperature T will be

$$\begin{aligned} a &= \sqrt{32.17 \times 53.36 \times 1.4\,T} \\ &= 49.05\sqrt{T} \end{aligned}$$

The velocity of sound in helium will be

$$\begin{aligned} a &= \sqrt{32.17 \times 386.33 \times 1.67\,T} \\ &= 144\sqrt{T} \end{aligned}$$

The velocity of sound in helium is approximately three times as high as that in air at the same temperature.

8.4 Stagnation-Point Properties in Terms of the Mach Number

In Sec. 8.2(a), the internal energy and the enthalpy were expressed for a perfect gas in terms of the specific heats and the temperature change:

$$dh = c_p\,dT$$

According to Eqs. (8.8) and (8.9), $R = J(c_p - c_v)$ and $\gamma = c_p/c_v$. From these two equations the specific heats can be evaluated:

$$\begin{aligned} c_v &= \frac{R}{J(\gamma - 1)} \\ c_p &= \frac{\gamma R}{J(\gamma - 1)} \end{aligned} \tag{8.25}$$

The change of enthalpy becomes

$$dh = \frac{\gamma R}{J(\gamma - 1)}\,dT;$$

and, after integration,

$$h = \frac{\gamma R}{J(\gamma - 1)} T \tag{8.26}$$

In the stream moving at the velocity U, with a temperature T and enthalpy h, according to Eq. (6.31) the stagnation enthalpy is

$$h^\circ = h + \frac{1}{2J} U^2 \tag{8.27}$$

As mentioned earlier in this chapter, the gravity does not play an important part in the motion of compressible gases and therefore has been neglected in Eq. (8.27). The value of h derived in Eq. (8.26) can now be substituted in the stagnation-enthalpy relation.

$$h^\circ = \frac{\gamma R}{J(\gamma - 1)} T + \frac{1}{2J} U^2$$

$$= h\left(1 + \frac{\gamma - 1}{2\gamma RT} U^2\right) \tag{8.28}$$

Since h and T are related through Eq. (8.26), a similar temperature equation for the stagnation point can be derived.

$$\frac{\gamma R}{J(\gamma - 1)} T^\circ = \frac{\gamma - 1}{J(\gamma - 1)} T + \frac{1}{2J} U^2$$

$$T^\circ = T + \frac{\gamma - 1}{2\gamma R} U^2$$

$$T^\circ = T\left(1 + \frac{\gamma - 1}{2\gamma RT} U^2\right) \tag{8.29}$$

These two relations for the stagnation enthalpy and the stagnation temperature were developed with the assumptions of a perfect gas and no changes in altitude; in the derivation there was no mention of any process at all. Therefore, they are valid for any thermodynamic process.

In the case of isentropic flow, the stagnation-temperature equation can be modified to the stagnation-pressure or density equation through Eq. (8.16) and the equation of state for a perfect gas.

$$p = \text{constant } T^{\frac{\gamma}{\gamma - 1}}$$

$$\frac{p^\circ}{p} = \left(\frac{T^\circ}{T}\right)^{\frac{\gamma}{\gamma - 1}}$$

$$= \left(1 + \frac{\gamma - 1}{2\gamma RT} U^2\right)^{\frac{\gamma}{\gamma - 1}} \tag{8.30}$$

The speed of sound in the undisturbed stream at the temperature T was found, from Eq. (8.23), to be

$$a^2 = \gamma RT$$

This relation for the velocity of sound can be substituted into Eqs. (8.28), (8.29), and (8.30); and, using the definition of the Mach number, the stagnation-point properties become

$$h^\circ = h\left(1 + \frac{\gamma - 1}{2}\mathfrak{M}^2\right)$$

$$T^\circ = T\left(1 + \frac{\gamma - 1}{2}\mathfrak{M}^2\right)$$

$$p^\circ = p\left(1 + \frac{\gamma - 1}{2}\mathfrak{M}^2\right)^{\frac{\gamma}{\gamma-1}}$$

$$\rho^\circ = \rho\left(1 + \frac{\gamma - 1}{2}\mathfrak{M}^2\right)^{\frac{1}{\gamma-1}} \tag{8.31}$$

These equations establish the stagnation-point properties in terms of the properties of the undisturbed flow h, T, and $\mathfrak{M}$. It should be emphasized that, in the case of adiabatic flow between *any two points* in the stream, the relations for the enthalpy and the temperature in Eq. (8.31) can be generalized as adiabatic forms of the energy equation. In the case of the pressure and the density, they are restricted to the isentropic case. This relation for the pressure was derived in Eq. (4.36).

Illustrative Example 8.2

Argon, a monoatomic gas, at 14.7 psia and 70°F flows at the velocity of 800 ft/sec. Determine the free-stream Mach number and the stagnation temperature and pressure.

$$a = \sqrt{32.17 \times 38.73 \times 1.68 \times 530}$$
$$= 1{,}052 \text{ ft/sec}$$
$$\mathfrak{M} = \frac{800}{1{,}052}$$
$$= 0.761$$

From Eq. (8.31),

$$\frac{T^\circ}{T} = \left(1 + \frac{1.68 - 1.0}{2}(0.761)^2\right)$$
$$= 1.197$$
$$T^\circ = 634°\text{R}$$
$$= 174°\text{F}$$

The stagnation pressure is

$$p^\circ = 14.7\,(1.197)^{\frac{1.68}{0.68}}$$
$$= 22.9 \text{ psia}$$

8.5 Propagation of Waves in Subsonic, Sonic, and Supersonic Flows

It was stated in Sec. 8.4 that when a pressure disturbance is caused in the fluid, this disturbance, when weak, travels from the point in circular waves at the speed of sound a. This speed of sound was found to vary with the type of fluid and with temperature. It is a measure of the velocity of the disturbance wave relative to the stationary fluid. Since the fluid may move with a velocity U, the propagation of these waves in the moving fluid will display various patterns, depending on the relative ratio of the velocity of the fluid to that of sound in the same fluid, that is, the Mach number.

For simplicity, this phenomenon is compared to the surface waves generated on a liquid when a stone is suddenly dropped into it. In a still liquid the propagating waves will be circular, and all the waves will travel at the same speed with the same interval L from each successive

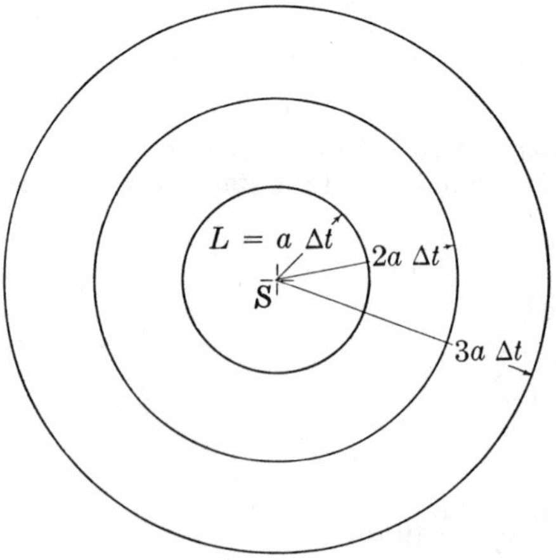

Figure 8.4
Waves from an oscillating disturbance S.

disturbance caused by the vibration of the liquid surface where the stone landed on the liquid.

Assume, now, a compressible gas in which a source of disturbance S, such as a small sphere, changes its radius periodically, with a period Δt. These disturbances, when produced in a stationary fluid, will travel the same way, as shown in Fig. 8.4. The pressure waves will be spherical, and the distance separating two successive wave fronts will be $L = a\,\Delta t$, the wave length of the disturbance. Now, if the fluid is also moving at a velocity U with respect to the stationary location of the disturbance, then the wave-propagation pattern relative to the source will be different from Fig. 8.4. The disturbance will propagate in the fluid in spherical waves, and at the same time these waves will be carried downstream in the fluid. For the case when $U < a$, shown in Fig. 8.5, the waves

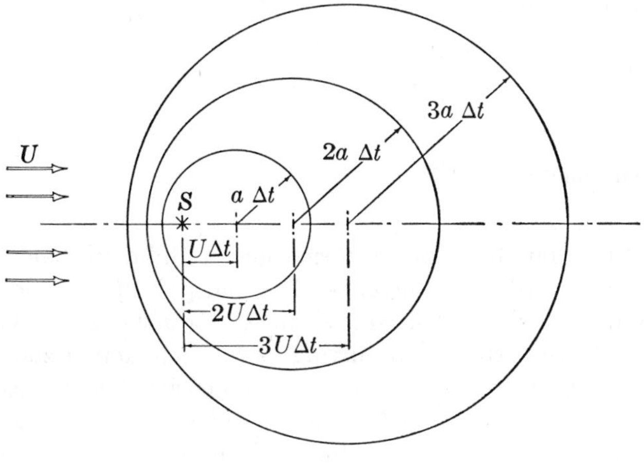

Figure 8.5
Wave propagation with fluid velocity $U < a$.

propagate faster in the direction of motion owing to a higher resultant velocity. Since the wave velocity is larger than the velocity of the fluid, the source remains always inside of the circular excentric waves. The pressure waves of the disturbance travel upstream at a velocity $(a - U)$ and downstream at a velocity $(a + U)$.

In the case when $U > a$, *supersonic flow*, the waves do not have a chance to travel upstream of the source, since the velocity of the fluid is faster than that of the wave-propagation velocity in the fluid. The source is always outside of the circular waves, as shown in Fig. 8.6.

They are carried downstream faster than they propagate. From the construction in Fig. 8.6, it can be seen that all waves are tangent to the cone with a half-angle α. The fluid upstream of the cone surface,

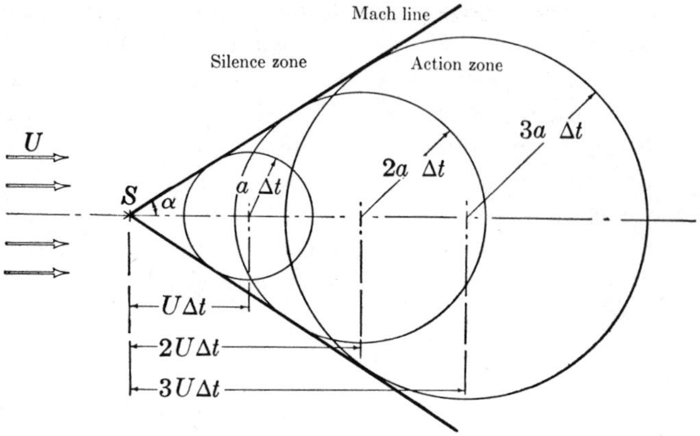

Figure 8.6
Wave propagation with fluid velocity $U > a$.

"the silence zone," does not have any information of the disturbance produced at S, since the wave front never reaches that part of the fluid. The flow in the right-hand side of the cone surface, *"the action zone,"* is always informed of the disturbances occurring at S. The action zone is more often called the *Mach cone.* In a two-dimensional flow this cone reduces to a pair of intersecting lines on the plane of the paper. These are often referred to as the *Mach lines.* The half-angle of the cone is called the *Mach angle,* and its value, according to Fig. 8.6, is

$$\sin \alpha = \frac{a\,\Delta t}{U\,\Delta t} = \frac{a}{U} = \frac{1}{\mathfrak{M}}$$

$$\mathfrak{M} = \operatorname{cosec} \alpha \tag{8.32}$$

8.6 Subsonic and Supersonic Motion over a Thin Body

The flow past certain aerodynamic bodies for subsonic and nonviscous motion has already been discussed in some detail in Chap. VII. An important fact was then discovered, namely that, if a flow of undisturbed velocity U_0 passes around a body, the velocity of the stream is altered in the vicinity of the body. First, along the approach stagnation streamline, there is a gradual deceleration of the flow. This flow reaches the condition of zero velocity at the stagnation point. Then the flow around the body begins accelerating, accompanied by a drop in pressure; for most bodies it accelerates to a velocity higher than the free-stream condition. Later, the flow decelerates ultimately to the free-stream conditions. Much of these effects will occur at high-speed flows with additional effects which will be discussed here.

For a flow with $U_0 \ll a$, the regime is considered subsonic, with no Mach waves forming anywhere in the fluid, since the pressure disturbances owing to the presence of the body can be propagated throughout the fluid. If the speed of the fluid U_0 is increased to equal nearly that of the speed of sound, as the fluid approaches the stagnation point it decelerates even further and thus remains in the subsonic regime. After passing the stagnation point, however, when it starts accelerating again around the surface of the body toward the trailing edge, it may reach a speed higher than the speed of sound and become supersonic. Where the pressure begins to rise and the flow returns subsonic, a shock wave (Mach wave) is formed on the surface of the body. This is much the same as the compression shock described in Fig. 8.6. This flow is described in Fig. 8.7(*a*). Across each shock wave (top and bottom of the airfoil) there is a sudden rise in pressure and a subsequent dropping back to subsonic flow toward the trailing edge of the wing.

When the speed is increased, the strength of the shocks are increased, and they are made to move toward the trailing edge. These two shocks will be the only ones on the surface of the wing until the free stream U_0 becomes supersonic. These local disturbances of the shock waves will play an important role in affecting the lift and drag of the airfoil.

Let the velocity of the undisturbed flow or the velocity of the body relative to the undisturbed fluid U_0 accelerate above the speed of sound. The pressure pulse resulting from this change of conditions builds into a single steep-fronted wave, the same as the Mach wave shown in Fig. 8.6, and moves upstream of the stagnation point to a place where the stream velocity relative to the body is supersonic again. This final settling of the shock in front of the airfoil is shown in Fig. 8.7(*b*) with the leading-edge shock wave and two oblique shock waves stemming from the vicinity of the trailing edge. The slope of these waves depends on the free-stream Mach number. The Mach number of the flow will

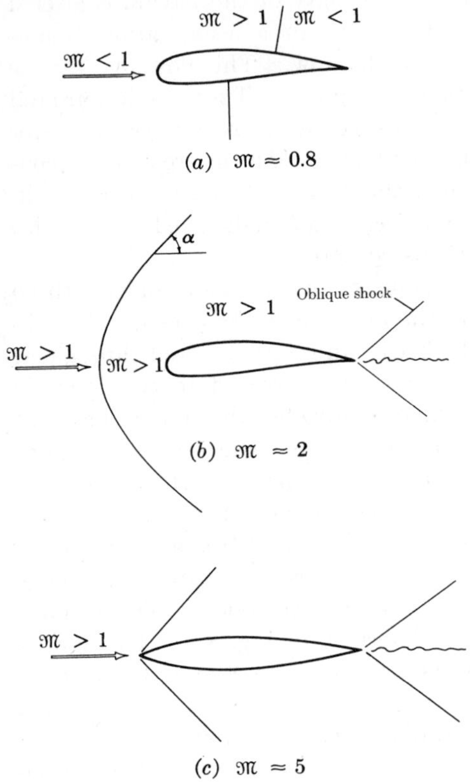

Figure 8.7
Flow over a wing for various Mach numbers.

be larger than unity everywhere except for a decelerated region between the leading-edge shock wave and the stagnation point. The pressure rise across the wave will be larger where the leading shock wave is normal to the flow direction U_0 or the axis of the body. Away from the axis of the body the magnitude of the wave, characterized by its pressure rise, will diminish, since it is farther removed from the main stagnation-point disturbance. Therefore, the propagation velocity of the part of the flow farther from the axis of the body is less, and consequently the angle of the wave decreases with distance from the axis.

The angle of the leading-edge shock reaches a limiting value α, giving the value of the Mach angle with the axis of the flow. Since the shock is weak away from the axis of the body, the limiting angle α will determine the Mach number of the undisturbed flow.

As the speed of the body is further increased relative to the free stream, the leading-edge shock approaches the leading edge of the body, and the magnitude of the shock becomes greater. Figure 8.7(*c*) shows the shock patterns of a thin body as the Mach number is appreciably larger than unity. The shocks are then said to be *attached* to the stagnation points of the body. For bodies having a blunt nose, the shock remains ahead of the nose even at very high values of the Mach number. The slope of the shock wave at the trailing edge is different from that at the leading edge, since the velocity at the trailing edge entering the shock is different from that at the leading edge U_0. The entire flow in Fig. 8.7(*c*) is supersonic. Again, in the case of supersonic flow throughout, the pressure coefficient, the drag, and the lift on the body differ from those of the subsonic cases explained.

8.7 Velocity of Propagation of a Strong Normal Shock Wave

Consider a tube in which a compressible gas is initially at rest at a pressure p_0. If a piston at the left-hand side of the tube is suddenly moved at the velocity U, causing, as a result of the compressibility, a pressure p behind the piston, this pressure jump will travel down the tube at the velocity c, which is the propagation velocity of the wave. This experiment is shown in Fig. 8.8. As was done in Sec. 8.3 to apply the momentum and energy relations to the flow through the wave, the flow of the medium is considered relative to the shock front in the second illustration. If A is the cross section of the tube and the flow is one-dimensional, the continuity of mass, the momentum, and the energy relations for the adiabatic case are

$$
\begin{aligned}
Ac\rho_0 &= A\rho(c - U) \\
(p_0 - p)A &= A\rho_0 c[(c - U) - c] \\
\frac{(c - U)^2 - c^2}{2} &= J(h_0 - h) \\
&= c_p J(T_0 - T) + \left(\frac{p_0}{\rho_0} - \frac{p}{\rho}\right)
\end{aligned}
$$

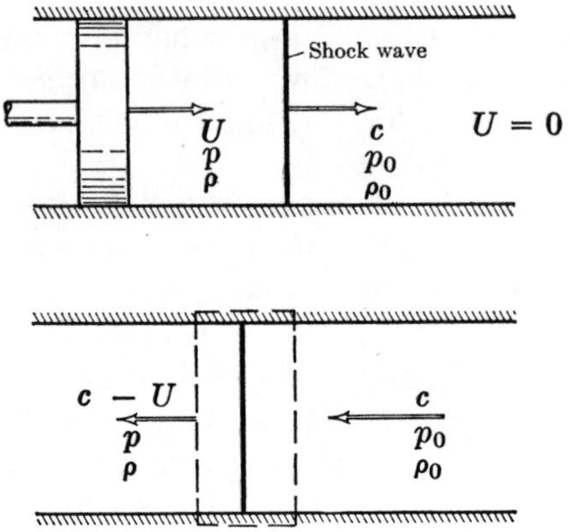

Figure 8.8
Propagation of a strong normal shock.

From Eq. (8.25), c_v can be substituted, and the energy equation takes the form:

$$\frac{U^2 - 2cU}{2} = \frac{R}{\gamma - 1}(T_0 - T) + \left(\frac{p_0}{\rho_0} - \frac{p}{\rho}\right)$$

$$= \frac{1}{\gamma - 1}\left(\frac{p_0}{\rho_0} - \frac{p}{\rho}\right) + \left(\frac{p_0}{\rho_0} - \frac{p}{\rho}\right)$$

$$= \frac{\gamma}{\gamma - 1}\left(\frac{p_0}{\rho_0} - \frac{p}{\rho}\right) \tag{8.33}$$

The mass-continuity equation and the momentum equation are

$$c\rho_0 = c\rho - U\rho$$

$$\rho = \frac{c\rho_0}{c - U} \tag{8.34}$$

$$p_0 - p = -\rho_0 c U$$

$$U = \frac{p - p_0}{\rho_0 c} \tag{8.35}$$

Substitution of ρ and U into the energy equation changes it into the following form:

$$\frac{(p - p_0)^2}{2(\rho_0 c)^2} - \frac{p - p_0}{\rho_0} = \frac{\gamma}{\gamma - 1}\left[\frac{p_0}{\rho_0} - \frac{p}{\rho_0}\left(1 - \frac{p - p_0}{\rho_0 c^2}\right)\right]$$

$$\frac{1}{(\rho_0 c)^2}\left[\frac{(p - p_0)^2}{2} - \frac{\gamma}{\gamma - 1}p(p - p_0)\right] = \frac{1}{\gamma - 1}\left(\frac{p_0 - p}{\rho_0}\right)$$

The propagation velocity c^2 can be solved after arranging terms:

$$c^2 = \frac{\gamma p_0}{\rho_0}\left[\frac{\gamma - 1}{2\gamma}\left(1 - \frac{p}{p_0}\right) + \frac{p}{p_0}\right]$$

$$= \frac{\gamma p_0}{\rho_0}\left(\frac{\gamma + 1}{2\gamma}\frac{p}{p_0} + \frac{\gamma - 1}{2\gamma}\right)$$

$$= a^2\left(\frac{\gamma + 1}{2\gamma}\frac{p}{p_0} + \frac{\gamma - 1}{2\gamma}\right) \tag{8.36}$$

From this equation it can easily be verified that, when dealing with weak pressure waves such that the pressure rise across the wave is very nearly unity, the last expression for the wave propagation becomes the velocity of sound.

$$c^2 = a^2 = \frac{\gamma p_0}{\rho_0}$$

This relation was derived and presented in Eq. (8.23). For very high shock strengths p/p_0, the second term in Eq. (8.36) can be neglected; and

$$\frac{c}{a} = \left(\frac{\gamma + 1}{2\gamma}\frac{p}{p_0}\right)^{1/2} \tag{8.37}$$

The relationship of the wave speed c/a with wave strength p/p_0 is plotted in Fig. 8.9 for adiabatic air with a specific-heat ratio of $\gamma = 1.4$ and for helium for which $\gamma = 1.67$.

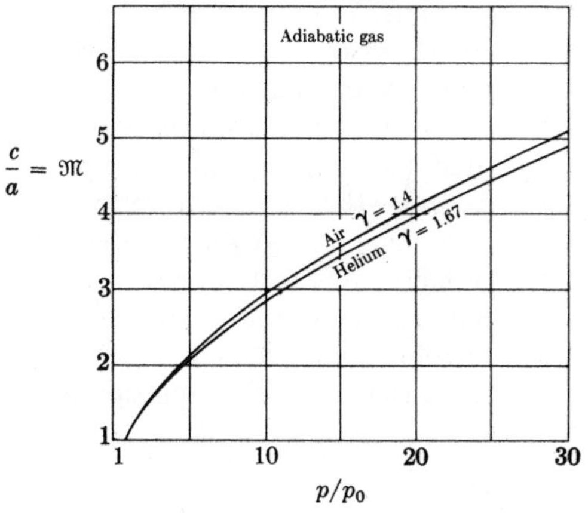

Figure 8.9
The Mach number as a function of its strength.

Illustrative Example 8.3

What pressure rise will occur across a shock wave when it moves three times as fast as the velocity of sound upstream of the wave? The gas is sulfur dioxide.

$$\begin{aligned}\frac{p}{p_0} &= \frac{2\gamma c^2}{a^2(\gamma + 1)} - \frac{\gamma - 1}{\gamma + 1} \\ &= \frac{2 \times 1.25 \times 9}{2.25} - \frac{0.25}{2.25} \\ &= 10 - 0.09 \\ &= 9.91\end{aligned}$$

8.8 The Flow Through Strong Stationary Shock Waves. The Normal Shock

In the investigation of flows through weak waves, it was learned that the flow undergoes a frictionless isentropic process. When the waves become strong, the assumption of constant entropy through the wave no longer holds. This amount of entropy rise across the shock wave will be discussed after establishing the relations of the pressure, density, and temperature changes across the same shock. The analysis of the flow through a stationary shock, in essence, is the same as that described in Sec. 8.7. The flow of fluid through a stationary shock is analyzed by considering the three principal equations of continuity of mass, of momentum, and of energy.

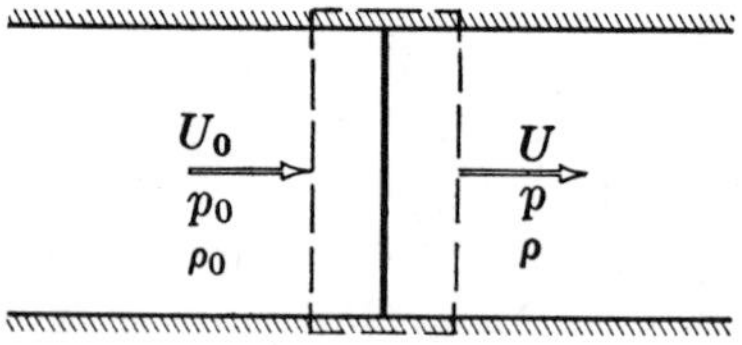

Figure 8.10
Flow through a stationary normal shock.

Consider a uniform stream of fluid moving at the conditions U_0, p_0, and ρ_0 through a stationary shock in a channel.[2] After the shock the properties of the flow are p, ρ, and U. Since the flow at any cross section of the channel is treated as being uniform, the continuity equation reads:

$$\rho_0 U_0 = \rho U$$

The momentum equation reads:

[2] The conditions considered do not need to be those of a channel; they could be those of the shock waves discussed in Fig. 8.7, but the flow must be such that it can be treated as being one-dimensional.

$$\rho U^2 - \rho_0 U_0^2 = p_0 - p$$

The adiabatic energy equation, as derived in Sec. 8.7, can be rewritten as

$$\frac{U^2 - U_0^2}{2} = J(h_0 - h)$$

$$= \frac{\gamma}{\gamma - 1}\left(\frac{p_0}{\rho_0} - \frac{p}{\rho}\right)$$

Dividing the momentum equation by the equation of continuity gives

$$\frac{\rho U^2 - \rho_0 U_0^2}{\rho_0 U_0} = \frac{p_0 - p}{\rho_0 U_0}$$

$$U - U_0 = \frac{p_0 - p}{\rho_0 U_0}$$

Multiplication of this result by $(U + U_0)$ and substitution into the energy equation yields

$$(U - U_0)(U + U_0) = (p_0 - p)\,\frac{U + U_0}{\rho_0 U_0}$$

$$U^2 - U_0^2 = (p_0 - p)\left(\frac{1}{\rho} + \frac{1}{\rho_0}\right)$$

Then

$$\tfrac{1}{2}(p_0 - p)\left(\frac{1}{\rho} + \frac{1}{\rho_0}\right) = \frac{\gamma}{\gamma - 1}\left(\frac{p_0}{\rho_0} - \frac{p}{\rho}\right)$$

Multiplying throughout by ρ/p_0, one obtains

$$\frac{1}{2}\left(1 - \frac{p}{p_0}\right)\left(1 + \frac{\rho}{\rho_0}\right) = \frac{\gamma}{\gamma - 1}\left(\frac{\rho}{\rho_0} - \frac{p}{p_0}\right)$$

Here, either the pressure or the density can be factored out. Doing so, the Rankine-Hugoniot relations are obtained.

$$\frac{p}{p_0} = \frac{\dfrac{\gamma + 1}{\gamma - 1}\dfrac{\rho}{\rho_0} - 1}{\dfrac{\gamma + 1}{\gamma - 1} - \dfrac{\rho}{\rho_0}} \tag{8.38}$$

or

$$\frac{\rho}{\rho_0} = \frac{U_0}{U} = \frac{\dfrac{\gamma + 1}{\gamma - 1}\dfrac{p}{p_0} + 1}{\dfrac{\gamma + 1}{\gamma - 1} + \dfrac{p}{p_0}} \tag{8.39}$$

After eliminating the downstream properties on the right-hand side of the equation and using the upstream Mach number $\mathfrak{M}_0 = U_0/a_0$, the Rankine-Hugoniot equations become

$$\frac{p}{p_0} = \frac{2\gamma}{\gamma + 1}\mathfrak{M}_0^2 - \frac{\gamma - 1}{\gamma + 1} \tag{8.40}$$

$$\frac{\rho}{\rho_0} = \frac{U_0}{U} = \frac{(\gamma + 1)\mathfrak{M}_0^2}{(\gamma - 1)\mathfrak{M}_0^2 + 2} \tag{8.41}$$

After dividing these two expressions, one obtains the relationship for the temperature rise across the shock in terms of the upstream Mach number.

$$\frac{p}{\rho}\frac{\rho_0}{p_0} = \frac{T}{T_0} = \frac{[2\gamma\mathfrak{M}_0^2 - (\gamma - 1)][(\gamma - 1)\mathfrak{M}_0^2 + 2]}{(\gamma + 1)^2\mathfrak{M}_0^2} \tag{8.42}$$

These equations give the rise of pressure, density, velocity, and temperature through a normal shock. It must be pointed out here that Eq. (8.40) could have been obtained more directly from Eq. (8.36),

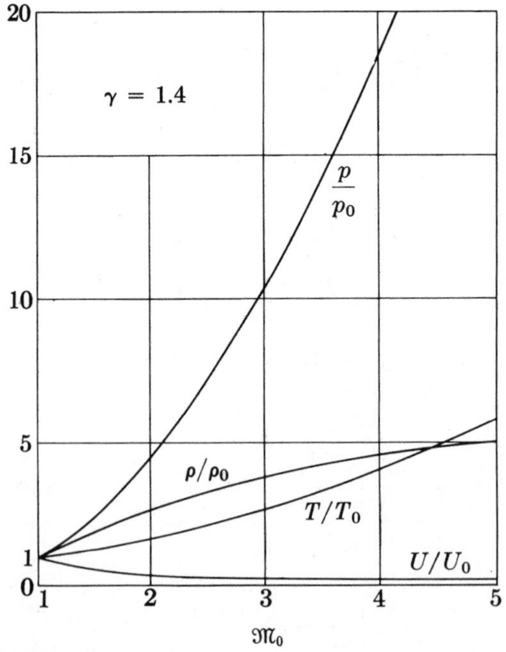

Figure 8.11
Property change across a shock as a function of upstream Mach number.

where c would correspond to the free-stream velocity of the fluid relative to the stationary wave.

The results of Eqs. (8.40), (8.41), and (8.42) have been plotted in Fig. 8.11. This figure shows the rise of pressure, density, and temperature, and the drop in velocity through the shock wave. The result of Eq. (8.38), representing the pressure change through the shock as a function of the density change, is compared with the isentropic change:

$$\frac{p}{p_0} = \left(\frac{\rho}{\rho_0}\right)^\gamma$$

This comparison is shown in Fig. 8.12. It shows that the isentropic pressure rise is smaller than that across a strong shock for the same density change.

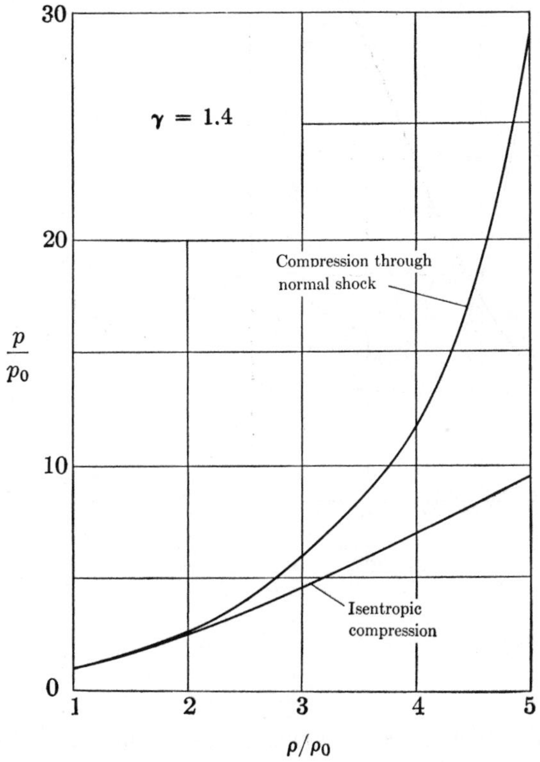

Figure 8.12
Compression through a normal shock as compared with the isentropic case.

The entropy rise across the wave can easily be found in terms of the upstream Mach number from Eqs. (8.18), (8.40), and (8.41):

$$\frac{s - s_0}{c_v} = \ln \left[\frac{2\gamma \mathfrak{M}_0^2 - (\gamma - 1)}{\gamma + 1}\right]\left[\frac{(\gamma - 1)\mathfrak{M}_0^2 + 2}{(\gamma + 1)\mathfrak{M}_0^2}\right]^{\gamma} \tag{8.43}$$

This distribution of the entropy rise across the shock is plotted in Fig. 8.13.

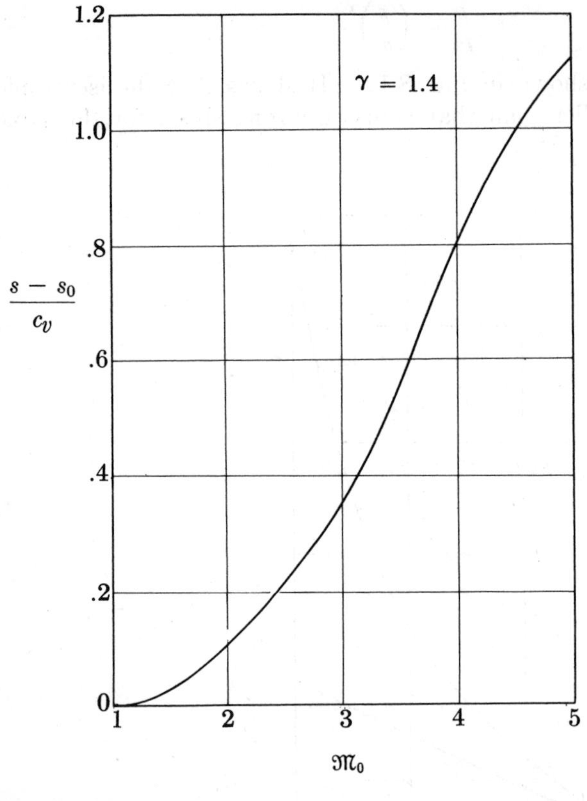

Figure 8.13
Entropy rise through a normal shock.

A relationship of the Mach number downstream of the shock to that upstream of the shock can be found from the fact that the Mach number is a function of the velocity U and temperature T. The ratio of the Mach number downstream of the shock to that upstream is

$$\frac{\mathfrak{M}}{\mathfrak{M}_0} = \frac{U}{U_0}\frac{a_0}{a}$$

$$= \frac{U}{U_0}\left(\frac{T_0}{T}\right)^{1/2} \tag{8.44}$$

But the velocity ratio was the inverse of the density ratio as given by Eq. (8.41); also, using the equation of state of the perfect gas, the ratio of the Mach numbers takes the form:

$$\frac{\mathfrak{M}}{\mathfrak{M}_0} = \frac{\rho_0}{\rho}\left(\frac{T_0}{T}\right)^{1/2}$$

$$= \left(\frac{\rho_0 p_0}{\rho p}\right)^{1/2}$$

$$= \left[\frac{(\gamma+1)}{2\gamma\mathfrak{M}_0^2 - (\gamma-1)}\,\frac{2 + (\gamma-1)\mathfrak{M}_0^2}{(\gamma+1)\mathfrak{M}_0^2}\right]^{1/2}$$

$$\mathfrak{M} = \sqrt{\frac{2 + (\gamma-1)\mathfrak{M}_0^2}{2\gamma\mathfrak{M}_0^2 - (\gamma-1)}} \tag{8.45}$$

This drop in the downstream Mach number is illustrated in Fig. 8.14 as a function of the upstream Mach number for air with $\gamma = 1.4$.

Illustrative Example 8.4

At $\mathfrak{M}_0 = 3$ and $\gamma = 1.4$, find the per cent change in pressure and the per cent change in density when they are due to a small increase in γ.

The per cent change in pressure and density with a change in γ can be found by differentiating p and ρ, in Eqs. (8.40) and (8.41), with respect to γ.

$$\frac{dp}{p_0} = \frac{(\gamma+1)(2\mathfrak{M}_0^2 - 1) - 2\gamma\mathfrak{M}_0^2 + (\gamma-1)}{(\gamma+1)^2}\,d\gamma$$

$$= \frac{2(\mathfrak{M}_0^2 - 1)}{(\gamma+1)^2}\,d\gamma$$

The density is treated in the same fashion:

$$\frac{d\rho}{\rho_0} = \frac{[(\gamma-1)\mathfrak{M}_0^2 + 2]\mathfrak{M}_0^2 - (\gamma+1)\mathfrak{M}_0^4}{[(\gamma-1)\mathfrak{M}_0^2 + 2]^2}\,d\gamma$$

$$= -\frac{2\mathfrak{M}_0^2[\mathfrak{M}_0^2 - 1]}{[(\gamma-1)\mathfrak{M}_0^2 + 2]^2}\,d\gamma$$

In the first place, it is seen from these derived relations that, on account of the minus sign, the density decreases with increase of γ. The pressure increases

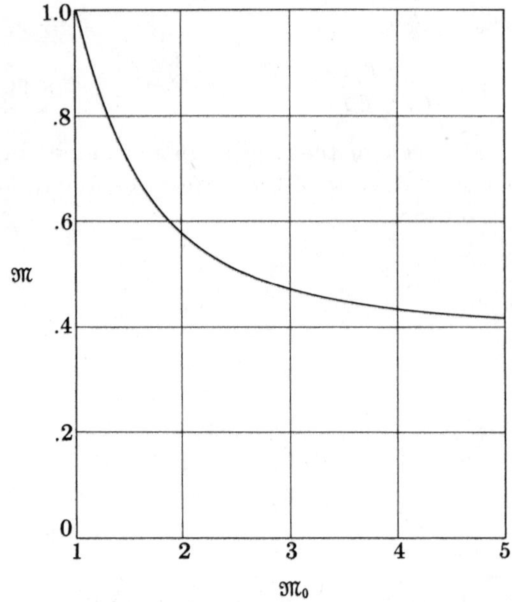

Figure 8.14
Relation of Mach number downstream of the shock as a function of the upstream Mach number.

with increase in γ. At the prescribed conditions of $\mathfrak{M}_0 = 3$ and $\gamma = 1.4$, these per cent variations become

$$\frac{dp}{p_0} = 2.78\, d\gamma$$

and

$$\frac{d\rho}{\rho_0} = -4.58\, d\gamma$$

For the same change of $d\gamma$ around the value of $\gamma = 1.4$, the absolute value of the per cent change in the density is larger than the per cent change in pressure. This indicates that the density is more sensitive to variations in γ than is the pressure. If the gas is changed to one with $\gamma = 1.6$, the per cent difference in pressure and density downstream of the shock is

$$\frac{dp}{p_0} = 0.556$$

$$\frac{d\rho}{\rho_0} = -0.916$$

8.9 The Pitot Tube in a Supersonic Stream

The response of the Pitot tube in a compressible isentropic stream was discussed in Sec. 4.10(*d*). The stagnation pressure for the isentropic flow was given in Eqs. (4.36) and (8.31) in terms of the upstream and undisturbed Mach number.

Consider, now, a supersonic free stream passing over the nose of a Pitot tube. As pointed out in Sec. 8.6, a shock wave will be formed upstream of the stagnation point, as shown in Fig. 8.15. The fluid

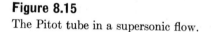

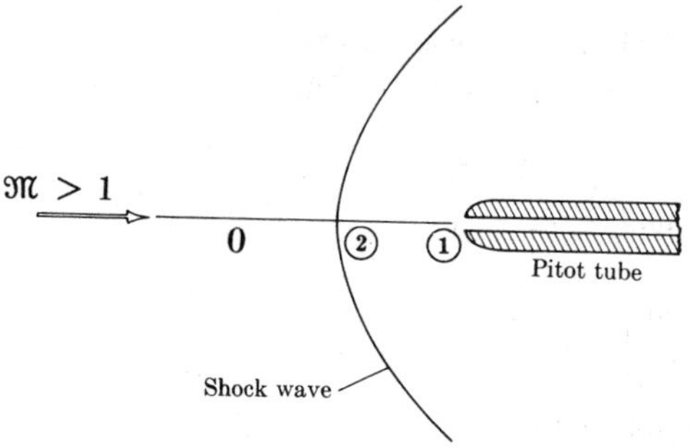

Figure 8.15
The Pitot tube in a supersonic flow.

moving along the approach stagnation streamline 021 will undergo a change in properties through the shock wave from 0 to 2, and then, from the subsonic conditions at 2, it will decelerate isentropically to the stagnation point 1.

Essentially, there are two regimes here which need separate consideration. The first regime is the flow across the shock wave, where the property changes are given in Sec. 8.8. If the conditions of the flow before the shock can be assumed to be those of the undisturbed flow, the pressure rise through the shock is

$$\frac{p_2}{p_0} = \frac{2\gamma\mathfrak{M}_0^2 - (\gamma + 1)}{\gamma + 1} \tag{8.40}$$

The second regime is after the shock from 2 to 1, where the flow process can be considered isentropic. Thus, the pressure rise to the stagnation point is given by Eq. (8.31):

$$\frac{p_1^\circ}{p_2} = \left(1 + \frac{\gamma - 1}{2}\mathfrak{M}_2^2\right)^{\frac{\gamma}{\gamma-1}} \tag{8.31}$$

To find the pressure ratio p_1°/p_0, these two equations must be combined, and, in addition, Eq. (8.45) must be used in order to change $\mathfrak{M}_2$ into $\mathfrak{M}_0$:

$$\mathfrak{M}_2^2 = \frac{2 + (\gamma - 1)\mathfrak{M}_0^2}{2\gamma\mathfrak{M}_0^2 - (\gamma - 1)} \tag{8.45}$$

The substitution of Eq. (8.45) into Eq. (8.31) yields

$$\frac{p_1^\circ}{p_2} = \left\{1 + \frac{\gamma - 1}{2}\left[\frac{2 + (\gamma - 1)\mathfrak{M}_0^2}{2\gamma\mathfrak{M}_0^2 - (\gamma - 1)}\right]\right\}^{\frac{\gamma}{\gamma-1}}$$

Therefore, the relationship between the stagnation pressure and the free-stream pressure, in terms of the upstream Mach number, is

$$\frac{p_1^\circ}{p_0} = \frac{p_1^\circ}{p_2}\frac{p_2}{p_0} = \left\{1 + \frac{\gamma - 1}{2}\left[\frac{2 + (\gamma - 1)\mathfrak{M}_0^2}{2\gamma\mathfrak{M}_0^2 - (\gamma - 1)}\right]\right\}^{\frac{\gamma}{\gamma-1}} \frac{2\gamma\mathfrak{M}_0^2 - (\gamma - 1)}{(\gamma + 1)}$$

$$= \left[\frac{(\frac{1}{2}\mathfrak{M}_0^2)^\gamma(\gamma + 1)^{\gamma+1}}{2\gamma\mathfrak{M}_0^2 - (\gamma - 1)}\right]^{\frac{1}{\gamma-1}} \tag{8.46}$$

This equation is now plotted in Fig. 8.16 curve (*c*). The pressure rise to the stagnation point of the Pitot tube is shown as a function of the upstream Mach number. At the same time it is compared with the simple isentropic compression, as given by Eq. (8.31):

$$\frac{p_1^\circ}{p_0} = \left(1 + \frac{\gamma - 1}{2}\mathfrak{M}_0^2\right)^{\frac{\gamma}{\gamma-1}}$$

The comparison is also made with the incompressible-stagnation-point equation:

$$p_1^\circ = p_0 + \frac{\rho_0}{2}U_0^2$$

$$\frac{p_1^\circ}{p_0} = 1 + \frac{\rho_0}{2p_0}U_0^2$$

$$= 1 + \frac{\gamma}{2}\mathfrak{M}_0^2 \tag{8.47}$$

The comparison in the figure is done among the pressure ratio for (*a*) incompressible flow, (*b*) a purely isentropic flow between the same two points, and finally (*c*) a shock followed by an isentropic compression. The gas for which Fig. 8.16 has been computed is air with $\gamma = 1.4$. The cases of the incompressible flow (*a*) and the purely isentropic flow are fictitious beyond $\mathfrak{M}_0 > 1$; they are plotted just for the purpose of comparison. A similar comparison of the pressure rise for the two sub-

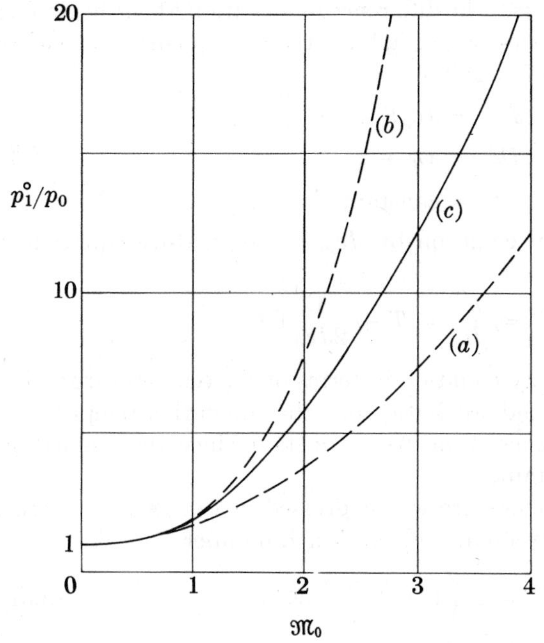

Figure 8.16
The Pitot-tube response.

sonic cases (*a*) and (*b*) was given in Fig. 4.18. Equations (8.31) and (8.46) start at the same value at $\mathfrak{M}_0 = 1$ and depart from there on, because in one case the entropy is considered constant and in the other it varies across the shock.

The static-pressure orifice on the Pitot tube, on account of the shock wave, does not give the correct upstream undisturbed static pressure. The probe and the analysis just described should be used for total stagnation-pressure measurements only, which, in turn, give the value of the free-stream Mach number.

8.10 Adiabatic Flows in Channels

Most compressible flows through channels take place without any external work and without any external heat transfer from or into the surroundings. In most cases the difference of elevation at the beginning and at the end of the process is negligible, and consequently the energy equation given in Eq. (8.7) applies.

$$Jh^\circ = Jc_pT + \tfrac{1}{2}U^2$$
$$Jh^\circ = Jh + \tfrac{1}{2}U^2 \tag{8.7}$$
$$= \text{constant}$$

Dividing this energy equation by Jc_p, a temperature equation is obtained:

$$T^\circ = \frac{h^\circ}{Jc_p} = T + \frac{1}{2Jc_p}U^2$$

This is a form of the energy equation in terms of the temperature which states that, for no work and adiabatic flow, the stagnation temperature throughout the fluid process remains a constant since the stagnation enthalpy remains a constant.

This stagnation temperature was expressed in Eq. (8.31) in terms of the temperature at any point and the Mach number.

$$T^\circ = T\left(1 + \frac{\gamma - 1}{2}\mathfrak{M}^2\right) \tag{8.31}$$

Since T° is derived directly from h°, which is a constant everywhere, the ratio of any two temperatures in the flow is obtained by dividing two identical equations, Eq. (8.31):

$$\frac{T_1}{T_2} = \frac{1 + \dfrac{\gamma - 1}{2}\mathfrak{M}_2^2}{1 + \dfrac{\gamma - 1}{2}\mathfrak{M}_1^2} \tag{8.48}$$

For an adiabatic flow with internal losses, it was found in Sec. 4.12 that the stagnation pressure is not a constant everywhere in the flow. The internal losses will increase the entropy of the fluid which, in turn, will decrease the stagnation pressure at a point downstream. In Eq. (8.31), a relation is given for the value of the stagnation point at one particular point in the flow field. If this relation represents the definition of the stagnation pressure at a point of an adiabatic flow, p° will not remain constant from point to point, as in the case of T°; it will vary, depending on the internal losses incurred in the flow process. This variation of the stagnation pressure can be easily evaluated from the modified form of the system's equation, Eq. (6.35).

$$JT\,ds - p\,d\left(\frac{1}{\rho}\right) = J\,de \tag{6.35}$$

Introducing the enthalpy equation,

$$J\,dh = J\,de + \frac{p}{\rho}$$

the system equation for the stagnation properties becomes

$$JT^\circ\,ds^\circ + \frac{dp^\circ}{\rho^\circ} = J\,dh^\circ$$

It was just found that for the adiabatic process the stagnation enthalpy remained constant, and therefore $dh^\circ = 0$. Dividing by T° and using the perfect-gas law $p^\circ = \rho^\circ RT^\circ$, the modified-system equation becomes

$$-J\,ds^\circ = R\frac{dp^\circ}{p^\circ}$$

The integration of this equation for any two points in the adiabatic flow becomes

$$R \ln \frac{p_2^\circ}{p_1^\circ} = -J(s_2^\circ - s_1^\circ)$$

and

$$\frac{p_2^\circ}{p_1^\circ} = e^{(s_1^\circ - s_2^\circ)J/R}$$

$$= e^{(s_1 - s_2)J/R} \qquad (8.49)$$

Here, it must be said that if, in order to find the stagnation entropy, the fluid is by choice made to stagnate isentropically, then the stagnation entropy at any point is the actual entropy at the same point. The ratio of the stagnation pressures is then given in Eq. (8.49) in terms of the entropy change between two points. The same stagnation pressures at the two points in consideration can be evaluated according to Eq. (8.31). The only assumption in the use of this equation is that the stagnation pressure at any point is obtained in an isentropic fashion. This assumption does not place any isentropic limitation to the general flow process considered, except, as has already been stated, that the stagnation points are obtained by stagnating the flow isentropically.

Now, for every point in the fluid,

$$p_2^\circ = p_2\left(1 + \frac{\gamma - 1}{2}\,\mathfrak{M}_2^2\right)^{\frac{\gamma}{\gamma-1}}$$

$$p_1^\circ = p_1\left(1 + \frac{\gamma - 1}{2}\,\mathfrak{M}_1^2\right)^{\frac{\gamma}{\gamma-1}}$$

From these two equations and Eq. (8.49), an expression for the pressure ratio similar to Eq. (8.48) can be obtained:

$$\frac{p_2}{p_1} = \left(\frac{1 + \frac{\gamma - 1}{2} \mathfrak{M}_1^2}{1 + \frac{\gamma - 1}{2} \mathfrak{M}_2^2} \right)^{\frac{\gamma}{\gamma - 1}} e^{(s_1 - s_2)J/R} \tag{8.50}$$

From this equation and Eq. (8.48) the density ratio is readily found with the use of the perfect-gas law.[3]

$$\frac{\rho_2}{\rho_1} = \frac{p_2}{p_1} \frac{T_1}{T_2}$$

$$= \left(\frac{1 + \frac{\gamma - 1}{2} \mathfrak{M}_1^2}{1 + \frac{\gamma - 1}{2} \mathfrak{M}_2^2} \right)^{\frac{1}{\gamma - 1}} e^{(s_1 - s_2)J/R} \tag{8.51}$$

From the mass-continuity equation

$$\rho_2 A_2 U_2 = \rho_1 A_1 U_1$$

and the Mach-number definition

$$U = \mathfrak{M} \sqrt{\gamma R T}$$

the velocity can be eliminated, and an expression for the area ratio can be obtained.

$$\frac{A_2}{A_1} = \frac{\mathfrak{M}_1}{\mathfrak{M}_2} \left(\frac{1 + \frac{\gamma - 1}{2} \mathfrak{M}_2^2}{1 + \frac{\gamma - 1}{2} \mathfrak{M}_1^2} \right)^{\frac{\gamma + 1}{2(\gamma - 1)}} e^{-(s_1 - s_2)J/R} \tag{8.52}$$

Finally, the velocity ratio is obtained from the mass-continuity relation

$$\frac{U_2}{U_1} = \frac{\rho_1}{\rho_2} \frac{A_1}{A_2}$$

$$= \frac{\mathfrak{M}_2}{\mathfrak{M}_1} \left(\frac{1 + \frac{\gamma - 1}{2} \mathfrak{M}_1^2}{1 + \frac{\gamma - 1}{2} \mathfrak{M}_2^2} \right)^{1/2} \tag{8.53}$$

From these relationships the isentropic-flow case can be obtained by making the entropy change $(s_1 - s_2) = 0$ and eliminating the exponen-

[3] For additional information on this subject, consult Newman A. Hall, *Thermodynamics of Fluid Flow*, 2nd Ed., Prentice-Hall, Inc., Englewood Cliffs, N.J., 1956, Chap. 8.

tial term in the pressure, density, and area-ratio expressions. Instead of using the stagnation-point property as a reference, the properties where the flow becomes sonic, $\mathfrak{M} = 1$, are often used in the equations above. Say that $\mathfrak{M}_1 = 1$ is replaced in the equation above for the isentropic case. If the corresponding properties at the sonic point are identified with an asterisk, then

$$\frac{T}{T^*} = \frac{(\gamma + 1)/2}{1 + \frac{\gamma - 1}{2}\mathfrak{M}^2}$$

$$\frac{p}{p^*} = \left[\frac{(\gamma + 1)/2}{1 + \frac{\gamma - 1}{2}\mathfrak{M}^2}\right]^{\frac{\gamma}{\gamma - 1}}$$

$$\frac{\rho}{\rho^*} = \left[\frac{(\gamma + 1)/2}{1 + \frac{\gamma - 1}{2}\mathfrak{M}^2}\right]^{\frac{1}{\gamma - 1}} \tag{8.54}$$

$$\frac{A}{A^*} = \frac{1}{\mathfrak{M}}\left[\frac{1 + \frac{\gamma - 1}{2}\mathfrak{M}^2}{(\gamma + 1)/2}\right]^{\frac{\gamma + 1}{2(\gamma - 1)}}$$

$$\frac{U}{U^*} = \mathfrak{M}\left[\frac{(\gamma + 1)/2}{1 + \frac{\gamma - 1}{2}\mathfrak{M}^2}\right]^{1/2}$$

Figure 8.17 shows the property ratios as a function of the local Mach number. For a given geometry of a passage A/A^*, the Mach number can be evaluated at every cross section, and consequently the rest of the properties are known if the conditions at the sonic point are known. For these relationships to apply, the flow must be isentropic. Consequently, these relationships are not applicable if a normal shock exists between the two points in consideration.

Illustrative Example 8.5

Let an isentropic flow in a converging nozzle reach sonic speed at the throat. Find the velocity and the area of the nozzle upstream of the throat where the pressure is 1.5 times the throat pressure. Assume the fluid to be air.

From the pressure equation, Eq. (8.54), the Mach number can be deduced.

$$\frac{(\gamma + 1)/2}{1 + \frac{\gamma - 1}{2}\mathfrak{M}^2} = 1.5^{\frac{\gamma - 1}{\gamma}} = 1.126$$

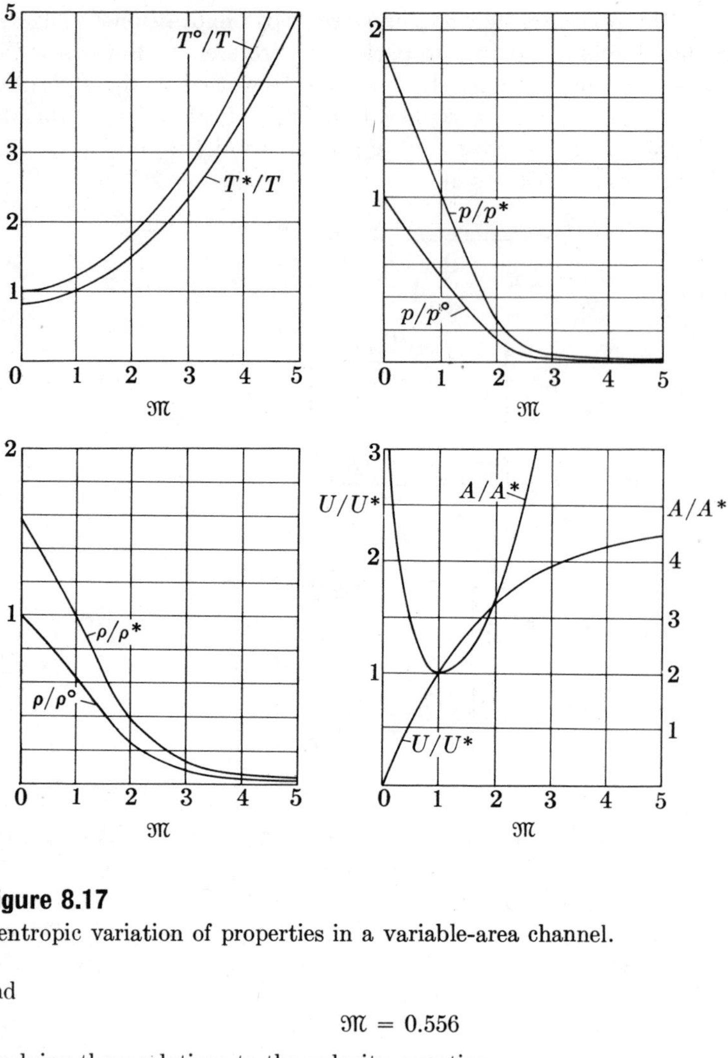

Figure 8.17
Isentropic variation of properties in a variable-area channel.

and

$$\mathfrak{M} = 0.556$$

Applying these relations to the velocity equation,

$$\frac{U}{U^*} = 0.556\sqrt{1.126}$$

$$= 0.59$$

The area ratio is then

$$\frac{A}{A^*} = \frac{1}{0.556}\left(\frac{1}{1.126}\right)^{\frac{2.4}{0.8}}$$

$$= 1.26$$

If the conditions at the exit are given, the properties at any other point in the nozzle are then determined from Eq. (8.54).

8.11 The Mass Rate of Flow Through a Nozzle

The preceding section established the relation of the fluid properties at two different sections of a channel such as the nozzle. Here an analysis will be presented for the mass rate of flow, going through a channel such as a nozzle, in terms of the stagnation properties of the fluid.

The integration of Eq. (8.1) gives a relation between the velocity change and the enthalpy change:

$$J(h - h_0) = \tfrac{1}{2}(U_0^2 - U^2)$$

In the case when the flow starts from a big *plenum chamber* with $U_0 = 0$, then the value of the enthalpy in the chamber is the stagnation enthalpy $h^\circ = h_0$. The velocity at any point in the nozzle shown in Fig. 8.18 is

$$U = \sqrt{2J(h^\circ - h)} \qquad (8.55)$$

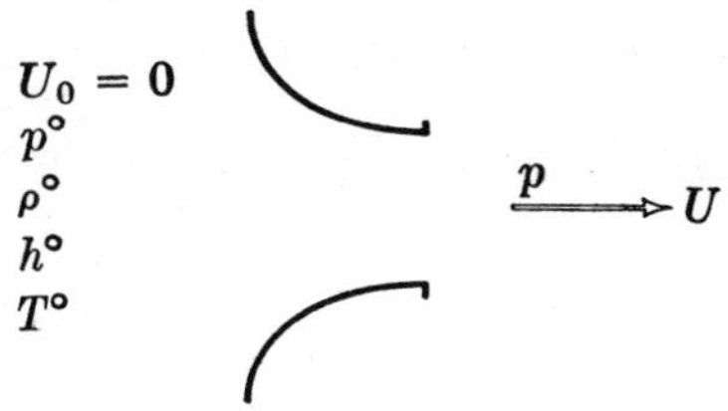

Figure 8.18
Compressible flow through nozzle.

For a perfect gas

$$U = \sqrt{2Jc_p(T^\circ - T)} \qquad (8.56)$$

The specific heat at constant pressure can be expressed in terms of the gas constant R, using Eq. (8.8):

$$\frac{R}{J} = c_p - c_v$$

$$= c_p - \frac{c_p}{\gamma}$$

$$= c_p \frac{\gamma - 1}{\gamma}$$

and, therefore,

$$c_p = \frac{\gamma}{\gamma - 1} \frac{R}{J}$$

The velocity in the nozzle becomes, after substitution,

$$U = \sqrt{\frac{2\gamma}{\gamma - 1} RT^\circ \left(1 - \frac{T}{T^\circ}\right)}$$

This velocity relationship in terms of the temperature is valid for the no-work and adiabatic-flow condition. Furthermore, the difference in elevation has been neglected. Now, for the isentropic case, the temperature ratio can be expressed in terms of the pressure ratio, and the nozzle velocity then becomes

$$U = \sqrt{\frac{2\gamma}{\gamma - 1} RT^\circ \left[1 - \left(\frac{p}{p^\circ}\right)^{\frac{\gamma-1}{\gamma}}\right]}$$

$$U = \sqrt{\frac{2\gamma}{\gamma - 1} \frac{p^\circ}{\rho^\circ} \left[1 - \left(\frac{p}{p^\circ}\right)^{\frac{\gamma-1}{\gamma}}\right]} \tag{8.57}$$

The mass rate of flow is obtained by multiplying this velocity by the density ρ and the area A. Using again the isentropic relation $(\rho/\rho^\circ) = (p/p^\circ)^{\frac{1}{\gamma}}$, the mass rate of flow becomes

$$Q = \rho A U$$

$$= A \sqrt{\frac{2\gamma}{\gamma - 1} p^\circ \rho^\circ \left[\left(\frac{p}{p^\circ}\right)^{\frac{2}{\gamma}} - \left(\frac{p}{p^\circ}\right)^{\frac{\gamma+1}{\gamma}}\right]} \tag{8.58}$$

For a given plenum-chamber pressure (stagnation pressure) p°, the equation of the mass rate of flow varies as a function of the discharge pressure p. For the same stagnation conditions and the same discharge area, there will be a maximum flow Q_{max} for one particular discharge pressure called the critical pressure p_c. This pressure is found by differentiating Eq. (8.58) with respect to p and equating the result to zero. After performing the differentiation and simplifying, the critical discharge pressure p_c as a ratio to the stagnation pressure is

$$\frac{p_c}{p^\circ} = \left(\frac{2}{\gamma + 1}\right)^{\frac{\gamma}{\gamma-1}} \tag{8.59}$$

This ratio is approximately equal to 0.53 for air with $\gamma = 1.4$. Then the maximum flow is obtained when the critical pressure ratio is substituted in Eq. (8.58). It can be seen from Fig. 8.19 that this maximum flow occurs when the throat Mach number reaches unity. The ratio of the mass rate of the flow to the maximum value is then

$$\frac{Q}{Q_{\max}} = \sqrt{\frac{\left(\frac{p}{p^\circ}\right)^{\frac{2}{\gamma}} - \left(\frac{p}{p^\circ}\right)^{\frac{\gamma+1}{\gamma}}}{\left(\frac{2}{\gamma+1}\right)^{\frac{2}{\gamma-1}} - \left(\frac{2}{\gamma+1}\right)^{\frac{\gamma+1}{\gamma-1}}}} \tag{8.60}$$

This equation is plotted in Fig. 8.19. In the isentropic flow for which the analysis was made, given a pressure ratio p/p°, a ratio of the actual mass flow to the maximum mass flow is obtained from Eq. (8.60). Also at the same pressure ratio the Mach number can be found from

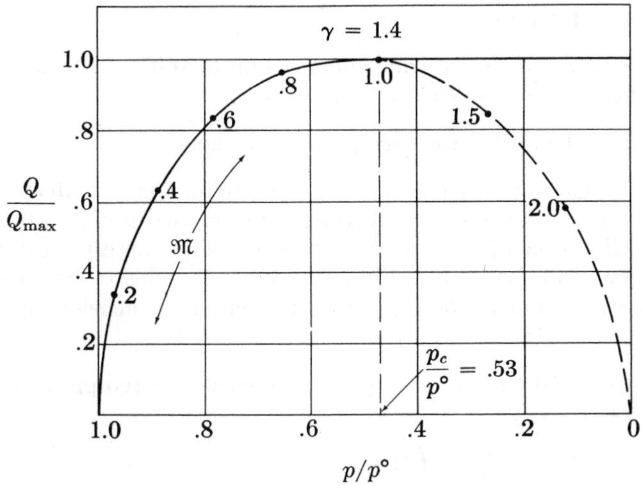

Figure 8.19
Mass rate of flow through the nozzle.

Eq. (8.31). This value of the Mach number is shown on the mass-rate-of-flow curve in Fig. 8.19. It can be seen that, when the Mach number reaches the value of unity, the throat pressure of the nozzle reaches the critical pressure and the mass rate of flow reaches the maximum value. For discharge pressures lower than the critical pressure, the velocity at the low-pressure end is supersonic, and consequently this pressure is never transmitted upstream. Thus, since the upstream flow is not informed of throat pressures lower than the critical pressure, the mass rate of flow through the nozzle remains the same for discharge pressures less than the critical pressure. Figure 8.19 shows a horizontal solid line for the mass rate of flow corresponding to discharge pressures lower than the critical pressure.

Problems

8.1 From Table 1.2, compute the specific heats at constant pressure and constant volume for air.

8.2 Give the enthalpy and the internal energy of air at 160°F. Assume that the specific heats in Prob. 8.1 are applicable.

8.3 Repeat Probs. 8.1 and 8.2 for argon and hydrogen.

8.4 A one-dimensional flow through a divergent channel is considered. The area change in a downstream direction between two neighboring points along the direction of flow is 10 per cent. The corresponding drop in the density is 14 per cent. Find the per cent velocity change between the same neighboring points. State whether an acceleration or deceleration takes place.

8.5 Show from Eq. 8.16 that, for an isentropic case, the temperature ratio can be expressed as

$$\frac{T_1}{T_2} = \left(\frac{\rho_1}{\rho_2}\right)^{\gamma-1}$$

$$= \left(\frac{p_1}{p_2}\right)^{\frac{\gamma-1}{\gamma}}$$

8.6 Find the velocity of sound in carbon dioxide at 1000°F. Compare it with the value at ordinary room temperature of 60°F.

8.7 Compare the difference in the velocity of sound in sulfur dioxide and in argon at the same temperature.

8.8 From the definition in Eq. (8.22), determine the velocity of sound in water at 50°F. Use the data given in Table 1.4.

8.9 Helium at 60°F flows at the speed of 2,400 ft/sec. Find (*a*) the enthalpy of the flowing gas; (*b*) the speed of sound in the gas; (*c*) the Mach number; (*d*) the stagnation enthalpy; (*e*) the stagnation pressure.

8.10 In Prob. 8.9, determine the ratio of the fluid pressure to the stagnation pressure. Also determine the ratio of the density of the fluid to that of the stagnation density.

8.11 Argon flows at a temperature of 100°F at a pressure one half the value of the stagnation pressure. If the flow is considered isentropic, find the velocity of the flow.

8.12 If, in Prob. 8.11, the flowing pressure is atmospheric, determine the stagnation density of the fluid.

8.13 Carbon monoxide flows through an insulated channel. The velocity at point 1 is 600 ft/sec at the temperature of 140°F. If, at a second point 2, the temperature is 60°F, what is the Mach number at the two points? What are the stagnation enthalpies at the two points? What is the Mach number at 2?

8.14 A piston is suddenly activated in a tube containing air and consequently sending a wave down the tube with a pressure ratio across the wave of 1.5. At what Mach number with reference to the undisturbed flow does the wave move in the tube?

8.15 What pressure rise occurs across a blast wave in hydrogen when the wave moves five times faster than the speed of sound in the undisturbed hydrogen?

8.16 Show that Eqs. (8.36) and (8.40) are equivalent if a common reference is considered.

8.17 The absolute temperature rise in gaseous nitrogen across a normal shock is $T/T_0 = 1.5$. T_0 is the free-stream absolute temperature. Determine the pressure, density, and velocity ratios across the shock.

8.18 In Prob. 8.17, state the entropy rise and the Mach number of the flow downstream of the shock.

8.19 A stream of argon moves at a Mach number of 0.8. If a total pressure probe (Pitot tube) is used to determine the stagnation pressure, find the per cent error involved if the stagnation pressure is computed with the assumption of an incompressible motion.

8.20 For the Pitot tube in Prob. 8.19, in a stream of sulfur dioxide, evaluate the same per cent error by treating the flow as incompressible.

8.21 A stream of carbon dioxide at atmospheric pressure is moving at a Mach number of 3.0. What is the stagnation pressure measured with a Pitot tube? What error would be involved if the flow were considered to be completely isentropic?

8.22 If the stagnation pressure of air reduces in an adiabatic flow in a pipe by 0.85, find the entropy change between the same two points.

8.23 In Prob. 8.22, what would be the ratio of the pressure, density, area, and velocity between the two points of the flow if the Mach number drops from 0.90 to 0.80?

8.24 Air is discharged isentropically through a nozzle with a throat diameter of 1 in. It is necessary that the thermodynamic conditions of the air at the discharge be standard: 14.7 psia and 60°F and the Mach number equal 1.0. Find the pressure, temperature, density, area, and velocity where $\mathfrak{M} = 0.5$ in the nozzle.

8.25 What is the maximum rate of mass flow that can be obtained from a 2-in.-diameter nozzle when the pressure and temperature in a settling box upstream of the nozzle are 350 $lb_f/in.^2$ and 70°F?

8.26 What is the critical discharge pressure in Prob. 8.25?

Theory and Applications of Viscous Fluids

chapter IX

9.1 Introduction

The concept of viscosity and shearing stress was introduced in Sec. 1.10. It was stated that the viscosity is a characteristic property distinguishing a fluid from a solid when the substance is in motion, and that a fluid cannot sustain a finite deformation under a tangential shear stress but will deform continuously in such a manner that the *rate of deformation will be proportional to the shear stress applied.* The proportionality-constant in the shearing motion of a fluid is then the viscosity of the fluid.

This proportionality between the shear stress and the rate of deformation, often called Newton's law of viscosity, applies to a great number of fluids called *Newtonian fluids.* The linear relationship between the shear stress and the rate of deformation is shown in Fig. 9.1. According to Eq. (1.7) or [1.7(*a*)], the slope of this straight line for the Newtonian-fluid behavior is the absolute viscosity of the fluid. According to the same figure, there are other substances that behave differently from a Newtonian fluid. Since the viscosity of a perfect fluid is zero, its behavior in Fig. 9.1 will be represented as the abscissa.

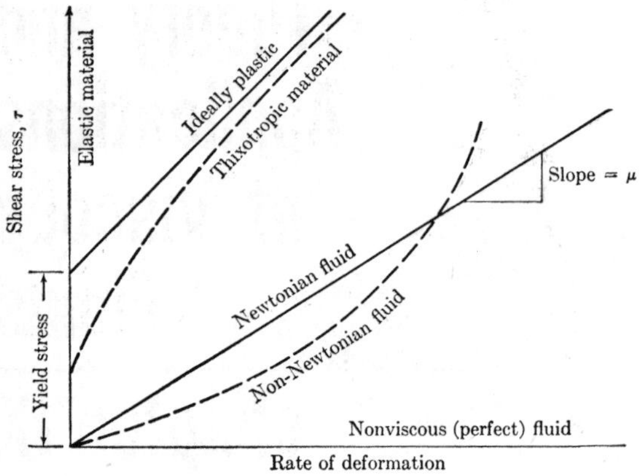

Figure 9.1
Relationship between shear stress and rate of deformation for various substances.

This indicates that in the perfect fluid any rates of deformation can be set up without a tangential shear stress; the perfect fluid does not display any tangential shear stresses. The dynamics of a perfect fluid motion was the subject of Chap. VII.

Following the diagram, a *non-Newtonian* fluid is one whose relationship between the shear stress and the rate of deformation is nonlinear; but, to classify it as a fluid, when the rate of deformation is zero, the applied shear stress is also zero. In other words, a fluid cannot be prestressed before it displays a rate of change of deformation. Thick liquids such as tar are generally non-Newtonian fluids.

A purely *elastic* material will always display a finite deformation under a tensile, compressive, or shear load. Since the deformation is finite and constant for a given load, the rate of deformation is zero. Consequently, the behavior of the elastic material will be represented as the ordinate of the diagram shown. This is, then, the behavior of a solid substance in the elastic regime. Since most solid substances have a limiting stress, called the yield stress, at which point they cease to be elastic, the stress versus rate-of-deformation relationship will change beyond this limiting yield stress. The solid will become *plastic*, and, for all shear loads beyond the yield stress, there will be a continuous deformation associated with a certain rate. The so-called *ideally plastic* materials display, like a viscous fluid, a linear relationship between the shear stress applied and the rate of deformation, the distinguishing characteristic of the solid being that, up to the yield stress, it can still sustain a finite deformation.

A *thixotropic* material is a substance that displays some elasticity at small loads, and in the plastic regime the rate of deformation is not linearly dependent on the shear stress. The behavior of such a material is also shown in the diagram. In some cases, for instance, a substance such as printer's ink will have a shear stress not only a function of the rate of deformation but also of the level of the deformation itself. The study of the motion of such substances is beyond the scope of this book. In fact, the viscous motion that will be considered here will deal solely with the Newtonian fluids.

In Secs. 4.12 and 4.13 an over-all concept of viscous losses was introduced into Bernoulli's equation. No attempt was made in those sections, however, to interpret these viscous losses in terms of the motion of the fluid. This chapter will attempt to explain these viscous losses in terms of the flow properties.

9.2 The Shear Stresses in a Three-Dimensional Fluid Element

Consider a fluid element as shown in Fig. 9.2. Surface forces are to be applied in such a way that their effect is that of pure shearing defor-

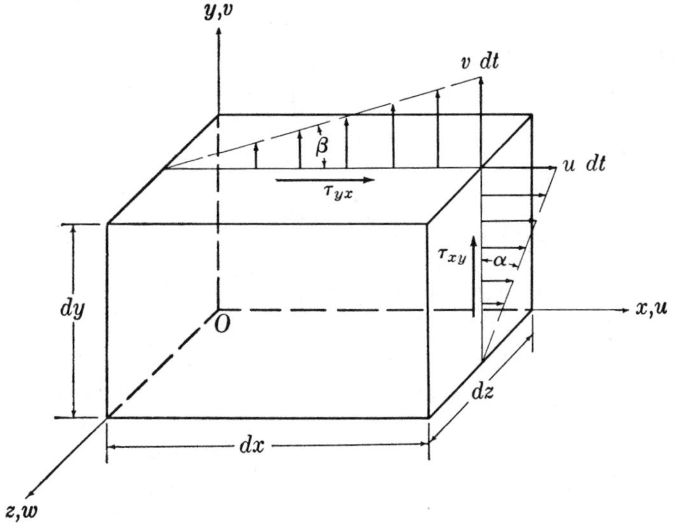

Figure 9.2
Fluid element under pure shear of the x–y-plane.

mation and not rotation. Following the convention of the subscripts of the shearing stress already set up in Sec. 1.10, there will be, for the deformation of the x–y-plane, two shearing stresses τ_{xy} and τ_{yx} equal in strength but opposite in moment around the z-axis. At an instant of time as shown in the figure, the total deformation produced by this set of surface forces is the sum of the angular displacements $(\alpha + \beta)$ which represent the strain. Then, according to Newton's law of viscosity, the shearing stress will be equal to the rate of deformation times the viscosity of the fluid

$$\tau_{xy} = \tau_{yx} = \mu \frac{d}{dt} (\alpha + \beta)$$

For small angles the tangent of the angle can be used for the angle. Here, $\alpha = \dfrac{u\,dt}{dy}$ and $\beta = \dfrac{v\,dt}{dx}$. Substitution of these angles into the previous shearing-stress equation yields

$$\tau_{xy} = \tau_{yx} = \mu \left(\frac{du}{dy} + \frac{dv}{dx} \right)$$

Since the velocity components u and v are, in general, functions of the other coordinates as well, the derivatives in the previous equation must be replaced with partial derivatives:

$$\tau_{xy} = \tau_{yx} = \mu \left(\frac{\partial u}{\partial y} + \frac{\partial v}{\partial x} \right) \qquad [9.1(a)]$$

With similar steps, the deformation on the other two planes can be evaluated if the other four shear stresses are considered. Consequently,

$$\tau_{xz} = \tau_{zx} = \mu \left(\frac{\partial u}{\partial z} + \frac{\partial w}{\partial x} \right) \qquad [9.1(b)]$$

$$\tau_{yz} = \tau_{zy} = \mu \left(\frac{\partial v}{\partial z} + \frac{\partial w}{\partial y} \right) \qquad [9.1(c)]$$

It is worth while to remark at this point that the terms in the parentheses of Eqs. [9.1(a)], [9.1(b)], and [9.1(c)] are the same as those of the vorticity in Eqs. (3.32) and (3.33), with the exception of the signs inside the parentheses. This difference in the sign indicates the difference between pure shear and pure rotation. In fact, if one of the shear stresses in Fig. 9.1 were drawn in the opposite direction, the over-all effect would be one of pure rotation.

The fluid element in Fig. 9.2 could easily be taken in a cylindrical form, and the shear stresses in terms of the cylindrical coordinates would be

$$\tau_{r\theta} = \tau_{\theta r} = \mu \left[r \frac{\partial}{\partial r}\left(\frac{v_\theta}{r}\right) + \frac{1}{r}\frac{\partial v_r}{\partial \theta} \right] \qquad [9.2(a)]$$

$$\tau_{z\theta} = \tau_{\theta z} = \mu \left(\frac{1}{r}\frac{\partial v_z}{\partial \theta} + \frac{\partial v_\theta}{\partial z} \right) \qquad [9.2(b)]$$

and

$$\tau_{zr} = \tau_{rz} = \mu \left(\frac{\partial v_r}{\partial z} + \frac{\partial v_z}{\partial r} \right) \qquad [9.2(c)]$$

In general, shear stresses are not the only internal surface stresses present in the fluid when in motion. Like the pressure which already has been discussed, there are additional normal forces on the surface of the element owing to the viscous deceleration. These normal elemental forces will be discussed also in this chapter.

9.3 Incompressible Viscous Flow in Long Pipes and Channels

Consider an incompressible steady viscous flow entering a pipe or a channel with uniform cross section. If the fluid is introduced uniformly into the conduit, the velocity distribution of the fluid at the entrance will be uniform, as shown in Fig. 9.3. Since, because of the viscosity, the fluid cannot slip over the boundaries of the conduit, the velocity of the fluid at the boundary will be zero and will reach uniformly the uniform value in a short distance from the boundary. The presence of this frictional layer in moving real fluids in the neighborhood of solid

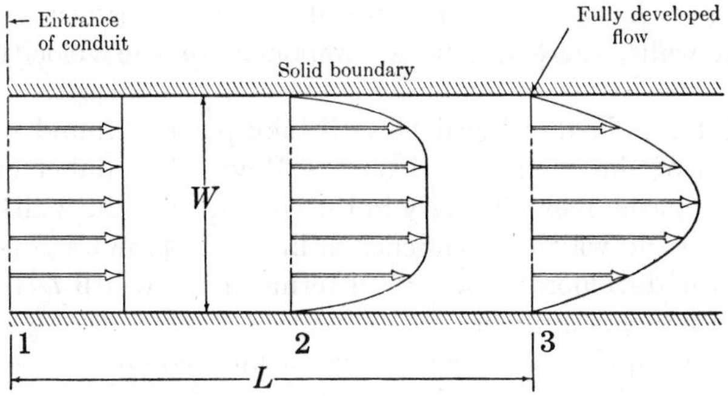

Figure 9.3
Viscous-flow development in a conduit.

boundaries was discussed in Sec. 1.13. This frictional layer, called the boundary layer, will be extremely thin at the entrance of the conduit. As the flow proceeds downstream of the entrance, however, viscous forces dependent on the velocity gradient and the viscosity of the fluid will keep on slowing down the fluid layers in the neighborhood of the solid boundary. As more and more layers of fluid are slowed down in the neighborhood of the solid boundary, the thickness of this frictional layer will grow in size and will occupy more and more of the flow inside the channel. Since the velocity of the fluid in the growing frictional layer is being decelerated, to preserve mass continuity the center layers of the flow must experience an acceleration such that the total mass flow remains constant. The process of deceleration of the frictional layer will persist downstream of the conduit until this frictional layer has extended to the center of the channel from all sides. When this state has been reached, and the viscous forces have progressively altered the velocity distribution of the flow all the way to the center of the conduit, there is no further development of the flow field. The velocity profile remains unchanged from there on in the direction of motion. This state is called the *fully developed state.*

In the development length L of Fig. 9.3 there is a deceleration of the flow in the neighborhood of the solid boundaries and an acceleration in the center of the conduit. The stream surfaces at the entrance of the conduit are parallel to the solid boundaries. As the flow develops from station 1 to station 3, these stream surfaces deflect toward the center of the conduit. Downstream of the fully developed station 3, since any further development has stopped, the stream surfaces remain parallel again. This fact indicates that the velocity at the entrance and in the fully developed region is parallel to the walls of the conduit. In the development region L, however, since the stream surfaces are not parallel to the solid walls, there will be a component of the velocity normal to the wall.

The distance L for fully developed flow to take place is found to depend on the width of the conduit and on the Reynolds number of the flow based on the spatial mean velocity in the conduit and the width of the conduit. Since the width dependence is linear, it is more convenient to say that the development length in terms of the width L/W is a function of the Reynolds number.

The preceding description of viscous flows in long conduits is as applicable for turbulent flows as it is for laminar flows. The dependence of L/W on the Reynolds number, however, is different in both cases. For laminar flows in pipes with diameter D, the ratio L/D has been found theoretically by Langhaar[1] to equal 0.058 times the Reynolds number based on the diameter and the spatial mean velocity in the pipe. Consequently, the development length L is 58 diameters when the Reynolds number is 1,000. On account of additional turbulent shear stresses, this development of the flow is, in general, shorter. Experiments show that, in the turbulent case, this development length is less dependent on the Reynolds number.

9.4 Equation of Motion of Incompressible Viscous Fluids

(a) Fully Developed Flow in Conduits

In the preceding section it was found that, when the flow in a conduit becomes fully developed, the stream surfaces are parallel to the walls of the conduit. This implies that the velocity of the fluid has a direction parallel to the walls of the conduit. If a rectangular conduit is chosen for discussion, letting the coordinate x be along the axis of the conduit, u along x will be the only velocity represented. The other two components $v = w = 0$ because they are normal to the walls of the conduit. Furthermore, it was mentioned in Sec. 9.3 that when the flow reaches the state of full development, the velocity profile does not alter in a downstream direction. Since u is the only velocity component, then it does not vary with x.

Equation [4.8(a)] gives the components of acceleration of the fluid. Since the flow has been considered to be steady, the time-dependent terms vanish. Furthermore, in the fully developed case, $v = w = 0$ eliminates the acceleration terms in v and w. Since, by definition of fully developed state, the velocity u is not a function of x the direction of flow, it follows that all the terms in the acceleration equation are zero. Therefore, fully developed flows in conduits have zero acceleration. The only forces, then, keeping the viscous fluid element in equilibrium are the surface forces. (Assume the gravitational body forces to be negligible.)

The surface forces acting on the fully developed fluid element are the pressure forces and the shear forces, as shown in Fig. 9.4. Here, x is the direction of the velocity u along the axis of the conduit. The

[1] H. L. Langhaar, "Steady Flow in the Transition Length of a Straight Tube," *J. Appl. Mechanics*, Vol. 9, 1942 pp. 55–58.

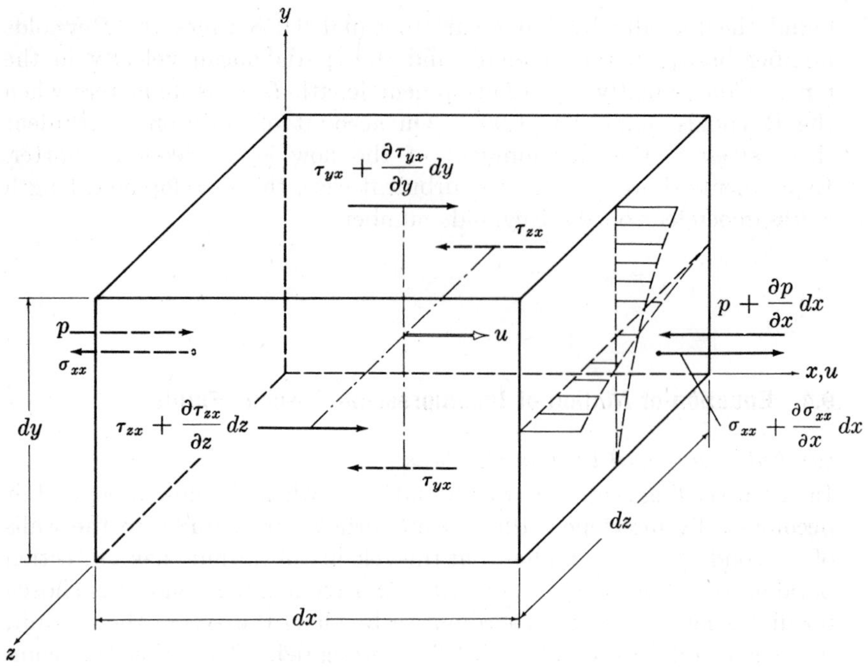

Figure 9.4
Surface forces on a fully developed element of fluid.

surface $dy\,dz$ is the only surface through which the flow is flowing; all other surfaces are parallel to the walls of the rectangular conduit. Since u is the only component of the velocity present, the only deformation taking place is along u through shear stresses τ_{yx} and τ_{zx}. Because $v = w = 0$ and according to Eqs. [9.1(*a*)] and [9.1(*b*)], the only velocity gradients that will be considered are those in u alone.

Following Fig. 9.4 with surface forces drawn so that they increase in an increasing direction of the coordinate system, the equilibrium equation reads:

$$p\,dy\,dz - \left(p + \frac{\partial p}{\partial x}\,dx\right) dy\,dz - \tau_{yx}\,dx\,dz + \left(\tau_{yx} + \frac{\partial}{\partial y}\,\tau_{yx}\,dy\right) dx\,dz$$
$$- \tau_{zx}\,dy\,dx + \left(\tau_{zx} + \frac{\partial}{\partial z}\,\tau_{zx}\,dz\right) dy\,dx = 0$$

After simplification and division by the unit volume $dx\,dy\,dz$, the equilibrium equation for the fully developed element becomes

$$\frac{\partial p}{\partial x} = \frac{\partial}{\partial y}\tau_{yx} + \frac{\partial}{\partial z}\tau_{zx} \tag{9.3}$$

(b) General, Incompressible Viscous Motion

The fully developed flow is a simplified physical condition that occurs in long conduits. Equation (9.3) is, therefore, a simplified form of the general equation of dynamics of viscous motion. If the flow field is not fully developed, implying that the components v and w are nonzero and that there is a possibility of further development in the x-, y-, and z-directions, then, in the equations of motion of the element of Fig. 9.4, one must include the acceleration terms of Eq. [4.8(a)] and take into account the normal stresses due to the viscous dilation of the fluid element. These stresses σ_{xx}, σ_{yy} and σ_{zz} are respectively on surfaces[2] normal to x, y and z and in the x-, y-, and z-directions. Therefore, they have the same sense as the pressure as shown in Fig. 9.4, but in opposite directions. For instance, σ_{xx} is positive in the positive x-direction. These normal stresses arise from the viscous resistance to dilation or compression. Although they are in the same sense as the thermodynamic pressure p, they arise from different effects, namely viscous. As will be seen shortly, since these normal viscous stresses in Newtonian fluids are proportional to $\partial u/\partial x$, $\partial v/\partial y$ and $\partial w/\partial z$, respectively, they did not appear in the previous discussion of fully developed flow. The reason being that, by definition, $u \neq f(x)$, $v \neq f(y)$ and $w \neq f(z)$ in a fully developed flow.

Since there is a change of σ_x from one face to another along the distance dx, the net resistance force owing to elongation is

$$\left(\sigma_{xx} + \frac{\partial \sigma_{xx}}{\partial x}\,dx\right) dy\,dz - \sigma_{xx}\,dy\,dz = \frac{\partial \sigma_{xx}}{\partial x}\,dx\,dy\,dz$$

In the general case, the inertial force must also be taken into account, the x-component, according to Eq. [4.8(a)], will be

$$\rho a_x\,d\mathcal{V} = \rho\left(\frac{\partial u}{\partial t} + u\frac{\partial u}{\partial x} + v\frac{\partial u}{\partial y} + w\frac{\partial u}{\partial z}\right) dx\,dy\,dz$$

With these two additional forces, the force balance leading to Eq. (9.3) becomes, for an incompressible flow,

$$\rho a_x = \rho\left(\frac{\partial u}{\partial t} + u\frac{\partial u}{\partial x} + v\frac{\partial u}{\partial y} + w\frac{\partial u}{\partial z}\right) = -\frac{\partial p}{\partial x} + \frac{\partial}{\partial x}\sigma_x + \frac{\partial}{\partial y}\tau_{yx} + \frac{\partial}{\partial z}\tau_{zx} \tag{9.4}$$

[2] The significance of the subscripts on the viscous stresses was discussed in Sec. 1.10.

This is the x-component of the equation of motion. Two other similar equations can be written for the force balance in the other two directions. If z is the gravitational direction, the force owing to gravity should be taken into account if its magnitude is comparable to the other forces. By inspection we can write the other two equations

$$\rho a_y = \rho\left(\frac{\partial v}{\partial t} + u\frac{\partial v}{\partial x} + v\frac{\partial v}{\partial y} + w\frac{\partial v}{\partial z}\right) = -\frac{\partial p}{\partial y} + \frac{\partial}{\partial x}\tau_{xy} + \frac{\partial}{\partial y}\sigma_{yy} + \frac{\partial}{\partial z}\tau_{zy} \tag{9.5}$$

$$\rho a_z = \rho\left(\frac{\partial w}{\partial t} + u\frac{\partial w}{\partial x} + v\frac{\partial w}{\partial y} + w\frac{\partial w}{\partial z}\right) = \rho g - \frac{\partial p}{\partial z} + \frac{\partial}{\partial x}\tau_{xz} + \frac{\partial}{\partial y}\tau_{yz} + \frac{\partial}{\partial z}\sigma_{zz} \tag{9.6}$$

These equations include stresses on planes normal to x, y and z and in directions of y and z. These stress components are not shown in Fig. 9.4, but can be visualized easily. The body force ρg is made to coincide with the z-direction. In other words, $\boldsymbol{g}$ is in the direction of positive z. In the case of gravitational force, z is then known as depth.

Although the velocity field is a *vector field* with three components, it is apparent that the *stress field* has nine components; they are:

$$\begin{pmatrix} -p+\sigma_{xx} & \tau_{yx} & \tau_{zx} \\ \tau_{xy} & -p+\sigma_{yy} & \tau_{zy} \\ \tau_{xz} & \tau_{yz} & -p+\sigma_{zz} \end{pmatrix} = \begin{pmatrix} -p & 0 & 0 \\ 0 & -p & 0 \\ 0 & 0 & -p \end{pmatrix} + \begin{pmatrix} \sigma_{xx} & \tau_{yx} & \tau_{zx} \\ \tau_{xy} & \sigma_{yy} & \tau_{zy} \\ \tau_{xz} & \tau_{yz} & \sigma_{zz} \end{pmatrix} \tag{9.7}$$

$$\mathbf{S} = \begin{pmatrix} \sigma_{xx} & \tau_{yx} & \tau_{zx} \\ \tau_{xy} & \sigma_{yy} & \tau_{zy} \\ \tau_{xz} & \tau_{yz} & \sigma_{zz} \end{pmatrix} \qquad [9.8(a)]$$

Where $\mathbf{S}$ is the *viscous stress tensor*, and the *viscous stress vectors* on each of the surfaces normal to x, y and z are

$$\begin{aligned} \boldsymbol{P}_x &= \boldsymbol{i}\sigma_{xx} + \boldsymbol{j}\tau_{xy} + \boldsymbol{k}\tau_{xz} \\ \boldsymbol{P}_y &= \boldsymbol{i}\tau_{yx} + \boldsymbol{j}\sigma_{yy} + \boldsymbol{k}\tau_{yz} \\ \boldsymbol{P}_z &= \boldsymbol{i}\tau_{zx} + \boldsymbol{j}\tau_{zy} + \boldsymbol{k}\sigma_{zz} \end{aligned} \qquad [9.8(b)]$$

respectively. In other words, the components of the stress vectors in Eq. (9.7) form the three columns of the tensor matrix. It is at once apparent that the stress tensor is a quantity made up of nine components and obviously, more elaborate in its description than a vector. Inspecting the balance of forces in Eqs. (9.4), (9.5), and (9.6) we see that the derivatives of the viscous stresses are given by

$$\nabla \cdot \mathbf{S} = \frac{\partial}{\partial x} \boldsymbol{P}_x + \frac{\partial}{\partial y} \boldsymbol{P}_y + \frac{\partial}{\partial z} \boldsymbol{P}_z \tag{9.9}$$

or the divergence of the stress tensor $\nabla \cdot \mathbf{S}$. Thus in vector form, the three component Eqs. (9.4), (9.5), and (9.6) can be written as

$$\rho \boldsymbol{a} = \rho \left[\frac{\partial \boldsymbol{U}}{\partial t} + (\boldsymbol{U} \cdot \nabla) \boldsymbol{U} \right] = \rho \boldsymbol{g} - \nabla p + \nabla \cdot \mathbf{S} \tag{9.10}$$

This is the *Navier-Stokes* equation, giving the balance of forces in a viscous fluid with body and surface forces. The external body force is given by $\rho \boldsymbol{g}$ and the external surface force[3] by $\nabla \cdot \mathbf{S}$.

Special cases of Eq. (9.10) have been discussed already. For instance, in the absence of viscous forces, Eq. (9.10) will ignore $\nabla \cdot \mathbf{S}$, and it will become Euler's equation discussed in Sec. 4.8. In the absence of viscous and inertia forces, Eq. (9.10) reduces to the hydrostatic equation of Eq. (2.2). Furthermore, in the absence of inertia forces, as in the case of fully developed parallel flow of Sec. [9.4(*a*)], we obtain Eq. (9.3).

The shear stresses appearing in Eqs. (9.4), (9.5), and (9.6) are related for a Newtonian fluid with constant density to the velocity derivatives as in Eqs. [9.1(*a*)], [9.1(*b*)] and [9.1(*c*)] given by

$$\begin{aligned} \sigma_{xx} &= 2\mu \frac{\partial u}{\partial x} \\ \sigma_{yy} &= 2\mu \frac{\partial v}{\partial y} \\ \sigma_{zz} &= 2\mu \frac{\partial w}{\partial z} \end{aligned} \tag{9.11}$$

Thus, in Eq. (9.4),

$$\begin{aligned} \frac{\partial}{\partial x} \sigma_x + \frac{\partial}{\partial y} \tau_{yx} + \frac{\partial}{\partial z} \tau_{zx} &= \frac{\partial}{\partial x} \left(2\mu \frac{\partial u}{\partial x} \right) + \frac{\partial}{\partial y} \left[\mu \left(\frac{\partial u}{\partial y} + \frac{\partial v}{\partial x} \right) \right] \\ &\quad + \frac{\partial}{\partial z} \left[\mu \left(\frac{\partial u}{\partial z} + \frac{\partial w}{\partial x} \right) \right] \\ &= \mu \left[2 \frac{\partial^2 u}{\partial x^2} + \frac{\partial^2 u}{\partial y^2} + \frac{\partial^2 u}{\partial z^2} + \frac{\partial}{\partial x} \left(\frac{\partial v}{\partial y} + \frac{\partial w}{\partial z} \right) \right] \\ &= \mu \left(\frac{\partial^2 u}{\partial x^2} + \frac{\partial^2 u}{\partial y^2} + \frac{\partial u^2}{\partial z^2} \right) \end{aligned} \tag{9.12}$$

[3] Note here that the divergence of a tensor is a vector and no longer a scalar as in the case of the divergence of a vector.

A change in the order of differentiation and the continuity equation, Eq. (3.17), for an incompressible flow have been used to obtain the result of Eq. (9.12). The components of this Navier-Stokes equation as given in Eqs. (9.4), (9.5), and (9.6), in terms of the velocity derivatives take the form

$$\frac{d\boldsymbol{U}}{dt} = \boldsymbol{g} - \nabla p + \nu \nabla^2 \boldsymbol{U}$$

$$\frac{\partial u}{\partial t} + u\frac{\partial u}{\partial x} + v\frac{\partial u}{\partial y} + w\frac{\partial u}{\partial z} = -\frac{1}{\rho}\frac{\partial p}{\partial x} + \nu\left(\frac{\partial^2 u}{\partial x^2} + \frac{\partial^2 u}{\partial y^2} + \frac{\partial^2 u}{\partial z^2}\right) \tag{9.13}$$

$$\frac{\partial v}{\partial t} + u\frac{\partial v}{\partial x} + v\frac{\partial v}{\partial y} + w\frac{\partial v}{\partial z} = -\frac{1}{\rho}\frac{\partial p}{\partial y} + \nu\left(\frac{\partial^2 v}{\partial x^2} + \frac{\partial^2 v}{\partial y^2} + \frac{\partial^2 v}{\partial z^2}\right) \tag{9.14}$$

$$\frac{\partial w}{\partial t} + u\frac{\partial w}{\partial x} + v\frac{\partial w}{\partial y} + w\frac{\partial w}{\partial z}$$

$$= -\frac{1}{\rho}\frac{\partial p}{\partial z} + \nu\left(\frac{\partial^2 w}{\partial x^2} + \frac{\partial^2 w}{\partial y^2} + \frac{\partial^2 w}{\partial z^2}\right) + g \tag{9.15}$$

9.5 The Reynolds Number Derived from the Equation of Motion

The concept of the Reynolds number was fully discussed in Sec. (3.5). The Reynolds number was defined as the ratio of the inertial force to the viscous force. When the inertial force and the viscous force are of importance, this ratio of forces, called the Reynolds number, is an important dimensionless independent variable upon which similitude of flow performance depends.

Consider, for instance, the incompressible flow around a sphere of diameter d. Let the undisturbed velocity of the fluid be U, its density ρ, and its absolute viscosity μ. Then, by definition, $\nu = \mu/\rho$. The drag on the sphere, for instance, will be completely caused by the viscous effects in the neighborhood of the sphere. This fact was discussed in Chap. VII, and the conclusion was that, in the absence of viscosity, moving immersed bodies do not experience any drag. At any point x,y,z in the viscous layer that causes the drag, the velocity components u, v, and w are proportional to the free-stream velocity U. If U is doubled, for instance, one expects the velocities around the sphere to double. So any velocity in the flow field, as, for example, given in Eq. (9.13), can be replaced by U times a proportionality factor. Also, for equal velocity U but different sized spheres, it can be said that similar flow conditions will be encountered at corresponding points with same x/d, y/d, and z/d distances from the center of the sphere. Therefore, the corresponding distance for similarity of two spherical flow fields is proportional to the diameter of the particular sphere, and any dimension that appears in Eq. (9.13) can be replaced by the diameter of the sphere times a proportionality constant.

For two spheres, since the geometric similarity is automatically satisfied, for dynamic similarity of two flows the ratio of corresponding forces as they appear in the equation of motion must be the same. Equation (9.13) represents a balance of forces in the x-direction per unit mass. The ratio of the inertial force to the viscous force is typically represented by

$$\frac{\text{Inertial force}}{\text{Viscous force}} = \frac{u\,\partial u/\partial x}{\nu\,\partial^2 u/\partial x^2}$$

Substituting the proportionality of u with U and of x with d, the ratio of inertial to viscous forces becomes

$$\mathcal{R} = \frac{UU/d}{\nu U/d^2} = \frac{Ud}{\nu} \tag{9.16}$$

This is the same equation as Eq. (3.1).[4]

Therefore, if two flows are considered around geometrically similar bodies and if the quantity Ud/ν is the same, then the streamlines of both flow fields are geometrically similar. Of course, this conclusion is true for flows in which the inertial and viscous forces predominate.

In the case of flow within a pipe, the Reynolds number is based on a characteristic velocity valid for the whole system, and that is the space mean velocity in the pipe; the characteristic dimension is taken as the diameter of the pipe.

[4] The analysis of Sec. 4.15 can be extended here. The acceleration terms in the two flows have the proportions given by Eq. (4.49). If the ratio of the kinematic viscosities in the two flows is $\nu_1/\nu_2 = h$, then the proportion of the viscous terms in Eq. (9.13) will be

$$\nu_1 \frac{\partial^2 u_1}{\partial x_1^2} = \frac{h}{cb}\,\nu_2 \frac{\partial^2 u_2}{\partial x_1^2}$$

For the same differential equation to be valid for both flows, the coefficient of the inertial term must equal that of the viscous term.

$$\frac{b}{c^2} = \frac{h}{cb} \quad \text{or} \quad \frac{hc}{b^2} = 1$$

This results in

$$\frac{U_1 L_1}{\nu_1} = \frac{U_2 L_2}{\nu_2} = \mathcal{R}$$

For a flow along an infinite flat plate, the characteristic velocity in the Reynolds number is again conveniently taken as the undisturbed free-stream velocity. The search for a characteristic dimension does not offer a single choice. The boundary-layer thickness may be chosen for the length, and, since it increases with distance downstream, the Reynolds number also increases. Often, the distance along the plate is taken as a characteristic length, but, since the growth of the boundary-layer thickness can be related analytically or experimentally to the distance downstream, a Reynolds number based on either one of these dimensions can be easily converted into that of the other.

9.6 Laminar Flow Between Two Stationary Parallel Plates

When a steady and incompressible fluid is allowed to flow between two stationary solid plates, and if the flow passage is longer than approximately 100 times the distance between the plates, the flow, as in the case of the pipe, will reach a fully developed state. This will occur when the retarding viscous effects have progressed to the center of the passage.

The velocity profile between the plates will remain unaltered by the viscous forces. The fluid velocity will vary across the plates but without any variations in the direction of flow.

Consider the fully developed flow between the two plates as shown in Fig. 9.5. Let x be the direction of flow and y the coordinate in the direction normal to the flow and to the surface of the plates. If the flow had started uniformly at the entrance of the passage and if the dimension c is large compared with the distance between the plates, the flow properties will not show any changes in the z-direction.

Thus, with stream surfaces parallel to the plates, $v = w = 0$; the third component u is a function of y alone; consequently, all the terms in Eqs. (9.14) and (9.15) reduce to zero. The only terms that are not zero in Eq. (9.13) are

$$\frac{1}{\rho}\frac{\partial p}{\partial x} = \nu \frac{\partial^2 u}{\partial y^2} \tag{9.17}$$

This is the differential equation that governs the motion of the flow described. From the other two equations it follows that

$$\frac{\partial p}{\partial y} = \frac{\partial p}{\partial z} = 0$$

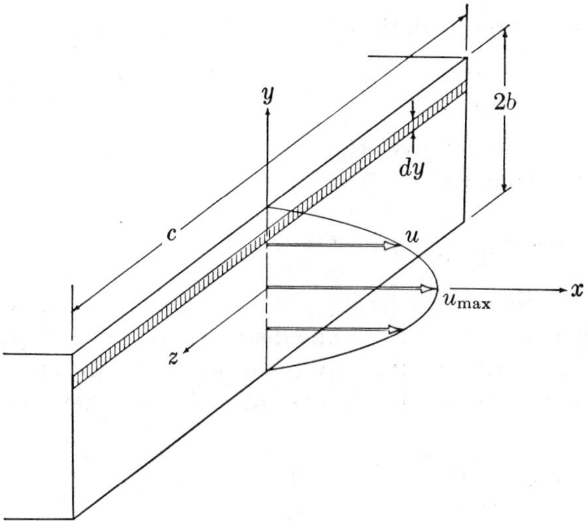

Figure 9.5
Flow between two parallel plates.

meaning that p is not a function of y or of z. Therefore, Eq. (9.17) is really a total differential equation:

$$\frac{1}{\rho}\frac{dp}{dx} = \nu \frac{d^2u}{dy^2}$$

$$= \frac{1}{\rho}\frac{d\tau}{dy} \tag{9.18}$$

A further study of this equation reveals that, since u is a function of y alone, the right-hand term in Eq. (9.18) can be either a function of y or a constant. Since the pressure p is a function of x alone, the term dp/dx can be either a function of x or a constant. It is impossible to have an equation with one side dependent on y alone and the other dependent on x alone, so both sides must be equal to the same constant. For the fully developed flow between two parallel plates, the pressure must decrease linearly with x, and consequently dp/dx must be a negative constant. In that case, Eq. (9.18) can be readily integrated.

$$\mu \frac{du}{dy} = \tau = \frac{dp}{dx} y + A \tag{9.19}$$

This first integration states that the shear stress τ is a linear function of y. Because of the symmetry of the velocity profile $du/dy = 0$ at the center of the channel where $y = 0$, the constant of integration $A = 0$.

$$\mu \frac{du}{dy} = \tau = \frac{dp}{dx} y \tag{9.20}$$

A second integration of Eq. (9.20) gives the velocity distribution across the channel between the two plates

$$u = \frac{1}{2\mu} \frac{dp}{dx} (y^2 - b^2) \tag{9.21}$$

According to this solution, the velocity profile of the laminar flow between two parallel plates is parabolic. The distribution of the shear stress is linear, according to Eq. (9.20). By factoring b in Eq. (9.21), the velocity distribution in terms of the dimensionless distance between the two plates becomes

$$u = \frac{b^2}{2\mu} \frac{dp}{dx} \left[\left(\frac{y}{b} \right)^2 - 1 \right] \tag{9.22}$$

(*a*) *The Maximum Velocity in the Passage*

Equation (9.22) indicates that when $y = 0$, $y/b = 0$, the velocity at the center of the channel, u_{max}, the highest value attained, is equal to

$$u_{max} = -\frac{b^2}{2\mu} \frac{dp}{dx} \tag{9.23}$$

This relationship for the maximum velocity is always positive, since the pressure decreases in the direction of flow. The maximum value of the shear stress occurs, according to Eq. (9.20), at the wall where $y = \pm b$.

$$\tau_w = b \frac{dp}{dx} \tag{9.24}$$

The velocity and shear-stress distribution in the flow between the two plates are shown in Fig. 9.6. The level of the maximum velocity is dependent on the width between the plates, the viscosity, and the pressure drop. The shear stress at the wall is dependent on the width of the channel and the pressure drop.

Illustrative Example 9.1

Consider a laminar flow of water at 50°F between two parallel plates separated by a distance of 1.0 in. If the pressure drop per foot of channel is recorded to be 0.003 in. of water, find the maximum velocity, the shear stress at the wall, and the velocity distribution between the plates.

The pressure drop in appropriate units is

$$\frac{dp}{dx} = -\frac{0.003 \times 62.4}{12} = -0.0156 \frac{\text{lb}_f/\text{ft}^2}{\text{foot of channel}}$$

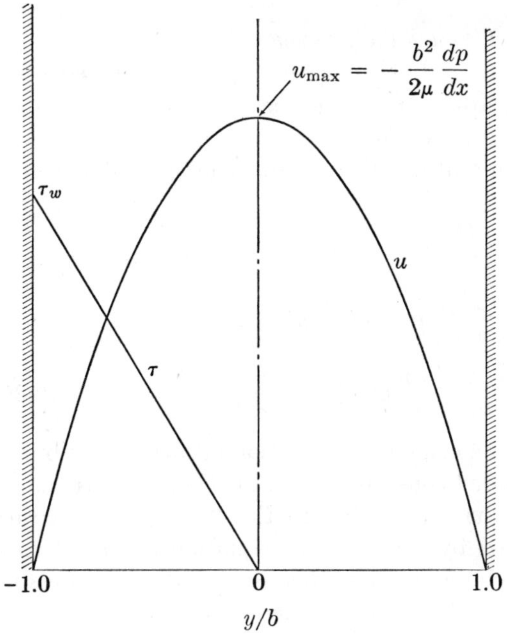

Figure 9.6
Velocity and shear-stress distribution between parallel plates.

The viscosity of the water at 50°F, from Table 1.5, is $\mu = 2.74 \times 10^{-5}$ $lb_f \times sec/ft^2$. From Eq. (9.23) the maximum velocity at the center of the flow is

$$u_{max} = \frac{(0.5)^2 \times 10^5 \times 0.0156}{144 \times 2 \times 2.74}$$

$$= 0.494 \text{ ft/sec.}$$

The shear stress at the wall is given by Eq. (9.24) as

$$\tau_w = \frac{0.5 \times 0.0156}{12}$$

$$= 0.00065 \text{ lb}_f/\text{ft}^2$$

The velocity profile between the plates will be, according to Eq. (9.22),

$$u = 0.494 \, [(2y)^2 - 1]$$

where y is measured in inches. Figure 9.6 represents such a profile.

(b) The Mass Rate of Flow Through the Passage

Since the velocity is a function of the distance across the passage, the mass rate of flow per unit area across the passage varies. The total mass rate of fluid between the two plates can be found by integrating the mass flow crossing an infinitesimal element of area $c\,dy$, as shown in Fig. 9.5.

$$Q = c\int_{-b}^{b} \rho u\, dy$$

$$= \frac{c\rho}{2\mu}\frac{dp}{dx}\int_{-b}^{b}(y^2 - b^2)\, dy$$

$$= -\frac{2}{3}\frac{c\rho}{\mu}\frac{dp}{dx}b^3 \tag{9.25}$$

Here, complying with the original assumption of incompressibility, the density has been considered constant across the channel. It should be remarked at this point that, according to Eq. (9.25), the viscosity of liquids can be determined by solving that equation for μ. A flow field between two plates can be set up in such a manner that the pressure drop in the direction of the flow can be measured with a sensitive manometer, and the liquid accumulated in a tank for a period of time will give the mass rate of flow Q. Knowing the distance between the plates, the viscosity of the liquid can be evaluated.

(c) The Space Average Velocity

Let a space average velocity u_{av} be defined in such a way that the mass rate of flow just derived is equal to the product of the density of the fluid, the total cross-sectional area of the channel, and the space average velocity.

$$Q = -\frac{2}{3}\frac{c\rho}{\mu}\frac{dp}{dx}b^3 = 2bc\rho u_{av}$$

Solving,

$$u_{av} = -\frac{b^2}{3\mu}\frac{dp}{dx} \tag{9.26}$$

Comparing this expression with Eq. (9.23), it follows that the space average velocity in the laminar flow between two plates is two-thirds the value of the maximum velocity in the center.

Illustrative Example 9.2

Determine the mass rate of flow per unit breadth c, the space average velocity, and the Reynolds number of the flow based on the average velocity and the width $2b$ for Illustrative Example 9.1.

$$u_{av} = \frac{2 \times 0.494}{3}$$

$$= 0.329 \text{ ft/sec}$$

Then,

$$Q = \frac{0.329 \times 62.4}{12}$$

$$= 1.71 \text{ lb}_m/\text{sec}$$

and

$$\mathcal{R} = \frac{0.329 \times 1 \times 10^5}{12 \times 1.41}$$

$$= 1{,}945$$

(d) The Pressure Drop

In a channel with constant width, in order to preserve the mass continuity of the flow, the space average velocity must be constant for an incompressible flow. A study of Eq. (9.26) reveals that the pressure drop in the passage for laminar flow is a linear function of the mean velocity

$$\frac{dp}{dx} = -\frac{3\mu}{b^2} u_{av} \tag{9.27}$$

The same pressure drop for turbulent flows is found to be approximately proportional to the square of the space average velocity. This fact was discovered experimentally before the laminar-flow analysis shown here was ever solved.

If the pressure is made dimensionless by dividing with the dynamic pressure of the mean flow, and if the distance x is made dimensionless dividing by the width of the channel $2b$, then the *resistance coefficient* between parallel plates is defined as

$$f = -\frac{d\left(\dfrac{p}{\dfrac{\rho}{2} u_{av}^2}\right)}{d\left(\dfrac{x}{2b}\right)}$$

$$= -\frac{2b}{\dfrac{\rho}{2} u_{av}^2} \frac{dp}{dx}$$

$$= \frac{4\tau_w}{\rho u_{av}^2}$$

Substitution of the value of the pressure drop given in Eq. (9.27) gives

$$f = \frac{4b}{\rho u_{\text{av}}^2} \frac{3\mu}{b^2} u_{\text{av}}$$

$$= \frac{12\mu}{\rho b u_{\text{av}}}$$

$$= \frac{12}{\mathcal{R}} \tag{9.28}$$

where $\mathcal{R} = \rho b u_{\text{av}}/\mu$ is the Reynolds number of the flow between the flat plates based on the space average velocity and the half distance between the plates. It can be shown experimentally that Eq. (9.28) holds true for laminar flows up to a critical Reynolds number of approximately 2,300. Flows with higher Reynolds number become turbulent, and the over-all flow pattern is entirely different from that of the laminar case. Re-examining the definition of the resistance coefficient, the pressure was divided by u_{av}^2. Since it has already been stated, that in the turbulent case the pressure drop is proportional to u_{av} raised to a power approximately 2.0 (between 1.7 and 2.0), the resistance coefficient is approximately a constant.

The resistance coefficient for the laminar flow between two flat plates is plotted on logarithmic coordinates in Fig. 9.7. The range of

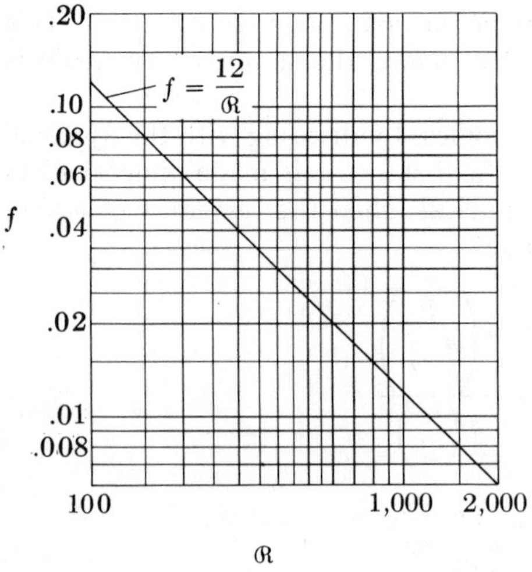

Figure 9.7
Resistance coefficient for laminar flow between two flat plates.

this resistance law should be extended only to the critical $\mathfrak{R}$ approximately equal to 2,300.

(e) Dissipation of Energy Owing to Friction

The flow between the two plates was considered to be incompressible. For the fully developed state, the velocity of the fluid does not vary in the direction of the motion, and thus this motion excludes any kinetic-energy variation in the direction of the motion. Since no shaft work is introduced to the fluid element, the difference between the work done by the surroundings on the element and by the element on the surroundings through the pressure and shear forces is the energy dissipated through friction into heat.

Figure 9.8 shows such a fully developed element removed from the flow in Fig. 9.5. In this case, defining the properties of the fluid at the center of the element as u, p, and τ, the properties at the corresponding surfaces can be obtained by Taylor's expansion. For the fully developed

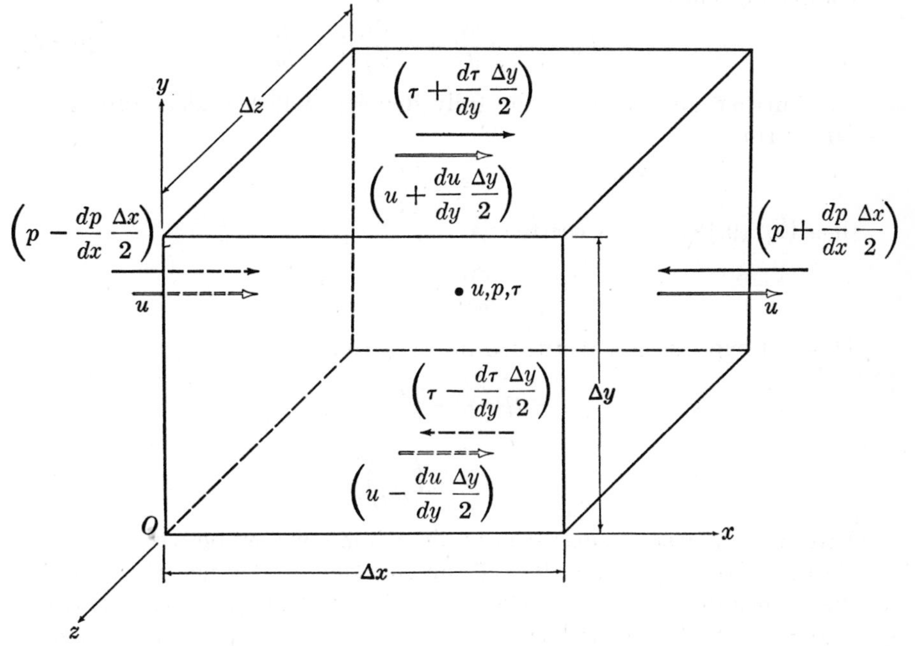

Figure 9.8
Surface forces and velocities on the surface of a fully developed element of fluid.

flow, the variation of properties across the faces of the element is represented by total derivatives.

The work done per unit time by the surroundings on the fluid element considered comes from the action of the pressure and shear force moving the element in the direction of motion. In the absence of inertia forces, this total power input is then:

$$\left[\left(p - \frac{dp}{dx}\frac{\Delta x}{2}\right)\Delta y\,\Delta z\right]u + \left[\left(\tau + \frac{d\tau}{dy}\frac{\Delta y}{2}\right)\Delta x\,\Delta z\right]\left[\left(u + \frac{du}{dy}\frac{\Delta y}{2}\right)\right]$$

The work per unit time performed by the element on its surroundings through the pressure and shear forces that retard the motion is

$$\left[\left(p + \frac{dp}{dx}\frac{\Delta x}{2}\right)\Delta y\,\Delta z\right]u + \left[\left(\tau - \frac{d\tau}{dy}\frac{\Delta y}{2}\right)\Delta x\,\Delta z\right]\left[\left(u - \frac{du}{dy}\frac{\Delta y}{2}\right)\right]$$

The difference between the power input and the power out of the element is what dissipates into heat through friction. This difference can be obtained readily, and the energy dissipated per unit time and unit volume becomes

$$dP_d = -u\frac{dp}{dx} + u\frac{d\tau}{dy} + \tau\frac{du}{dy} \tag{9.29}$$

Furthermore, since in the fully developed flow and according to Eq. [9.1(*a*)],

$$\tau = \mu\frac{du}{dy}$$

then Eq. (9.18) can be written as

$$\frac{dp}{dx} = \frac{d\tau}{dy}$$

This last expression, substituted into Eq. (9.29), gives

$$dP_d = \tau\frac{du}{dy}$$

$$= \mu\left(\frac{du}{dy}\right)^2 \tag{9.30}$$

This is the power dissipated per unit volume of flow between the two plates.[5] Looking at Fig. 9.5, if one considers a channel of length L, then, since du/dy given by Eq. (9.20) varies along y, the infinitesimal volume to be considered is $cL\,dy$, and the power dissipated of that

[5] This result was derived in a much simpler fashion in Illustrative Example 1.5. A more general approach will be shown in Sec. 10.7.

volume is Eq. (9.30). The total dissipated power across the channel is found by integration

$$P_d = \int_{-b}^{b} cL\mu \left(\frac{du}{dy}\right)^2 dy$$

$$P_d = \frac{cL\left(\frac{dp}{dx}\right)^2}{\mu} \int_{-b}^{b} y^2\, dy$$

$$= \frac{2cLb^3}{3\mu}\left(\frac{dp}{dx}\right)^2$$

According to Eq. (9.25), the mass rate of flow Q can be substituted into the preceding equation, giving

$$P_d = -\frac{Q}{\rho}\frac{dp}{dx} L$$

and, since dp/dx is constant with x, the product $(dp/dx)L$ can be replaced by the finite pressure drop in a length L.

$$P_d = \frac{Q\,\Delta p}{\rho} \tag{9.31}$$

Consequently, for the laminar case of a fully developed flow between two parallel plates, the power dissipated in a length of passage L is equal to the volume flow times the pressure drop between the two ends of the passage.

Illustrative Example 9.3

A 10-in.-thick wall holds water at 50°F on one side. At a depth 12 in. below the surface of the water, a 0.015-in. crack has developed on the wall for a length of 24 ft. Determine (*a*) the average velocity, the mass rate of flow through the crack, and the maximum velocity in the crack; (*b*) the Reynolds number of the flow based on the average velocity and the width of the crack; (*c*) the shear-stress distribution, the velocity distribution, and the distribution of the power dissipation per unit volume; (*d*) the total power dissipated in the entire length of the crack, assuming fully developed flow throughout.

The pressure drop of the water through the crack is equal to the 12-in. head of water, and in the distance of 10 in. this drop of pressure will be

$$\frac{dp}{dx} = -\frac{62.4 \times 12}{10}$$

$$= -75\ \text{lb}_f/\text{ft}^3$$

The space average velocity is given by Eq. (9.26) as

$$u_{av} = -\frac{b^2}{3\mu}\frac{dp}{dx}$$
$$= \frac{(0.015)^2 \times 10^5 \times 75}{4 \times 144 \times 3 \times 2.74}$$
$$= 0.356 \text{ ft/sec}$$

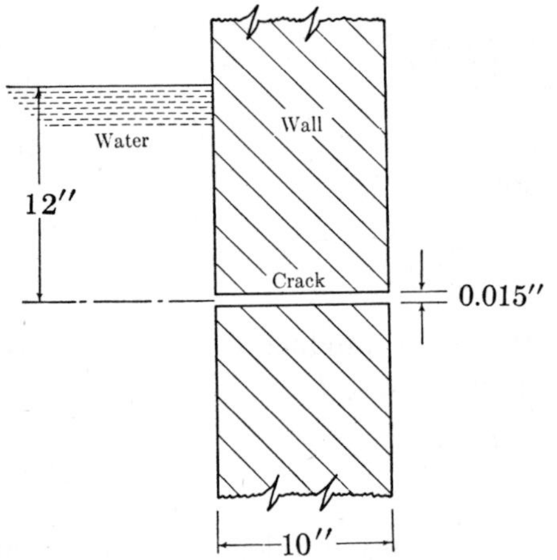

Figure 9.9
Flow out of a crack in a wall.

The cross-sectional area of the crack is $A = \frac{0.015 \times 24}{12} = 0.030$ ft²; consequently, the mass rate of flow coming out of the crack will be

$$Q = 0.356 \times 0.030 \times 62.4$$
$$= 0.666 \text{ lb}_m\text{/sec}$$

The maximum velocity in the crack is 3/2 times the space average velocity, and therefore $u_{max} = 0.534$ ft/sec.

The Reynolds number of the flow is

$$\mathcal{R} = \frac{0.356 \times 0.015 \times 10^5}{12 \times 1.41}$$
$$= 31.6$$

The shear-stress distribution is given by Eq. (9.20) and shown in Fig. 9.10. The maximum value of the shear stress which occurs at the wall of the crack is

$$\tau_w = \frac{75 \times 0.0075}{12}$$
$$= 0.0468 \text{ lb}_f/\text{ft}^2$$

Since the maximum velocity is known, the velocity distribution can be obtained from Eq. (9.22). This distribution is also shown in Fig. 9.10. The power dissipation per unit volume of fluid was derived in Eq. (9.30) as

$$dP_d = \mu \left(\frac{du}{dy}\right)^2$$
$$= \frac{1}{\mu}\left(\frac{dp}{dx}\right)^2 y^2$$

This last expression is obtained with the use of Eq. (9.20) for the velocity derivative. This equation is a parabola and is plotted in Fig. 9.10. The maximum power dissipation occurs at the wall, where it assumes the value of

$$dP_d = \frac{10^5 \times (75)^2 \times (0.015)^2}{2.74 \times 4 \times 144}$$
$$= 80.3 \frac{\text{ft} \times \text{lb}_f}{\text{sec}} \Big/ \text{ft}^3$$

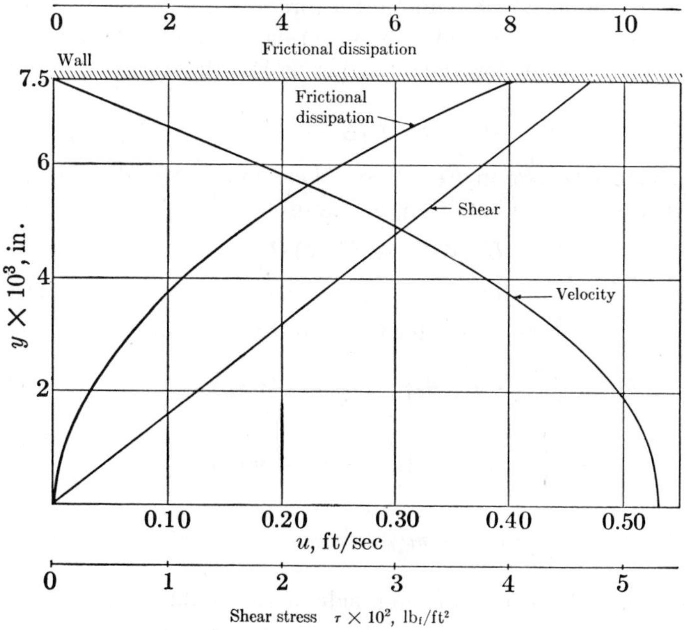

Figure 9.10
Properties of the flow in a crack.

The total power dissipation in the entire crack is the volume integration of the local power dissipation plotted. This value is given by Eq. (9.31)

$$P_d = \frac{Q\,\Delta p}{\rho}$$

$$= \frac{0.666 \times 62.4}{62.4}$$

$$= 0.666 \text{ ft} \times \text{lb}_f/\text{sec}$$

9.7 Power Owing to Stresses

In Sec. 6.4, the mechanical power equation owing to the motion of a fluid was considered. In that discussion, the *flow work* or work owing to the hydrostatic pressure was considered only. Here the entire stress tensor acted upon by a velocity vector $\boldsymbol{U}$ will be considered. In the previous section, a very simplified form of this analysis was done for a fully developed flow in which, the inertia forces being zero, the pressure and shear forces were the only forces acting on the fluid element.

In analogy to the considerations leading to Eq. (9.29), the viscous power is

$$\delta P_v = \nabla \cdot (\boldsymbol{U} \cdot \mathbf{S}) \tag{9.32}$$

where $\mathbf{S}$ is the stress tensor in Eq. (9.8). Developing the divergence of a product in the previous equation, we have

$$\delta P_v + \boldsymbol{U} \cdot (\nabla \cdot \mathbf{S}) + (\mathbf{S} \cdot \nabla) \cdot \boldsymbol{U} \tag{9.33}$$

From the definition of the divergence of the stress tensor in Eq. (9.9) and the components of $\mathbf{S}$ and $\boldsymbol{U}$, Eq. (9.32) in component form is

$$\begin{aligned} \delta P_v &= \frac{\partial}{\partial x}\left[u(\sigma_{xx} - p) + v\tau_{yx} + w\tau_{zx}\right] \\ &+ \frac{\partial}{\partial y}\left[u\tau_{xy} + v(\sigma_{yy} - p) + w\tau_{zy}\right] \\ &+ \frac{\partial}{\partial z}\left[u\tau_{xz} + v\tau_{yz} + w(\sigma_{zz} - p)\right] \end{aligned} \tag{9.34}$$

of which the first term in the right-hand side of Eq. (9.33) is the useful work and the second term is the power dissipated into heat. To check the relationships for a fully developed flow as in Eqs. (9.29) and (9.30) we use the definition of a fully developed channel flow implying that

$v = w = 0$, $\partial p/\partial y = \partial p/\partial z = 0$, $\partial u/\partial x = \partial u/\partial z = 0$. The first row in Eq. (9.34) gives only $-u\,\frac{\partial p}{\partial x}$. The second row gives $u\,\frac{\partial \tau_{xy}}{\partial y}$ and $\tau_{xy}\,\frac{\partial u}{\partial y}$. The third row is zero. Thus, the viscous power becomes

$$\delta P_v = -u\,\frac{\partial p}{\partial x} + u\,\frac{\partial \tau_{xy}}{\partial y} + \tau_{xy}\,\frac{\partial u}{\partial y}$$

This is the special result sought. The partial derivatives, here, can be changed to total since they represent the only changes in p and u. The rest of the analysis follows as in Sec. 9.6.

9.8 Incompressible, Laminar, Couette Flow

The case considered here refers to the motion of an incompressible laminar flow between two parallel plates but with one of the plates moving relative to the other. As shown in Fig. 9.11, let the lower plate

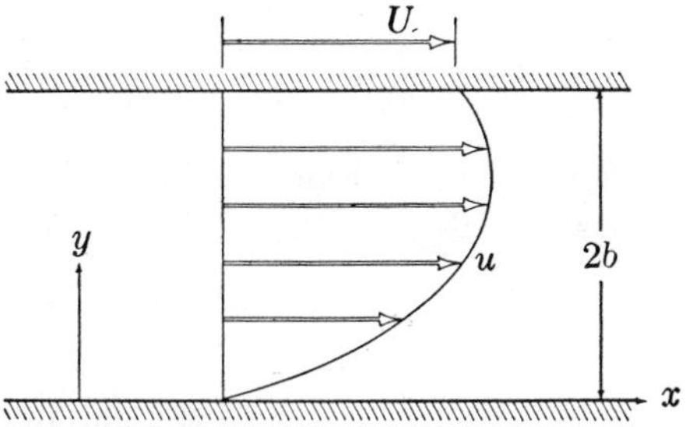

Figure 9.11
Incompressible, laminar, Couette flow.

be stationary and the upper plate be moving at the velocity U. If the plates are long enough in the direction of motion, the flow will eventually reach a fully developed state such that the stream surfaces will be parallel to the plates, $v = w = 0$ and $u = f(y)$ alone. Therefore, Eq. (9.18) will again be applicable to this case. The boundary conditions, however, will be different from the previous case in that $y = 0$, $u = 0$; $y = 2b$, $u = U$.

The first integration of Eq. (9.18) yields Eq. (9.19).

$$\frac{du}{dy} = \frac{1}{\mu}\frac{dp}{dx}y + \frac{A}{\mu}$$

The second integration gives the velocity distribution:

$$u = \frac{1}{\mu}\frac{dp}{dx}\frac{y^2}{2} + \frac{A}{\mu}y + B \tag{9.35}$$

The first boundary condition at the stationary wall where $u = 0$ for $y = 0$, when substituted in this solution, specifies that the integration constant B must be zero. The second boundary condition when $y = 2b$ yields

$$U = \frac{1}{\mu}\frac{dp}{dx}2b^2 + \frac{A}{\mu}2b$$

Then the constant of integration A is

$$A = \frac{\mu U}{2b} - \frac{dp}{dx}b$$

Replacing this constant in the solution given by Eq. (9.35) gives

$$u = \frac{U}{2b}y - \frac{1}{\mu}\frac{dp}{dx}\left(yb - \frac{y^2}{2}\right)$$

$$= U\frac{y}{2b} - \frac{2b^2}{\mu}\frac{dp}{dx}\frac{y}{2b}\left(1 - \frac{y}{2b}\right) \tag{9.36}$$

Dividing by U, the velocity distribution becomes dimensionless. Letting ϕ represent the dimensionless pressure gradient,

$$\phi = \frac{2b^2}{\mu U}\frac{dp}{dx}$$

the dimensionless velocity distribution in the space between the moving plate and the stationary plate becomes

$$\frac{u}{U} = \frac{y}{2b} - \phi\frac{y}{2b}\left(1 - \frac{y}{2b}\right) \tag{9.37}$$

This dimensionless velocity is plotted in Fig. 9.12 as a function of the distance from the stationary plate for various dimensionless pressure gradients ϕ. In particular, one can observe that, when the pressure gradient along the passage is zero, the velocity distribution between the two plates is linear. From the velocity distributions it can also be seen that, for positive dimensionless pressure gradients $\phi > 1.0$, there is a reverse flow in the vicinity of the stationary wall.

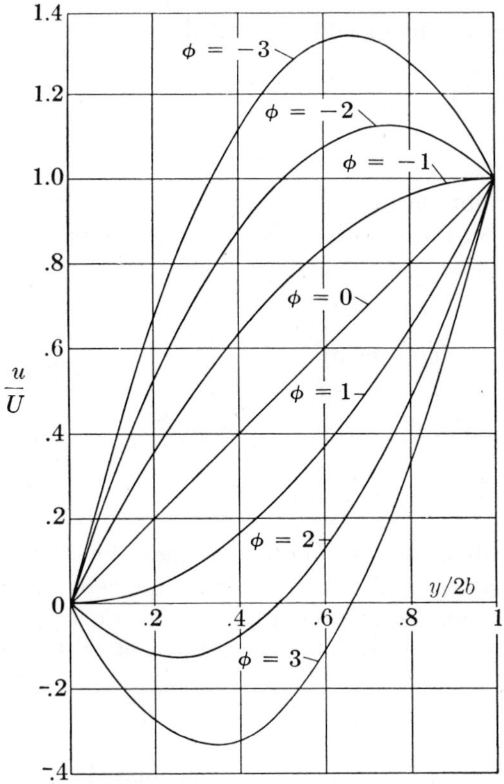

Figure 9.12
Velocity profiles of Couette flows.

(a) The Mass Rate of Flow

The velocity distribution is given by Eq. (9.36), and the mass rate of flow per unit depth of passage is the velocity integrated across the passage times the density of the fluid.

$$Q = \int_0^{2b} \rho u \, dy$$

$$= \rho \int_0^{2b} \left[U \frac{y}{2b} - \frac{2b^2}{\mu} \frac{dp}{dx} \frac{y}{2b} \left(1 - \frac{y}{2b}\right) \right] dy$$

$$= \rho \left(Ub - \frac{2b^3}{3\mu} \frac{dp}{dx} \right) \tag{9.38}$$

In dimensionless form, this mass rate of flow per unit depth is

$$\frac{Q}{\rho U b} = 1 - \frac{\phi}{3} \tag{9.39}$$

(*b*) *The Space Average Velocity*
The space average velocity is obtained by dividing the mass rate of flow by the density and the area per unit depth or the width of the passage

$$u_{\text{av}} = \frac{Q}{2b\rho}$$

$$= \frac{U}{2} - \frac{b^2}{3\mu}\frac{dp}{dx} \tag{9.40}$$

and in dimensionless form it takes the form

$$\frac{u_{\text{av}}}{U} = \frac{1}{2} - \frac{\phi}{6} \tag{9.41}$$

As seen from Fig. 9.12, when the pressure drop is zero, the dimensionless velocity across the passage is linear, varying from a zero value at the stationary wall to 1.0 at the moving wall. Here, Eq. (9.40) gives $u_{\text{av}} = U/2$ when dp/dx is zero, which is in agreement with the mean height of a triangle.

(*c*) *The Shearing Stress*
From Eq. (9.36), the velocity derivative du/dy can be evaluated. This derivative is

$$\frac{du}{dy} = \frac{U}{2b} - \frac{b}{\mu}\frac{dp}{dx}\left(1 - \frac{y}{b}\right) \tag{9.42}$$

The shear stress is then

$$\tau = \frac{\mu U}{2b} - b\frac{dp}{dx}\left(1 - \frac{y}{b}\right)$$

In dimensionless form, this shear-stress distribution becomes

$$\frac{2b\tau}{\mu U} = 1 - \phi\left(1 - \frac{y}{b}\right) \tag{9.43}$$

Figure 9.13 shows the distribution of the dimensionless shear for various values of the dimensionless pressure gradient ϕ. It becomes apparent from the figure that the value of the shear stress at the center of the passage is the same for all pressure gradients. This result can be obtained from inspection of Eq. (9.42). At the center of the passage

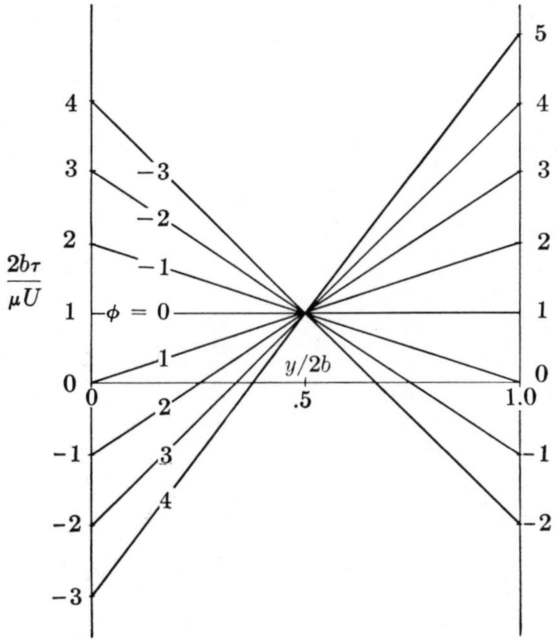

Figure 9.13
Shear-stress distribution in a Couette flow.

$y/b = 1.0$, and consequently for all values of dp/dx, the slope of the velocity profiles is the same, namely $U/2b$.

(d) The Maximum Velocity
The maximum or minimum velocity occurs at the place where the velocity derivative $du/dy = 0$. From Eq. (9.43), the velocity derivative or the shear stress is zero when

$$\frac{y}{2b} = \frac{1}{2} - \frac{1}{2\phi}$$

This is the position of the maximum velocity. Substitution of this value of the coordinate into the dimensionless velocity Eq. (9.37) gives the value of the maximum velocity as a ratio to the moving wall velocity:

$$\frac{u_{\max}}{U} = -\frac{1}{4}\frac{(\phi - 1)^2}{\phi} \tag{9.44}$$

For the purpose of comparison, this equation is plotted in Fig. 9.14.

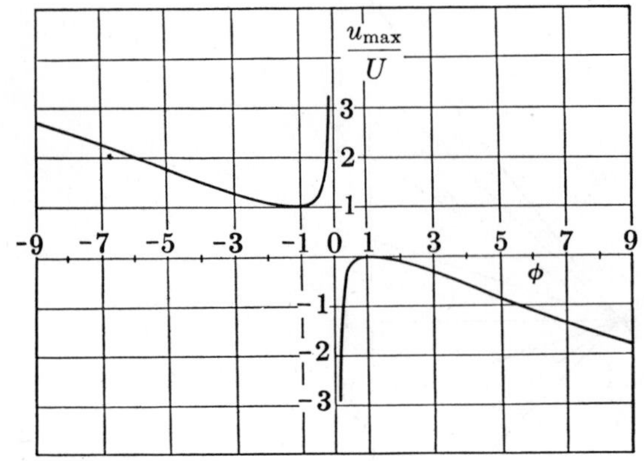

Figure 9.14
Value of the maximum velocity as a function of the dimensionless pressure gradient.

Illustrative Example 9.4
A platform AB weighs 120 lb_f/ft. The unit foot is in the direction normal to the paper. The platform is $L = 12$ in. and is supported by an oil film 0.020 in. thick with a viscosity of $\mu = 0.8 \times 10^{-3}$ $lb_f \times sec/ft^2$. The oil film is set in motion from left to right through the pressure gradient $p_1 - p_0$, and the linear motion of the lower platform at $U = 20$ ft/sec. If the density of the oil is

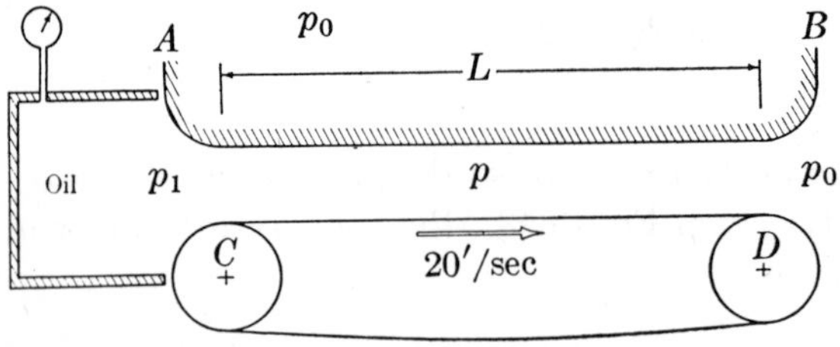

Figure 9.15
Floating bearing.

54.0 lb_m/ft^3, find the mass consumption of oil to produce a lift force equal to the weight of the plate.

The ratio of the platform length L to the gap is so large that the flow in the gap can be considered to be fully developed throughout. On account of the pressure inside the gap, the force supporting the platform AB is

$$F = \int_0^L (p - p_0)\, dx$$

but, since the pressure variation in the gap is linear,

$$p = p_1 - \frac{p_1 - p_0}{L} x$$

therefore,

$$F = \int_0^L \left[(p_1 - p_0) - \frac{(p_1 - p_0)}{L} x \right] dx$$

$$= \frac{(p_1 - p_0)L}{2}$$

$$= \frac{(p_1 - p_0)}{L} \frac{L^2}{2}$$

For the platform load to be supported,[6] F must be equal to its weight 120 lb_f/ft. The pressure drop can then be computed

$$\frac{dp}{dx} = \frac{(p_1 - p_0)}{L} = \frac{120 \times 2}{L^2}$$

$$= -240 \text{ lb}_f/\text{ft}^3$$

Equation (9.38) determines then the mass rate of oil flow through the gap

$$Q = 54.0 \left[20 \times \frac{0.10}{12} + \frac{2 \times (0.010)^3 \times 10^3 \times 240}{3 \times 0.8 \times 12^3} \right]$$

$$= 0.899 \text{ lb}_m/\text{sec ft}$$

9.9 The Slipper Bearing

The slipper bearing is a short sliding pad, straight or curved, moving at a velocity U relative to a stationary pad and inclined at a small angle with respect to the stationary pad. The small gap between the two pads is filled with a lubricant. A diagram of this bearing is shown in Fig. 9.16 and constitutes one segment of a thrust bearing of the Kingsbury type. Depending on the type of application, one of the surfaces shown in Fig. 9.16 is in uniform relative motion with respect to the other. For ease of analysis, it is always desirable to consider the

[6] The center of gravity and the center of pressure are not at the same point along the plate. If the plate was hinged at the right-hand end, the student should attempt to solve this problem for the plate to float.

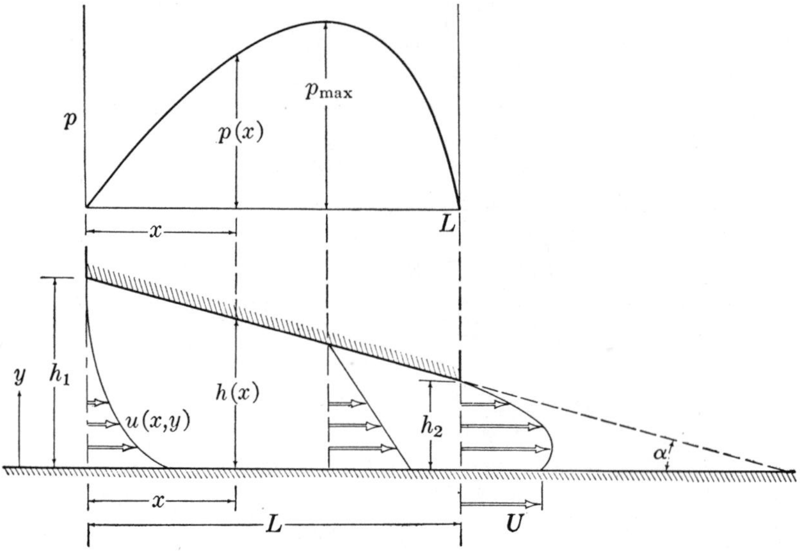

Figure 9.16
The slipper bearing.

over-all motion relative to the slipper pad. The figure is drawn in conformity with this convention. Newton's laws of motion can apply readily to the relative motion, since U is a constant. Since the ends of the bearing are generally open, the pressure of the lubricant there is ambient, say atmospheric p_0. If the upper pad is parallel to the base plate, since from previous analysis dp/dx in the gap must be a constant, then the pressure everywhere in the gap must be atmospheric. Thus a parallel pad with open ends is unable to support a transverse load in the y-direction, since the pressure on both sides of the pad is the same.

If the pad is inclined relative to the base plate, a pressure distribution is set up in the gap. At high speeds, this pressure distribution can be of such a magnitude as to support heavy loads in the direction normal to the base plate.

With the slipper pad inclined, the pressure distribution is no longer linear, and consequently dp/dx is no longer a constant, as in the previous cases, but a function of the coordinate x. Since the width of the gap and the angle of inclination are generally small, it can be assumed with good accuracy that p is not a function of y.

For a two-dimensional flow and a small angle α, the velocities v

and w can be omitted, and consequently Eqs. (9.14) and (9.15) are identically zero. Because of the two dimensionality, the term $\partial^2 u/\partial z^2$ is zero in Eq. (9.13). The normal viscous-stress gradient $\partial^2 u/\partial x^2$ is not zero in this case, but it can be neglected when compared with the larger magnitude of the shear-stress gradient $\mu \partial^2 u/\partial y^2 = \partial \tau/\partial y$. Therefore, as in the previous examples, the equation governing the motion of the lubricant between the two pads is

$$\frac{dp}{dx} = \mu \frac{\partial^2 u}{\partial y^2}$$

One must remember that dp/dx is a total derivative, since it is not a function of y but the equation is a partial differential equation since $u = f(x,y)$.

Integrating the differential equation twice, the velocity distribution becomes

$$\frac{\partial u}{\partial y} = \frac{1}{\mu}\frac{dp}{dx} y + f_1(x) \tag{9.45}$$

$$u = \frac{1}{2\mu}\frac{dp}{dx} y^2 + y f_1(x) + f_2(x) \tag{9.46}$$

This is similar to the integration in Sec. 9.8, except that the constants A and B are replaced by $f_1(x)$ and $f_2(x)$, since u here is a function of both variables x and y. These functions can easily be evaluated from the boundary conditions of the flow field. For $y = 0$, $u = U$ gives $f_2(x) = U =$ constant. The second boundary condition $y = h$, $u = 0$ gives $f_1(x) = -\dfrac{h(x)}{2\mu}\dfrac{dp}{dx} - \dfrac{U}{h(x)}$, and the velocity distribution of Eq. (9.46) becomes

$$u = U\left[1 - \frac{y}{h(x)}\right] - \frac{h^2(x)}{2\mu}\frac{dp}{dx}\frac{y}{h(x)}\left[1 - \frac{y}{h(x)}\right] \tag{9.47}$$

To satisfy the continuity of mass, the mass rate of flow Q at every cross section $h(x)$ must be the same. Evaluating the mass rate of flow per unit depth,

$$Q = \rho \int_0^{h(x)} u\, dy = \text{constant}$$

$$= \rho\left[\frac{Uh(x)}{2} - \frac{h^3(x)}{12\mu}\frac{dp}{dx}\right] \tag{9.48}$$

From this relation, knowing Q, the pressure gradient can be evaluated at every point x.

$$\frac{dp}{dx} = 12\mu\left[\frac{U}{2h^2(x)} - \frac{Q}{\rho h^3(x)}\right] \tag{9.49}$$

This is a total differential equation involving the pressure as a function of x. It can be integrated, and the variation of pressure along the bearing is obtained.

$$p(x) = p_0 + 6\mu U\int_0^x \frac{dx}{h^2(x)} - \frac{12\mu Q}{\rho}\int_0^x \frac{dx}{h^3(x)} \tag{9.50}$$

This is the value of the pressure in the gap as a function of x for a given slipper-pad contour $h(x)$. If $h(x)$ is given, then the integration can be performed and $p(x)$ obtained at various values of x.

Advantage can be taken of the fourth boundary condition which states that $p = p_0$ at $x = L$. Substituting it into Eq. (9.50), an expression for the mass rate of flow is obtained.

$$Q = \frac{\rho U}{2}\frac{\displaystyle\int_0^L \frac{dx}{h^2(x)}}{\displaystyle\int_0^L \frac{dx}{h^3(x)}} \tag{9.51}$$

In particular, when the contour of the pad $h(x)$ is linear as shown in Fig. 9.16, so that

$$h(x) = h_1 - \frac{h_1 - h_2}{L}x \tag{9.52}$$

and substituting this linear relation into Eq. (9.51), it follows that

$$Q = \frac{\rho U}{2}\frac{\left.\dfrac{1}{\dfrac{h_1 - h_2}{L}\left(h_1 - \dfrac{h_1 - h_2}{L}x\right)}\right|_0^L}{\left.\dfrac{1}{\dfrac{2(h_1 - h_2)}{L}\left(h_1 - \dfrac{h_1 - h_2}{L}x\right)^2}\right|_0^L}$$

$$= \frac{\rho U h_1 h_2}{h_1 + h_2} \tag{9.53}$$

When the linear relation for the gap width $h(x)$ given by Eq. (9.52) is substituted into the pressure equation, Eq. (9.50), it simplifies to the form

$$p - p_0 = \frac{6\mu U x(h - h_2)}{h^2(h_1 + h_2)} \tag{9.54}$$

(a) The Bearing Load and the Center of Pressure
The bearing load or the transverse load that the fluid exerts on the bearing pads can be evaluated by integrating Eq. (9.54) over the entire surface of the slipper pad. The total load per unit depth is

$$F = \int_0^L (p - p_0)\, dx$$

$$= \frac{\mu U L^2}{h_2^2}\, \phi_l \tag{9.55}$$

where ϕ_l, the *load factor*, is a function of the ratio of the bearing end widths $\epsilon = h_1/h_2$.

$$\phi_l = \frac{6}{(\epsilon - 1)^2}\left[\ln \epsilon - \frac{2(\epsilon - 1)}{(\epsilon + 1)}\right] \tag{9.56}$$

The load factor is a dimensionless quantity and is plotted in Fig. 9.17.

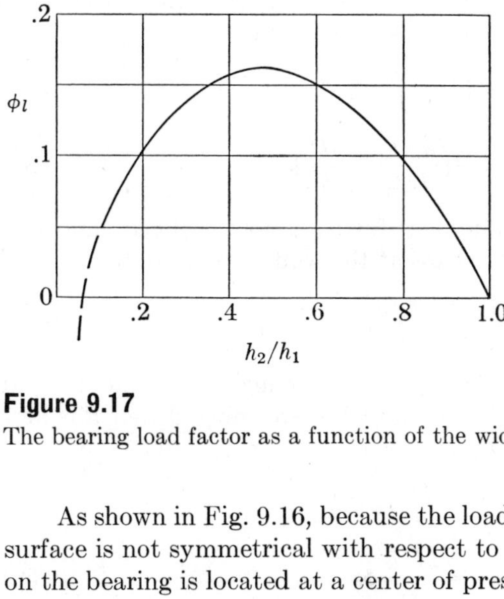

Figure 9.17
The bearing load factor as a function of the width ratio h_2/h_1.

As shown in Fig. 9.16, because the load per unit area on the bearing surface is not symmetrical with respect to its center, the resultant load on the bearing is located at a center of pressure $x_p \geqslant L/2$. This center of pressure can readily be found by using Eq. (2.17):

$$x_p F = \int_0^L x(p - p_0)\, dx$$

$$x_p = \frac{1}{F}\int_0^L x(p - p_0)\, dx$$

After performing the first-moment integration of Eq. (9.54) and using Eq. (9.55), values of x_p can be calculated for various end-width ratios h_1/h_2. The location of x_p, measured in the x-direction from the wider end of the bearing, is tabulated below.[7]

h_1/h_2	x_p/L
1.0	0.50
2.0	0.56
3.0	0.61
4.0	0.64
5.0	0.66

(b) The Frictional Force

The velocity derivative $\partial u/\partial y$ was derived in Eq. (9.45). The shear stress at any point in the flow field is

$$\tau = \mu \frac{\partial u}{\partial y} = \frac{dp}{dx}\left(y - \frac{h}{2}\right) - \frac{\mu U}{h}$$

To evaluate the drag force on the moving base, the shear stress between the fluid and the moving base at $y = 0$ is

$$\tau_w = \mu \left(\frac{\partial u}{\partial y}\right)_{y=0}$$

$$= -\left(\frac{dp}{dx}\frac{h}{2} + \frac{\mu U}{h}\right) \tag{9.57}$$

Using Eq. (9.49) and the value of Q for a straight inclined slipper as given by Eq. (9.53), the shear stress at the wall is found to be

$$\tau_w = \mu\left[\frac{6Uh_1h_2}{(h_1 + h_2)h^2} - \frac{4U}{h}\right] \tag{9.58}$$

The total drag per unit depth on the moving base is the integral of τ_w throughout the length L. It must be remembered that h is here a function of x as prescribed by Eq. (9.52).

$$D = \int_0^L \tau_w \, dx$$

$$= \frac{\mu UL}{h_2}\phi_d \tag{9.59}$$

where ϕ_d is the *drag factor* which is a function of the ratio of the bearing end widths $\epsilon = h_1/h_2$

[7] These values are obtained from J. C. Hunsaker and B. G. Rightmire, *Engineering Applications of Fluid Mechanics*, McGraw-Hill Book Company, Inc., New York, 1947, p. 296.

$$\phi_d = \frac{2}{(\epsilon - 1)}\left[2 \ln \epsilon - \frac{3(\epsilon - 1)}{(\epsilon + 1)}\right] \tag{9.60}$$

(c) *The Ratio of the Load to the Drag*

Both the normal and the horizontal loads have been computed and given in Eqs. (9.55) and (9.59). As can be seen from Fig. 9.17, the maximum value of the load occurs at approximately $h_2/h_1 = 0.485$. This value can be obtained analytically by differentiating Eq. (9.56), setting it equal to zero, and solving for h_2/h_1. At this ratio of $h_2/h_1 = 0.485$, the optimum normal load per unit depth can be evaluated

$$F = 0.162 \frac{\mu U L^2}{h_2^2} \tag{9.61}$$

For the same slipper configuration which gives the optimum load, the shear force per unit depth can be evaluated

$$D = 0.753 \frac{\mu U L}{h_2} \tag{9.62}$$

Finally, the load-to-drag ratio for the optimum load configuration is

$$\frac{F}{D} = 0.215 \frac{L}{h_2} \tag{9.63}$$

Illustrative Example 9.5

Plot the dimensionless pressure distribution $L(p - p_0)/6\mu U$ as a function of the bearing dimensionless length x/L for a slipper angle $\alpha = 5°$ and $h_1/L = 0.15$.

Using Eq. (9.54), the dimensionless pressure distribution is

$$\frac{L(p - p_0)}{6\mu U} = \frac{Lx(h - h_2)}{h^2(h_1 + h_2)}$$

If the angle α is as shown in Fig. 9.16, the variable h can be expressed in terms of the known quantities according to Eq. (9.52). The dimensionless pressure distribution is then

$$\frac{L(p - p_0)}{6\mu U} = \frac{\frac{x}{L}\tan\alpha\left(1 - \frac{x}{L}\right)}{\left(\frac{h_1}{L} - \frac{x}{L}\tan\alpha\right)^2\left(\frac{h_1 + h_2}{L}\right)}$$

For an angle of 5°, the tangent is 0.1051. Since the dimensionless ratio $h_1/L = 0.15$, then the other ratio h_2/L can be deduced to be 0.0449. With these quantities known, the above expression takes the form of

$$\frac{L(p - p_0)}{6\mu U} = \frac{0.538\frac{x}{L}\left(1 - \frac{x}{L}\right)}{\left(0.15 - 0.1051\frac{x}{L}\right)^2}$$

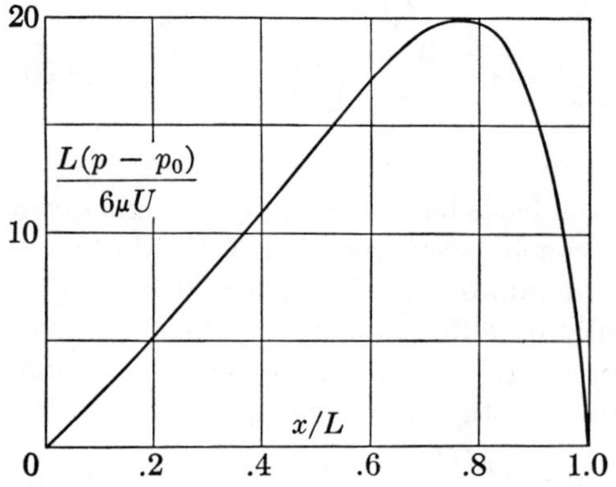

Figure 9.18
Pressure distribution for $\alpha = 5°$ and $h_1/L = 0.15$.

This expression is plotted in Fig. 9.18 as a function of the dimensionless bearing length x/L.

9.10 Viscous Flow Through a Pipe

(a) The Laminar Poiseuille[8] *Flow*

The geometry of the flow in a round pipe suggests that the problem should be treated in its inherent cylindrical-coordinate system. When fully developed flow is established in the motion of the fluid inside the pipe, any acceleration in the direction of motion will vanish. According to the two-dimensional Cartesian equation, Eq. (9.4), the pressure forces will identically balance the shear forces such that no acceleration or deceleration takes place. Equation (9.4) can be transformed into cylindrical coordinates by setting

$$r^2 = y^2 + z^2 \quad \text{and} \quad \frac{\partial r}{\partial y} = \frac{y}{r}, \qquad \frac{\partial r}{\partial z} = \frac{z}{r}$$

The derivatives of u, the axial component of the velocity (the only component in this parallel flow), can be written in cylindrical coordinates. Since $u = f(r)$ only,

[8] See footnote 17 in Sec. 1.10.

$$\frac{\partial u}{\partial y} = \frac{\partial u}{\partial r}\frac{\partial r}{\partial y}$$

$$= \frac{y}{r}\frac{\partial u}{\partial r}$$

$$\frac{\partial u}{\partial z} = \frac{\partial u}{\partial r}\frac{\partial r}{\partial z}$$

$$= \frac{z}{r}\frac{\partial u}{\partial r}$$

The second differentiation yields

$$\frac{\partial^2 u}{\partial y^2} = \frac{y^2}{r^2}\frac{\partial^2 u}{\partial r^2} + \left(\frac{1}{r} - \frac{y^2}{r^3}\right)\frac{\partial u}{\partial r}$$

$$\frac{\partial^2 u}{\partial z^2} = \frac{z^2}{r^2}\frac{\partial^2 u}{\partial r^2} + \left(\frac{1}{r} - \frac{z^2}{r^3}\right)\frac{\partial u}{\partial r}$$

The viscous terms given in the right-hand side of Eq. (9.4) are then

$$\mu\left(\frac{\partial^2 u}{\partial y^2} + \frac{\partial^2 u}{\partial z^2}\right) = \mu\left(\frac{\partial^2 u}{\partial r^2} + \frac{1}{r}\frac{\partial u}{\partial r}\right)$$

and the equation of motion in cylindrical coordinates is

$$\frac{dp}{dx} = \mu\left(\frac{\partial^2 u}{\partial r^2} + \frac{1}{r}\frac{\partial u}{\partial r}\right)$$

$$= \mu\frac{1}{r}\frac{d}{dr}\left(r\frac{du}{dr}\right) \tag{9.64}$$

In the last equation, total derivatives have been used, since u is a function of r alone. The coordinate x represents the axial direction. In Eq. (9.64), since dp/dx can be a function of x or a constant and the right-hand side of the equation a function of r or a constant, and since one side of an equation cannot be a function of x alone and the other side a function of r alone, they must be equal to the same constant. The first integration of Eq. (9.64) yields

$$r\frac{du}{dr} = \frac{1}{2\mu}\frac{dp}{dx}r^2 + A$$

The second integration yields

$$u = \frac{1}{4\mu}\frac{dp}{dx}r^2 + A\ln r + B \tag{9.65}$$

On account of symmetry, if the velocity derivative at the center of the pipe is zero, this boundary condition will specify that the integration constant A be zero. The second boundary condition is that $u = 0$

when $r = r_0$. The quantity r_0 is the inside radius of the pipe. Substitution of these conditions into Eq. (9.65) gives the axial velocity distribution of the fully developed, steady, incompressible, and laminar flow through a pipe.

$$u = \frac{1}{4\mu}\frac{dp}{dx}(r^2 - r_0^2) \tag{9.66}$$

This velocity profile has the form of a paraboloid of revolution, as shown in Fig. 9.19. Since, in this axisymmetric Poiseuille flow there is an

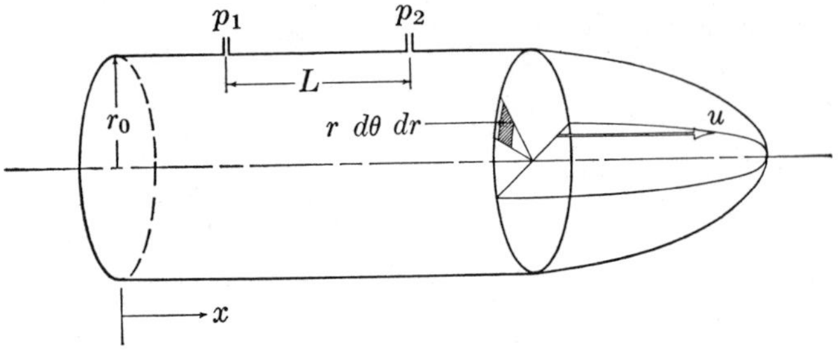

Figure 9.19
Fully developed flow through a pipe.

axial velocity alone, for $u = v_z$ from Eq. [9.2(*c*)] the only shear stress is $\tau_{rz} = \mu\, du/dr$. This stress is in the z-direction and on a surface perpendicular to r, which is a cylindrical shell. From the solution of the velocity in Eq. (9.66), the shear stress becomes, after differentiation,

$$\tau = \mu\frac{du}{dr} = \frac{r}{2}\frac{dp}{dx} \tag{9.67}$$

Although this relationship for the shear stress in a fully developed flow was derived for the laminar case, it is also valid for the turbulent case,[9] with the exception that its magnitude is different owing to the fact that the pressure drop is different. At the wall $r = r_0$ and

$$\tau_w = \frac{r_0}{2}\frac{dp}{dx} \tag{9.68}$$

The maximum velocity occurs at the center of the pipe where $r = 0$. Then, from Eq. (9.66),

$$u_{\max} = -\frac{1}{4\mu}\frac{dp}{dx}r_0^2 \tag{9.69}$$

[9] This will be shown in part (*b*) of this section.

This is a positive quantity, since $dp/dx < 0$. The mass rate of flow through the pipe is the density times the integral of the velocity through the infinitesimal area $r\, d\theta\, dr$.

$$Q = \frac{\rho}{4\mu}\frac{dp}{dx}\int_0^{2\pi}\int_0^{r_0}(r^2 - r_0^2)r\, d\theta\, dr$$

$$= -\frac{\pi\rho}{8\mu}\frac{dp}{dx}r_0^4 \qquad (9.70)$$

The space average velocity u_{av} is obtained by dividing the mass rate of flow by the density and the cross-sectional area of the pipe

$$u_{av} = \frac{Q}{\rho\pi r_0^2}$$

$$= -\frac{1}{8\mu}\frac{dp}{dx}r_0^2 \qquad (9.71)$$

When compared with u_{max} as given by Eq. (9.69), the value of the space average velocity is one half the value of the maximum velocity. In the case of the two-dimensional channel, this ratio u_{av}/u_{max} was 2/3 [Sec. 9.6(*c*)].

As already discussed in the two-dimensional channel flow, Eq. (9.70) can be used to determine the viscosity of liquids. An experiment can be prepared so that a liquid of unknown viscosity is made to flow in a long capillary tube of known diameter r_0. If the wall-pressure difference between two points at an axial distance L apart is measured, and if the fluid is discharged into a tank where the mass accumulated per unit time is measured, these measured quantities will give the value of the viscosity through Eq. (9.70). The following example illustrates the experiment.

Illustrative Example 9.6

Mercury at 70°F is pumped through a long tube 1/8 in. in diameter. The density of the mercury is 826 lb_m/ft^3, the mass collected at the end of the tube is 10 lb_m/min, and the pressure drop in a 1-ft length is 0.14 lb_f/in^2. Determine the viscosity of the mercury.

From Eq. (9.70), the viscosity is found to be

$$\mu = -\frac{\pi\rho}{8Q}\frac{dp}{dx}r_0^4$$

$$= \frac{3.14 \times 826 \times 0.14 \times 144 \times 60}{8 \times 10 \times (16 \times 12)^4}$$

$$= 2.88 \times 10^{-5}\ lb_f \times sec/ft^2$$

If the dimensionless pressure drop is again called the *resistance coefficient*, as in Sec. 9.6(d),

$$f = -\frac{d\left(\dfrac{p}{\frac{1}{2}\rho u_{av}^2}\right)}{d\left(\dfrac{x}{2r_0}\right)}$$

$$= -\frac{2r_0}{\frac{\rho}{2}u_{av}^2}\frac{dp}{dx} \tag{9.72}$$

$$= \frac{8\tau_w}{\rho u_{av}^2}$$

The value of the pressure drop can be taken from Eq. (9.71) and substituted into the resistance coefficient.

$$f = 64\frac{\mu}{\rho u_{av}(2r_0)}$$

$$= \frac{64}{\mathcal{R}} \tag{9.73}$$

where $\mathcal{R}$ is the Reynolds number of the flow in the pipe based on the pipe diameter. This relationship is, of course, valid for the laminar regime and is plotted in Figs. 9.20 and 9.21.

Figure 9.20, often called the *Moody diagram*, shows the dependence of the resistance coefficient in a pipe as a function of the Reynolds number. These curves are obtained experimentally for commercially rough pipes. It can be noticed that in the laminar regime the resistance coefficient is not at all a function of the roughness coefficient k/D which expresses the ratio of the average roughness to the diameter of the pipe. The laminar results are identical with the analytical solution of Eq. (9.73). In the turbulent case, however, the resistance coefficient is not a unique function of the Reynolds number; it is also a function of the roughness coefficient k/D. Thus, for the turbulent case,

$$f = f(\mathcal{R}, k/D) \tag{9.74}$$

Notice that the transition from laminar flow to turbulent flow occurs at a Reynolds number a little over 2,000. This indicates that, for flows in pipe with a Reynolds number larger than, say, 2,300, the laminar-flow analysis described here is no longer valid. Experiments also show that the turbulent velocity profile of the flow in the pipe is very much different from the laminar velocity profile described in this section. The shear forces at the wall of the pipe are also different in the two

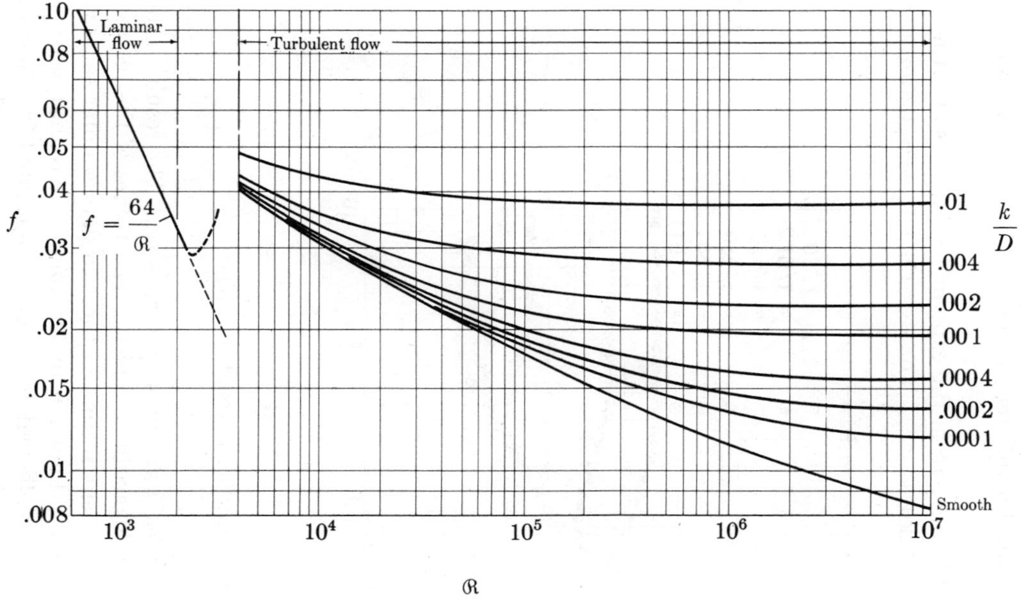

Figure 9.20
Resistance coefficient of a viscous pipe flow as a function of Reynolds number for commercial pipes of various roughness.
(After L. F. Moody, "Friction Factors for Pipe Flow," *Trans. ASME*, November, 1944.)

regimes, and this is what accounts for the difference in the resistance coefficient.

The average roughness dimension k for some commercial pipes is: cast iron, 0.010 in.; wrought iron, 0.0018 in.; galvanized iron, 0.006 in. Other roughness values for different pipes may be obtained from engineering handbooks.

Figure 9.21 is obtained from the experimental results of artificially roughened pipes by Nikuradse.[10] The experiments were performed in

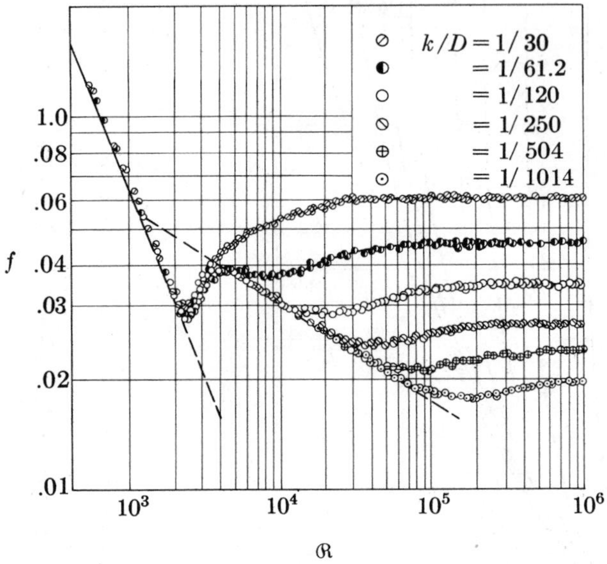

Figure 9.21
Resistance coefficient for artificially roughened pipes.

pipes roughened with sand grains of uniform size. The results in both figures are plotted on logarithmic scales. The values of the resistance coefficient for the turbulent regime in the two figures differ somewhat because they represent data taken under different circumstances. In general, the resistance coefficient is a more complicated function than Eq. (9.74), which is valid for one particular configuration of roughness as in Nikuradse's spherical sand roughness experiments. In general, the friction coefficient is also a function of the spacing between the

[10] J. Nikuradse, Verein Deutscher Ingenieure (VDI) *Forschungsheft*, 356, 1932; (VDI) *Forschungsheft* 361, 1933.

roughness elements and their shape. Figure 9.20 is a representative distribution of the resistance coefficient for commercially available pipes.

In 1913 Blasius[11] established an empirical formula for the resistance of turbulent flows in smooth pipes. His equation reads:

$$f = \frac{0.3164}{\mathcal{R}^{1/4}} \tag{9.75}$$

The limiting tangent straight line in the turbulent regime of Nikuradse's experiments agrees fairly well with Blasius' empirical relation. This behavior for the smooth pipe is shown in Fig. 9.21.

According to the definition of the resistance coefficient in Eq. (9.72), it is equal to the dimensionless pressure drop in the pipe over the dimensionless distance downstream. Since the pressure drop in the fully developed flow in the pipe was found to be linear, Eq. (9.72) can be replaced by the finite pressure difference over a pipe length L and a diameter D. This equation becomes

$$f = \frac{p_1 - p_2}{L} D \frac{1}{\frac{\rho}{2} u_{\text{av}}^2}$$

According to the integrated forms of Eqs. (4.41) and (6.36), in the absence of external work done and heat transfer, the energy loss per unit mass of an incompressible flow in the pipe is

$$\frac{p_1 - p_2}{\rho} + g(z_1 - z_2) - gH = 0$$

The kinetic-energy change between the two points has not been considered here, since the discussion applies to a fully developed flow along which the velocity does not change. By the same token, if the difference in elevation is neglected, then the head loss H in feet of flowing substance is identically equal to the pressure drop $(p_1 - p_2)g$ in feet of flowing substance. The resistance coefficient then becomes

$$f = \frac{p_1 - p_2}{\rho g} \frac{D}{L} \frac{2g}{u_{\text{av}}^2}$$

$$= H \frac{D}{L} \frac{2g}{u_{\text{av}}^2}$$

The head loss in the pipe owing to friction is then

$$H = f \frac{L}{D} \frac{u_{\text{av}}^2}{2g} \tag{9.76}$$

[11] H. Blasius, Verein Deutscher Ingenieure (VDI) *Forschungsheft*, 131, 1913.

This equation is often known as the Darcy-Weisbach relation for the energy loss in a steady, fully developed, incompressible flow in a pipe without external mechanical or heat-energy transfer. Equation (9.76) is applicable to laminar as well as turbulent flows in conduits. The resistance coefficient f changes for different cases.

Illustrative Example 9.7

Two liquids of different density and viscosity flow through the same pipe at the same Reynolds number. (*a*) Find the ratio of the velocities, head losses, and power dissipated as a function of the viscosity ratio. (*b*) If one of the liquids is mineral oil with density $\rho = 1.7$ slugs/ft³ and a viscosity $\mu = 2.7 \times 10^{-3}$ $\text{lb}_f \times \text{sec/ft}^2$ flowing in a $\frac{1}{2}$-in. nominal pipe with a diameter of 0.622 in. at a rate of 0.11 slug/sec, find the head loss in a 100-ft length. (*c*) What would be the head loss if water at 50°F flowed at the same Reynolds number?

(*a*) If Q is the mass rate of flow equal to $\rho u_{av}\pi(D)^2/4$, according to the Reynolds-number definition,

$$\mathcal{R} = \frac{\rho u_{av} D}{\mu} = \frac{4Q}{\pi D \mu}$$

For the same diameter of pipe and the same Reynolds number, the mass rate of flow of two liquids will take the proportions

$$\frac{Q_1}{Q_2} = \frac{\mu_1}{\mu_2}$$

and also

$$\frac{Q_1}{Q_2} = \frac{\rho_1 (u_{av})_1}{\rho_2 (u_{av})_2}$$

consequently,

$$\frac{(u_{av})_1}{(u_{av})_2} = \frac{\nu_1}{\nu_2}$$

For the same Reynolds number, the coefficient of resistance is the same in both flow cases; therefore, for the same diameter and length of pipe, the ratio of the head losses is proportional to the ratio of the square of the average velocities as shown by the Darcy-Weisbach relation, Eq. (9.76). Therefore,

$$\frac{H_1}{H_2} = \left[\frac{(u_{av})_1}{(u_{av})_2}\right]^2 = \left(\frac{\nu_1}{\nu_2}\right)^2$$

According to Eq. (9.31), the power dissipated into heat is the product of the volume rate of flow and the pressure drop. For the same pipe, the ratio of the volume flow is proportional to the ratio of the average velocities. Furthermore, the pressure drop which constitutes the head loss is proportional to the ratio of the square of the velocities as just found. Therefore, the ratio of the power loss in the line is proportional to the ratio of the cube of the average velocities or the ratio of the cube of the kinematic viscosity.

$$\frac{P_1}{P_2} = \left(\frac{\nu_1}{\nu_2}\right)^3$$

(*b*) According to the Reynolds-number expression just derived, its value for the mineral oil flow is

$$\begin{aligned} \mathcal{R} &= \frac{4Q}{\pi D \mu} \\ &= \frac{4 \times 0.11 \times 12}{3.14 \times 0.622 \times 2.7 \times 10^{-3}} \\ &= 1{,}000 \end{aligned}$$

According to the laminar-law-of-resistance coefficient, Eq. (9.73), $f = 64/1{,}000$ for all flows at that same $\mathcal{R}$. The average velocity in the pipe is

$$\begin{aligned} u_{\text{av}} &= \frac{0.11 \times 4 \times 144}{1.7 \times 3.14 \times (0.622)^2} \\ &= 30.7 \text{ ft/sec} \end{aligned}$$

From Eq. (9.76), the head loss for the flow of mineral oil is

$$\begin{aligned} H &= 0.064 \frac{100 \times 12 \times (30.7)^2}{0.622 \times 64.4} \\ &= 1{,}810 \text{ ft of mineral oil} \end{aligned}$$

(*c*) For the case of water at 50°F, the kinematic viscosity is $\nu_w = 1.41 \times 10^{-5}$ ft²/sec. For the oil $\nu_o = 1.59 \times 10^{-3}$ ft²/sec. For the same Reynolds number and the same pipe configuration, the head loss for the water will be

$$\begin{aligned} H &= 1{,}810 \left(\frac{1.41 \times 10^{-5}}{1.59 \times 10^{-3}}\right)^2 \\ &= 0.1425 \text{ ft of water} \end{aligned}$$

(*b*) *Turbulent Flow Through Pipes*

The velocity profile in the pipe for the fully developed turbulent flow is very different from the parabolic laminar profile. This results from the fact that the stresses in the turbulent fluid differ from the stresses in the laminar regime. This is because the turbulent flow, besides sustaining stresses dependent on the velocity gradient $\mu\, du/dr$, also displays much larger shear stresses owing to the agitation or turbulent transfer of momentum from one fluid layer to the other. The difference in velocity profile from the laminar to the turbulent case is roughly demonstrated in Fig. 9.22. The profiles have been drawn for an equal mass rate of

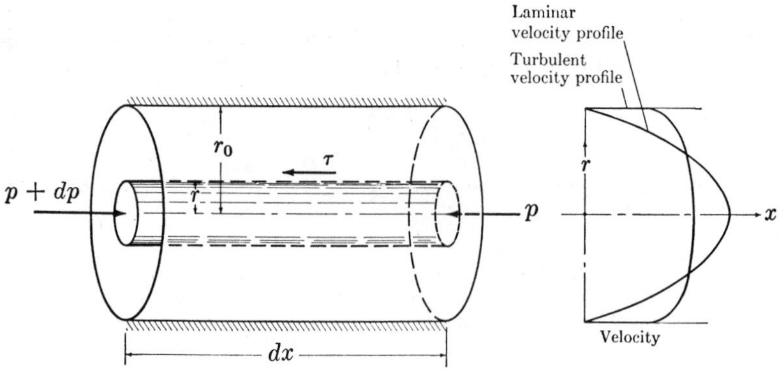

Figure 9.22
Control volume for the flow in a pipe.

flow. It can be remarked, from the shown distributions, that the shear stress owing to the velocity gradient at the wall of the pipe is much larger in the turbulent case than in the laminar case. Near the center of the pipe, although the gradient of velocity in the turbulent case is milder than in the laminar case, the total turbulent shear stress as a result of turbulent agitation is larger than in the laminar case.

It was mentioned in the preceding section that the turbulent shear-stress distribution in the fully developed turbulent pipe flow is also linear with r. As long as the fully developed condition is assumed to prevail, dp/dx, the pressure drop along the pipe, is a constant, and, for any possible distribution $u = f(r)$, the shear stress is a linear distribution in r. This is demonstrated with the help of the diagram of Fig. 9.22.

Consider a cylindrical control volume of radius r concentric to the pipe. Although fluid is going through this control volume, there is no net change of momentum within the volume, since the flow has been considered to be fully developed and the velocity u for every r is the same at all x-positions; that is, since $\partial u/\partial x = 0$, the momentum crossing both faces of the control volume is the same. Therefore, since there is no net momentum change within the volume, the summation of external forces on the control volume must be equal to zero.

$$\pi r^2(p + dp) - \pi r^2 p - 2\pi r\tau\, dx = 0$$

The sense of the shear stress τ has been chosen in such a manner that it represents the opposing force per unit area of the fluid surrounding that in the control volume. The solution of this equation gives

$$\frac{r}{2}\frac{dp}{dx} = \tau \tag{9.67}$$

This is the result expected. Since dp/dx, representing the head loss, changes roughly[12] as the square of the velocity, according to Eq. (9.76), it is larger for the turbulent flow than in the case of laminar flow. Therefore, the shear stress is also larger. The shear stress at the wall is obtained by replacing r by r_0 in Eq. (9.67).

$$\tau_w = \frac{r_0}{2}\frac{dp}{dx} \tag{9.77}$$

In the Darcy-Weisbach relation, Eq. (9.76), the quantity H/L represents the pressure drop dp/dx, and combining Eq. (9.77) with Eq. (9.76) yields a modified friction-law equation in terms of the shear stress at the wall

$$\tau_w = \frac{f}{4}\frac{\rho u_{\text{av}}^2}{2} \tag{9.78}$$

This also shows that for small variations of f the shear stress at the wall of the pipe varies as the square of the average velocity.

As shown in Fig. 9.22 and as already discussed in this section, the velocity profile of a turbulent flow in a pipe is entirely different from the velocity distribution of the laminar flow in the same pipe. A typical turbulent velocity profile in a smooth pipe is shown in Fig. 9.23. The newly introduced quantity u_*, having the dimensions of velocity, is called the shearing velocity, and it is $(\tau_w/\rho)^{1/2}$. It is noted that the velocity profile is divided into three important regions, namely the *laminar sublayer*, the *transition buffer zone*, and the *turbulent core*. At the present there is no one mathematical relation to satisfy the complete range of experimental measurements shown. Instead, the mathematical analysis is performed separately for the laminar sublayer and the turbulent core.

In the laminar sublayer, the shear stress in the fluid, including the wall shear, is primarily laminar $\tau = \mu \dfrac{du}{dy}$. It has been verified experimentally that the velocity distribution in the sublayer is linear in y. (Here, the dimension y is the radial distance measured from the wall of the pipe.) Therefore, the slope of the velocity profile in the laminar

[12] The word "roughly" is used here since the resistance coefficient f also varies slightly with velocity contained in the Reynolds number, as shown in Figs. 9.20 and 9.21. For the laminar flow, $\dfrac{dp}{dx}$ varies as u_{av}, since f varies as $1/\mathcal{R}$ or $1/u_{\text{av}}$.

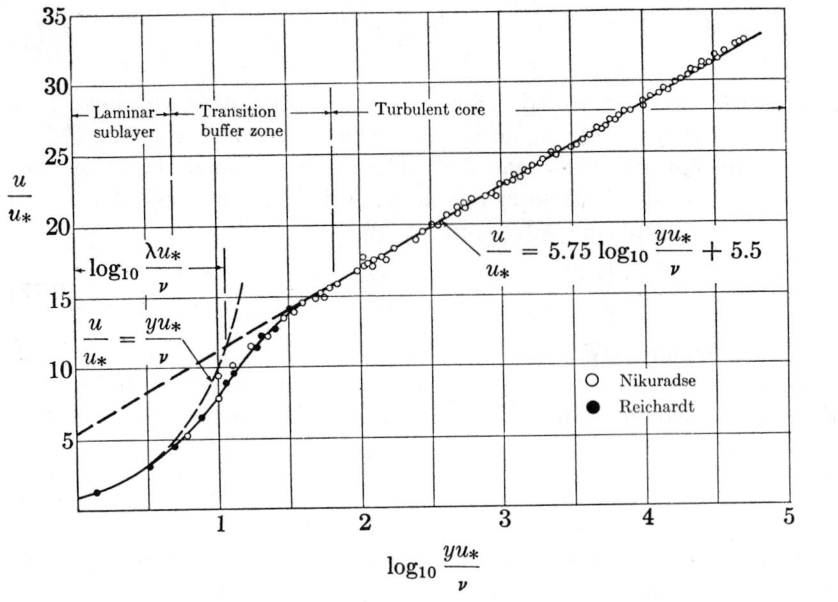

Figure 9.23

Turbulent velocity-distribution law for a smooth pipe. ○ = Nikuradse's experiments for a range of Reynolds numbers 4×10^3 to 3.2×10^6; ● = Reichardt's measurements near the wall.
(By permission of the publishers, from Herman Schlichting, *Boundary Layer Theory*, Pergamon Press Limited, Oxford, 1955.)

sublayer is a constant, and the shear stress at the wall $\tau_w = \mu \dfrac{du}{dy} = \mu \dfrac{u}{y}$. Care should be taken that this linear law is not extended beyond the limits of the sublayer. Dividing this last expression by the density,

$$\frac{\tau_w}{\rho} = \nu \frac{u}{y}$$

According to the definition of the shearing velocity u_*, the shear-stress relation becomes

$$u_*^2 = \nu \frac{u}{y}$$

and

$$\frac{u}{u_*} = \frac{yu_*}{\nu} \tag{9.79}$$

This equation is plotted in Fig. 9.23, and it can be seen that, for a region of $yu_*/\nu = 5$ or $\log_{10} yu_*/\nu = 0.699$, the experimental points of Reichardt[13] satisfy it very well.

The buffer zone extends from the laminar sublayer to the turbulent core. Generally, this region is considered for $5 < yu_*/\nu < 70$, and in it the laminar and turbulent shear stresses are of the same order of magnitude. In the logarithmic scale this range is $0.699 < \log_{10} yu_*/\nu < 1.845$.

In the turbulent core for $yu_*/\nu > 70$, the turbulent shear stress predominates the laminar shear based on the product of viscosity and the mean velocity gradient. The turbulent shear stress, according to Prandtl's *mixing-length* theory, is given as

$$\tau = \rho l^2 \left(\frac{du}{dy}\right)^2 \tag{9.80}$$

where l, called the mixing length, is a distance in the y-direction that a fluid lump with a velocity u will move into a neighboring lamina in such a manner that it will create a velocity fluctuation equal to the turbulent velocity fluctuation. This concept of Prandtl's mixing length is somewhat analogous to the mixing length in the kinetic theory of gases, the difference being that the *mean-free path,* the average distance traveled by a molecule, in the kinetic theory of gases is based on microscopic motions, whereas the mixing length is based on macroscopic motion of large lumps of fluid particles.

The mixing-length concept of Prandtl, although it helps predict the turbulent behavior of some flows, cannot be considered general enough to apply to all turbulent-flow fields; therefore, it must be used with caution. In the case of turbulent pipe flow, it is assumed that the mixing length is a linear function of the radial distance from the wall y. Thus,

$$l = ay$$

Here a denotes a dimensionless constant which is derived from experiment. Therefore, from Eq. (9.80) the turbulent shear is

$$\tau = \rho a^2 y^2 \left(\frac{du}{dy}\right)^2 \tag{9.81}$$

Besides the assumption of the linearity of the mixing length with the distance y, Prandtl introduced an additional far-reaching assumption which claims that in the turbulent region near the wall the turbulent shear stress essentially remains constant. Therefore, $\tau = \tau_w$. Naturally, there are limitations to this assumption; nevertheless, it leads

[13] H. Reichardt, *Z. angew. Math. u. Mech.*, Vol. 20, 1940, p. 297.

to interesting and accurate results. Thus, the second assumption and Eq. (9.81) give

$$\tau_w = \rho a^2 y^2 \left(\frac{du}{dy}\right)^2$$

$$u_* = \left(\frac{\tau_w}{\rho}\right)^{1/2} = ay\frac{du}{dy}$$

It must be remembered that τ_w is a constant for a given pressure drop, Eq. (9.77), and so is u_*. The variables in the preceding equation can be separated.

$$\frac{1}{u_*}\,du = \frac{1}{a}\frac{dy}{y}$$

After integration, this equation becomes

$$\frac{u}{u_*} = \frac{1}{a}\ln y + C \qquad (9.82)$$

This solution indicates that, in the turbulent region near the wall, the velocity distribution is logarithmic instead of parabolic as in the laminar case. In Fig. 9.23 the experimental points of Nikuradse for a smooth pipe are shown to be in agreement with this analysis. This can be shown by modifying Eq. (9.82) to the coordinates of Fig. 9.23, as follows:

Consider the entire flow to consist of a laminar sublayer and a turbulent core. Let the apparent thickness of the sublayer be λ. The two distinct types of velocity distribution are shown, in Fig. 9.23, to meet at $\log_{10} \lambda u_*/\nu$ approximately equal to 1.0. Let the corresponding value of $\lambda u_*/\nu$, approximately 10, be equal to a number n. Since the experiments in Fig. 9.23 represent flows at many Reynolds numbers, it can be said with certainty that the number n will be the same for all turbulent flows. Therefore, according to Eq. (9.79), the velocity at the end of the sublayer is

$$\frac{u_\lambda}{u_*} = \frac{\lambda u_*}{\nu} = n$$

At the same distance λ from the wall, according to Eq. (9.82), the velocity there will be also

$$\frac{u_\lambda}{u_*} = \frac{1}{a}\ln\lambda + C = n$$

$$= \frac{1}{a}\ln\frac{n\nu}{u_*} + C$$

Therefore, the constant of integration C is

$$C = n - \frac{1}{a} \ln \frac{n\nu}{u_*}$$

Substitution of this constant into Eq. (9.82) yields

$$\frac{u}{u_*} = \frac{1}{a} \ln y + n - \frac{1}{a} \ln \frac{n\nu}{u_*}$$

$$= \frac{1}{a} \ln \frac{yu_*}{\nu} + B \qquad (9.83)$$

If $A = 1/a$ and $B = n - A \ln n$, then the *universal* velocity profile of the turbulent core of the flow in the pipe is

$$\frac{u}{u_*} = A \ln \frac{yu_*}{\nu} + B \qquad (9.84)$$

or

$$\frac{u}{u_*} = A' \log_{10} \frac{yu_*}{\nu} + B$$

Experiments in a smooth pipe show that the constants for this universal velocity profile are $A = 2.5$, $A' = 5.75$, and $B = 5.5$ and that Eq. (9.84) applies to the major portion of the turbulent core.

Using this velocity profile, a space average velocity u_{av} can be computed and introduced into the friction equation, Eq. (9.78). The resultant friction law for the *smooth pipes* is

$$\frac{1}{\sqrt{f}} = 2.0 \log_{10} (\mathcal{R}\sqrt{f}) - 0.8 \qquad (9.85)$$

where $\mathcal{R}$ is the Reynolds number based on the spatial average velocity and the diameter of the pipe. This expression is often known as Prandtl's universal law of turbulent friction for flow through a smooth pipe. Equation (9.85), Blasius' simple law [Eq. (9.75)], and some experimental values are compared in Fig. 9.24. It is seen that Eq. (9.85) agrees very well with the experimental points of Nikuradse.

In completely rough pipes the universal velocity distribution is a function of the distance from the wall divided by the height of the roughness protrusion k. Therefore, the following law satisfies most experimental values obtained in a *rough pipe:*

$$\frac{u}{u_*} = 5.75 \log_{10} \frac{y}{k} + 8.5 \qquad (9.86)$$

From this velocity profile a resistance law can be obtained, as was sug-

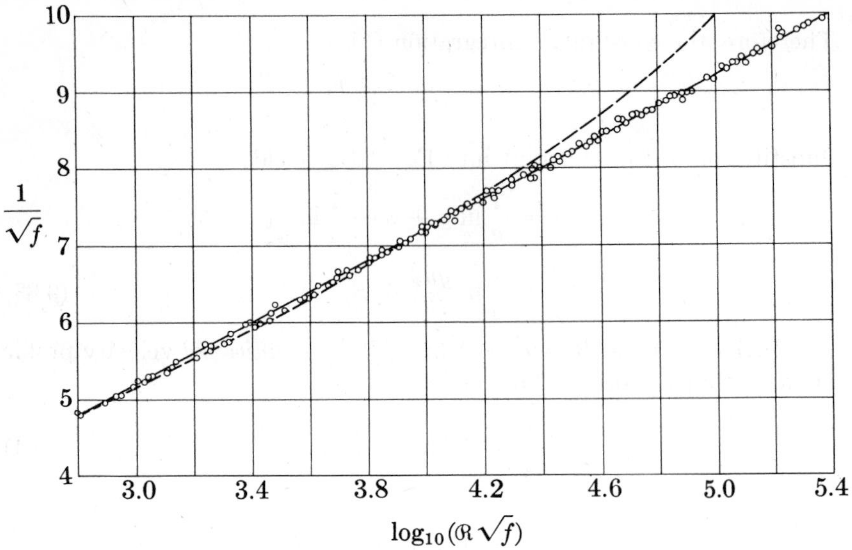

Figure 9.24
Universal law of turbulent friction in a smooth pipe. Dotted line is Eq. (9.75). (By permission of the publishers, from Herman Schlichting, *Boundary Layer Theory*, Pergamon Press Limited, Oxford, 1955.)

gested in the preceding case for the smooth pipe. This resistance law for *rough pipes* reads:

$$\frac{1}{\sqrt{f}} = 2 \log_{10} \frac{r_0}{k} + 1.74$$

$$= 1.14 - 2 \log_{10} \frac{k}{D} \tag{9.87}$$

Here r_0 is the radius of the pipe and D is its diameter.

Colebrook[14] has developed an empirical resistance function which correlates the region from hydraulically smooth to rough pipes. His equation applicable to commercial pipes of various roughnesses forms the basis for the charts in Fig. 9.20. This empirical expression reads:

$$\frac{1}{\sqrt{f}} = 1.74 - 2 \log_{10} \left(\frac{k}{r_0} + \frac{18.7}{\mathcal{R}\sqrt{f}} \right) \tag{9.88}$$

The three equations, Eqs. (9.85), (9.87), and (9.88), can be compared on the same graph if the following procedure is followed.

[14] C. F. Colebrook, *J. Inst. Civil Engrs.* (*London*), Vol. 11, 1939, pp. 133–156.

Add the quantity $2 \log_{10} k/r_0$ on both sides of Eq. (9.85). The result will be

$$\frac{1}{\sqrt{f}} + 2 \log_{10} \frac{k}{r_0} = 2 \log_{10} \frac{\mathcal{R}k}{r_0} \sqrt{f} - 0.8 \tag{9.89}$$

Equation (9.87) can also be changed into this form:

$$\frac{1}{\sqrt{f}} + 2 \log_{10} \frac{k}{r_0} = 1.74 \tag{9.90}$$

The same is done for Eq. (9.88) by adding the quantity $2 \log_{10} k/r_0$ on both sides of the equation:

$$\frac{1}{\sqrt{f}} + 2 \log_{10} \frac{k}{r_0} = 1.74 - 2 \log_{10} \left(1 + \frac{18.7}{\mathcal{R} \dfrac{k}{r_0} \sqrt{f}}\right) \tag{9.91}$$

These three equations are compared in Fig. 9.25.

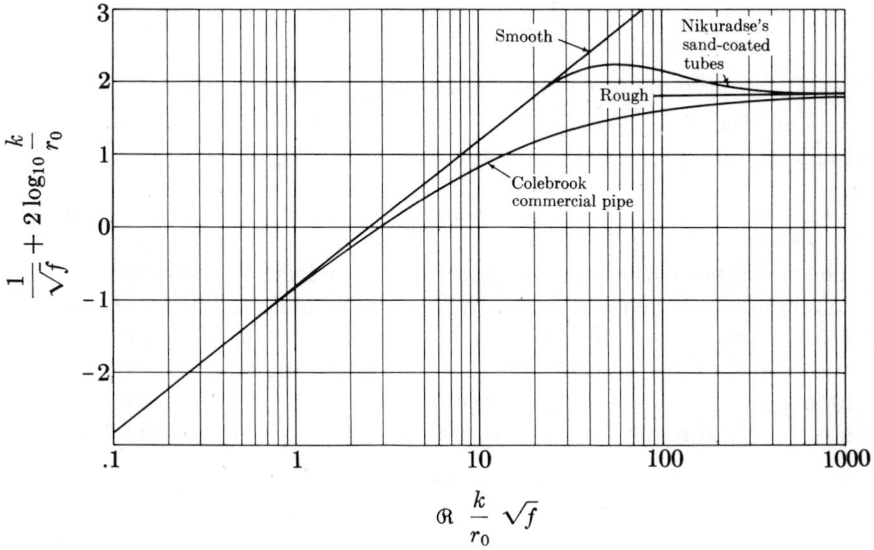

Figure 9.25
Comparison of roughness universal laws.

Illustrative Example 9.8

From Colebrook's equation, determine the resistance coefficient f for a commercial pipe of relative roughness $k/D = 0.0005$ and operating at a Reynolds number of 100,000.

From the nature of Colebrook's equation, one can see that the evaluation of f must be done by trial and error. The roughness ratio $k/r_0 = 0.001$, and $\mathcal{R}\frac{k}{r_0} = 100$. The second term in Eq. (9.91) can be readily evaluated, and it is equal to

$$2 \log_{10} k/r_0 = -6.0$$

If all the terms of the equation are gathered on one side, the result is

$$\frac{1}{\sqrt{f}} - 7.74 + 2 \log_{10}\left(1 + \frac{18.7}{100\sqrt{f}}\right) = 0$$

Using Fig. 9.20 as a guide, the first value of f tried is 0.025. Substitution of this value of f into the equation gives -0.74 instead of zero. The next value tried is $f = 0.02$. This substitution gives a positive result $+0.092$ instead of zero. The exact solution for f must be between 0.020 and 0.025. By linear interpolation, the value of f turns out to be 0.0205. This value agrees fairly well with the resistance-coefficient chart of Fig. 9.20.

Instead, if a smooth-pipe relationship [Eq. (9.85)] is considered, the interpolated value for the resistance coefficient is found to be $f = 0.0183$. The error involved in the use of this equation is 10.7 per cent.

(c) *Losses of Turbulent Flows Through Pipes and Pipe Fittings*

The head-loss equation in a pipe flow, either laminar or turbulent, was found to be represented in the form given by Eq. (9.76),

$$H = f\frac{L}{D}\frac{u_{av}^2}{2g} \tag{9.76}$$

The resistance coefficient f is a function of the Reynolds number and the roughness coefficient, as given by Eq. (9.74) and Fig. 9.20. L and D are the length and diameter of the pipe. Consequently, the units of this head loss are in length of a column of flowing fluid. The loss in a fitting such as a valve, elbow, or coupling has been found to be estimated adequately through the same equation, Eq. (9.76), written in the form

$$H = K\frac{u_{av}^2}{2g} = f\frac{L_e}{D}\frac{u_{av}^2}{2g}$$

Here, K is a constant appropriate to the fitting, and L_e is an equivalent length of pipe that would give the same loss as the fitting. It is evident here that K is not a function of Reynolds number. In the turbulent case this has been verified experimentally with a degree of approximation. Since f is a function of the Reynolds number, however, then the equivalent length L_e is dependent on the Reynolds number inversely as f is. Table 9.1 gives some reasonable values of K and L_e/D for various fittings.

Besides the fitting losses that occur in viscous flows through pipes and tubes, there are losses for sudden expansion or sudden contraction

Table 9.1
Values of K and L_e/D for turbulent flows in pipe fittings.

	K	L_e/D
Standard 90° elbow	0.8	30
Standard 45° elbow	0.4	15
Standard tee	1.8	67
Gate valve (open)	0.17	6.4
Gate valve (half-open)	4.5	170
Globe valve (open)	9.0	340
Angle valve (open)	4.0	150
Close return bend	2.5	95

that may occur in the fluid. The following analysis is worked out for the sudden expansion shown in Fig. 9.26, but it applies also to the sudden contraction shown in Fig. 9.27.

Let the control volume 122′1′ be considered here. The momentum theorem states that the sum of all external forces on the boundaries of the volume must be equal to the net momentum rate transferred across its boundaries. Then for this steady motion, according to Eq. (5.10),

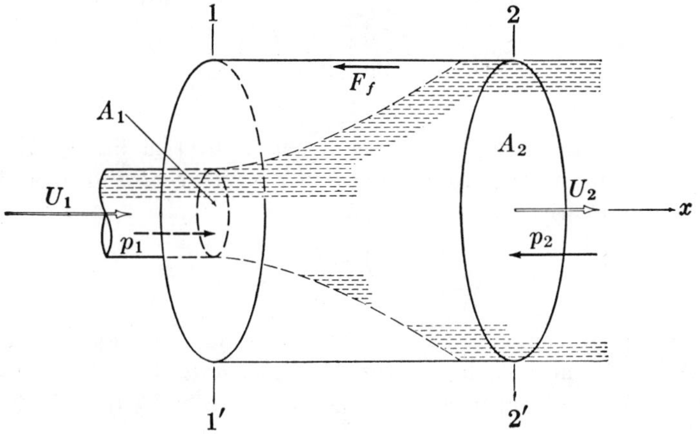

Figure 9.26
Sudden expansion.

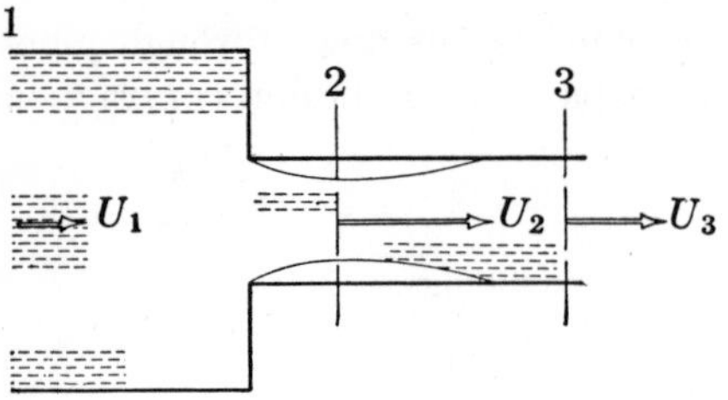

Figure 9.27
Sudden contraction.

$$\sum F_x = Q(U_2 - U_1)$$

$$(p_1 - p_2)A_2 - F_f = \rho A_1 U_1(U_2 - U_1); \qquad A_1U_1 = A_2U_2$$

where F_f is the frictional force.

From the incompressible Bernoulli energy equations, Eqs. (4.41) and (6.36), a second relationship of the pressures, velocity, and head loss $H_{1\text{-}2}$ can be written as

$$\frac{p_1 - p_2}{\rho g} = H_{1\text{-}2} - \frac{U_1^2 - U_2^2}{2g}$$

From the momentum equation, the Bernoulli equation, and the continuity equation, the pressures and U_2 can be eliminated, and the total head loss H owing to friction in the fluid and the walls is

$$H = H_{1\text{-}2} - \frac{F_f}{\rho A_2 g} = \frac{U_1^2}{2g}\left[1 - \left(\frac{A_1}{A_2}\right)\right]^2$$

The dimensions of H are in feet of flowing fluid.

The analysis is identical for the contraction in Fig. 9.27. The results there will apply to the cross sections of the *vena contracta* A_2 and the downstream pipe area A_3,

$$H = \frac{U_2^2}{2g}\left[1 - \left(\frac{A_2}{A_3}\right)\right]^2$$

It is not at all convenient to express the head loss in a sudden contraction in terms of the velocity at the *vena contracta,* since it is not always known. Instead, using the continuity equation $U_2A_2 = U_3A_3$, the previous loss equation can be changed into

$$H = \frac{U_3^2}{2g}\left[\frac{A_3}{A_2} - 1\right]^2$$

If A_2/A_3 is defined as the contraction coefficient C_c, as in Sec. 4.13, then the head loss becomes

$$H = \frac{U_3^2}{2g}\left(\frac{1}{C_c} - 1\right)^2$$

Table 9.2
Contraction coefficients.

A_3/A_1	C_c
0.0	0.585
0.2	0.632
0.4	0.659
0.6	0.712
0.8	0.813
1.0	1.000

Julius Weisbach[15] in his *Experimental Hydraulics*, has given some of these contraction coefficients for various contractions A_3/A_1.

When the contraction is very small, as in the case of a circular pipe emanating from a very large reservoir, the loss is very nearly one half the dynamic head. If the entrance to the pipe, in the same case, however, is rounded, the loss is negligible.

9.11 Laminar Flow Between Two Concentric Cylinders

(a) Axial Flow with Both Cylinders Stationary

The simplified form of the Navier-Stokes equation in cylindrical coordinates that governs the fully developed axial flow between two concentric cylinders is given by Eq. (9.64).

$$\frac{dp}{dx} = \mu \frac{1}{r}\frac{d}{dr}\left(r\frac{du}{dr}\right) \tag{9.64}$$

Since for this case also the shear stress $\tau_{rz} = \mu \frac{du}{dr}$, then the equation of motion is also written in the form

[15] J. Weisbach, *Die experimental Hydraulik*, J. S. Engelhardt, Freiburg, 1855, p. 133.

$$\frac{dp}{dx} = \frac{1}{r}\frac{d}{dr}(\tau r) \tag{9.92}$$

With similar reasoning, the velocity and the shear stress here are functions of the radial distance only; the pressure being a function of the axial distance alone, both sides of Eqs. (9.64) and (9.92) must be a constant. Equation (9.64) has already been integrated, and its result was given by Eq. (9.65),

$$u = \frac{1}{4\mu}\frac{dp}{dx} r^2 + A \ln r + B \tag{9.65}$$

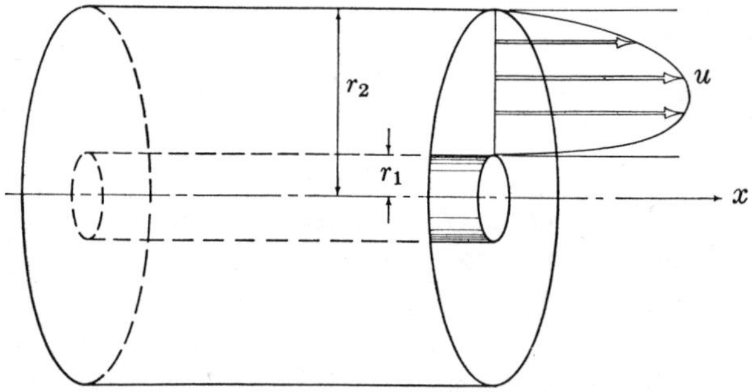

Figure 9.28
Axial flow between two concentric cylinders.

The boundary conditions, according to Fig. 9.28, are

$$u = 0 \quad \text{when} \quad r = r_1$$

$$u = 0 \quad \text{when} \quad r = r_2$$

The two constants of integration can be evaluated

$$A = -\frac{1}{4\mu}\frac{dp}{dx}\frac{(r_2^2 - r_1^2)}{\ln r_2/r_1}$$

$$B = \frac{1}{4\mu}\frac{dp}{dx}\left[\frac{(r_2^2 - r_1^2)}{\ln r_2/r_1}\ln r_1 - r_1^2\right]$$

The laminar solution for the axial velocity becomes

$$u = \frac{1}{4\mu}\frac{dp}{dx}\left[(r^2 - r_1^2) - \frac{r_2^2 - r_1^2}{\ln r_2/r_1}\ln\frac{r}{r_1}\right] \tag{9.93}$$

The shear stress is

$$\tau = \mu \frac{du}{dr}$$

$$= \frac{1}{2}\frac{dp}{dx} r - \frac{1}{4}\frac{dp}{dx}\frac{r_2^2 - r_1^2}{r \ln r_2/r_1} \tag{9.94}$$

The first term on the right-hand side of this expression is that for the circular pipe as given by Eq. (9.67). The second term is the effect of the new geometry. Owing to this new geometry, the slope du/dr changes sign from one wall to the other. This does not imply that the shear stress at the two walls has opposite directions. The wall shear stresses have the same direction at both walls, and therefore, to remove this difficulty, one must think of r as the radial distance measured in a direction toward the wall.

The rate of mass flow for the incompressible, steady, and laminar flow considered is determined by integrating the quantity

$$Q = 2\pi\rho \int_{r_1}^{r_2} ur\, dr$$

$$= \frac{\pi\rho}{8\mu}\frac{dp}{dx}\left[\frac{(r_2^2 - r_1^2)^2}{\ln r_2/r_1} + r_1^4 - r_2^4\right] \tag{9.95}$$

The velocity profile can also be written in the form

$$u = \frac{1}{4\mu}\frac{dp}{dx} r_1^2 \left[\left(\frac{r}{r_1}\right)^2 - 1 - \frac{(r_2/r_1)^2 - 1}{\ln r_2/r_1} \ln \frac{r}{r_1}\right]$$

If the coefficient $-\frac{1}{4\mu}\frac{dp}{dx} r_1^2$ having the dimensions of velocity is called K_1, the pipe-radius ratio $r_2/r_1 = \eta_0$, and the variable radial distance $r/r_1 = \eta$, then the dimensionless velocity distribution is

$$\frac{u}{K_1} = \frac{\eta_0^2 - 1}{\ln \eta_0} \ln \eta - \eta^2 + 1 \tag{9.96}$$

In the same fashion the shear-stress distribution of Eq. (9.94) can be made dimensionless in the following way:

$$\tau = \frac{1}{4}\frac{dp}{dx} r_1 \left(2\frac{r}{r_1} - \frac{r_2^2 - r_1^2}{r r_1 \ln r_2/r_1}\right)$$

Letting $K_2 = -\frac{1}{4}\frac{dp}{dx} r_1$, then

$$\frac{\tau}{K_2} = \frac{\eta_0^2 - 1}{\eta \ln \eta_0} - 2\eta \tag{9.97}$$

These dimensionless forms of the velocity and the shear stress are plotted

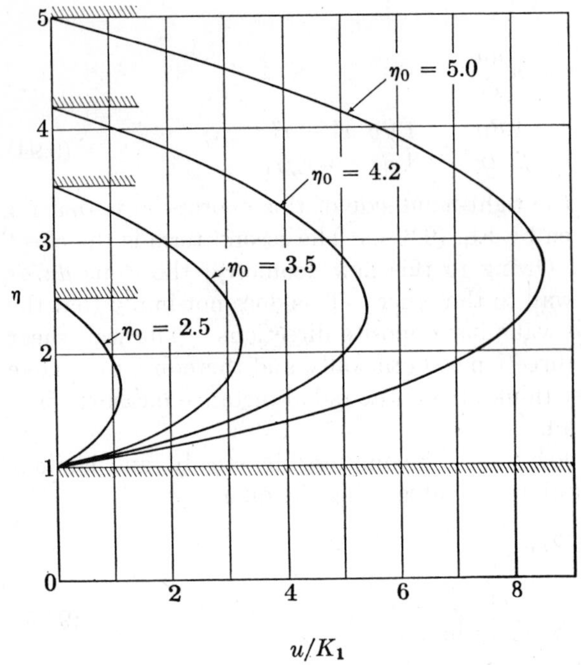

Figure 9.29
Laminar axial velocity between two concentric cylinders for different diameter ratios.

in Figs. 9.29 and 9.30. The point where the shear stress becomes zero is the maximum-velocity point. Notice that it does not coincide with the center of the passage, as in the case of the pipe flow.

The point at which the velocity gradient is zero or the shear stress is zero can be obtained by differentiating Eq. (9.93) and setting it to zero. The derivative of u with respect to r reads:

$$\frac{du}{dr} = \frac{1}{4\mu}\frac{dp}{dx}\left(2r - \frac{r_2^2 - r_1^2}{\ln r_2/r_1}\frac{1}{r}\right)$$

Setting this expression equal to zero and solving for r whose particular radial distance will be at the maximum velocity point,

$$r_{u_{\max}} = \sqrt{\frac{r_2^2 - r_1^2}{2 \ln r_2/r_1}}$$

$$= \sqrt{\frac{r_2^2 - r_1^2}{\ln r_2^2/r_1^2}} \tag{9.98}$$

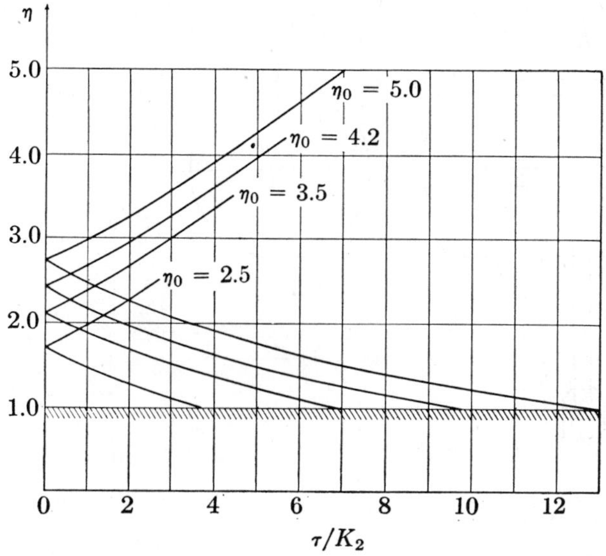

Figure 9.30
Laminar shear stress between two concentric cylinders for different diameter ratios.

The space average velocity in the annulus can be determined as in previous cases:

$$u_{\text{av}} = \frac{\int_{r_1}^{r_2} 2\pi r u \, dr}{\pi(r_2^2 - r_1^2)}$$

$$= \frac{1}{4\mu}\frac{dp}{dx}\left(\frac{r_2^2 - r_1^2}{\ln r_2^2/r_1^2} - \frac{r_2^2 + r_1^2}{2}\right) \tag{9.99}$$

Illustrative Example 9.9

A device such as that shown in Fig. 9.31 is constructed for measuring the rate of mass flow between two concentric cylinders. It consists of a free portion L of the outer cylinder mounted on a pivot O' and restrained at A by a spring with a pointer which indicates on a scale the mass rate of flow Q. If r_1 and r_2 are the radial dimensions of the inner and outer cylinders, respectively, and if the flow is steady, laminar, fully developed, and incompressible, find an analytical method for calibrating the scale in terms of Q.

The only tangential forces on the surface of the free portion of the outer tube are the wall shear stresses. For an element of area this elemental force is $\tau_w \, dA$. Having postulated that the flow within the free section is fully

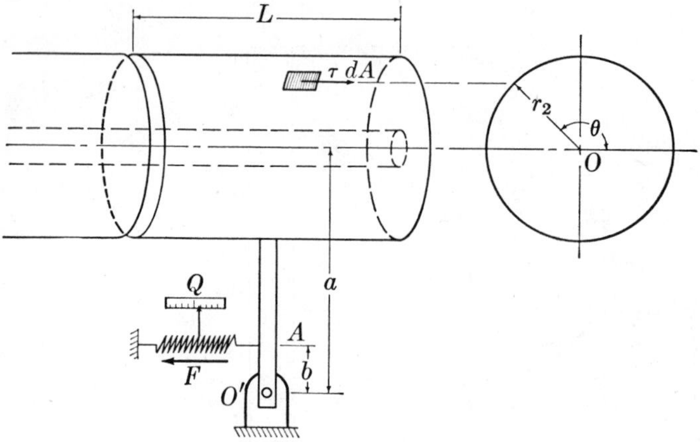

Figure 9.31
Device to measure mass rate of flow.

developed, the shear stress is not a function of its length L. The elemental shear force will be

$$(\tau_w L r_2\, d\theta)$$

Taking moments around the fixed point O' yields

$$Fb = \int_0^{2\pi} (\tau_w L r_2\, d\theta)(r_2 \sin\theta + a)$$

$$F = \frac{2\pi L r_2 a}{b} \tau_w$$

But at the outer pipe where $r = r_2$, the shear stress is given by Eq. (9.94), and it equals

$$\tau_w = \frac{1}{4}\frac{dp}{dx}\left(2r_2 - \frac{r_2^2 - r_1^2}{r_2 \ln r_2/r_1}\right)$$

If s is the displacement of the spring pointer so that its force $F = ks$ where k is the spring constant, then

$$F = ks = \frac{1}{2}\frac{\pi L r_2 a}{b}\left(2r_2 - \frac{r_2^2 - r_1^2}{r_2 \ln r_2/r_1}\right)\frac{dp}{dx}$$

For a given geometry, every term in the above expression is constant except for s and dp/dx. But, according to Eq. (9.95), for a given density and viscosity of the fluid, Q is expressed in terms of dp/dx. Finally s from our last expression can be expressed in terms of Q.

(*b*) *Peripheral Flow Between Two Concentric Rotating Cylinders*
Consider the flow between the two concentric cylinders shown in Fig. 9.32. Let the flow be peripheral only such that $v_r = v_z = 0$. Assume also axisymmetry such that $v_\theta = f(r)$ only. In the case of nonviscous flow in

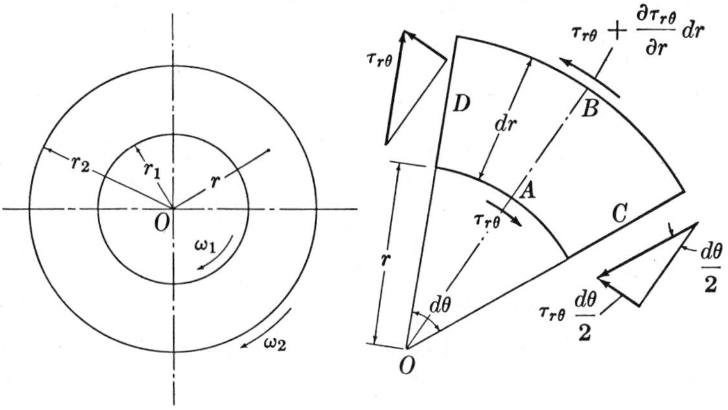

Figure 9.32
Peripheral flow between two concentric cylinders.

Sec. 3.16, it was shown that the flow assumes the distribution of a free vortex $v_\theta r =$ constant.

For the viscous, steady, and axisymmetric case treated here, there are no acceleration components in the peripheral direction θ. In that direction the pressure forces cancel, and consequently there are only shear forces to be considered. Let us consider the forces per unit height of cylinder on the faces of the element shown. The force on the face A is

$$-\tau_{r\theta} r \, d\theta$$

The force on the face B is

$$\left(\tau_{r\theta} + \frac{\partial \tau_{r\theta}}{\partial r} dr\right) (r + dr) \, d\theta$$

The contribution from the shear forces on the faces D and C in the direction of θ at OAB is

$$2\tau_{\theta r} \frac{d\theta}{2} dr = \tau_{\theta r} \, d\theta \, dr$$

In the absence of any other force, the peripheral-equilibrium equation must read:

$$\left(\tau_{r\theta} + \frac{\partial \tau_{r\theta}}{\partial r}\,dr\right)(r + dr)\,d\theta - \tau_{r\theta} r\,d\theta + \tau_{\theta r}\,d\theta\,dr = 0$$

It was stated in Sec. 9.2 that, in order for the element to be in pure shear, $\tau_{r\theta} = \tau_{\theta r}$, and therefore the above equation reduces to

$$2\tau_{r\theta} + r\,\frac{\partial \tau_{r\theta}}{\partial r} = 0 \tag{9.100}$$

The shear stress $\tau_{r\theta}$ has already been given in Eq. [9.2(*a*)]. In the absence of v_r, it simplifies to

$$\tau_{r\theta} = \mu r\,\frac{\partial}{\partial r}\left(\frac{v_\theta}{r}\right) \tag{9.101}$$

Substituting this expression into Eq. (9.100) yields

$$\frac{\partial^2 v_\theta}{\partial r^2} + \frac{1}{r}\frac{\partial v_\theta}{\partial r} - \frac{v_\theta}{r^2} = 0 \tag{9.102}$$

Since v_θ is only a function of r, the preceding equation can be changed to total derivatives and can be rewritten in a more compact form as

$$\frac{d^2 v_\theta}{dr^2} + \frac{d}{dr}\left(\frac{v_\theta}{r}\right) = 0 \tag{9.103}$$

The radial-equilibrium equation will be the same in this case as Eq. (4.18),

$$\frac{dp}{dr} = \rho\,\frac{v_\theta^2}{r} \tag{9.104}$$

When Eq. (9.102) is solved, the pressure field is obtained by integrating Eq. (9.104).

The boundary conditions of this flow are

$$v_\theta = r_1\omega_1 \quad \text{when} \quad r = r_1$$
$$v_\theta = r_2\omega_2 \quad \text{when} \quad r = r_2$$

The solution of Eq. (9.103) is[16]

$$v_\theta = \frac{1}{r_2^2 - r_1^2}\left[r(\omega_2 r_2^2 - \omega_1 r_1^2) - \frac{r_1^2 r_2^2}{r}(\omega_2 - \omega_1)\right] \tag{9.105}$$

In the case of a viscometer, when the inner cylinder is stationary and the

[16] The student may verify this by substituting Eq. (9.105) into the differential equation, Eq. (9.103).

outer cylinder rotates at an angular velocity ω_2, the velocity distribution in the passage is

$$v_\theta = \frac{1}{r_2^2 - r_1^2}\left(r\omega_2 r_2^2 - \frac{r_1^2 r_2^2}{r}\,\omega_2\right) \tag{9.106}$$

This indicates that the motion is a combined solid-body motion with apparent angular velocity $\omega_2 r_2^2/(r_2^2 - r_1^2)$ and a free vortex with a strength or $r_1^2 r_2^2 \omega_2/(r_2^2 - r_1^2)$.

The shear stress according to Eq. (9.101) can be evaluated

$$\tau = \frac{2\mu}{r_2^2 - r_1^2}\,\frac{r_1^2 r_2^2}{r^2}\,\omega_2 \tag{9.107}$$

At the outer wall the shear stress is

$$\tau_{r_2} = \frac{2\mu}{r_2^2 - r_1^2}\,r_1^2\omega_2 \tag{9.108}$$

If the height of the cylinder is h, the total force on the outer cylinder is

$$F_{r_2} = 2\pi r_2 h\,\frac{2\mu}{r_2^2 - r_1^2}\,r_1^2\omega_2$$

and the torque on the outer cylinder is

$$T_{r_2} = \frac{4\pi\mu h}{r_2^2 - r_1^2}\,r_1^2 r_2^2 \omega_2 \tag{9.109}$$

If this torque can be measured, then the value of the viscosity can be obtained from Eq. (9.109).

A more useful viscometer is shown in Fig. 9.33, where the outer cylinder of radius r_2 rotates at ω_2 and the inner cylinder is stationary and suspended by a flexible elastic wire. The fluid transmits a torque on the inner cylinder, and the torsion on the wire actuates a pointer that measures viscosity on a dial. In addition, if the gap $r_2 - r_1$ is made small, the shear stress at the inner cylinder is approximately

$$\tau_{r_1} = \frac{2\mu}{r_2^2 - r_1^2}\,r_2^2\omega_2$$

$$= \frac{\mu r_2 \omega_2}{r_2 - r_1} \tag{9.110}$$

since $r_2 + r_1 \approx 2r_2$.

The force on the inner cylinder is

$$F_{r_1} = \frac{2\pi h \mu r_1 r_2 \omega_2}{r_2 - r_1} \tag{9.111}$$

and the torque

$$T_{r_1} = 2\pi h\mu\omega_2 \frac{r_1^2 r_2}{r_2 - r_1} \qquad (9.112)$$

The value of the viscosity can be solved

$$\mu = \frac{T_{r_1}(r_2 - r_1)}{2\pi h\omega_2 r_1^2 r_2} \qquad (9.113)$$

As shown in Fig. 9.33, in case the bottom separation between the two cylinders also exists, the total torque on the inner cylinder owing to the rotation of the outer cylinder will be larger than Eq. (9.112) because

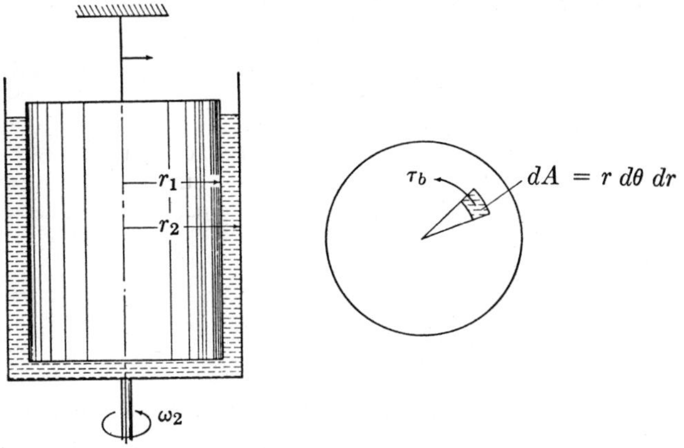

Figure 9.33
Viscometer.

of the contribution of torque from the bottom gap. Again assuming the gap to be small and equal to $(r_2 - r_1)$, the shear stress at any point in the bottom of the inner cylinder is

$$\tau_b = \mu \frac{\omega_2 r}{r_2 - r_1}$$

This value varies with the radius, since the peripheral velocity entrained by the rotation of the outer cylinder also varies with the radial distance. The elemental force on a small area $dA = r\,d\theta\,dr$ is

$$dF_b = \mu \frac{\omega_2 r}{r_2 - r_1} r\,d\theta\,dr$$

and the elemental torque,

$$dT_b = \frac{\mu\omega_2}{r_2 - r_1} \int_0^{2\pi} \int_0^{r_1} r^3 \, d\theta \, dr$$

$$T_b = \frac{\pi\mu\omega_2}{2(r_2 - r_1)} r_1^4 \tag{9.114}$$

The total torque is the sum of Eq. (9.112) and Eq. (9.114),

$$T = \frac{\pi\mu\omega_2 r_1^2}{r_2 - r_1}\left(\frac{r_1^2}{2} + 2hr_2\right) \tag{9.115}$$

For this case again, the viscosity can be solved in terms of the total torque and the geometry of the viscometer.

Illustrative Example 9.10

Show that when $r_2 \to \infty$ and $\omega_2 = 0$ the solution given in Eq. (9.105) becomes that of a free vortex. Find the torque on the inner cylinder.

First, the peripheral velocity in Eq. (9.105) is evaluated when $r_2 \to \infty$. The direct substitution of $r_2 = \infty$ gives an indeterminate value. To evaluate v_θ, the derivative of the numerator and the denominator must be taken separately. This leads to

$$v_\theta = r\omega_2 - \frac{r_1^2}{r}(\omega_2 - \omega_1)$$

For the case of $\omega_2 = 0$

$$v_\theta = \frac{r_1^2\omega_1}{r}$$

According to the definition of circulation in Sec. 3.16 and Illustrative Example 3.7

$$\begin{aligned}\Gamma &= 2\pi r v_\theta \\ &= 2\pi r_1^2\omega_1\end{aligned}$$

and consequently the velocity, according to Eq. (7.77), is

$$v_\theta = \frac{\Gamma}{2\pi}\frac{1}{r}$$

that of a free vortex.

The torque on the inner cylinder may be found by evaluating first the shear stress [Eq. (9.101)] at $r = r_1$:

$$\tau = -2\mu\omega_1$$

Then,

$$\begin{aligned}F &= -4\pi\mu\omega_1 r_1 h \\ T &= -4\pi\mu\omega_1 r_1^2 h\end{aligned}$$

9.12 Drag on a Sphere and a Cylinder

The force acting on an immersed body moving relative to an undisturbed stream is equal to the surface integral of normal pressure and tangential shear stresses acting on it. In the study of irrotational fluid motions past solid bodies, it was found in Chap. VII that such bodies do not experience any forces at all when they move in the fluid. In the case of rotational motion of a nonviscous fluid past a body such as a cylinder, it was demonstrated in Sec. 7.20 that a lift force on the cylinder exists but that there is no drag force. The lift force is again defined here as the component of the force on the submerged body normal to the direction of flow of the undisturbed fluid relative to the body. The drag force is the component of that force in the direction of the faraway, undisturbed flow.

In viscous rotational fluid motions around solid bodies, a drag as well as a lift force exists on submerged bodies. The drag force is completely dependent on the viscous effects produced by the fluid motion in the neighborhood of the immersed body. These viscous effects contributing to the total drag on the body can be classified into two distinct categories. First, because of the boundary layer developing on the surface of the immersed body, the flow at a given point on the body separates from the body owing to the final depletion of momentum of the flow in that layer because of the continuous retardating action of the shear forces. This separated region of low momentum extends downstream of the body and is called the *wake*. Models of these wakes are shown in Fig. 1.11 for various sizes of bodies moving at various velocities.

For a given body, a laminar flow on that body separates from the surface sooner than when turbulent flow passes over the same body. Consequently, for blunt bodies this indicates that the separated wake region will be wider for the laminar than for the turbulent case. This difference in behavior is due to the fact that in the turbulent case, because of the transverse velocity fluctuations in the flow, regions of high momentum in the boundary layer can transport momentum into the deficient regions, therefore delaying the position of separation. This remarkable difference is shown in Fig. 9.34. The first photograph shows the laminar separation upstream of the equator of a bowling ball upon smooth entry into the water. The second photograph was taken under the same conditions, except that a patch of sandpaper was glued around the stagnation point in order to induce turbulence in the boundary layer. The separation in this second case is downstream of the equator.

Because of the separated low-energy flow in wakes, the pressure there is smaller than that in the nonseparated region. This difference in pressure, multiplied by the projected surface area of the body, yields a drag force in the direction of motion called the *pressure* or *form drag.* This pressure drag is therefore larger for laminar flows than for turbulent flows around the same bodies. This drag force due to the difference in pressure between the two sides of the body is different from the *viscous* or *shear drag* which is caused by the friction of the fluid on the surface of the body.

For bodies with increasing slenderness, the value of the pressure drag has little variation between the laminar and the artificially turbulent case at the same conditions. In fact, a *streamlined body* can be defined as one with a minimum pressure drag.

From dimensionless reasoning, the total drag D can be made dimensionless by dividing it by a characteristic pressure of the flow $\frac{1}{2}\rho U^2$, the dynamic pressure, and a characteristic area of the body, the frontal exposed area A. This dimensionless quantity is called the *drag coefficient,*

$$C_D = \frac{D}{\frac{1}{2}\rho U^2 A}$$

Dimensional analysis leads to the conclusion that for geometrically similar systems the drag coefficient C_D is a unique function of the Reynolds number $\mathcal{R}$ in the incompressible regime. This fact is experimentally verified by Figs. 9.35 and 9.36 obtained from test results of moving spheres and cylinders. It must be remembered that the unique dependence of C_D on $\mathcal{R}$ holds true as long as the forces acting on the flow are due to friction and inertia only. In the case of compressible fluids or motions under the action of gravity, this simple dependence will no longer be true.

Figure 9.36 shows the variation of the drag coefficient for an immersed, circular, smooth cylinder moving relative to an undisturbed flow. The Reynolds number is based on the relative velocity of the cylinder or sphere with respect to the undisturbed flow, the diameter of the cylinder, and the viscosity of the fluid.

For slow moving laminar flows, the viscous drag increases as the velocity of the fluid, while the dynamic pressure increases as the velocity squared. This indicates that the drag coefficient will drop for increasing $\mathcal{R}$, as shown in Figs. 9.35 and 9.36. At a Reynolds number of approximately 5×10^5 in the case of the circular cylinder and one of 3×10^5 for the case of the sphere, a sudden decrease in the value of the drag coefficient occurs. This decrease is due to the transition of the flow from the laminar to the turbulent state and consequently, as already explained, reduces the pressure drag.

In the case of a sphere, an analytical solution is available for flows at low Reynolds numbers where the inertial forces are negligible compared with the pressure and viscous forces. Since this regime was first analyzed by G. G. Stokes, it is called the *Stokes flow*. For this flow the total drag on the sphere has been found to be

$$D = 6\pi\mu r U \tag{9.116}$$

Here, r is the radius of the sphere, and U is its velocity relative to the undisturbed stream. It can be shown also that this total drag is composed one-third from the pressure drag and the remaining two-thirds from the viscous drag.

From the definition of the drag coefficient,

$$D = C_D \pi r^2 (\tfrac{1}{2}\rho U^2)$$

and the drag equation, Eq. (9.116), gives the drag coefficient for the sphere in a Stokes-flow regime

$$C_D = \frac{24}{\mathcal{R}} \tag{9.117}$$

where the Reynolds number is based on the sphere diameter. This equation is plotted in Fig. 9.35 and is seen to agree fairly well with experiments at Reynolds numbers less than unity. The modified Oseen's solution,

$$C_D = \frac{24}{\mathcal{R}}\left(1 + \frac{3}{16}\,\mathcal{R}\right) \tag{9.118}$$

is valid to a Reynolds number of approximately 5.

9.13 The Flat Plate Accelerated Suddenly in an Infinite Fluid

The simplified form of the differential equation applicable to this unsteady flow is obtained from Eq. (9.13). If the motion of the infinite

---

Figure 9.34

Laminar and turbulent separation. An 8.5 in. bowling ball entering the water at 25 ft/sec. (*a*) Separation on a smooth ball. (*b*) Separation with a patch of sand on the nose of the ball.

(By permission of U. S. Naval Ordinance Test Section, Pasadena Annex.)

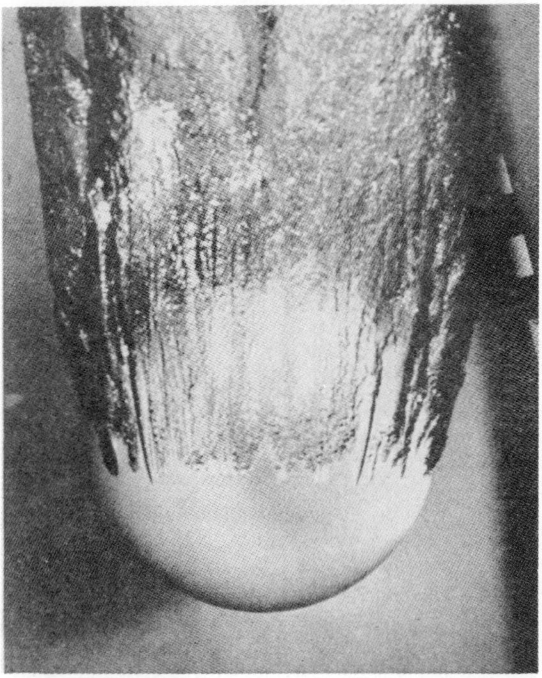

(a)

(b)

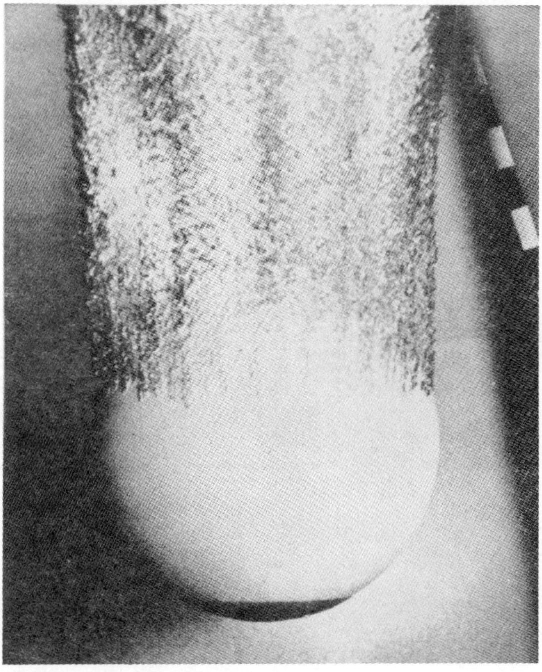

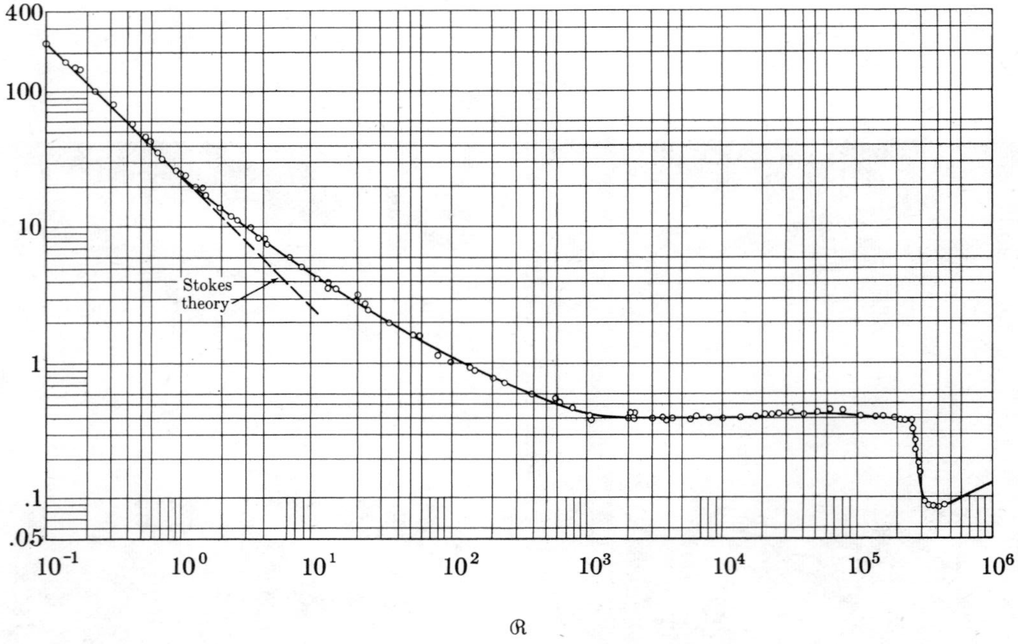

Figure 9.35

Drag coefficient for an immersed moving sphere.
(By permission of the publishers, from Herman Schlichting, *Boundary Layer Theory*, Pergamon Press Limited, Oxford, 1955.)

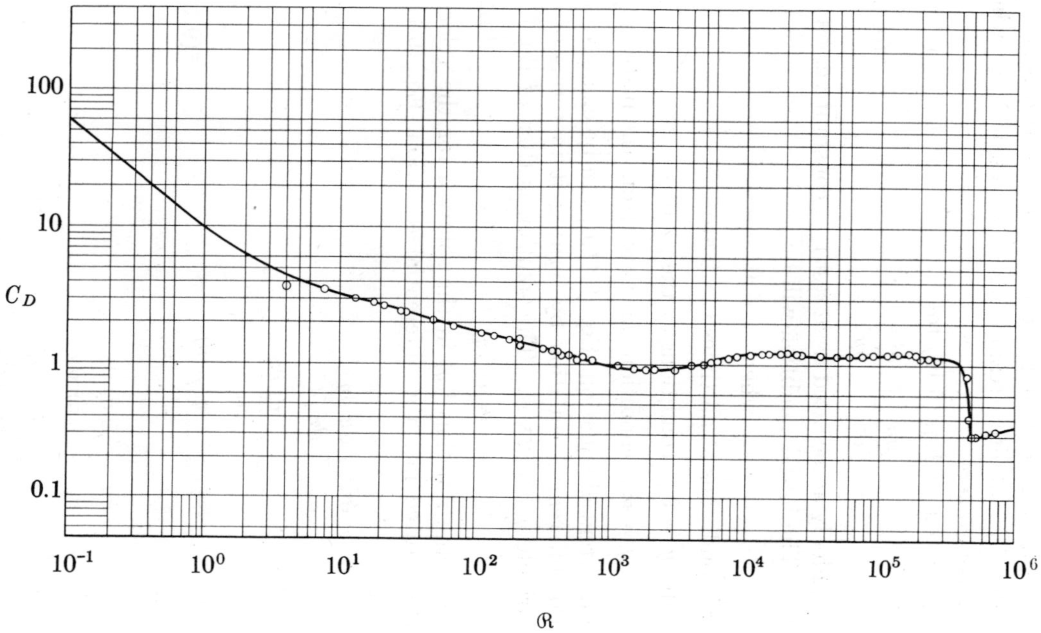

Figure 9.36

Drag coefficient for an immersed moving cylinder with a length which is long compared with the diameter.

(By permission of the publishers, from Herman Schlichting, *Boundary Layer Theory*, Pergamon Press Limited, Oxford, 1955.)

flat plate is in the x-direction and the induced velocities are in the same direction, the two components, Eqs. (9.14) and (9.15), are identically zero. Since the streamlines are parallel to the plate, $v = w = 0$, and all derivatives of u are zero except those in y and t. Also, since the plate is situated in a free infinite stream where the pressure everywhere is constant, $\partial p/\partial x$ is also zero.

These conditions reduce Eq. (9.13) to

$$\frac{\partial u}{\partial t} = \nu \frac{\partial^2 u}{\partial y^2} \tag{9.119}$$

Let the plate be suddenly accelerated from rest to a constant velocity U in the x-direction. The initial condition will be

$$u = 0 \quad \text{when} \quad t \leqslant 0$$

and the boundary conditions at all times $t > 0$ are

$$u = U \quad \text{at} \quad y = 0 \quad \text{conditions at the plate}$$

$$u = 0 \quad \text{at} \quad y = \infty \quad \text{conditions far away from the plate}$$

The partial differential equation, Eq. (9.119), can be changed into an ordinary total differential equation by writing it in terms of the dimensionless variable $\eta = y/2\sqrt{\nu t}$. The solution is then of the form

$$u = Uf(\eta) \tag{9.120}$$

To find the form of the function $f(\eta)$ in the solution for the velocity, Eq. (9.120) is substituted into the differential equation, Eq. (9.119). Thus

$$\begin{aligned} \frac{\partial u}{\partial t} &= \frac{du}{d\eta}\frac{\partial \eta}{\partial t} \\ &= U\frac{df}{d\eta}\frac{\partial \eta}{\partial t} \\ &= -\frac{\eta}{2t}U\frac{df}{d\eta} \end{aligned} \tag{9.121}$$

Similarly,

$$\begin{aligned} \frac{\partial u}{\partial y} &= U\frac{df}{d\eta}\frac{\partial \eta}{\partial y} \\ &= \frac{U}{2\sqrt{\nu t}}\frac{df}{d\eta} \\ \frac{\partial^2 u}{\partial y^2} &= \frac{U}{2\sqrt{\nu t}}\frac{d}{d\eta}\left(\frac{df}{d\eta}\right)\frac{\partial \eta}{\partial y} \\ &= \frac{U}{4\nu t}\frac{d^2 f}{d\eta^2} \end{aligned} \tag{9.122}$$

Combining Eqs. (9.121) and (9.122) to form Eq. (9.119), the differential equation that the function $f(\eta)$ satisfies is

$$\frac{d^2f}{d\eta^2} + 2\eta \frac{df}{d\eta} = 0 \tag{9.123}$$

The boundary conditions can be transformed to the new variable η. For $y = 0$, $\eta = 0$ and $f(\eta) = u/U = 1$. Also, when $y = \infty$, $\eta = \infty$ and $f(\eta) = 0$. With these boundary conditions, in which the initial condition is automatically satisfied, the solution[17] of $f(\eta)$ is

$$f(\eta) = 1 - \frac{2}{\sqrt{\pi}} \int_0^\eta e^{-\eta^2}\, d\eta$$

The velocity distribution is therefore

$$u = U\left[1 - \frac{2}{\sqrt{\pi}} \int_0^\eta e^{-\eta^2}\, d\eta\right]$$

$$= U(1 - \operatorname{erf} \eta) \tag{9.124}$$

The integral in the solution of Eq. (9.124) is called the *error function*, which is tabulated in many mathematical handbooks.[18] The velocity distribution is plotted in Fig. 9.37 in terms of the dimensionless variable η containing the distance from the wall y and time t. This viscous layer near the plate extends asymptotically to the infinity in the direction of y. For convenience, by definition, the width of this viscous layer is from the solid plate to a dimensionless distance η, where the velocity of the fluid is 1 per cent that of the plate velocity. This implies that the value of η when u/U is 0.01 is, according to the tables, approximately 1.82, and from the definition of η the actual thickness $y = \delta$ of the boundary layer is

$$\delta = 3.64\sqrt{\nu t} \tag{9.125}$$

Table 9.3 gives a few values of the error function.

At any given time t the quantity of volume flow moving above the plate owing to the motion of the plate is

$$\int_0^\infty u\, dy$$

This flow is per unit depth of plate. If this quantity is made equal to a width of fluid δ^* above the plate moving at the velocity U, then

$$\delta^* U = U \int_0^\infty (1 - \operatorname{erf} \eta)\, dy$$

[17] The student should verify this solution by substituting it into Eq. (9.123).
[18] B. O. Peirce, *A Short Table of Integrals*, Ginn & Company, Boston, 1929.

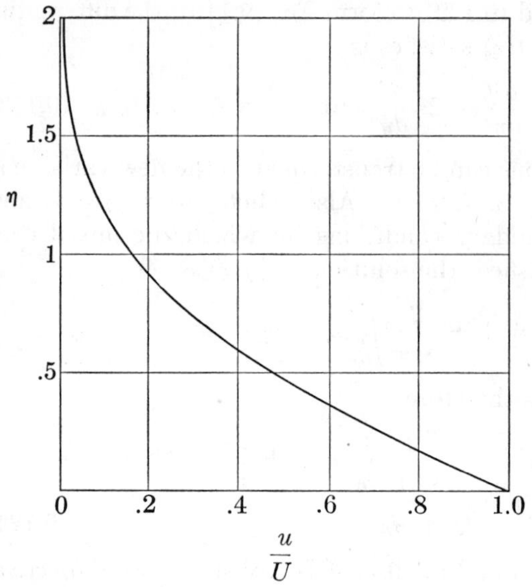

Figure 9.37
Velocity of the fluid near an accelerated flat plate.

At one particular time t, from the definition of η the value of dy can be obtained as $dy = 2\sqrt{\nu t}\, d\eta$. Substitution of this in the preceding equation gives

$$\delta^* = 2\sqrt{\nu t}\int_0^\infty (1 - \operatorname{erf}\eta)\, d\eta$$

$$= 2\sqrt{\frac{\nu t}{\pi}} \qquad (9.126)^{19}$$

The width δ^* is called the *displacement thickness.* It is a fictitious transverse distance that a plate can be moved in order to replace the boundary-layer flow with a nonviscous slip flow. On the other hand, if, instead of moving the plate, the outside stream is suddenly moved at the velocity U, the same solution will be valid. In that case δ^* will be the transverse displacement of the streamlines owing to the formation and presence of the boundary layer.

[19] The evaluation of this integral is, for instance, given in H. S. Carslaw and J. C. Jaeger, *Conduction of Heat in Solids,* Oxford University Press, New York, 1948, footnote p. 41, and Eq. (11), p. 372.

Table 9.3
Values of the error function.

η	erf η
0.0	0.0
0.1	0.11246
0.2	0.22270
0.3	0.32863
0.4	0.42839
0.5	0.52050
0.6	0.60386
0.7	0.67780
0.8	0.74210
0.9	0.79691
1.0	0.84270
1.1	0.88021
1.2	0.91031
1.3	0.93401
1.4	0.95229
1.5	0.96611
1.6	0.97635
1.7	0.98379
1.8	0.98909
1.9	0.99279
2.0	0.99532
2.1	0.99702
2.2	0.99814
2.3	0.99886
2.4	0.99931
2.5	0.99959
2.6	0.99976
2.7	0.99987

The ratio of the boundary-layer thickness to the displacement thickness is, in this case,

$$\frac{\delta}{\delta^*} = \frac{3.64\sqrt{\pi}}{2} = 3.22 \tag{9.127}$$

9.14 The Steady Laminar Boundary Layer on a Flat Plate

The preceding section has discussed the unsteady laminar boundary layer developing on a flat plate when suddenly accelerated from rest to

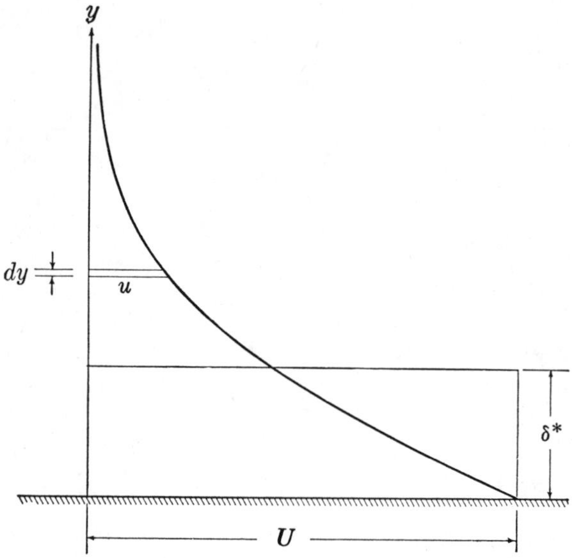

Figure 9.38
Velocity profile at a particular time.

a velocity U. In this section, the incompressible laminar boundary layer developed on a flat plate by the steady motion of a uniform stream moving at the velocity U will be studied. Figure 9.39 shows a thin flat plate starting at O and extending infinitely in the x-direction. The velocity of the potential flow outside the boundary layer is the same as that upstream of the plate, U, and, since this is constant along the plate, the pressure drop $\partial p/\partial x = 0$. Since the flow is two-dimensional,

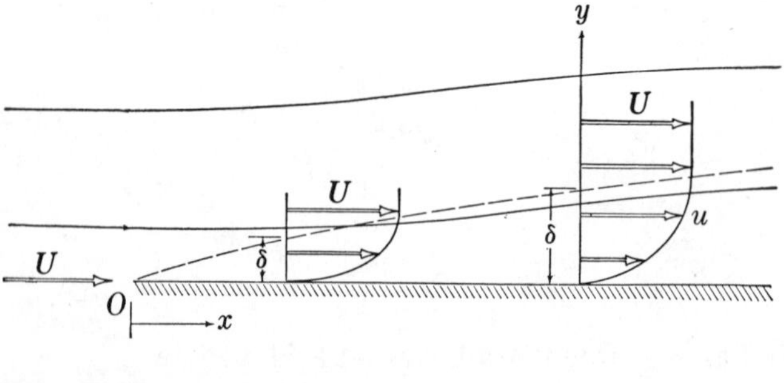

Figure 9.39
Steady, laminar boundary layer on a flat plate.

every term in the z-component of the Navier-Stokes equation, Eq. (9.15), is zero. Furthermore, since v is appreciably smaller than u, the y-component of the Navier-Stokes equation, Eq. (9.14), can also be neglected when its terms are compared with those in Eq. (9.13).

In the x-component equation, $\partial u/\partial t = w\partial u/\partial z = \partial p/\partial x = \partial^2 u/\partial z^2 = 0$. Furthermore, as established from experiments and shown in Fig. 9.39, the velocity derivative $\partial u/\partial x < \partial u/\partial y$ in approximately the same proportion as $v < u$. Consequently, the second derivative $\partial^2 u/\partial x^2 \ll \partial^2 u/\partial y^2$ and therefore can be neglected, leaving three important terms in the equation of motion.

$$u\frac{\partial u}{\partial x} + v\frac{\partial u}{\partial y} = \nu\frac{\partial^2 u}{\partial y^2} \tag{9.128}$$

The steady incompressible form of the mass-continuity equation for two-dimensional flow, Eq. (3.19), must also be satisfied:

$$\frac{\partial u}{\partial x} + \frac{\partial v}{\partial y} = 0$$

The boundary conditions of the flow are

$$y = 0, \qquad u = v = 0 \quad \text{and} \quad y = \infty, \qquad u = U$$

In 1908 H. Blasius[20] succeeded in solving the differential equation, Eq. (9.128), with the help of the continuity equation and the boundary conditions. As in the preceding case of the accelerated plate, Blasius was able to show that if the transverse distance y is made dimensionless with $\sqrt{\nu t}$, or in this case since t is estimated by x/U, the dimensionless variable $\eta = y\sqrt{\frac{U}{\nu x}}$ reduces the partial differential equation, Eq. (9.128), into an ordinary total differential equation. The solution is given in a series form

$$\frac{u}{U} = \sum_{n=0}^{\infty}\left(-\frac{1}{2}\right)^n \frac{A^{n+1}B_n}{(3n+1)!}\eta^{3n+1} \tag{9.129}$$

where A and B_n are a constant and coefficients determined by the boundary conditions.

$$A = 0.33206 \qquad B_0 = 1 \qquad B_1 = 1$$

$$B_2 = 11 \qquad B_3 = 375 \qquad B_4 = 27{,}897 \ldots$$

Table 9.4 gives a numerical tabulation of the velocity profile.[21]

[20] H. Blasius, *Zeitschrift f. Math. u. Phys.* Vol. 56, 1, 1908, also NACA TM 1256.
[21] For more detailed tabulations, see H. Schlichting, *Boundary Layer Theory*, McGraw-Hill Book Company, Inc., New York, 1955, p. 107.

Table 9.4
Velocity in Blasius' profile.

η	u/U
0.0	0.0
0.5	0.16586
1.0	0.32979
1.5	0.48651
2.0	0.62977
2.5	0.75072
3.0	0.84605
3.5	0.91255
4.0	0.95552
4.5	0.97928
5.0	0.99155
5.5	0.99682
6.0	0.99898
6.5	0.99969
7.0	0.99992
7.5	0.99999
8.0	1.00000

It must be observed here, that the boundary layer grows with distance downstream as it grew with time in the previous unsteady example. The fact that there is a unique solution in terms of η [Eq. (9.129)] for all velocity profiles in x indicates that, although the boundary layer grows in thickness, the profiles remain similar. In other words, dividing the coordinate y by $\sqrt{\nu x/U}$ reduces all profiles to a unique and universal one.

The velocity distribution at every x will not be the same. This is observed from Fig. 9.40, which shows that u/U will be the same at the same value of η. Consequently, for larger x-distances, the same u/U value will occur at larger y to give the same η. Therefore, the constant velocity line or constant η line is a parabola of the form $y^2 = \eta_0^2 \nu x/U$.

If only five terms of the solution, Eq. (9.129), are considered, after evaluating the coefficients, the expression can be written as

$$\frac{u}{U} = 0.332\eta - 0.00229\eta^4 + 1.996 \times 10^{-5}\eta^7 - 1.567 \times 10^{-7}\eta^{10} + 1.129 \times 10^{-9}\eta^{13} \cdots \qquad (9.130)$$

This approximation is shown in Fig. 9.40, together with the exact solution. For most of the boundary-layer calculations that follow, this approximation is quite adequate.

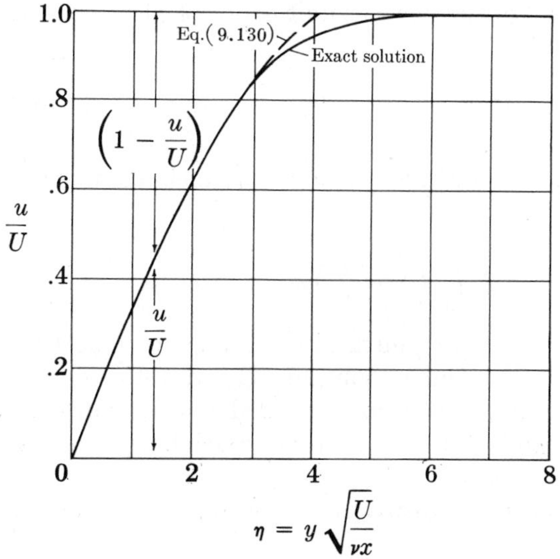

Figure 9.40
Laminar velocity profile over a flat plate.

(a) The Boundary-Layer Thickness

As in the accelerated-plate problem, the boundary-layer thickness will arbitrarily be defined as the distance from the solid plate where the velocity is 1 per cent smaller than the free-stream velocity U, or equal to $0.99U$. According to Table 10.4, this velocity occurs approximately at a dimensionless distance $\eta = 5.0$, and therefore this corresponds to a transverse distance:

$$y = \delta = 5.0\sqrt{\frac{\nu x}{U}} \tag{9.131}$$

$$\frac{\delta}{x} = 5.0\sqrt{\frac{\nu}{Ux}} = \frac{5.0}{\sqrt{\mathcal{R}_x}} \tag{9.132}$$

where $\mathcal{R}_x$ is the Reynolds number based on the plate length x. The boundary-layer thickness grows as the square root of the distance downstream. In other words, as shown in Fig. 9.39, the line joining the position of the edge of the boundary layer is a parabola.

(b) The Displacement Thickness

The displacement thickness was defined as the transverse distance from the solid plate such that, when multiplied by U, it gives the volume rate of flow deficiency in the boundary layer per unit depth of plate. Thus the velocity deficiency is $(U - u)$, and

$$\delta^* U = \int_0^\delta (U - u)\, dy \tag{9.133}$$

At any given x, $dy = \sqrt{\frac{\nu x}{U}}\, d\eta$, and the displacement thickness integral becomes

$$\delta^* = \sqrt{\frac{\nu x}{U}} \int_0^4 \left(1 - \frac{u}{U}\right) d\eta$$

The upper limit of the preceding integral has been chosen as 4 for the following reason: The approximate solution, Eq. (9.130), is seen, from Fig. 9.40, to be valid fairly well up to around $\eta = 4$, and, since the contribution of the integral of $(1 - u/U)$ is not much beyond $\eta = 4$, the error introduced will be small.

Substituting Eq. (9.130) in the displacement-thickness integral and integrating gives

$$\delta^* = 1.69 \sqrt{\frac{\nu x}{U}} \tag{9.134}$$

Therefore, the ratio of the boundary-layer thickness to the displacement thickness is

$$\frac{\delta}{\delta^*} = \frac{5.0}{1.69}$$

$$= 2.96 \tag{9.135}$$

This is approximately the same ratio as was found in Eq. (9.127).

(c) The Momentum Thickness

The momentum deficiency in the boundary-layer flow per unit mass is the velocity deficiency $(U - u)$ times the velocity u at which this deficient mass would have traveled. The *momentum thickness* is then defined as a thickness of flow θ moving at the velocity U and having the same momentum as the deficient momentum in the boundary layer. Thus

$$\theta U^2 = \int_0^\delta (U - u) u\, dy \tag{9.136}$$

$$\theta = \int_0^\delta \left(1 - \frac{u}{U}\right) \frac{u}{U}\, dy$$

or

$$= \sqrt{\frac{\nu x}{U}} \int_0^4 \left(1 - \frac{u}{U}\right) \frac{u}{U}\, d\eta$$

Again, substitution of Eq. (9.130) into the integral yields

$$\theta = 0.62\sqrt{\frac{\nu x}{U}} \tag{9.137}$$

and

$$\frac{\delta}{\theta} = 8.06$$

Figure 9.41 shows the velocity profile at a given x on the flat plate and the various thicknesses as defined in this section.

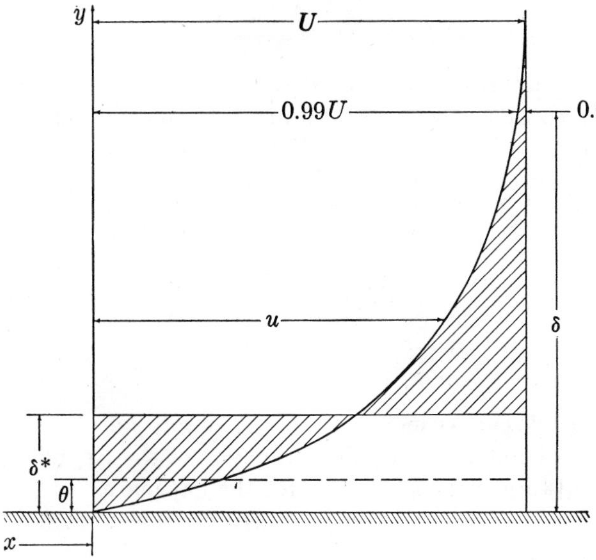

Figure 9.41
Various thicknesses of the boundary layer.

(d) The Drag on the Plate

Since the velocity distribution of the flow is given either in Table 9.4 or by Eq. (9.130), the shear stress at the wall can be found by differentiation at $y = 0$:

$$\tau_w(x) = \mu\left(\frac{\partial u}{\partial y}\right)_{y=0} \tag{9.138}$$

To evaluate this from Eq. (9.130), the chain differentiation rule must be used.

$$\frac{\partial u}{\partial y} = U\,\frac{d(u/U)}{d\eta}\,\frac{\partial \eta}{\partial y}$$

At the wall, this shear stress becomes

$$\tau_w(x) = 0.332\mu U \sqrt{\frac{U}{\nu x}} \tag{9.139}$$

If the width of the plate is b and its length is L, the total viscous drag on both sides of the plate is

$$D = 2b \int_0^L \tau_w \, dx \tag{9.140}$$

$$= 0.664b\sqrt{U^3\mu\rho} \int_0^L \frac{dx}{\sqrt{x}}$$
$$= 1.328b\sqrt{U^3\mu\rho L} \tag{9.141}$$

If the dimensionless drag, the *drag coefficient* C_D, is defined as the drag divided by the free-stream dynamic pressure $\frac{1}{2}\rho U^2$ and the plate's total exposed area $2bL$,

$$C_D = \frac{D}{\rho U^2 bL}$$

$$= 1.328 \sqrt{\frac{\mu}{\rho UL}}$$

$$= \frac{1.328}{\sqrt{\mathcal{R}_L}} \tag{9.142}$$

The drag coefficient was discussed in Sec. 9.12, and it was stated that, for geometrically similar bodies, it is a unique function of the Reynolds number. Equation (9.142) confirms this fact for the flat plate.

As in the case of a pipe discussed in Sec. 9.10(a), turbulent flow on the plate can occur as early as

$$\mathcal{R}_\delta = \frac{U\delta}{\nu} = 2{,}300$$

Since the relationship of δ in terms of x is given in Eq. (9.131), a corresponding critical Reynolds number, based on the length of the plate, can be derived for the limit when turbulence may set in. Substitution of Eq. (9.131) into the preceding relation gives

$$\mathcal{R}_x = \frac{Ux}{\nu} = 2.1 \times 10^5$$

Experiments have shown, however, that if the flat plate is very smooth and the free-stream flow is free of disturbances, a laminar state can be maintained up to a Reynolds number of $\mathcal{R}_x = 3 \times 10^6$. For most applications one can say that the transition from laminar to turbulent flow along a flat plate occurs when the critical Reynolds number, based on the length of the flat plate, is $\mathcal{R}_x = 5 \times 10^5$.

9.15 The Steady Turbulent Boundary Layer on a Flat Plate

In the turbulent case, owing to the lack of an analytical solution such as Eq. (9.129) which covers the entire turbulent boundary layer, the calculations performed in the preceding section will here have to be done in a different fashion.

When the critical Reynolds number of approximately 5×10^5 has been reached along the length of the plate, the laminar boundary layer becomes turbulent, and consequently all its properties will assume new relationships. Figure 9.42 shows schematically this process of the

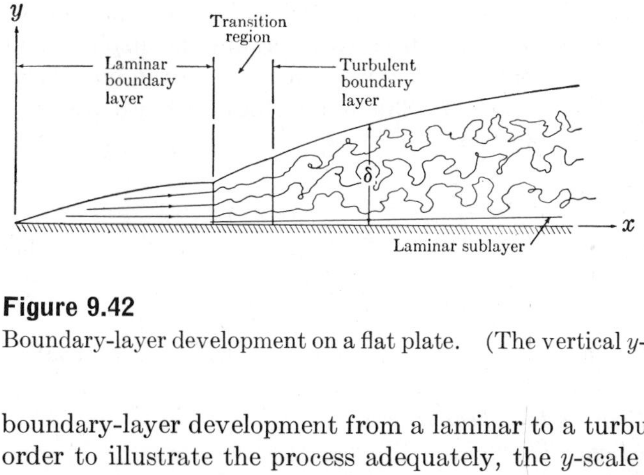

Figure 9.42
Boundary-layer development on a flat plate. (The vertical y-scale is magnified.)

boundary-layer development from a laminar to a turbulent regime. In order to illustrate the process adequately, the y-scale has been grossly magnified when compared with the x-scale. In this figure the edge of the boundary layer is shown. For the laminar regime, this thickness δ has been given in Eq. (9.131).

(a) *The Velocity Profile*

Based on experimental results, Prandtl and von Kármán,[22] independ-

[22] T. von Kármán (1881–1967), one of the most noted contributors to the fields of general mechanics in the 20th century.

ently, assumed that the velocity profile in the turbulent boundary layer over a flat plate was of the form

$$\frac{u}{U} = \left(\frac{y}{\delta}\right)^{1/7} \tag{9.143}$$

This expression satisfies the major part of the boundary layer but fails to satisfy the two most important regions of the flow, namely, the flow in the vicinity of the plate and the flow in the boundary layer near the free stream. Consequently, the shear stress and the thickness δ cannot be directly derived from this relationship.

It has also been shown that the relationships, Eqs. (9.78) and (9.84) in Sec. 9.10(*b*), also apply to the turbulent boundary layer on the flat plate. Right now these relations will not be used, since the shear stress at the wall or u_* is not yet known.

(b) The Displacement and Momentum Thickness

Although Eq. (9.143) is not adequate for determining the shear stress or the boundary-layer thickness δ, since it satisfies the major part of the turbulent boundary layer, it can be used to determine the displacement thickness δ^* and the momentum thickness θ in terms of the boundary-layer thickness δ. Using Eqs. (9.133) and (9.136) with Eq. (9.143), the following ratios are obtained:

$$\frac{\delta}{\delta^*} = 8 \qquad \frac{\delta}{\theta} = \frac{72}{7} \tag{9.144}$$

The variation of each of these thicknesses with x will be found later.

(c) Relationship Between the Shear Stress and the Boundary-Layer Thickness

In order to establish the relationship of the shear stress at the wall of the plate in terms of the boundary-layer thickness, the momentum relationships developed in Chap. V are applied here to the boundary layer.

As shown in Fig. 9.43, consider a control volume *ABCD* of length dx and height from the plate to the edge of the boundary layer. Since outside the boundary layer U = constant, then dp/dx and dp/dy must be zero. Consequently, the only external force acting on the elemental control volume is the wall shearing force per unit depth $\tau_w\, dx$. This force must be balanced by the net exchange of momentum through the three open surfaces of the volume. The rate of flow entering at face AB is $\int_0^\delta \rho u \, dy$; that leaving at CD is

$$\int_0^\delta \rho u \, dy + \frac{\partial}{\partial x}\left[\int_0^\delta \rho u \, dy\right] dx$$

The difference of flow between these two faces is

$$\frac{\partial}{\partial x}\left[\int_0^\delta \rho u \, dy\right] dx$$

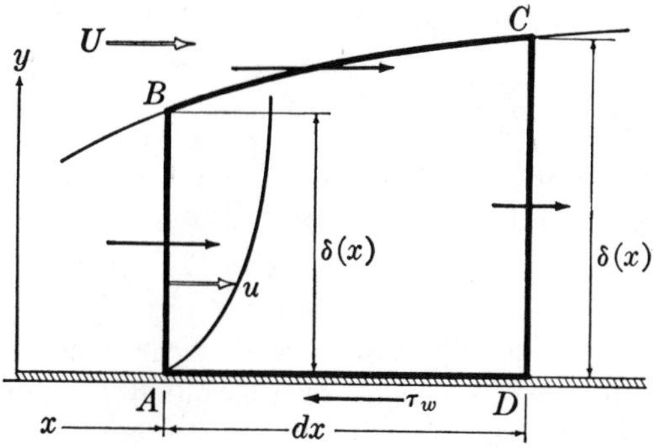

Figure 9.43
An elemental control volume in the turbulent boundary layer.

and represents the amount of flow entering the face BC. Since the flow there is moving at the velocity U, its momentum entering the face BC per unit width of plate is

$$U \frac{\partial}{\partial x}\left[\int_0^\delta \rho u \, dy\right] dx \tag{9.145}$$

The momentum entering the face AB is $\int_0^\delta \rho u^2 \, dy$, and that leaving the face CD is

$$\int_0^\delta \rho u^2 \, dy + \frac{\partial}{\partial x}\left[\int_0^\delta \rho u^2 \, dy\right] dx$$

The net momentum exchange must be equal to the shear force $\tau_w \, dx$; then

$$\begin{aligned}\tau_w &= U\frac{\partial}{\partial x}\int_0^\delta \rho u\, dy - \frac{\partial}{\partial x}\int_0^\delta \rho u^2\, dy \\ &= \frac{\partial}{\partial x}\int_0^\delta \rho(U-u)u\, dy \\ &= \frac{\partial}{\partial x}(\rho U^2\theta)\end{aligned}$$

according to Eq. (9.136). Thus for a flat plate flow the stream velocity U is constant and

$$\frac{\tau_w}{\rho U^2} = \frac{d\theta}{dx} \tag{9.146}$$

In Eq. (9.144), δ is given in terms of θ; then

$$\frac{\tau_w}{\rho U^2} = \frac{7}{72}\frac{d\delta}{dx} \tag{9.147}$$

This is the differential equation sought. Now, if τ_w can be found in terms of x, then δ, δ^*, and θ can also be evaluated in terms of x.

(d) The Shear Stress at the Wall

Experiments have shown that the dependence of the wall shear stress on the Reynolds number and the dynamic pressure for a turbulent flow on a flat plate is the same as that for a turbulent flow in a pipe, provided that appropriate choices of the velocity and the boundary-layer thickness are obtained.

Combining Eqs. (9.68), (9.72), and (9.75),

$$\begin{aligned}\tau_w &= \frac{0.03955}{\mathcal{R}^{1/4}}\rho u_{\mathrm{av}}^2 \\ &= 0.03955\rho\nu^{1/4}d^{-1/4}u_{\mathrm{av}}^{-7/4}\end{aligned}$$

In fully developed turbulent flows in a pipe, it has been found experimentally that the ratio of the maximum velocity $u_{\max}$ to the average velocity u_{av} is 1.235. Changing the previous equation in terms of $u_{\max}$ and in terms of the radius $d/2 = r_0$, then

$$\tau_w = \frac{0.0229}{\mathcal{R}^{1/4}}\rho u_{\max}^2$$

Here, the Reynolds number is on the basis of the pipe radius and the maximum velocity. This shear-stress expression holds for a flat plate as well, provided that $u_{\max}$ is replaced by U and the Reynolds number is based on U and the boundary-layer thickness δ.

$$\tau_w = \frac{0.0229}{\mathcal{R}^{1/4}}\,\rho U^2$$

$$\frac{\tau_w}{\rho U^2} = 0.0229\left(\frac{\nu}{U\delta}\right)^{1/4} \tag{9.148}$$

(*e*) *Solution of the Displacement and Momentum Thickness*

Equations (9.147) and (9.148) can now be equated, and a differential equation in δ is obtained:

$$0.0229\left(\frac{\nu}{U\delta}\right)^{1/4} = \frac{7}{72}\frac{d\delta}{dx}$$

$$0.2355\left(\frac{\nu}{U}\right)^{1/4} dx = \delta^{1/4}\,d\delta$$

Integrating,

$$\delta = 0.376\left(\frac{\nu}{U}\right)^{1/5} x^{4/5}$$

$$= \frac{0.376x}{\mathcal{R}_x^{1/5}} \tag{9.149}$$

Compared with the laminar boundary-layer thickness, Eq. (9.131), the turbulent boundary-layer thickness grows faster, to the 4/5 power of x. Similarly, the displacement and momentum thicknesses are

$$\delta^* = \frac{0.047x}{\mathcal{R}_x^{1/5}}$$

$$\theta = \frac{0.0366x}{\mathcal{R}_x^{1/5}} \tag{9.150}$$

(*f*) *The Drag and Drag Coefficient*

The shear stress at the wall in terms of the plate length x can be found by replacing $\delta(x)$ in Eq. (9.148) by the value given in Eq. (9.149). This substitution yields

$$\frac{\tau_w}{\rho U^2} = \frac{0.0229}{(0.376)^{1/4}}\left(\frac{\nu\mathcal{R}_x^{1/5}}{Ux}\right)^{1/4}$$

$$= \frac{0.0292}{\mathcal{R}_x^{1/4}} \tag{9.151}$$

The drag on the plate can be obtained in two ways. Both ways will involve the evaluation of

$$D = 2b\int_0^L \tau_w\,dx$$

The factor of 2 is to cover the area on both sides of the plate, as in the laminar case. This result can be achieved either by integrating Eq. (9.151) or by integrating Eq. (9.151) which is the simpler, since the value of θ is already available.

$$D = 2b\rho U^2\theta(L)$$
$$= 0.0732 b\rho U^2 L \mathcal{R}_L^{-1/5} \tag{9.152}$$

Here L is the length of the plate being considered. $\mathcal{R}_L$ is the Reynolds number of the flow based on the free-stream velocity and the length of the plate. The drag coefficient C_D is the drag divided by the free-stream dynamic pressure and the total area of the plate:

$$C_D = \frac{D}{\frac{1}{2}\rho U^2(2bL)}$$
$$= \frac{0.0732}{\mathcal{R}_L^{1/5}} \tag{9.153}$$

The results of the investigation for the drag coefficient are plotted for the laminar as well as the turbulent case in Fig. 9.44. The laminar

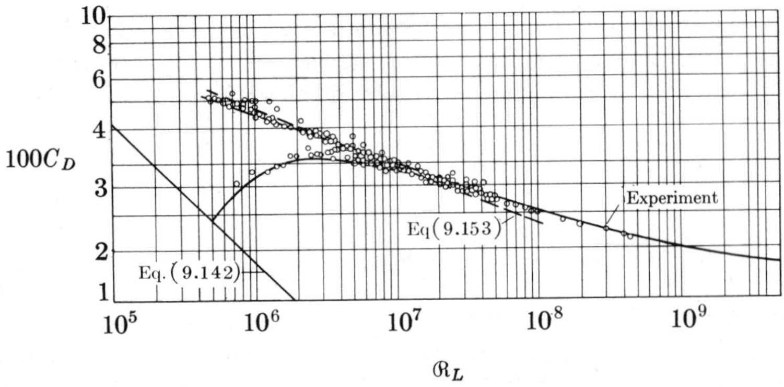

Figure 9.44
Drag coefficient of flow over a flat plate with zero angle of attack.
(By permission of the publishers, from Herman Schlichting, *Boundary Layer Theory*, Pergamon Press Limited, Oxford, 1955.)

solution agrees very well with the experimental results. In the turbulent case, Eq. (9.153) is seen to agree well with the experiments for a Reynolds-number region between 5×10^5 and 10^7. In the range $2 \times 10^5 < \mathcal{R}_L < 6 \times 10^5$, both laminar and turbulent flows over a flat plate are possible.

9.16 The Boundary-Layer Separation

The boundary layer on a flat plate without pressure gradient in the direction of flow was considered in the preceding section. The existence of pressure gradients in the direction of flow alters considerably the boundary-layer development. Consequently, the preceding analysis is applicable strictly to boundary-layer flows with zero pressure gradients in the direction of flow.

For an example of a boundary-layer flow with pressure gradients, negative and positive, consider the flow through a convergent and divergent channel, as shown in Fig. 9.45. The flow enters the channel

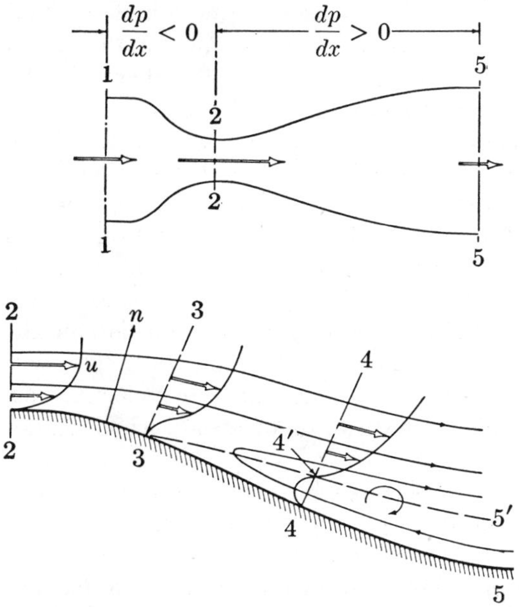

Figure 9.45
Boundary-layer separation in an adverse pressure gradient.

at section 1-1 and converges into section 2-2 by increasing its speed. Since the area 2-2 is smaller than that at 1-1, if the flow is essentially incompressible, the velocity at 2-2 will be larger. Since no changes of elevation are involved, the energy equation must require that the flow energy, or pressure, at 2-2 must be smaller than that at 1-1, since the kinetic energy at 2-2 has increased from 1-1 to 2-2. This pressure decrease in the direction of flow or $dp/dx < 0$ has, naturally, some influence on the boundary layer at the walls between 1-1 and 2-2. Here, the viscous forces trying to retard the motion are now confronted not only with the momentum of the flow but with a *favorable pressure gradient* giving the fluid an additional push in the direction of flow. On account of this net acceleration of the flow in the convergent section, the thickness of the boundary layer at 2-2 becomes smaller than that at 1-1.

The situation of the boundary layer on the walls between sections 2-2 and 5-5, however, is entirely opposite. Since from 2-2 to 5-5 the area of the channel is increasing, the velocity reduces and the pressure increases in the direction of flow. This region is identified by $dp/dx > 0$; that is, the pressure increases in the direction of flow. The pressure gradient, here, is called *adverse,* since it opposes the motion of the fluid in the same way that the shear stresses do. A fluid element in this region has a higher pressure downstream than upstream. Together with the shear stresses, this pressure rise decelerates the fluid.

The fluid element in the boundary layer at section 2-2 had a large momentum per unit volume as compared with the other sections. As this boundary layer proceeds from 2-2 to 5-5, the shear forces, together with the adverse pressures, constantly reduce the momentum of this flow. This situation persists as long as the velocity gradient in the boundary layer du/dn is positive. The pressure and shear stresses acting on the fluid continuously, the layers of fluid in the immediate neighborhood of the wall will suffer first a momentum depletion. This will be characterized by a region near the wall having zero velocity, and consequently $du/dn = 0$. This is shown to occur at 3-3, which marks the beginning of *separation.*

As the flow proceeds farther downstream, the net pressure and shear forces are still acting in the direction opposite to the motion. The boundary layer will be decelerated further, and the region near the wall will start flowing in a direction opposite to the main flow in the channel. The zero-velocity points will be at the wall and also at a distance from the wall 4-4′, as shown in the figure. The line 3-4′-5′ represents the zero-velocity *separation line.* Above the separation line the flow moves in one direction, while below it moves in the opposite direction. This causes a strong vorticity field there, which often, in channels, appears as a standing vortex circulating in an isolated pocket. The separation line 3-4′-5′ is also a streamline now replacing the wall for the fluid above. Owing to the divergence, the streamlines have been moved away from the wall, and the boundary layer, before separation, thickens faster in this region of adverse pressure gradient.

The separation picture just described is not particular to divergent channels alone; it is also common on the surface of blunt bodies moving in a stream. As Fig. 9.46 shows, the flow from the stagnation point O moves along the body, accelerating to a point 1. The pressure in this

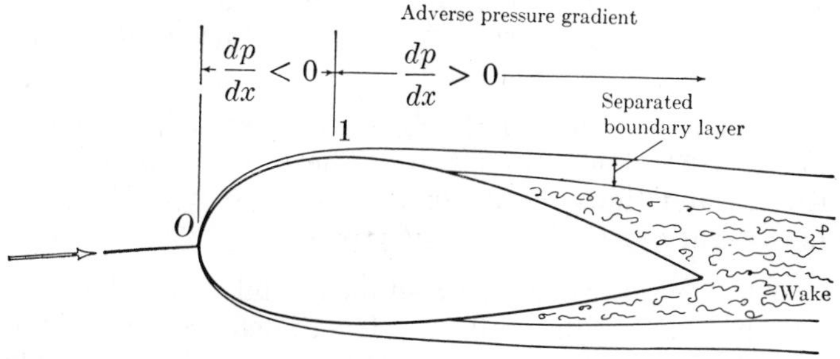

Figure 9.46
Separated flow and the wake.

region drops in the direction of flow, and a thin boundary layer builds on the surface. At point 1 the flow reaches the maximum velocity, and the pressure from there on increases in the direction of flow. This adverse pressure gradient imposes decelerative forces to the boundary layer and eventually makes it separate from the surface of the body. The *wake* is the strong vorticity field which is generated behind the body owing to the boundary layer and its separation. It has already been stated in Sec. 9.12 that the presence of this wake is what produces the pressure or *form drag*. A streamlined body was also defined as one on which separation does not occur and consequently one which does not generate a wake from separation.

The phenomenon of separation described pertains to laminar flows as well as to turbulent flows. There is one distinction, however, and that is that turbulent boundary layers resist separation better than do the laminar boundary layers. In other words, turbulent separation occurs farther downstream than does a laminar separation on the same object. This was shown in Fig. 9.34. The reason for this, as explained, is that, in the turbulent boundary layer, owing to the fluctuations of velocity in the direction normal to the mean flow, turbulence brings into these layers near the wall a momentum from upper layers. The net result is that it retards the effects of the shear and pressure forces which eventually separate the boundary layer.

Problems

9.1 Ethyl alcohol flows at the rate of 1.9 ft³/min through a 2-in. wrought-iron pipe. The internal diameter of the pipe is 2.067 in., and the viscosity of the alcohol at 70°F is 2.34×10^{-5} ft²/sec. Find the approximate length of the pipe necessary for fully developed flow to occur.

9.2 Fully developed flow occurs in 10 ft of 1-in. wrought-iron pipe when mineral oil at 70°F flows through it. The internal diameter of the pipe is 1.049 in., and the viscosity of the oil is 1.6×10^{-3} ft²/sec. Find the average velocity of the flow in the pipe.

9.3 Water at 50°F flows through a two-dimensional channel with a velocity distribution of $u = -6y^2 + 0.54$. The dimension y is in fractions of an inch and is measured from the center of the channel. The velocity is in feet per second. Find the pressure drop, in inches, of water for a 100-ft-long channel.

9.4 Based on the velocity equation, find the Reynolds number of the flow of Prob. 9.3 in terms of the maximum velocity in the channel and the width of the channel.

9.5 If air having a viscosity of 1.41×10^{-4} ft²/sec is to flow through the channel of Prob. 9.3 at the same Reynolds number, find the maximum velocity of the air in the channel.

9.6 In Prob. 9.3, what would be the space average velocity in the channel? Using the results of Prob. 9.4, what is the frictional resistance coefficient?

9.7 A dam with water on one side has a 0.006-in. crack 10 ft below the surface of the water. The horizontal length of the crack is 4 ft, and the thickness of the dam at that location is 3 ft. If the water is at 50°F, calculate the following: (*a*) the pressure drop per unit length through the crack; (*b*) the velocity distribution in the crack (let y be the distance in inches from the center of the crack); (*c*) the maximum velocity at the center; (*d*) the shear stress at the wall; (*e*) the space average velocity; (*f*) the volume rate of flow through the crack in gallons per hour; (*g*) the Reynolds number of the flow based on the average velocity and the width of the crack; (*h*) the resistance coefficient.

9.8 Find the total power loss to friction in Prob. 9.7.

9.9 One of the bearings in a power-plant engine is 12 in. in diameter and 18 in. long. The shaft, when rotating, has an assumed uniform clearance of 0.020 in., and it rotates at 3,600 rpm. Because of the uniform-clearance assumption, there are no pressure gradients in the bearing. At the temperature of the bearing, the lubricating oil has a viscosity of 36 centipoises. On the basis of the assumption of uniform clearance, calculate the horsepower dissipated in the bearing.

9.10 The piston of an internal-combustion engine is 10 in. in diameter and 12 in. long. When operating, the clearance with the cylinder walls is 0.010 in., and the stroke is 12 in. The engine runs at 720 rpm, and the lubricating oil used has a viscosity of 0.86×10^{-3} $lb_f \times sec/ft^2$ at operating conditions. The mean pressure in the cylinder head is 100 psi above the crankcase. Find the velocity distribution, the shear stress at the wall, and the power dissipated by the piston on its forward and backward strokes. Assume the mean pressure in the cylinder and the mean speed of the piston to prevail at all times.

9.11 Find the dimensionless pressure drop ϕ of Prob. 9.10 and determine the average and maximum velocities of the lubricating oil for the forward and backward strokes.

9.12 What is the value of the pressure drop in the incompressible, laminar, and steady Couette flow such that there will be no net flow of fluid across the passage between the two plates?

9.13 Find the rate of mass flow Q between the two parallel plates in the Couette flow of Prob. 9.12 for the condition that the shear stress on the stationary plate is zero. The answer should be in terms of ρ, U, and b.

9.14 What happens to the rate of flow of Prob. 9.13 if the shear stress on the moving wall is specified to be zero?

9.15 A slipper bearing is 2 in. long and moves at a velocity of 50 ft/sec relative to the stationary pad. The lubricating oil at running conditions has a viscosity of 0.86×10^{-3} $lb_f \times sec/ft^2$ and a specific gravity of 0.86. The bearing gap is 0.006 in. at one end and 0.002 in. at the other. Find the flow of oil through the bearing per unit depth. Plot the pressure distribution in the bearing in pounds per square inch as a function of bearing length. Estimate the maximum pressure in the bearing and where it occurs.

9.16 A thrust bearing of a vertical turbine is made up of 12 flat rocker plates 2 by 6 in., with its long dimension along the radius of the shaft. The centers of these plates are on a circle 18 in. from the axis of the shaft, and they carry a total thrust of 75,000 lb_f. The viscosity of the lubricant is 1.49×10^{-3} $lb_f \times sec/ft^2$, and the shaft revolves at 750 rpm. If the rocker plates take the angle for the maximum load, calculate the clearance in the bearing and the frictional power loss.

9.17 The fixed shoe of a slider bearing is $L = 2$ in., and 4 in. wide. The angle of inclination of the slider is 10 min., and the oil in the bearing has a viscosity of 36 centipoises. What is the load on the bearing if $h_2 = 0.002$ in. and the speed of the slider is 50 ft/sec?

9.18 A $\frac{1}{2}$-in. wrought-iron pipe having an internal diameter of 0.622 in. carries a liquid with a viscosity of 0.001 $\text{lb}_f \times \text{sec/ft}^2$ and a specific gravity of 0.86. If the Reynolds number of the flow based on the average velocity and the diameter of the pipe is 2,000, what is the shear stress at the wall in pounds per square foot?

9.19 If the liquid in Prob. 9.18 is pumped through a pipe 100 ft long, find the power necessary.

9.20 What would be the vorticity distribution of the fully developed laminar flow in a pipe?

9.21 A tube having an inside diameter of $\frac{1}{4}$ in. is L ft long, is held vertically, and is filled with oil of a viscosity of 30 centipoises and a density of 50 lb_m/ft^3. If the bottom of the tube is suddenly opened, state the mass discharge and the Reynolds number of the flow. As long as the flow remains fully developed, does the rate of flow vary as the oil drains out of the pipe?

9.22 Helium at 2 atm and 300°F flows through a $\frac{1}{4}$-in.-inside-diameter pipe 150 ft long. Determine the highest average velocity for which the flow within the pipe is laminar. Also determine the pressure difference at the two ends of the pipe and the power necessary to pump it. Use Sutherland's equation for the viscosity.

9.23 What is the head loss in feet of water in a 1,000-ft smooth 4-in. pipe carrying 1 ft^3/sec of water at 50°F? Compare the results when the water is at 100°F.

9.24 Compare the results of Prob. 9.23 if the fluid is air.

9.25 What is the shear stress at the wall of the pipe for Probs. 9.23 and 9.24?

9.26 Compute the shearing velocity u_* for Probs. 9.23 and 9.24 at 50°F. Evaluate the thickness of the laminar sublayer.

9.27 Turbulent flow of air at 100°F flows through a 4-in.-diameter pipe with a pressure drop of 3 in. of water in 30 ft of pipe. Find the shearing velocity. If the velocity profile is logarithmic, find the ratio of the average velocity to the maximum velocity by integrating between the limits $\frac{yu_*}{\nu} = 5$ and $\frac{r_0 u_*}{\nu}$. Here, y is the distance from the pipe wall, and r_0 is the inner radius of the pipe.

9.28 A turbulent flow in a smooth pipe is considered at a Reynolds number of 10^6. Compute the resistance coefficient by trial and error and compare with the values obtained from Figs. 9.20 and 9.21.

9.29 Justify the two expressions given in Eqs. (9.87) and (9.90).

9.30 A rough pipe, with a roughness coefficient $k/D = 1/60$, carries a fluid in a completely turbulent state. What would be its resistance coefficient? Compare the calculated value with the data in Fig. 9.21.

9.31 Try Colebrook's equation, Eq. (9.88), for a turbulent flow of Reynolds number 10^6 in a galvanized-iron pipe of roughness coefficient $k/D = 0.0005$. Solve for the resistance coefficient f by trial and error and compare with the results of Fig. 9.20.

9.32 A piping system is connected at the bottom of a very large open tank containing water at 50°F. The piping system of galvanized iron starts at the tank with square edges and runs horizontally for 200 ft and is 1.049 in. inside diameter. Four 90° elbows and a fully opened globe valve are also in the line. The piping is 50 ft below the surface of the water in the tank. Considering entrance losses from the tank to the pipe, pipe losses, elbow losses, and valve losses, find by trial and error the velocity of the flow that is being discharged at the end of the pipe system opened to the atmosphere. What is the Reynolds number? Find the discharge velocity if the flow is frictionless.

9.33 A water pump operates at an efficiency of 77 per cent and delivers water into an atmospheric tank 100 ft above. The piping is 4 in. inside diameter and 1,000 ft long, with a resistance coefficient of 0.020. The pressure in the pipe at the discharge of the pump is 100 psig. Determine the velocity through the pipe, the volume rate of flow, and the horsepower of the motor driving the pump. How much of the power goes into frictional loss?

9.34 For cooling purposes, helium at 200°F is circulated in the space between two concentric pipes. The concentric pipes are 4 and 2 in. in diameter. The flow of helium at approximately atmospheric pressure is $\pi/4$ ft^3/sec. First calculate the absolute and kinematic viscosity of the helium at 200°F. Then determine the pressure drop per foot of pipe and the shear stresses at both walls.

9.35 Where is the shear stress zero in Prob. 9.34, and what is the space average velocity?

9.36 Compute the pressure distribution for Illustrative Example 9.10. If the inner cylinder with radius r_1 and height h spins at an angular velocity of ω_1 and if the pressure inside the inner tank and at $r = \infty$ is atmospheric, find the total normal pressure on the entire cylindrical wall.

9.37 Consider the viscometer in Fig. 9.33. Here $r_1 = 2$ in., $h = 4$ in., and $r_2 - r_1 = 1/8$ in. The outer cylinder revolves at 720 rpm, and the inner cylinder is suspended with a filament easy to deflect in torsion. Find the relationship between the torque T and the viscosity μ if the bottom gap is neglected. Also evaluate the error involved if the bottom gap of the order of $r_2 - r_1$ is considered.

9.38 A 1-in.-diameter sphere falls through water at a Reynolds number of 10^4. If the water is at 50°F, find the drag on the sphere.

9.39 A sphere falls in a liquid of viscosity μ in a Reynolds-number range where the drag is in the Stokes-flow regime. The radius of the sphere is r, its density is ρ_s, and the density of the liquid is ρ. By making a balance of the buoyant force, the drag force, and the weight of the sphere, determine the so-called terminal velocity of the sphere moving without acceleration.

9.40 A 12-in.-long rod with a 0.2-in. diameter is immersed in 100°F and 3 atm of hydrogen moving at 100 ft/sec. Determine the drag on the rod.

9.41 Compute the decrease in drag when a cylinder is immersed in a fluid and its Reynolds number varies from 3×10^5 to 5×10^5. The size of the cylinder and the density of the fluid remain the same.

9.42 Compute the error in the drag coefficient of a sphere when evaluated from Oseen's approximate-drag coefficient at $\mathcal{R} = 10$.

9.43 Verify Eq. (9.126) by graphic integration of data given in Table 9.3.

9.44 A flat plate is suddenly moved to a velocity U in water at 50°F. Plot the velocity ratio u/U as a function of y distance from the plate for times 0.001 sec, 0.01 sec, 0.1 sec, and 1.0 sec.

9.45 By numerical integration of values in Table 9.4, compute the ratio of the average velocity to the maximum velocity in the laminar boundary layer on a flat plate.

9.46 Transition, in air at 50°F, from laminar to turbulent flow occurs 12 in. downstream of the leading edge of a flat plate. The transition Reynolds number is 2×10^5, based on the plate length. Find the laminar boundary-layer thickness just before transition, the free-stream velocity, the displacement thickness, and the momentum thickness.

9.47 What is the laminar drag in Prob. 9.46 if the dimensions of the plate are 1 ft long and 2 ft wide?

9.48 The thickness of a turbulent boundary layer at the end of a 10-ft plate is 1.655 in. What is the Reynolds number at the end of the plate? If water at 50°F is the fluid, find the free-stream velocity and the shear stress at the wall and at the end of the plate. If the width of the plate is 3 ft, what is the total drag?

Dimensional Analysis

chapter X

10.1 Introduction

The purpose of dimensional analysis is to find, without actually solving the problem, certain relationships which measurable quantities pertaining to the problem must satisfy on the basis of pure dimensional reasoning. Dimensional analysis is not a tool for solving problems explicitly but a powerful method for establishing the grouping of the pertinent variables that are likely to appear if the analytical solution is at all possible. The advantages of this method are that it is rapid and that, without knowledge of the dynamic equations, some fruitful generalizations about the solution can be made.

When mathematical knowledge is not available to solve analytically a given problem, dimensional analysis, together with a thorough experiment, does bring a complete graphic or empirical solution. In fact, then, dimensional analysis is necessary to control the experiments according to the independent grouping of variables it suggests.

The method followed in dimensional analysis is essentially one in which the physical quantities influencing the solution are known a priori. Then these quantities are combined into a functional relationship such that the relationship remains always true, regardless of the magnitude of the units used to describe the measured quantities. Thus, if the quantities influencing a physical phenomenon are known, dimensional analysis can put these quantities into a useful form for the planning of experiments or the interpretation of data. The major advantage of the use of dimensional analysis is most apparent where complete analytical solution of the physical problem is not possible. Thus, by establishing the *form* of the dimensionless solution, the number of experiments needed to establish the phenomenon experimentally is greatly reduced. For instance, it was evident from Chap. IX that, for incompressible viscous flows through pipes, the Reynolds number, which is a dimensional grouping of four physical quantities, uniquely determines the value of the resistance coefficient for a given surface geometry of the pipe. Therefore, if this much knowledge can be obtained from dimensional analysis without necessarily knowing the form of the dependence of f on the Reynolds number $\mathcal{R}$ and the surface roughness, then there is no need to run experiments at all possible densities, viscosities, pipe diameter, roughness, and flow velocities. It is necessary only to run the experiments at varying $\mathcal{R}$ and roughness ratio, regardless of the absolute magnitude of each quantity making up the Reynolds number and the roughness ratio.

In dimensional analysis it is basically implied that, since physical laws express natural phenomena, they are independent of the units of dimensions used. Thus one can say that in the formulation of such laws it must be possible to express them in dimensionless form.

10.2 Dimensional Units

Every essential property, such as the velocity, the viscosity, or the diameter, that enters into the description of physical phenomena has its own units which differentiate it from other properties. A quantity, with or without units which help describe a physical phenomenon but which do not vary in the particular phenomenon, is called a dimensional or a dimensionless constant, respectively.

Although every physical quantity has its own units, one will notice that all such quantities are made up of a very limited number of *fundamental dimensions.* Therefore, if these fundamental dimensions are established, then any quantity describing a physical phenomenon can be expressed in terms of them. In Chap. I the fundamental units of dimensions were discussed for a mechanical system involving *force, mass, length,* and *time.* At the same time, it was also disclosed that all these four basic fundamental units need not be specified together. Since

Newton's inertial law related through an equation these four fundamental dimensions, one of these dimensions can always be related in terms of the other three. Thus, for problems in mechanics, all quantities describing a mechanical phenomenon can be expressed in terms of the three fundamental dimensions: *force* (F), *length* (L), and *time* (T) or as an alternative *mass* (M), *length* (L), and *time* (T). Consequently, it can be said that an FLT or an MLT system can describe all mechanical quantities. Table 10.1 shows how this is done.

Since thermodynamics enters into the description of fluid-flow problems, two new independent fundamental dimensions appear. Because they are independent, they cannot be expressed in terms of F, M, L, or T. These fundamental dimensions are the temperature Θ and the heat transfer H. The dimension of quantities appearing in fluid mechanics can thus be, in general, expressed in either of the two fundamental dimensional systems: $FLT\Theta H$ or $MLT\Theta H$. For the most part, in problems involving dynamics alone, the three dimensions FLT or MLT are sufficient.

A dimensionless constant is a constant that appears in the description of a physical event but does not have units. For example, in the period of the roll in Sec. 2.15, the quantity 2π is a dimensionless constant which does not depend on the magnitude of the units chosen for the weight, the metacentric height, or the moment of inertia.

A dimensional constant is a quantity that does not vary in the phenomenon involved but is one in which its magnitude is dependent on the magnitude of the units of the other dimensional quantities in the equation. For instance, R, the gas constant in Eq. (1.3), is a constant in a sense that it does not vary in the problem, but its magnitude is dependent on the magnitude of the units chosen for the rest of the terms in the equation. This was illustrated in Table 1.2. Similarly, C in Newton's gravitational equation in Chap. I is a dimensional constant.

10.3 Dimensional Homogeneity

When an equation representing a physical phenomenon is written down, it is absolutely necessary that the equation be dimensionally homogeneous. By this it is implied that all the terms in the equation must have the same units, whatever they may be. In fact, a student should develop the habit of checking his equations for homogeneity of units. If

Table 10.1
Dimensions of physical quantities used in fluid mechanics.

Quantity	Symbol	Dimensional system M, L, T, Θ, H	F, L, T, Θ, H
	Kinematics		
Angle (radians)	Θ	no dimensions	no dimensions
Length	l	L	L
Time	t	T	T
Mass	m	M	$FL^{-1}T^2$
Area	A	L^2	L^2
Volume	$\mathcal{V}$	L^3	L^3
Linear velocity	V, U	LT^{-1}	LT^{-1}
Angular velocity	ω	T^{-1}	T^{-1}
Acceleration	a, g	LT^{-2}	LT^{-2}
Moment of inertia	I	ML^2	FLT^2
Volume rate of flow	Q	L^3T^{-1}	L^3T^{-1}
Mass density	ρ	ML^{-3}	$FL^{-4}T^2$
Mass rate of flow	Q	MT^{-1}	$FL^{-1}T$
Circulation	Γ	L^2T^{-1}	L^2T^{-1}
Kinematic viscosity	ν	L^2T^{-1}	L^2T^{-1}
	Dynamics		
Force	F	MLT^{-2}	F
Pressure	p	$ML^{-1}T^{-2}$	FL^{-2}
Shear stress	τ	$ML^{-1}T^{-2}$	FL^{-2}
Specific weight	ρg	$ML^{-2}T^{-2}$	FL^{-3}
Modulus of elasticity	E	$ML^{-1}T^{-2}$	FL^{-2}
Coefficient of compressibility	β	$M^{-1}LT^2$	$F^{-1}L^2$
Surface-tension coefficient	σ	MT^{-2}	FL^{-1}
Momentum	M	MLT^{-1}	FT
Angular momentum		ML^2T^{-1}	FLT
Torque	T	ML^2T^{-2}	FL
Absolute viscosity	μ	$ML^{-1}T^{-1}$	$FL^{-2}T$
	Energy and power		
Energy (mechanical)	W	ML^2T^{-2}	FL
Energy (heat)	E, Q	H	H
Power (mechanical)	P	ML^2T^{-3}	FLT^{-1}
Power (heat)	P	HT^{-1}	HT^{-1}
	Thermodynamics and heat transfer		
Temperature	T	Θ	Θ
Thermal-expansion coefficient	β	Θ^{-1}	Θ^{-1}
Thermal conductivity	k	$HL^{-1}T^{-1}\text{-}\Theta^{-1}$	$HL^{-1}T^{-1}\Theta^{-1}$
Specific heat (mass)	c	$HM^{-1}\Theta^{-1}$	$HF^{-1}LT^{-2}\Theta^{-1}$
Specific heat (volume)	c'	$HL^{-3}\Theta^{-1}$	$HL^{-3}\Theta^{-1}$
Gas constant	R	$L^2T^{-2}\Theta^{-1}$	$L^2T^{-2}\Theta^{-1}$
Film coefficient of heat transfer	h	$HL^{-2}T^{-1}\Theta^{-1}$	$HL^{-2}T^{-1}\Theta^{-1}$

the units of all the terms in the equation do not appear to be the same, then one can be sure that some important quantity was lost or misplaced in the derivation.

Based on this concept of maintaining dimensional homogeneity, a clue to the solution of many problems may be arrived at by simply keeping track of the dimensions. For instance, let the following problem be analyzed dimensionally. Consider a small droplet formed by surface tension and, at the same time, imagine that the size of the drop is such that its weight is of no consequence to the discussion. Suppose it is necessary to determine the period of oscillation of such a droplet when, owing to an original external force, its shape changes periodically from spherical to oval. This period of oscillation will, without a doubt, depend on the surface-tension coefficient, the density, and the diameter of the drop.[1]

$$[t] = T$$
$$[\sigma] = MT^{-2}$$
$$[\rho] = ML^{-3}$$
$$[D] = L$$

The brackets around the physical quantities indicate *units of*, and the equality in the equations above pertains to the units alone. Thus, in general, it could be said that the period is

$$t = f(\sigma,\rho,D) \tag{10.1}$$

where f is a functional relationship that makes the equation correct in magnitude and dimensions. In Eq. (10.1), since the left-hand side of the equation does not have the units of mass M, then it must not appear explicitly in the right-hand side. The same argument holds true for the dimensions of length in D, which should not appear by itself. Thus, in order for Eq. (10.1) to involve units of time alone, it must be written as

$$t = f\left(\frac{\rho D^3}{\sigma}\right) \tag{10.2}$$

Furthermore, the function f must be the square root, since the units of $[\rho D^3/\sigma] = T^2$. Then the solution for the period of deformation is

$$t = C\sqrt{\frac{\rho D^3}{\sigma}} \tag{10.3}$$

Here C is a dimensionless constant which cannot be determined from

[1] The *MLT* system is used throughout this analysis and in what is to follow. This is a matter of choice. The *FLT* system could have been used just as easily.

this dimensional reasoning. It must be determined from the dynamic solution or by experiment.

It must be emphasized here that the form of the solution of the preceding problem was obtained purely by dimensional reasoning. What was known, a priori, was the quantities which influenced the solution. For more complicated problems, a more systematic method of this dimensional reasoning will be used later.

Another application of this method to a simple problem is as follows: Consider the nonviscous flow of an incompressible fluid emptying from the bottom of a tank. The elevation of the free surface from the bottom of the tank is l, and the efflux velocity is sought. With just a small amount of physical knowledge about this problem, one can say that the efflux velocity U will vary with the length l and the gravitational acceleration g.

$$[U] = LT^{-1}$$
$$[l] = L$$
$$[g] = LT^{-2}$$

Thus,

$$U = f(g,l) \tag{10.4}$$

If this equation must be dimensionally homogeneous, g and l must combine as a product and f must be the square root. Thus,

$$U = C\sqrt{gl} \tag{10.5}$$

The constant cannot be obtained from this analysis, but, from the analytical solution in Chap. IV, it is seen to be equal to $\sqrt{2}$.

With a little more experience, this deductive reasoning can be extended to somewhat more complicated problems. Let us, for instance, take the problem of a force imparted by an incompressible fluid on a solid boundary. For a viscous fluid this force will be the drag or the lift on a cylinder, sphere, or a flat plate. The quantity F (force) is dependent on the velocity U, the density ρ, the viscosity μ, and a characteristic geometrical dimension, say the diameter D. Because of some small familiarity with the phenomenon, these independent quantities U, ρ, μ, and D are postulated to be essential. Therefore,

$$[F] = MLT^{-2}$$
$$[U] = LT^{-1}$$
$$[\rho] = ML^{-3}$$
$$[D] = L$$
$$[\mu] = ML^{-1}T^{-1}$$

and, in general,

$$F = f(U,\rho,D,\mu) \tag{10.6}$$

This expression can be expanded in an infinite series of the form

$$F = U^{\alpha_1}\rho^{\beta_1}D^{\gamma_1}\mu^{\delta_1} + U^{\alpha_2}\rho^{\beta_2}D^{\gamma_2}\mu^{\delta_2} + \cdots \tag{10.7}$$

This equation must be dimensionally homogeneous, and therefore every term in it must have the same dimensions. Thus:

$$[F] = [U^{\alpha_1}\rho^{\beta_1}D^{\gamma_1}\mu^{\delta_1}] = [U^{\alpha_2}\rho^{\beta_2}D^{\gamma_2}\mu^{\delta_2}] \quad \text{etc.}$$

$$MLT^{-2} = (LT^{-1})^{\alpha_1}(ML^{-3})^{\beta_1}(L)^{\gamma_1}(ML^{-1}T^{-1})^{\delta_1} \tag{10.8}$$

Collecting powers in the last-dimension equation, three algebraic equations with four unknowns are obtained:

$$\begin{aligned} &\text{For } M \qquad & 1 &= \beta_1 + \delta_1 \\ &\text{For } L \qquad & 1 &= \alpha_1 - 3\beta_1 + \gamma_1 - \delta_1 \\ &\text{For } T \qquad & -2 &= -\alpha_1 - \delta_1 \end{aligned} \tag{10.9}$$

Obviously, the solution of these three equations can be obtained only in terms of a fourth variable, say δ_1. Then

$$\alpha_1 = 2 - \delta_1$$

$$\beta_1 = 1 - \delta_1$$

$$\gamma_1 = 2 - \delta_1$$

Substituting these values in Eq. (10.7), it follows that

$$F = U^{2-\delta_1}\rho^{1-\delta_1}D^{2-\delta_1}\mu^{\delta_1} + U^{2-\delta_2}\rho^{1-\delta_2}D^{2-\delta_2}\mu^{\delta_2} + \cdots$$

At once, it becomes apparent that a term ρU^2D^2 having the units of force can be factored out; then

$$F = \rho U^2D^2\left[\left(\frac{\mu}{U\rho D}\right)^{\delta_1} + \left(\frac{\mu}{U\rho \mathrm{D}}\right)^{\delta_2} + \cdots\right] \tag{10.10}$$

The terms in the bracket comprise a series $U\rho D/\mu = \mathcal{R}$ and can be represented in a general form as

$$F = \rho U^2D^2\phi(\mathcal{R}) \tag{10.11}$$

In particular, if F is the drag force, say on a sphere, then, by definition, the drag coefficient C_D is

$$\frac{F}{\frac{\pi}{8}\rho U^2D^2} = C_D = \frac{\pi}{8}\phi(\mathcal{R}) = \psi(\mathcal{R}) \tag{10.12}$$

Here, C_D is the drag coefficient. This was found to be true in Chap. IX. Equation (10.12) will be applicable for a cylinder or a flat plate. It can be shown just as easily, from Eq. (10.11), that Eq. (10.12) could also be derived for the lift coefficient.

Again, it is seen that this analysis is very fruitful, provided that the important variables influencing the problem are known. For someone who is at all familiar with the physical phenomenon, this knowledge of the important variables is easily obtained. The next section will deal with the same dimensional reasoning, but in a more systematic fashion for more complex problems.

10.4 The Π Theorem.[2] The General Form of the Physical Equation

It was found in the preceding example that, although originally the force on a submerged body was a function of four dimensional variables, the final dimensionless force C_D was a function of only one dimensionless independent variable $\mathcal{R}$.

This theorem will now show in more general terms that for the previous example,

$$\phi(F,U,\rho,D,\mu) = \psi(C_D,\mathcal{R}) = 0$$

Here the number of variables has been reduced by dimensionless groupings to two instead of five, the reduction in variables being equal to the number of *fundamental dimensions* in the problem, MLT.

Buckingham's Π theorem states that, given a physical equation,

$$f(x_1,x_2,x_3, \ldots, x_n) = 0 \tag{10.13}$$

where the x's are dimensional physical quantities pertinent to the physical phenomenon that Eq. (10.13) describes, there can be $(n - m)$ dimensionless Π quantities that describe the same phenomenon as

$$f(x_1,x_2,x_3, \ldots, x_n) = \phi(\Pi_1,\Pi_2,\Pi_3, \ldots, \Pi_{n-m}) = 0 \tag{10.14}$$

The number of variables is reduced by m the number of fundamental units involved in the phenomenon. In pure mechanics problems, there are three fundamental units MLT, and thus the expected reduction in the number of variables is $m = 3$, as in the preceding problem.

The proof of this theorem can be made as general as one wishes,

[2] This theorem is the contribution of E. Buckingham, published under the title, "On Physically Similar Systems," *Phys. Rev.*, Vol. 4, 1914, pp. 354–376.

but, for the sake of clarity, it will be confined here to five physical properties such that the phenomenon may be described as

$$f(x_1,x_2,x_3,x_4,x_5) = 0 \tag{10.15}$$

It is further assumed that this last equation can be expressed in the form of an infinite power series.

$$f(x_1,x_2,x_3,x_4,x_5) = C_1(x_1^\alpha x_2^\beta x_3^\gamma x_4^\delta x_5^\epsilon) + C_2(x_1^\alpha x_2^\beta x_3^\gamma x_4^\delta x_5^\epsilon)^2 + \cdots$$
$$+ C_k(x_1^\alpha x_2^\beta x_3^\gamma x_4^\delta x_5^\epsilon)^k = 0 \tag{10.16}$$

The quantities C_k are dimensionless coefficients and the exponents are dimensionless numbers, since all the dimensions are contained in the x's. For dimensional homogeneity all the terms in the above equation must have the same dimensions. Thus:

$$[(x_1^\alpha x_2^\beta x_3^\gamma x_4^\delta x_5^\epsilon)] = M^a L^b T^c$$
$$[(x_1^\alpha x_2^\beta x_3^\gamma x_4^\delta x_5^\epsilon)^k] = M^{ka} L^{kb} T^{kc}$$

For equal dimensions,

$$M^a L^b T^c = M^{ka} L^{kb} T^{kc}$$

and for $k \neq 0$, the exponents $a = b = c = 0$, which means that every term in Eq. (10.16) must be dimensionless. Thus the typical term

$$[x_1^\alpha x_2^\beta x_3^\gamma x_4^\delta x_5^\epsilon] = M^0 L^0 T^0 \tag{10.17}$$

has zero dimensions, and yet each term in the product has the dimensions of

$$[x_1] = M^{a_1} L^{b_1} T^{c_1}$$
$$\vdots$$
$$[x_5] = M^{a_5} L^{b_5} T^{c_5}$$

such that substitution in Eq. (10.17) gives

$$(M^{1a} L^{b_1} T^{c_1})^\alpha (M^{a_2} L^{b_2} T^{c_2})^\beta (M^{a_3} L^{b_3} T^{c_3})^\gamma (M^{a_4} L^{b_4} T^{c_4})^\delta (M^{a_5} L^{b_5} T^{c_5})^\epsilon = M^0 L^0 T^0$$

Collecting powers of M, L, and T, three algebraic equations are obtained:

$$\begin{aligned} a_1\alpha + a_2\beta + a_3\gamma + a_4\delta + a_5\epsilon &= 0 \\ b_1\alpha + b_2\beta + b_3\gamma + b_4\delta + b_5\epsilon &= 0 \\ c_1\alpha + c_2\beta + c_3\gamma + c_4\delta + c_5\epsilon &= 0 \end{aligned} \tag{10.18}$$

Since there are only three equations, only three exponents α, β, γ can be evaluated in terms of the others. One of these solutions will be

$$\gamma = \frac{(a_4b_1 - a_1b_4)(b_2c_1 - b_1c_2) - (b_4c_1 - c_4b_1)(a_2b_1 - a_1b_2)}{(a_3b_1 - a_1b_3)(b_2c_1 - b_1c_2) - (b_3c_1 - c_3b_1)(a_2b_1 - a_1b_2)}\,\delta$$
$$+ \frac{(a_5b_1 - a_1b_5)(b_2c_1 - b_1c_2) - (b_5c_1 - b_1c_5)(a_2b_1 - a_1b_2)}{(a_3b_1 - a_1b_3)(b_2c_1 - b_1c_2) - (b_3c_1 - b_1c_3)(a_2b_1 - a_1b_2)}\,\epsilon$$
$$= p_3\delta + q_3\epsilon \tag{10.19}$$

Similarly, the other two exponents α and β will have the form

$$\begin{aligned} \alpha &= p_1\delta + q_1\epsilon \\ \beta &= p_2\delta + q_2\epsilon \end{aligned} \tag{10.20}$$

Now Eq. (10.17), which pertains to one term in the original infinite power series, becomes

$$x_1^{(p_1\delta + q_1\epsilon)} x_2^{(p_2\delta + q_2\epsilon)} x_3^{(p_3\delta + q_3\epsilon)} x_4^{\delta} x_5^{\epsilon} = (x_1^{p_1} x_2^{p_2} x_3^{p_3} x_4)^{\delta} (x_1^{q_1} x_2^{q_2} x_3^{q_3} x_5)^{\epsilon}$$
$$= \Pi_1^{\delta} \Pi_2^{\epsilon} \tag{10.21}$$

Thus every term in the expansion of Eq. (10.16) can be modified into a two-Π-term product instead of the five-x product. Thus Eq. (10.16) becomes

$$f(x_1,x_2,x_3,x_4,x_5) = C_1\Pi_1^{\delta}\Pi_2^{\epsilon} + C_2(\Pi_1^{\delta}\Pi_2^{\epsilon})^2 + \cdots + C_k(\Pi_1^{\delta}\Pi_2)^k$$
$$= \phi(\Pi_1,\Pi_2)$$

which is the proof of the theorem.

Illustrative Example 10.1

Consider, for instance, the very general problem of fluid motion without heat transfer, where the geometry of the solid boundary is described by three typical linear dimensions x_1, x_2, and x_3 and the following properties are considered to be important:

$$\phi(U,\Delta p,\rho,\mu,\sigma,g,\beta,x_1,x_2,x_3) = 0 \tag{10.22}$$

In this relation, U is the characteristic velocity, Δp the pressure drop, ρ the density, μ the absolute viscosity, σ the surface-tension coefficient, g the gravitational acceleration, β the coefficient of compressibility defined in Eq. (1.6), and the x's are the three characteristic dimensions of the solid boundary. The most important part of dimensional analysis is the assumed knowledge of the important variables in the problem.

According to Eq. (10.17), the preceding equation can be expanded in an infinite power series, and each term will be of the form

$$[U^i \Delta p^j \rho^k \mu^l \sigma^m g^n \beta^q x_1^r x_2^s x_3^t] = M^0 L^0 T^0 \tag{10.23}$$

For each quantity in the preceding equation, substitute the dimensions MLT taken from Table 10.1.

$$(LT^{-1})^i(ML^{-1}T^{-2})^j(ML^{-3})^k(ML^{-1}T^{-1})^l (MT^{-2})^m(LT^{-2})^n(M^{-1}LT^2)^q(L)^r(L)^s(L)^t = M^0L^0T^0$$

This equation can be rewritten by collecting the same dimensions under one exponent

$$M^{j+k+l+m-q}L^{i-j-3k-l+n+q+r+s+t}T^{-i-2j-l-2m-2n+2q} = M^0L^0T^0$$

Equating the exponents, three algebraic equations are obtained:

$$j + k + l + m - q = 0$$
$$i - j - 3k - l + n + q + r + s + t = 0$$
$$-i - 2j - l - 2m - 2n + 2q = 0$$

There are 10 exponents and 3 equations. The best one can do is to solve 3 quantities in terms of the other 7. The proper selection of which ones to solve for will be determined as follows: As a rule, let the exponents of the quantity that will recur more often in the Π groupings be solved for. Here it is guessed that U, ρ, and one dimension, say x_1, will recur more often than the others, so solve for i, k, and r.

$$i = 2q - 2j - l - 2m - 2n$$
$$k = q - j - l - m$$
$$r = -l - m + n - s - t$$

Substitutions of these solutions in Eq. (10.23) yields

$$[U^{2q-2j-l-2m-2n}\,\Delta p^j\rho^{q-j-l-m}\mu^l\sigma^m g^n\beta^q x_1^{-l-m+n-s-t}x_2^s x_3^t] = M^0L^0T^0$$

Rewriting this equation by collecting terms with the same exponent, we have

$$\left[(\rho U^2\beta)^q\left(\frac{\Delta p}{\rho U^2}\right)^j\left(\frac{\mu}{\rho U x_1}\right)^l\left(\frac{\sigma}{\rho U^2 x_1}\right)^m\left(\frac{g x_1}{U^2}\right)^n\left(\frac{x_2}{x_1}\right)^s\left(\frac{x_3}{x_1}\right)^t\right] = M^0L^0T^0 \qquad (10.24)$$

Since Eq. (10.22) has been expanded in terms of Eq. (10.23) and since each term of Eq. (10.23), in turn, can be represented in terms of Eq. (10.24), then it is possible to write

$$\phi(U,\Delta p,\rho,\mu,\sigma,g,\beta,x_1,x_2,x_3) = \psi\left[(\rho U^2\beta), \left(\frac{\Delta p}{\rho U^2}\right), \left(\frac{\mu}{\rho U x_1}\right), \left(\frac{\sigma}{\rho U^2 x_1}\right), \left(\frac{g x_1}{U^2}\right), \left(\frac{x_2}{x_1}\right), \left(\frac{x_3}{x_1}\right)\right] = 0 \qquad (10.25)$$

The variables in the right-hand side of this equation are the new dimensionless Π terms. They are 7 in number instead of the original 10. Each Π term can now be analyzed individually.

The first is $(\rho U^2\beta)$, which is the Mach number squared $\mathfrak{M}^2$. This is because, as defined in Chap. VIII, the product $\rho\beta$ is the square of the velocity of sound. The second term is the pressure coefficient which, in general, is the dependent quantity for which Eq. (10.25) must be solved. The third term $\rho U x_1/\mu$ is theReynolds number $\mathfrak{R}$. The fourth term is the square of the Weber number $\mathcal{W}$. The fifth term U^2/gx_1 is the square of the Froude number $\mathfrak{F}r$, and the last two ratios represent the geometrical scaling ratios for the boundaries.

Solving for the pressure coefficient, Eq. (10.25) becomes

$$\frac{\Delta p}{\rho U^2} = \psi(\mathfrak{M}, \mathfrak{R}, \mathcal{W}, \mathfrak{F}r, x_2/x_1, x_3/x_1) \tag{10.26}$$

This dimensionless pressure change could be representative of the drag coefficient or the dimensionless pressure drop along a tube or channel. In the case of the flow in the pipe, x_2/x_1 will represent the roughness ratio, and x_3/x_1 will be the spacing between individual roughnesses.

Illustrative Example 10.2

The preceding problem was a purely dynamic one, and consequently only the three fundamental units M, L, and T were involved. Since heat transfer often takes place in fluid motion, let us consider the following problem.

A fluid moves at a characteristic velocity U around a body of characteristic dimension l. The density and viscosity of the fluid are represented by ρ and μ, and, since buoyant effects are to be considered, the gravitational acceleration g is of importance. Heat is being transferred from the body to the fluid or vice versa, and consequently the following additional heat properties of the fluid must be considered: the specific heat c_p, the thermal conductivity k, the film coefficient h, the temperature difference θ between the body and the fluid, and finally the volume-temperature expansion coefficient β. Three linear dimensions of the body could have been taken, as in the preceding problem, for describing a general shape of body, but, for the sake of simplicity, a spherically symmetric body, such as a sphere or a cube, or a two-dimensional infinite cylinder is used.

The relationship between these 10 independent quantities can be written, in general, as

$$f(U,l,\rho,\mu,g,c_p,k,h,\theta,\beta) = 0 \tag{10.27}$$

It was shown in Eq. (10.17) that this general functional relationship can be expanded in terms of an infinite power series, and a typical term will be

$$[U^a l^b \rho^c \mu^d g^e c_p^i k^j h^m \theta^n \beta^p] = M^0 L^0 T^0 \Theta^0 H^0 \tag{10.28}$$

It has already been shown that each of these terms will be dimensionless. A constant may be added to the terms of the expansion, but, since it is dimensionless, it is not considered in this analysis.

From Table 10.1, the units of each quantity in the preceding equation are substituted. Thus

$$(LT^{-1})^a(L)^b(ML^{-3})^c(ML^{-1}T^{-1})^d(LT^{-2})^e(HM^{-1}\Theta^{-1})^i(HL^{-1}T^{-1}\Theta^{-1})^j$$
$$(HT^{-1}L^{-2}\Theta^{-1})^m(\Theta)^n(\Theta)^p = M^0L^0T^0H^0\Theta^0$$

The following 5 algebraic equations are obtained when the powers of the same units are equated:

$$
\begin{aligned}
c + d - i &= 0 \\
a + b - 3c - d + e - j - 2m &= 0 \\
-a - d - 2e - j - m &= 0 \\
-i - j - m + n - p &= 0 \\
i + j + m &= 0
\end{aligned}
$$

There are 5 equations and 10 unknowns. Solving for b, c, d, j, and n,

$$
\begin{aligned}
b &= a + 3e + m \\
c &= a + 2e \\
d &= -a - 2e + i \\
j &= -i - m \\
n &= p
\end{aligned}
$$

Substitution of these values into Eq. (10.28) yields

$$[U^a l^{a+3e+m} \rho^{a+2e} \mu^{-a-2e+i} g^e c_p^i k^{-i-m} h^m \theta^p \beta^p] = M^0 L^0 T^0 H^0 \Theta^0$$

Combining into factors of same powers, the preceding expression becomes

$$\left[\left(\frac{\rho U l}{\mu}\right)^a \left(\frac{l^3 \rho^2 g}{\mu^2}\right)^e \left(\frac{hl}{k}\right)^m \left(\frac{c_p \mu}{k}\right)^i (\theta\beta)^p\right] = M^0 L^0 T^0 H^0 \Theta^0 \qquad (10.29)$$

These are the dimensionless Π terms. Thus, in general, all the Π terms of this type can be combined into a single function of the type

$$\phi\left(\frac{\rho U l}{\mu}, \frac{l^3 \rho^2 g}{\mu^2}, \frac{hl}{k}, \frac{c_p \mu}{k}, \beta\theta\right) = 0 \qquad (10.30)$$

From further physical reasoning, it becomes obvious that the second and fifth dimensionless terms must appear jointly as one term; in other words, that the power e and p must be the same. This conclusion is derived from the fact that the buoyant force per unit volume[3] is $(\rho_2 - \rho_1)g$, and, since the change in the density with temperature is $\rho_1 \beta\theta$, then $(\rho_2 - \rho_1)g = \rho\beta\theta g$. We shall see how these dimensionless ratios can also be obtained from the ratio of forces influencing the motion. Thus, since the buoyant force must appear as such, $\beta\theta$ must combine with the second dimensionless ratio. Thus

$$\phi\left(\frac{\rho U l}{\mu}, \frac{l^3 \rho^2 g \beta\theta}{\mu^2}, \frac{hl}{k}, \frac{c_p \mu}{k}\right) = 0 \qquad (10.31)$$

The first term in the last equation is the Reynolds number $\mathcal{R}$. The second dimensionless term, which is essential in buoyant convection, is the Grashof number $\mathcal{G}$. The third term, which is generally considered as the dependent variable in the problem, is the Nusselt number $\mathfrak{N}$. The last term, which is

[3] The buoyant force derived in Sec. 2.6 reduces to the value stated here, provided an unchanged unit volume is considered.

entirely made up only of the properties of the material, is the Prandtl number $\mathcal{P}$. Thus one can say that, in the problem considered,

$$\mathfrak{N} = \psi(\mathcal{R}, \mathcal{G}, \mathcal{P}) \tag{10.32}$$

Often in problems with heat transfer, the Reynolds and Prandtl numbers appear as a product. This new dimensionless product equal to $\rho U l c_p / k$ is called the *Péclet number*.

10.5 Dimensionless Considerations from the Equation of Motion

Geometric, kinematic, and dynamic similitude was discussed in Sec. 3.3. Consider now two flows past geometrically similar bodies with characteristic dimensions L_1 and L_2. Let also the characteristic velocity, say the free stream velocities, be V_1 and V_2. This immediately gives corresponding characteristic times $t_1 = L_1/V_1$ and $t_2 = L_2/V_2$. If the motions involved are affected by inertia, gravity, pressure and viscous forces, for instance, the governing equations of motion of a characteristic fluid particle in each case would be as in Eq. (9.13).

$$\rho_1 \frac{d\boldsymbol{U}_1}{dt_1} = \rho_1 \boldsymbol{g}_1 - \nabla_1 p_1 + \mu_1 \nabla_1^2 \boldsymbol{U}_1$$

$$\rho_2 \frac{d\boldsymbol{U}_2}{dt_2} = \rho_2 \boldsymbol{g}_2 - \nabla_2 p_2 + \mu_2 \nabla_2^2 \boldsymbol{U}_2 \qquad [10.33(a)]$$

For dynamic similitude to exist in each of these cases, the ratio of like forces must be the same. That is,

$$\frac{\rho_2\, d\boldsymbol{U}_2/dt_2}{\rho_1\, d\boldsymbol{U}_1/dt_1} = \frac{\rho_2 \boldsymbol{g}_2}{\rho_1 \boldsymbol{g}_1}$$

$$= \frac{\nabla_2 p_2}{\nabla_1 p_1} \qquad [10.33(b)]$$

$$= \frac{\mu_2 \nabla_2^2 \boldsymbol{U}_2}{\mu_1 \nabla_1^2 \boldsymbol{U}_1}$$

In considering the first equality, we rearrange as follows:

$$\frac{d\boldsymbol{U}_2/dt_2}{\boldsymbol{g}_2} = \frac{d\boldsymbol{U}_1/dt_1}{\boldsymbol{g}_1} \tag{10.34}$$

The rate of change of the velocity at each point and in each case depends on the boundary and initial conditions. In other words, $\boldsymbol{U}_1$ and $\boldsymbol{U}_2$

depend on V_1 and V_2; and t_1 and t_2 depend on L_1/V_1 and L_2/V_2. The ratios in Eq. (10.34) are not equal to but depend on

$$\frac{V}{L/V} \div g$$

For both cases then, the equality of the ratio of characteristic quantities is as valid as the equality in Eq. (10.34). Thus,

$$\mathfrak{F}r^2 = \frac{V_2^2}{L_2 g_2} = \frac{V_1^2}{L_1 g_1} \tag{10.35}$$

where g is the absolute value $\boldsymbol{g}$ or a characteristic value in a field where $\boldsymbol{g}$ is variable. The ratio in Eq. (10.35) is the *Froude number,* $\mathfrak{F}r$, also discussed soon after Eq. (10.25). It is easily seen from this that the Froude number derived from the ratio of the inertia force to the gravitational force is a characteristic dimensionless number that establishes similitude in flows where inertia and gravity forces are predominant.

The second ratio in Eq. [10.33(*b*)] is

$$\frac{\nabla_2 p_2}{\rho_2\, d\boldsymbol{U}_2/dt_2} = \frac{\nabla_1 p_1}{\rho_1\, d\boldsymbol{U}_1/dt_1}$$

If we choose to replace in each case ∇p by a characteristic pressure divided by a characteristic distance, then a new characteristic ratio is established.

$$\frac{p_2/L_2}{\rho_2 V_2/L_2/V_2} = \frac{p_1/L_1}{\rho_1 V_1/L_1/V_1},$$

or

$$C_p = \frac{p_2}{\rho_2 V_2^2} = \frac{p_1}{\rho_1 V_1^2} \tag{10.36}$$

This is the pressure coefficient already discussed in Eq. (10.26). Again, it is worth noting that in flows where inertia and pressure forces predominate, the pressure coefficient must be the same in order for dynamic similitude to exist.

For variable density flows, Eq. (10.36) takes another familiar form. Using the perfect-gas law and the definition of the velocity of sound, we have

$$p/\rho = RT \quad \text{and} \quad \gamma p/\rho = \gamma RT = a^2$$

where T is the temperature, R the gas constant, γ the ratio of specific heat, and a the speed of sound. Thus, Eq. (10.36) becomes

$$\mathfrak{M} = \frac{V_1}{a_1} = \frac{V_2}{a_2} \tag{10.37}$$

This is the *Mach number*.

The third and last ratio in Eq. [10.33(*b*)] is

$$\frac{\rho_2\, dU_2/dt_2}{\mu_2 \nabla_2^2 U_2} = \frac{\rho_1\, dU_1/dt_1}{\mu_1 \nabla_1^2 U_1}$$

The procedure to reduce to characteristic quantities is the same. The second derivative in ∇^2 must be replaced by one over the square of the characteristic dimension. Thus

$$\frac{\rho_2 V_2/L_2/V_2}{\mu_2 V_2/L_2^2} = \frac{\rho_1 V_1/L_1/V_1}{\mu_1 V_1/L_1^2}$$

or

$$= \frac{\rho_2 V_2 L_2}{\mu_2} = \frac{\rho_1 V_1 L_1}{\mu_1} \tag{10.38}$$

This is the *Reynolds number* discussed in Chaps. III, IX and X. It was obtained from the characteristic ratio of the inertia to viscous forces.

If in Eqs. [10.33(*a*)] the buoyant forces owing to temperature differences were considered, a force $\rho g \beta\, dT$ should have been added, where β is the volume coefficient of thermal expansion and dT is the infinitesimal difference of temperature. Again, the ratio of forces would have yielded

$$\frac{g_2 \beta_2\, dT_2 L_2}{V_2^2} = \frac{g_1 \beta_1\, dT_1 L_1}{V_1^2}$$

Multiplying this dimensionless quantity by the Reynolds number square yields the Grashof number discussed in Illustrative Example 10.2. Thus,

$$\mathcal{G} = \frac{g\beta L^3\, dT}{\nu^2}$$

is the characteristic, dimensionless number that establishes similitude when temperature-dependent buoyant forces and inertia forces are predominant.

Problems

10.1 A classic example of the application of dimensional analysis to a mechanics problem is the determination of the period of swing t of a pendulum. At first, one may think that the period is dependent on the mass m, the length l, the gravitational acceleration g, and finally the angular amplitude θ (in radians). Find t as a function of dimensionless groupings of the above variables.

10.2 Arrange the following groups of quantities into dimensionless ratios: (a) U,t,ν; (b) p,t,μ; (c) p,ρ,U; (d) U,g,L; (e) F,ρ,V,L; (f) p,ρ,L,t; (g) Q,ρ,t,L; (h) Q,L,μ; (i) ρ,g,L,σ; (j) μ,t,ρ,L.

10.3 Arrange the following groups of quantities into dimensionless ratios: (a) h,L,k where h is the heat-transfer film coefficient and k the thermal conductivity; (b) k,c_p,μ; (c) Q,c_p,k,L; (d) h,c_p,U,ρ; (e) h,k,μ,ρ,g.

10.4 The torque T of an axial-flow fan is believed to be a function of the blade diameter D, its angular velocity ω and the fluid properties ρ, μ, and the through-flow velocity U. Show that, if ω, ρ, and D occur more often in the dimensionless parameters,

$$\frac{T}{D^5\rho\omega^2} = f\left(\frac{\mu}{D^2\rho\omega}, \frac{U}{\omega D}\right)$$

10.5 The pressure drop in a pipe is figured to be a function of its length L, its diameter D, the spatial average velocity of the fluid U, the gravitational acceleration g, and the density and viscosity of the fluid ρ and μ. If the diameter, density, and velocity occur more often in the resultant dimensionless groupings, show that the dimensionless pressure drop is

$$\frac{\Delta p}{\rho U^2} = f\left(\frac{L}{D}, \mathcal{R}, \mathfrak{Fr}\right)$$

10.6 If the inclination of the pipe is neglected (gravitational effects are unimportant), show how the preceding result agrees well with the Darcy-Weisbach relationship for the pipe in Chap. IX. Ultimately, show that the frictional resistance coefficient is a unique function of the Reynolds number. It must be understood that, since in the original assumptions of the preceding problem the roughness did not enter, the results here would apply only to smooth pipes.

10.7 The drag coefficient of a solid shape is required at air speed of 400 ft/sec and air temperature of 50°F. If wind-tunnel facilities at this speed and the size of the body are not obtainable, what should be the speed of water in a water tunnel if the experiment is to be conducted at the same temperature with the same body?

10.8 The height of a liquid h in a capillary tube is thought of being a function of the specific weight of the liquid relative to that of the ambient air, to the surface-tension coefficient σ, and to the radius of the capillary tube. From dimensional reasoning, deduce that h/r is consistent with Eq. (2.37).

Survey of Vector Analysis

appendix A

A.1 General

This appendix is an introduction to vector algebra and vector calculus as preparatory material for students lacking an adequate mathematical background. The logical place for the introduction of this material, if it is needed, is immediately after Chap. I. Throughout the book, it has been assumed that the reader has an adequate background in vector calculus. When possible, reference has been made to this appendix to supply the necessary background information.

It should be clear to the reader that this appendix is, at best, a condensation of the necessary minimum principles in vector calculus. There are many excellent treatises on vector calculus available in print. The reader is referred to a number of these in various footnotes of this appendix.

A.2 Scalars and Vectors

Even with the limited experience afforded by Chap. I the reader should have made the important discovery that some physical quantities require a *number* or a *magnitude* with the proper units to describe a property, while others require, in addition, a direction relative to a frame of reference.

When temperature is described, it is sufficient to give a single number a accompanied by the proper units—degree Centigrade or degree Fahrenheit. The single, real number a does not have the same value when followed by different units, but the fact still remains that a physical quantity such as temperature requires only one number for its description and consequently is called a *scalar quantity.* For identification, symbols representing a scalar quantity are written in *italic.* Other scalar quantities are the *density, energy* and most *thermodynamic properties.* One can say that, in the absence of motion, thermodynamics is an exclusive science of scalar properties.

Other physical quantities such as the *velocity* or the *force* require for their description besides the magnitude and its proper units a *direction of action.* This is extremely important, for without their direction the position of a moving particle or the effect of a force cannot be determined. These physical quantities are then called *vectors* because they are directed quantities. To establish the direction of a vector, a frame of reference may be chosen, and its choice is just as arbitrary as the units associated with the magnitude.

Graphically, a vector can be represented completely by a pointed straight line originating at a point in space. Its length is representative of the magnitude, and its position in space establishes its *sense of action.* The arrow at the other end from the *origin* represents its direction. A *unit vector* is a vector whose magnitude is unity.

Two vectors are said to be equal when they have the same length and direction. For this to be true the two vectors need not coincide, but they must be parallel and of equal length. If the origin of a vector may be chosen arbitrarily, the vector is said to be *free* or *axial.*[1] A vector is said to be *bound* or *polar* when its origin is fixed in space. For instance, a force is a polar vector, since when moved to different positions it causes different moments, although its magnitude and direction are kept the same. In this volume a vector symbol has been distinguished by *bold face* type.

Since a vector needs a direction in order to be identified and since its direction can only be identified relative to a frame of reference, it is easy to see that one scalar number a is no longer sufficient for its descrip-

[1] The reason for the choice of this name is that vectors representing rigid body rotation are of this type, and they are along the *axis of rotation.* The position of the *rotation* on the body is of no importance as long as it maintains direction and magnitude.

tion. For instance, if a reference system of three mutually perpendicular axes is chosen, it will be necessary to specify at least three components of this vector, a_1, a_2 and a_3, on the respective axes. Now it becomes clear that unlike the scalar, a vector needs three independent scalar quantities for its description. Two vectors are equal only when their magnitude and directions are the same, this implies that their respective components are equal.

Since vector quantities have a magnitude as well as a direction, or, in other words, since three scalars are necessary to describe them, algebra and calculus must be extended for vector operations. We must regard at all times *a vector as an entity that has different components in different coordinate systems, while bearing in mind the fact that the resultant of any set of coordinates gives the same vector*. This is a property of vectors that is very important in vector operations.

A.3 Addition and Subtraction of Vectors

The rules of operations with vectors are analogous to those of operations with ordinary scalar numbers; namely, that the *result of the operation must be an entity and, therefore, not dependent on the frame of reference used to describe it*.

Let us define that the sum of two vectors a and b is a third vector c whose components are the sum of the components of a and b on the same axis.

$$\begin{aligned} a_x + b_x &= c_x \\ a_y + b_y &= c_y \\ a_z + b_z &= c_z \end{aligned} \tag{A.1}$$

To illustrate that the sum, as defined, gives an entity independent of the choice of coordinates, consider Fig. A.1. Two coordinate systems are chosen both on the plane formed by a and b. The z-component of the vectors is zero; some generality in the proof is lost. These results would be just as valid if the third coordinate were considered.

If the origin of b is brought to the end of a, as shown, then, from the projections on Oxy and $Ox'y'$, it is seen that

$$\begin{aligned} a_x + b_x &= c_x \\ a_y + b_y &= c_y \end{aligned}$$

conforms with the definition. It is also seen that the *commutative law* of addition is satisfied.

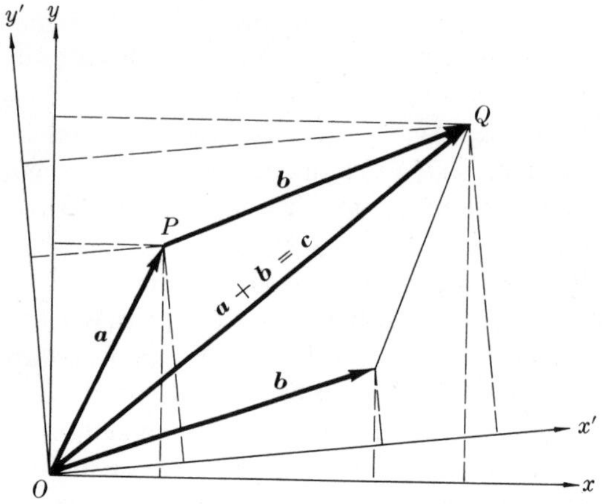

Figure A.1
Addition of two vectors.

$$\boldsymbol{a} + \boldsymbol{b} = \boldsymbol{b} + \boldsymbol{a}$$

Thus, to form an addition of two vectors, one needs to form a parallelogram with the vectors $\boldsymbol{a}$ and $\boldsymbol{b}$; the diagonal extending from the origin of the first to the end of the other determines the addition vector. The law of vector addition is often called the *parallelogram law*.

The rule for subtraction is obtained readily from the figure, since $\boldsymbol{c} - \boldsymbol{b} = \boldsymbol{a}$. The vector $\boldsymbol{b}$ is opposed to $\boldsymbol{c}$ in that the arrows oppose at Q and thus $\boldsymbol{a}$ starting at the origin of $\boldsymbol{c}$ becomes the result of the subtraction.

The *associative law* can be shown to hold such that

$$\boldsymbol{a} + (\boldsymbol{b} + \boldsymbol{c}) = (\boldsymbol{a} + \boldsymbol{b}) + \boldsymbol{c} = \boldsymbol{a} + \boldsymbol{b} + \boldsymbol{c} \qquad \text{(A.2)}$$

Finally, from Eq. (A.1) we see that a *vector equation* is equivalent to three scalar equations, and that the result of a summation of two vectors is *coplanar* with the two vectors.

A.4 Multiplication of a Vector by a Scalar

At least for the case when the scalar is an integer, it is easy to see that $m\boldsymbol{a}$ implies m additions of the same vector which result into a new vector in the same direction but with a magnitude m times larger. The same is true for the case when m is not an integer. The following relations are then true:

$$
\begin{aligned}
(m+n)\mathbf{a} &= m\mathbf{a} + n\mathbf{a} \\
m(n\mathbf{a}) - n(m\mathbf{a}) &= (mn)\mathbf{a} = mn\mathbf{a}
\end{aligned} \tag{A.3}
$$

A.5 Unit Vectors and Vector Addition of Components

Let a vector $\mathbf{a}$ be represented in a coordinate system as shown in Fig. A.5. Let $\mathbf{i}$, $\mathbf{j}$, and $\mathbf{k}$ be three unit vectors along the coordinate axis defined to be positive in the increasing direction of the coordinate. These unit vectors will have as components:

$$
\begin{array}{ll}
\mathbf{i} & (1,0,0) \\
\mathbf{j} & (0,1,0) \\
\mathbf{k} & (0,0,1)
\end{array}
$$

Now, according to Sec. A.4, the quantities $\mathbf{i}a_x$, $\mathbf{j}a_y$, and $\mathbf{k}a_z$ represent vectors of magnitude a_x, a_y, and a_z in the three corresponding direc-

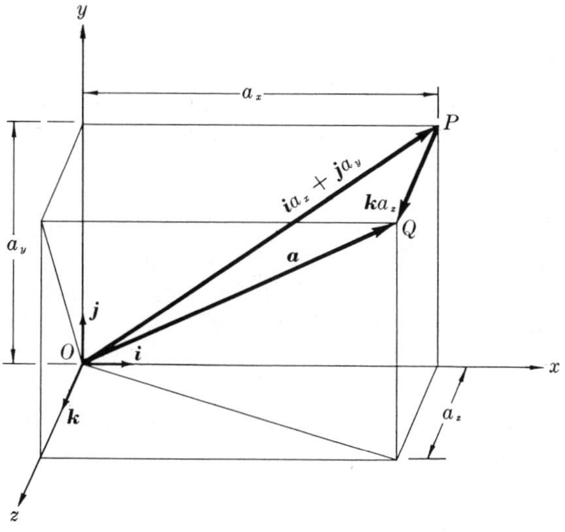

Figure A.2
Vector and components.

tions. According to the rule of addition $\boldsymbol{i}a_x + \boldsymbol{j}a_y$ is the vector $\overrightarrow{OP}$, and

$$\boldsymbol{i}a_x + \boldsymbol{j}a_y + \boldsymbol{k}a_z = \boldsymbol{a} \tag{A.4}$$

represents the vector $\boldsymbol{a}$ in terms of its components a_x, a_y, a_z, and the unit vectors. Equation (A.4) will be the basis for representing, in an equation form, any vector in terms of its components. The absolute value or magnitude of $\boldsymbol{a}$ is equal to

$$|\boldsymbol{a}| = a = \sqrt{a_x^2 + a_y^2 + a_z^2} \tag{A.5}$$

From Fig. A.1, the projection of the sum of two vectors on a coordinate was seen to equal the sum of the projections. Therefore, since

$$\boldsymbol{c} = \boldsymbol{a} + \boldsymbol{b},$$

then

$$\begin{aligned} \boldsymbol{c} &= \boldsymbol{i}c_x + \boldsymbol{j}c_y + \boldsymbol{k}c_z \\ &= \boldsymbol{i}(a_x + b_x) + \boldsymbol{j}(a_y + b_y) + \boldsymbol{k}(a_z + b_z), \end{aligned} \tag{A.6}$$

and

$$c = c_x^2 + c_y^2 + c_z^2 = (a_x + b_x)^2 + (a_y + b_y)^2 + (a_z + b_z)^2$$

When vector quantities are added the resultant quantity is no longer the sum of their magnitudes as in the case of scalars but a vector whose components are the sum of the components of each vector on the same axis. Equation (A.6) shows this relationship.

A.6 The Product of Vectors

A product of vectors must be defined so that the resultant is not a function of coordinate choice. The idea is to find which combination of coordinate multiplication gives a resultant, scalar or vector, that is independent of coordinate rotation. Obviously not any arbitrary combination of coordinate products will satisfy this requirement.

For instance, let a vector a make an angle θ with a vector b as shown in Fig. A.3. Let $\boldsymbol{e}_1$ and $\boldsymbol{e}_2$ be the unit vectors along $\boldsymbol{a}$ and $\boldsymbol{b}$ such that $\boldsymbol{e}_1 = \boldsymbol{a}/|\boldsymbol{a}|$ and $\boldsymbol{e}_2 = \boldsymbol{b}/|\boldsymbol{b}|$. The triangle $OA'B'$ is isosceles and, therefore, according to Eq. (A.6),

$$(\overrightarrow{A'B'})^2 = (e_{1x} - e_{2x})^2 + (e_{1y} - e_{2y})^2 + (e_{1z} - e_{2z})^2$$

But since $e_{1x}^2 + e_{1y}^2 + e_{1z}^2 = e_{2x}^2 + e_{2y}^2 + e_{2z}^2 = 1$, then,

$$(\overrightarrow{A'B'})^2 = 2 - 2(e_{1x}e_{2x} + e_{1y}e_{2y} + e_{1z}e_{2z}) \tag{A.7}$$

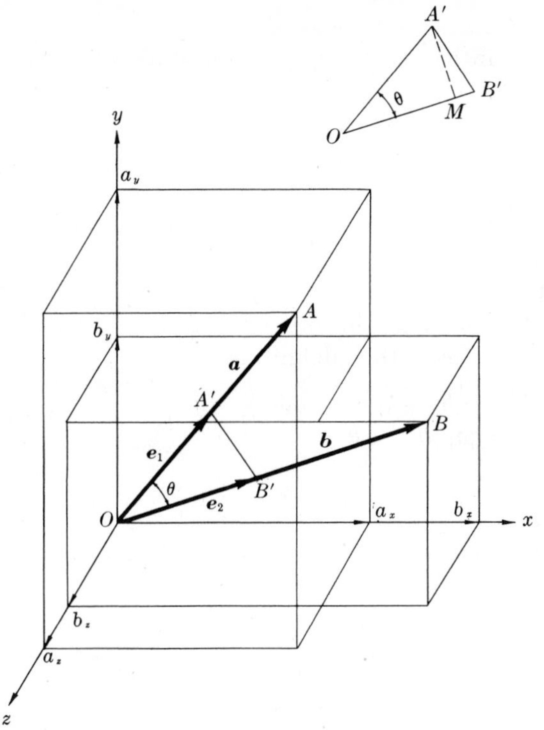

Figure A.3
Product of vectors.

Now, from triangle $OA'D'$,

$$\begin{aligned}(\overrightarrow{A'B'})^2 &= (\overrightarrow{A'M'})^2 + (\overrightarrow{MB'})^2 \\ &= \sin^2\theta + (1 - \cos\theta)^2 \\ &= 2 - 2\cos\theta \end{aligned} \tag{A.8}$$

From Eqs. (A.7) and (A.8),

$$\cos\theta = e_{1x}e_{2x} + e_{1y}e_{2y} + e_{1z}e_{2z}$$

Substituting values of $\boldsymbol{e}_1$ and $\boldsymbol{e}_2$ in terms of $\boldsymbol{a}$ and $\boldsymbol{b}$,

$$\cos\theta = \frac{a_xb_x + a_yb_y + a_zb_z}{|\boldsymbol{a}|\,|\boldsymbol{b}|} \tag{A.9}$$

Now when two vectors are given, the angle θ between them is fixed and so is $\cos\theta$. Therefore, the right hand side of Eq. (A.9) is independent of which orthogonal coordinate system is used at the origin 0, and consequently, the scalar quantity $a_x b_x + a_y b_y + a_z b_z$ is always a constant provided $\boldsymbol{a}$ and $\boldsymbol{b}$ are fixed.

A.7 The Scalar Product

On the basis of the results found in the previous section, the *scalar product* or the *inner* or *dot product* is then defined as

$$\begin{aligned} \boldsymbol{a} \cdot \boldsymbol{b} &= a_x b_x + a_y b_y + a_z b_z \\ &= |\boldsymbol{a}|\,|\boldsymbol{b}| \cos \theta \end{aligned} \tag{A.10}$$

and is read as "$\boldsymbol{a}$ dot $\boldsymbol{b}$".

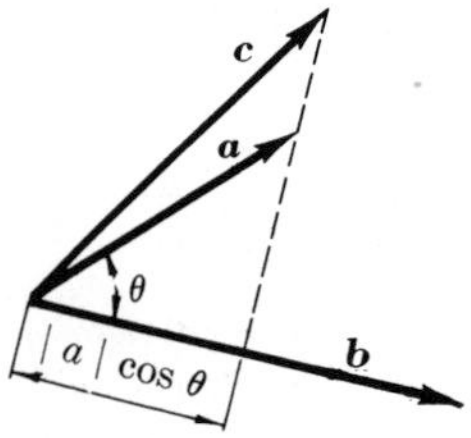

Figure A.4
Representation of the scalar product.

This definition of the dot product shows that it is equal to the product of the absolute value of $\boldsymbol{b}$ and the projection of $\boldsymbol{a}$ on $\boldsymbol{b}$. As long as this projection remains the same, as shown in Fig. A.4, $\boldsymbol{a} \cdot \boldsymbol{b} = \boldsymbol{c} \cdot \boldsymbol{b}$ and $\boldsymbol{a} \neq \boldsymbol{c}$.

From Eq. (A.10) we verify that since $\cos \theta$ is an even function the order of the product $\boldsymbol{a}$ to $\boldsymbol{b}$ or $\boldsymbol{b}$ to $\boldsymbol{a}$, or positive and negative θ gives the same result.

$$\boldsymbol{a} \cdot \boldsymbol{b} = \boldsymbol{b} \cdot \boldsymbol{a}$$

and that

$$\boldsymbol{a} \cdot \boldsymbol{a} = |\boldsymbol{a}|^2 = \boldsymbol{a}^2 = a^2 \tag{A.11}$$

If $\boldsymbol{a}$ is perpendicular to $\boldsymbol{b}$, then

$$\boldsymbol{a} \cdot \boldsymbol{b} = 0$$

The dot product of the unit vectors are then

$$\begin{aligned} \boldsymbol{i}\cdot\boldsymbol{i} &= \boldsymbol{j}\cdot\boldsymbol{j} = \boldsymbol{k}\cdot\boldsymbol{k} = 1 \\ \boldsymbol{i}\cdot\boldsymbol{j} &= \boldsymbol{j}\cdot\boldsymbol{k} = \boldsymbol{k}\cdot\boldsymbol{i} = 0 \end{aligned} \tag{A.12}$$

One can show easily that the *distributive law* applies to the dot product

$$\boldsymbol{a}\cdot(\boldsymbol{b} + \boldsymbol{c}) = \boldsymbol{a}\cdot\boldsymbol{b} + \boldsymbol{a}\cdot\boldsymbol{c}$$

An application of the dot product in mechanics is seen when it is necessary to find the energy involved in the movement of the point of application of a force. This energy is given by

$$E = \boldsymbol{F}\cdot\boldsymbol{r} \tag{A.13}$$

This shows that the maximum energy involved in the movement of a force $\boldsymbol{F}$ along a distance $\boldsymbol{r}$ is when the distance is along $\boldsymbol{F}$.

A.8 The Vector Product

The scalar product is a linear combination of three component products of the total nine possible. It will become evident that the other six can be combined in pairs to form a so-called *vector product.* To show which combination is independent of rotation of coordinates the following method is used: Let the resultant of the vector product of $\boldsymbol{a}$ and $\boldsymbol{b}$, making an angle θ, be a vector $\boldsymbol{c}$ perpendicular to the plane formed by $\boldsymbol{a}$ and $\boldsymbol{b}$. Then it follows that $\boldsymbol{a}\cdot\boldsymbol{c} = \boldsymbol{b}\cdot\boldsymbol{c} = 0$, or

$$\begin{aligned} a_xc_x + a_yc_y + a_zc_z &= 0 \\ b_xc_x + b_yc_y + b_zc_z &= 0 \end{aligned} \tag{A.14}$$

If c_x and c_y are solved in terms of c_z,

$$\frac{c_x}{a_yb_z - a_zb_y} = \frac{c_y}{a_zb_x - a_xb_z} = \frac{c_z}{a_xb_y - a_yb_x} = m \tag{A.15}$$

To preserve the symmetry of the dependence of the component $\boldsymbol{c}$ in terms of the components of $\boldsymbol{a}$ and $\boldsymbol{b}$ the quantity m must be a constant. Solving for c_x, c_y and c_z,

$$\begin{aligned} c_x &= m(a_yb_z - a_zb_y) \\ c_y &= m(a_zb_x - a_xb_z) \\ c_z &= m(a_xb_y - a_yb_x) \end{aligned} \tag{A.16}$$

The absolute value of $\boldsymbol{c}$ is

$$
\begin{aligned}
c^2 &= c_x^2 + c_y^2 + c_z^2 \\
&= m^2[a_x^2(b_y^2 + b_z^2) + a_y^2(b_z^2 + b_x^2) + a_z^2(b_x^2 + b_y^2) \\
&\quad - 2(a_yb_ya_zb_z + a_zb_za_xb_x + a_xb_xa_yb_y)] \\
&= m^2[a_x^2(b^2 - b_x^2) + a_y^2(b^2 - b_y^2) + a_z^2(b^2 - b_z^2) \\
&\quad - 2(a_yb_ya_zb_z + a_zb_za_xb_x + a_xb_xa_yb_y)] \\
&= m^2[a^2b^2 - (a_xb_x + a_yb_y + a_zb_z)^2]
\end{aligned}
$$

According to Eq. (A.10),

$$
\begin{aligned}
c^2 &= m^2a^2b^2(1 - \cos^2\theta) \\
&= m^2a^2b^2\sin^2\theta
\end{aligned}
\tag{A.17}
$$

This equation shows that the definition of the vector product gives a vector $\boldsymbol{c}$ whose magnitude is dependent on the magnitudes of $\boldsymbol{a}$ and $\boldsymbol{b}$ and the sine of the angle between them. Consequently, the result of the product is independent of the orthogonal coordinate system chosen. To evaluate m we can choose $\boldsymbol{a}$, $\boldsymbol{b}$, and $\boldsymbol{c}$ to be three mutually perpendicular unit vectors, say $\boldsymbol{i}, \boldsymbol{j}$, and $\boldsymbol{k}$ along x, y, and z. Then $a_x = b_y = c_z = 1$ and $a_y = a_z = b_x = b_z = c_x = c_y = 0$. From Eq. (A.16) $m = 1$ and in general,

$$
\begin{aligned}
c_x &= a_yb_z - a_zb_y \\
c_y &= a_zb_x - a_xb_z \\
c_z &= a_xb_y - a_yb_x
\end{aligned}
\tag{A.18}
$$

Thus, the *vector product* of two vectors $\boldsymbol{a}$ and $\boldsymbol{b}$ with an angle θ measured positive from $\boldsymbol{a}$ to $\boldsymbol{b}$ is a third vector $\boldsymbol{c}$ perpendicular to the plane formed by $\boldsymbol{a}$ and $\boldsymbol{b}$ and in the direction prescribed by the third axis of a conventional coordinate system (the right-handed system chosen here).

The *vector product*, or the *cross* or *outer product*, is then given by

$$
\begin{aligned}
\boldsymbol{a} \times \boldsymbol{b} &= \boldsymbol{c} \\
&= \boldsymbol{i}(a_yb_z - a_zb_y) + \boldsymbol{j}(a_zb_x - a_xb_z) + \boldsymbol{k}(a_xb_y - a_yb_x) \\
&= \boldsymbol{e}ab\sin\theta
\end{aligned}
\tag{A.19}
$$

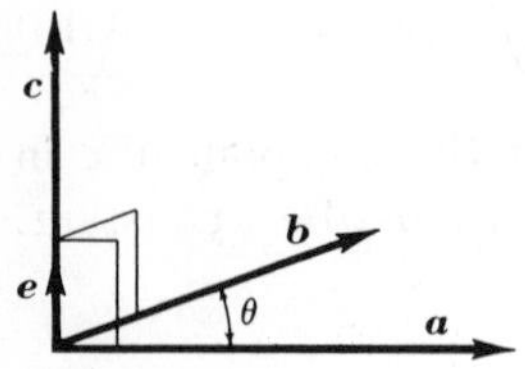

Figure A.5
Vector product.

Where $\boldsymbol{e}$ is a unit vector normal to the plane of $\boldsymbol{a}$ and $\boldsymbol{b}$ in the direction of the right-hand rule. Since $\sin\theta$ is an odd function, it shows that

$$\boldsymbol{a} \times \boldsymbol{b} = -\boldsymbol{b} \times \boldsymbol{a}$$

and that

$$\begin{aligned} &\boldsymbol{i} \times \boldsymbol{j} = \boldsymbol{k}; \quad \boldsymbol{j} \times \boldsymbol{k} = \boldsymbol{i}; \quad \boldsymbol{k} \times \boldsymbol{i} = \boldsymbol{j} \\ &\boldsymbol{i} \times \boldsymbol{i} = \boldsymbol{j} \times \boldsymbol{j} = \boldsymbol{k} \times \boldsymbol{k} = 0 \end{aligned} \tag{A.20}$$

The cross product of two parallel vectors is always zero.

From Eq. (A.19):

$$\boldsymbol{a} \times \boldsymbol{b} = \begin{vmatrix} \boldsymbol{i} & \boldsymbol{j} & \boldsymbol{k} \\ a_x & a_y & a_z \\ b_x & b_y & b_z \end{vmatrix} \tag{A.21}$$

If m and n are scalar numbers, then

$$m\boldsymbol{a} \times n\boldsymbol{b} = mn\boldsymbol{a} \times \boldsymbol{b} = mn(\boldsymbol{a} \times \boldsymbol{b}) \tag{A.22}$$

Physically, the cross product is involved, for instance, in the evaluation of the peripheral velocity of a point P around an axis OO' as shown in Fig. A.6. If $\boldsymbol{\omega}$ is the angular velocity of the point P and $\boldsymbol{r}$ the distance

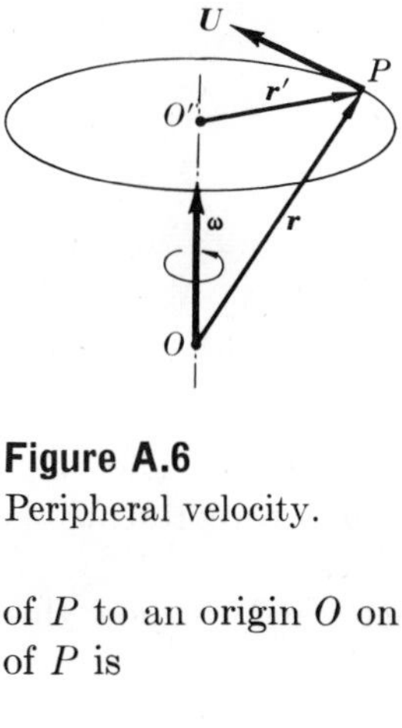

Figure A.6
Peripheral velocity.

of P to an origin O on the axis of rotation, then the peripheral velocity of P is

$$\begin{aligned} \boldsymbol{U} &= \boldsymbol{\omega} \times \boldsymbol{r} \\ &\boldsymbol{\omega} \times \boldsymbol{r}' \end{aligned} \tag{A.23}$$

This last equation does not imply that $\boldsymbol{r}$ is equal to $\boldsymbol{r}'$, but rather that any vector extending from P to any point on the axis will give the same cross product with $\boldsymbol{\omega}$, including $\boldsymbol{r}'$, that is perpendicular to the axis of rotation.

$$\begin{aligned} |\boldsymbol{U}| &= \omega(OP) \sin\theta \\ &\omega(OP') \end{aligned}$$

The direction of the vector product is along $\boldsymbol{U}$ perpendicular to the plane of $\boldsymbol{\omega}$ and $\boldsymbol{r}$ or $\boldsymbol{r}'$.

Another application is in the evaluation of the moment or the torque produced by a force $\boldsymbol{F}$ at a distance $\boldsymbol{r}$ from an axis

$$\boldsymbol{T} = \boldsymbol{r} \times \boldsymbol{F}$$

If, in Fig. A.6, $\boldsymbol{F}$ is put instead of $\boldsymbol{U}$ then $\boldsymbol{T}$ will be in the direction of $\boldsymbol{\omega}$.

Finally, the cross product of two vectors represents the area of the parallelogram formed by the two vectors. Here in Fig. A.7 it can be

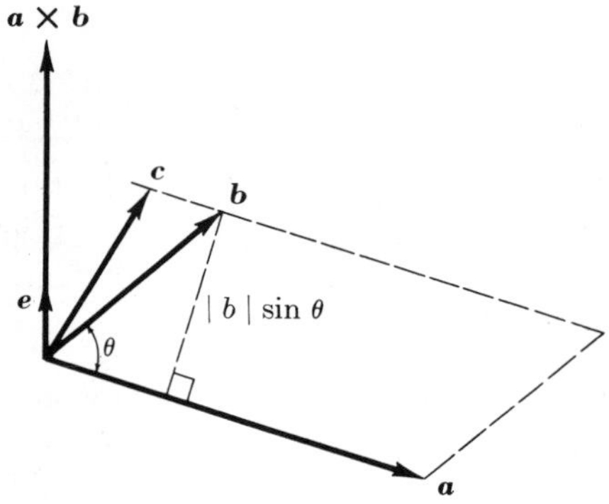

Figure A.7
The area vector.

seen that

$$\boldsymbol{a} \times \boldsymbol{b} = \boldsymbol{e}|\boldsymbol{a}|\,|\boldsymbol{b}| \sin \theta \tag{A.24}$$

where $\boldsymbol{e}$ is a unit vector normal to the plane of $\boldsymbol{a}$ and $\boldsymbol{b}$. The value $ab \sin \theta$ is the area of the parallelogram and thus $\boldsymbol{a} \times \boldsymbol{b}$ represents the area vector.

The distribution law applies to cross products, and to show this, it is necessary to prove that

$$\boldsymbol{a} \times (\boldsymbol{b} + \boldsymbol{c}) = \boldsymbol{a} \times \boldsymbol{b} + \boldsymbol{a} \times \boldsymbol{c} \tag{A.25}$$

From Eq. (A.19) it is easily seen[2] that the x-component, for instance, of this product is

$$[a_y(b_z + c_z) - a_z(b_y + c_y)] = (a_yb_z - a_zb_y) + (a_yc_z - a_zc_y)$$

[2] For an interesting geometrical proof of the distribution law, see R. Courant, *Differential and Integral Calculus*, Vol. II, Interscience Publishers, Inc., New York, 1936, pp. 15–16.

which is the sum of the x-components of $\boldsymbol{a} \times \boldsymbol{b}$ and $\boldsymbol{a} \times \boldsymbol{c}$. Repeating the same for the other two components proves the distributive law for a cross product given in Eq. (A.25).

A.9 The Triple Scalar Product

The combined vector-scalar products $(\boldsymbol{a} \times \boldsymbol{b}) \cdot \boldsymbol{c}$ of three vectors $\boldsymbol{a}$, $\boldsymbol{b}$, and $\boldsymbol{c}$ results in a scalar quantity. This is immediately verified by the fact that $(\boldsymbol{a} \times \boldsymbol{b})$ is a vector and when its dot product is taken with another vector $\boldsymbol{c}$ the result is a scalar. *The parentheses in these triple products are very meaningful. They imply that the operation in the parentheses must be completed before carrying out the rest of the operations.* From Eqs. (A.10) and (A.19), it is immediately verified that

$$\begin{aligned}(\boldsymbol{a} \times \boldsymbol{b}) \cdot \boldsymbol{c} &= \boldsymbol{c} \cdot (\boldsymbol{a} \times \boldsymbol{b}) \\ &= (a_x b_y c_z + a_y b_z c_x + a_z b_x c_y) - (a_x b_z c_y + a_y b_x c_z + a_z b_y c_x) \\ &= \begin{vmatrix} c_x & c_y & c_z \\ a_x & a_y & a_z \\ b_x & b_y & b_z \end{vmatrix} \end{aligned} \tag{A.26}$$

From the determinant in Eq. (A.26) it can be seen that as long as the sequence of the rows is maintained its value remains unchanged. That is,

$$\begin{aligned}\boldsymbol{c} \cdot (\boldsymbol{a} \times \boldsymbol{b}) &= \boldsymbol{a} \cdot (\boldsymbol{b} \times \boldsymbol{c}) = \boldsymbol{b} \cdot (\boldsymbol{c} \times \boldsymbol{a}) \\ &= -\boldsymbol{c} \cdot (\boldsymbol{b} \times \boldsymbol{a}) = -\boldsymbol{a} \cdot (\boldsymbol{c} \times \boldsymbol{b}) = -\boldsymbol{b} \cdot (\boldsymbol{a} \times \boldsymbol{c}) \end{aligned} \tag{A.27}$$

This is called the *cyclic rule of the triple scalar product.*

This product has a physical significance[3] in that it represents the volume of a parallelepiped with the three vectors for sides. From Fig. A.8 the product $\boldsymbol{a} \times \boldsymbol{b}$ represents a vector normal to the plane ab and with magnitude $ab \sin \theta$ the area of that plane. The triple scalar product then is equal to

$$\boldsymbol{c} \cdot (\boldsymbol{a} \times \boldsymbol{b}) = (c \cos \beta)(ab \sin \theta)$$

which is the volume of the parallelepiped. The following relations are now true:

$$\boldsymbol{i} \cdot (\boldsymbol{j} \times \boldsymbol{k}) = \boldsymbol{j} \cdot (\boldsymbol{k} \times \boldsymbol{i}) = \boldsymbol{k} \cdot (\boldsymbol{i} \times \boldsymbol{j}) = 1 \tag{A.28}$$

[3] For further physical significance of this product, consult H. Yeh and J. I. Abrams, *Principles of Mechanics of Solids and Fluids,* Vol. I, McGraw-Hill Book Co., Inc., New York, 1960, p. 42.

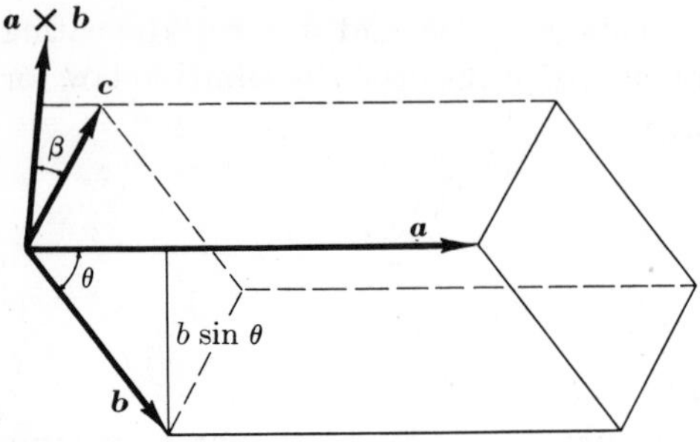

Figure A.8
The triple scalar product.

A.10 Triple Vector Product

The *triple vector product* is the cross product of three vectors which results in a fourth vector. This triple vector product can be shown[4,5] to be a linear combination of two vectors on the plane formed by $\boldsymbol{b}$ and $\boldsymbol{c}$

$$\boldsymbol{a} \times (\boldsymbol{b} \times \boldsymbol{c}) = (\boldsymbol{a}\cdot\boldsymbol{c})\boldsymbol{b} - (\boldsymbol{a}\cdot\boldsymbol{b})\boldsymbol{c} \tag{A.29}$$

This multiple product will occur often in this text. Since the quantities in the parentheses in the right-hand side of Eq. (A.29) are scalars, it shows that this triple vector product is on the plane formed by $\boldsymbol{b}$ and $\boldsymbol{c}$ and, consequently, is expressed in a linear combination of them.

A.11 Vector Functions of a Scalar

So far we have considered vectors as quantities with magnitude and direction that were fixed in space, time, or any other variable. When dealing with most statics problems in the mechanics of rigid bodies, the knowledge of vector algebra discussed so far is sufficient. In kinematics or dynamics of a continuous medium, the medium properties, scalar or vector, vary across the whole *field* to be studied. This concept of a *field of vectors* immediately brings the need of differential or integral

[4] A short algebraic verification of Eq. (A.29) is given in G. E. Hay, *Vector and Tensor Analysis,* Dover Publications, Inc., New York, 1953, p. 17.
[5] For a geometrical proof see S. Eskinazi, *Vector Mechanics of Fluids and Magnetofluids,* Academic Press, New York, 1967.

calculus in order to evaluate the changes in the field. Since fluids is the subject of this book, consider a fluid velocity field $\boldsymbol{U}$ a function of time and space. This velocity in terms of its Cartesian components can be written as

$$\boldsymbol{U} = \boldsymbol{i}u(x,y,z,t) + \boldsymbol{j}v(x,y,z,t) + \boldsymbol{k}w(x,y,z,t) \tag{A.30}$$

When u, v, and w are the x, y, and z scalar components of the velocity vector whose values depend on the position of a point $P(x,y,z)$ considered and the time t.

The value $\boldsymbol{U}$ can vary in time at the same point or at the same time at various points. When dealing with vector fields, it is important to determine the change of this vector with space and time. In calculus the student has learned to find the change of a single scalar function of x, y, z, and t. The question now arises as to whether the same method can be applied to vectors. Since $\boldsymbol{U}$ changes only if the component change, the total change of the vector is the vector sum of the change of the components

$$d\boldsymbol{U} = d(\boldsymbol{i}u) + d(\boldsymbol{j}v) = d(\boldsymbol{k}w)$$

If the description of these quantities is viewed with respect to a coordinate system that is fixed in time and space, then the unit vectors $\boldsymbol{i}$, $\boldsymbol{j}$, and $\boldsymbol{k}$ are constant, and, consequently,

$$d\boldsymbol{U} = \boldsymbol{i}\,du + \boldsymbol{j}\,dv + \boldsymbol{k}\,dw \tag{A.31}$$

If this were not the case then change of the unit vector must be taken into account. Since the scalar components of $\boldsymbol{U}$ are functions of x, y, z, and t, then this total change involves partial differentiation with respect to all four variables. A very useful application of Eq. (A.31) is encountered in the description of the change of position of a particle $P(x,y,z)$ in the Euclidean space. If $\boldsymbol{r} = \boldsymbol{i}x + \boldsymbol{j}y + \boldsymbol{k}z$ is its position at time $t = t_0$, in an infinitesimal time change the position change will be

$$d\boldsymbol{r} = \boldsymbol{i}\,dx + \boldsymbol{j}\,dy + \boldsymbol{k}\,dz \tag{A.32}$$

A.12 Differentiation with Respect to a Scalar Variable

Let a vector $\boldsymbol{a}$ be a function of a scalar σ. By convention, this is expressed in the form $a(\sigma)$. For a particular value of σ, $a(\sigma)$ has a value shown in Fig. A.9 by the vector OM. If the value of the independent

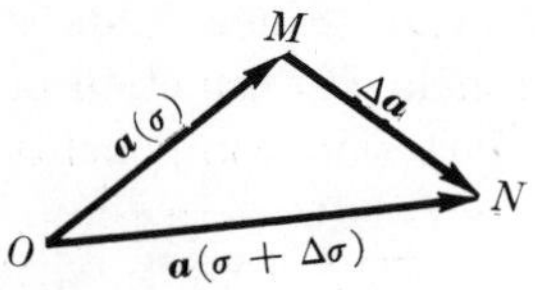

Figure A.9
Change of a vector with one variable.

quantity is increased by $\Delta\sigma$ then the vector corresponding to this new value $(\sigma + \Delta\sigma)$ will by $a(\sigma + \Delta\sigma)$ shown in Fig. A.9 by $\overline{ON}$. The change in $\boldsymbol{a}$ because of the change in $\Delta\sigma$ is

$$\Delta \boldsymbol{a} = \boldsymbol{a}(\sigma + \Delta\sigma) - \boldsymbol{a}(\sigma)$$

This is shown by the vector $\overrightarrow{MN}$. The average change of the vector $\boldsymbol{a}$ per unit change in σ is $\Delta\boldsymbol{a}/\Delta\sigma$. If $\Delta\sigma > 0$ then $\Delta a/\Delta\sigma$ is a vector in the direction of $\Delta\boldsymbol{a}$ but $1/\Delta\sigma$ as long. If $\Delta\sigma < 0$, then $\Delta\boldsymbol{a}/\Delta\sigma$ has the direction of $-\Delta\boldsymbol{a}$. If now $\Delta\sigma$ is made to approach zero without really reaching it, if, in other words, $\Delta\sigma$ is made very small and $\Delta\boldsymbol{a}$ is very small compared to $\boldsymbol{a}$, then

$$\frac{d\boldsymbol{a}}{d\sigma} = \lim_{\Delta\sigma \to 0} \frac{\boldsymbol{a}(\sigma + \Delta\sigma) - \boldsymbol{a}(\sigma)}{\Delta\sigma}$$

is called the *derivative* of $\boldsymbol{a}(\sigma)$ with respect to σ.

If we consider a point P moving on a circle of radius $\boldsymbol{r}$ with constant angular speed $\frac{d\theta}{dt}$ as shown in Fig. A.10, then

$$\boldsymbol{r} = \boldsymbol{i}r\cos\theta + \boldsymbol{j}r\sin\theta$$

and

$$\frac{d\boldsymbol{r}}{dt} = \boldsymbol{U} = \boldsymbol{i}r\frac{d}{dt}\cos\theta + \boldsymbol{j}r\frac{d}{dt}\sin\theta$$

Here the coordinate system has been fixed at O and thus $\boldsymbol{i}$ and $\boldsymbol{j}$ are constant with the motion of P. Then

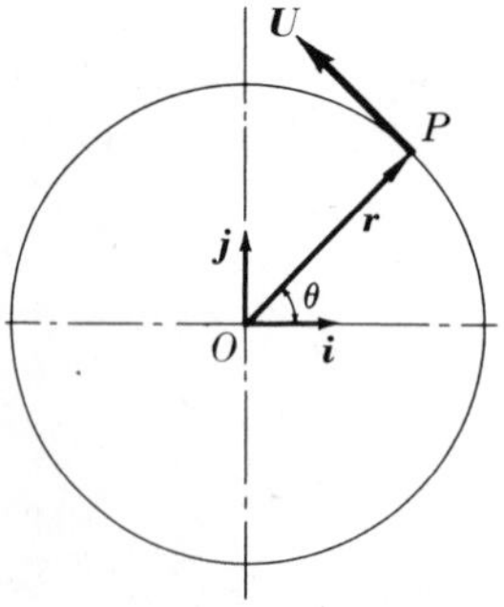

Figure A. 10
Angular motion.

$$U = (-\boldsymbol{i}r \sin \theta + \boldsymbol{j}r \cos \theta) \frac{d\theta}{dt} \tag{A.33}$$

The rotation vector $\boldsymbol{\omega}$ points perpendicular to the paper towards the reader and therefore is equal to $\boldsymbol{\omega} = \boldsymbol{k}\frac{d\theta}{dt}$. It is easily verified then that Eq. (A.23) is satisfied

$$\begin{aligned} \boldsymbol{U} &= \boldsymbol{\omega} \times \boldsymbol{r} \\ &= \left(\boldsymbol{k}\frac{d\theta}{dt}\right) \times (\boldsymbol{i}r \cos \theta + \boldsymbol{j}r \sin \theta) \end{aligned}$$

and that it is equal to Eq. (A.33).

The acceleration which is a rate of change of velocity is non-zero because, even though in this particular case the magnitude of the velocity is not changing, the direction of the velocity is changing. Then

$$\begin{aligned} \boldsymbol{a} &= \frac{d\boldsymbol{U}}{dt} = \frac{d^2\boldsymbol{r}}{dt^2} \\ &= (-\boldsymbol{i}r \cos \theta - \boldsymbol{j}r \sin \theta) \left(\frac{d\theta}{dt}\right)^2 \\ &= -\omega^2 \boldsymbol{r} \end{aligned}$$

This is the *centripetal acceleration* directed towards the center of rotation.

A.13 Differentiation Rules

Pursuing the line of reasoning in the previous section, it can be shown easily that if $\boldsymbol{a}$, $\boldsymbol{b}$, and m are functions of σ, then

$$\begin{aligned} \frac{d}{d\sigma}(m\boldsymbol{a}) &= m\frac{d\boldsymbol{a}}{d\sigma} + \frac{dm}{d\sigma}\boldsymbol{a} \\ \frac{d}{d\sigma}(\boldsymbol{a} + \boldsymbol{b}) &= \frac{d\boldsymbol{a}}{d\sigma} + \frac{d\boldsymbol{b}}{d\sigma} \\ \frac{d}{d\sigma}(\boldsymbol{a} \cdot \boldsymbol{b}) &= \boldsymbol{a} \cdot \frac{d\boldsymbol{b}}{d\sigma} + \frac{d\boldsymbol{a}}{d\sigma} \cdot \boldsymbol{b} \\ \frac{d}{d\sigma}(\boldsymbol{a} \times \boldsymbol{b}) &= \boldsymbol{a} \times \frac{d\boldsymbol{b}}{d\sigma} + \frac{d\boldsymbol{a}}{d\sigma} \times \boldsymbol{b} \end{aligned} \tag{A.34}$$

An important result appears from the third relation of Eq. (A.34). For a vector of constant magnitude, $\boldsymbol{a}\cdot\boldsymbol{a}$ is constant. Then

$$\boldsymbol{a}\cdot\frac{d\boldsymbol{a}}{d\sigma}+\frac{d\boldsymbol{a}}{d\sigma}\cdot\boldsymbol{a}=0$$

which means that $d\boldsymbol{a}/d\sigma$ is perpendicular to $\boldsymbol{a}$. Since $d\boldsymbol{a}/d\sigma$ has the same direction as $d\boldsymbol{a}$, $d\boldsymbol{a}$ is perpendicular to $\boldsymbol{a}$.

A.14 The Gradient of a Scalar Function

Let f, a scalar function of position such as the temperature, be represented in a three-dimensional Cartesian coordinate. The values of f for all x, y, z represent the scalar field. In Fig. A.11, given a point P a distance $\boldsymbol{r}$ from O, a surface f_P passes through P, where everywhere on this surface the value of the scalar is a constant. Let function f and its change in the neighborhood of P be continuous. If we draw a normal to f_P at P in the direction of the unit normal vector $\boldsymbol{n}$, this normal intersects another surface $f_Q = c_2$ at the point Q. For differential changes, since the limit of these two surfaces approaching each other must be taken, let the difference $f_Q - f_P$ be a differential change df

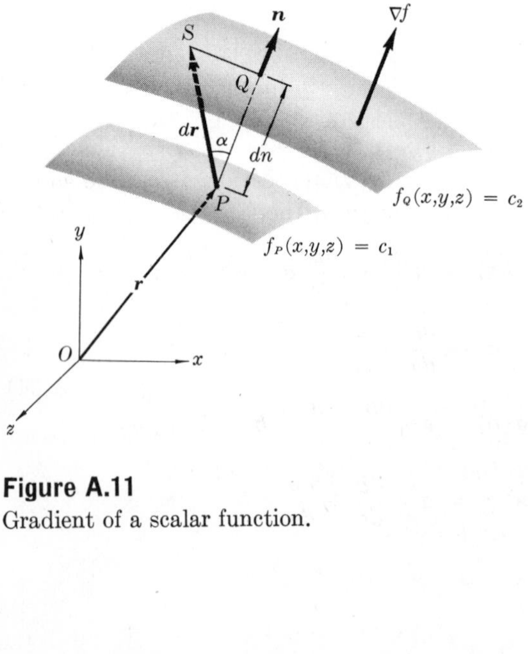

Figure A.11
Gradient of a scalar function.

in a distance dn. Then for small changes by Taylor's expansion along PQ

$$f_Q - f_P = PQ\left(\frac{df}{dn}\right)$$

Let S be any other neighboring point of P such that $f_S = f_Q$, then

$$f_S = f_Q = f_P + PQ\left(\frac{df}{dn}\right)$$

$$f_S - f_P = PQ\left(\frac{df}{dn}\right)$$

$$= PS\cos\alpha\left(\frac{df}{dn}\right) \tag{A.35}$$

Since f is a scalar, the total change of f is also a scalar. However, it is seen that this scalar change is the scalar product of two vectors $\overline{PS} = \boldsymbol{dr}$ and the directed unit change $\boldsymbol{n}\dfrac{df}{dn}$ of the scalar function f.

Therefore

$$df = \boldsymbol{n}\frac{df}{dn}\cdot \boldsymbol{dr}$$

It is seen from Eq. (A.35) that for no matter what displacement $\boldsymbol{dr}$ from P, it is its projection $\boldsymbol{n}\cdot\boldsymbol{dr} = dn$ along the normal that counts. The vector $\boldsymbol{n}\dfrac{df}{dn}$ is called the *gradient of the scalar function* f often expressed as **grad** f or $\boldsymbol{\nabla} f$ and points in the direction of maximum rate of change of f. The symbol $\boldsymbol{\nabla}$ is called "*nabla*" or "*del*" and is analogous to the scalar operator $D = d/dx$. From the previous equation, it is seen that the gradient can be symbolically expressed as $df/\boldsymbol{dr}$.

$$df = \frac{df}{\boldsymbol{dr}}\cdot \boldsymbol{dr}$$

$$= \boldsymbol{\nabla} f\cdot\boldsymbol{dr}$$

$$= \boldsymbol{dr}\cdot\boldsymbol{\nabla} f$$

$$= (\boldsymbol{dr}\cdot\boldsymbol{\nabla})f \tag{A.36}$$

Since $\boldsymbol{r}$ is generally used to represent the radius vector, in order to avoid confusion, any small directed displacement $\boldsymbol{ds}$ can be used instead of $\boldsymbol{dr}$, and this will establish the total change of f along $\boldsymbol{ds}$

$$df = \boldsymbol{\nabla} f\cdot\boldsymbol{ds} \tag{A.37}$$

In *Cartesian coordinates* $\boldsymbol{ds} = \boldsymbol{i}\,dx + \boldsymbol{j}\,dy + \boldsymbol{k}\,dz$, and since $f = f(x,y,z)$, its total change is also

$$df = \frac{\partial f}{\partial x}\,dx + \frac{\partial f}{\partial y}\,dy + \frac{\partial f}{\partial z}\,dz$$

Since ∇f is a vector, in terms of its Cartesian components

$$\nabla f = \boldsymbol{i}(\nabla f)_x + \boldsymbol{j}(\nabla f)_y + \boldsymbol{k}(\nabla f)_z$$

and according to Eq. (A.37)

$$df = (\nabla f)_x\,dx + (\nabla f)_y\,dy + (\nabla f)_z\,dz$$

Comparing this with the sum of the differential changes the components of the gradient in Cartesian coordinate are

$$(\nabla f)_x = \frac{\partial f}{\partial x}; \qquad (\nabla f)_y = \frac{\partial f}{\partial y}; \qquad (\nabla f)_z = \frac{\partial f}{\partial z}$$

and the vector operator[6]

$$\nabla \equiv \boldsymbol{i}\frac{\partial}{\partial x} + \boldsymbol{j}\frac{\partial}{\partial y} + \boldsymbol{k}\frac{\partial}{\partial z} \qquad [\text{A.38}(a)]$$

In cylindrical coordinates,

$$\nabla = \boldsymbol{i}\frac{\partial}{\partial r} + \boldsymbol{j}\frac{1}{r}\frac{\partial}{\partial \theta} + \boldsymbol{k}\frac{\partial}{\partial z} \qquad [\text{A.38}(b)]$$

With the background in this chapter the following relations can be shown to be true:

(a) $\nabla f = \dfrac{df}{d\phi}\nabla\phi = f'\nabla\phi$ if $\phi = \phi(x,y,z)$ and $f = f(\phi)$;

(b) $\nabla(\phi + \psi) = \nabla\phi + \nabla\psi$ (A.39)

(c) $\nabla(\phi\psi) = \phi\nabla\psi + \psi\nabla\phi$.

If, for instance, ϕ is a constant then

$$\nabla(\phi\psi) = \phi\nabla\psi$$

A.15 The Dot Product of a Vector with ∇

The product of a vector with the *vector operator* ∇ has already appeared in Eq. (A.36). The result is by the rules of scalar multiplica-

[6] See Appendix B for the form of the nabla in terms of components in other orthogonal coordinate systems.

tion or *scalar operator*. For instance, in Cartesian coordinates if $\boldsymbol{a} = \boldsymbol{i}a_x + \boldsymbol{j}a_y + \boldsymbol{k}a_z$, then

$$(\boldsymbol{a}\cdot\nabla) = a_x \frac{\partial}{\partial x} + a_y \frac{\partial}{\partial y} + a_z \frac{\partial}{\partial z} \qquad \text{(A.40)}$$

This operator is very important in fluid mechanics, since it appears in the Eulerean representations of the rate of change of a quantity (see Chap. V). As an example, if $\phi = \phi(x,y,z,t)$, then the total rate of change of ϕ, $d\phi/dt$ can be shown to be

$$\frac{d\phi}{dt} = \frac{\partial\phi}{\partial t} + \left(\frac{d\boldsymbol{r}}{dt}\cdot\nabla\right)\phi \qquad \text{(A.41)}$$

where $\boldsymbol{r} = \boldsymbol{i}x + \boldsymbol{j}y + \boldsymbol{k}z$.

The parentheses could be removed and the result will be the same

$$\left(\frac{d\boldsymbol{r}}{dt}\cdot\nabla\right)\phi = \frac{d\boldsymbol{r}}{dt}\cdot\nabla\phi \qquad \text{(A.42)}$$

Caution must be exercised in placing brackets in vector operations since their free use does not always give the same result.

A.16 The Cross Product of a Vector and the Operator ∇

According to Eqs. (A.19) and (A.21),

$$\boldsymbol{a}\times\nabla = \begin{vmatrix} \boldsymbol{i} & \boldsymbol{j} & \boldsymbol{k} \\ a_x & a_y & a_z \\ \dfrac{\partial}{\partial x} & \dfrac{\partial}{\partial y} & \dfrac{\partial}{\partial z} \end{vmatrix} \qquad \text{(A.43)}$$

$$= \boldsymbol{i}\left(a_y\frac{\partial}{\partial z} - a_z\frac{\partial}{\partial y}\right) + \boldsymbol{j}\left(a_z\frac{\partial}{\partial x} - a_x\frac{\partial}{\partial z}\right) + \boldsymbol{k}\left(a_x\frac{\partial}{\partial y} - a_y\frac{\partial}{\partial x}\right)$$

This resultant quantity is a vector operator. When applied to a scalar function ϕ it is also observed that

$$(\boldsymbol{a}\times\nabla)\phi = \boldsymbol{a}\times\nabla\phi \qquad \text{(A.44)}$$

A.17 The Divergence of a Vector

In vector calculus, so far, we have considered the vector sum of the changes of a scalar function in the three coordinate directions. This gave rise to the concept of the gradient. This concept could be applied to vectors as well but we can see right away that, since the gradient has three components and if it operates on a vector that also has three components, the complete operation involves nine derivatives to describe this concept. This then brings us to quantities more complex in their description called tensor quantities.

However, the scalar sum of the change of each vector component in its own direction has a real physical significance and is called the *divergence*. It represents the extent to which the vector field diverges away from a point. It is seen immediately that the divergence of a vector is just the dot product of the operator del with the vector.

$$\nabla \cdot \boldsymbol{a} = \left(\boldsymbol{i}\frac{\partial}{\partial x} + \boldsymbol{j}\frac{\partial}{\partial y} + \boldsymbol{k}\frac{\partial}{\partial t}\right) \cdot (\boldsymbol{i}a_x + \boldsymbol{j}a_y + \boldsymbol{k}a_z)$$

$$= \frac{\partial a_x}{\partial x} + \frac{\partial a_y}{\partial y} + \frac{\partial a_z}{\partial z} \qquad \text{(A.45)}$$

Here, in the Cartesian coordinate system, the unit vectors do not change in space. This is not true in cylindrical- or spherical-coordinate systems.

For instance, from Eq. [A.38(b)] in *cylindrical coordinates*

$$\nabla = \boldsymbol{i}\frac{\partial}{\partial r} + \boldsymbol{j}\frac{1}{r}\frac{\partial}{\partial \theta} + \boldsymbol{k}\frac{\partial}{\partial z}$$

Now, if a vector $\boldsymbol{a}$ is given in terms of its cylindrical components a_r, a_θ and a_z then the divergence is

$$\nabla \cdot \boldsymbol{a} = \left(\boldsymbol{i}\frac{\partial}{\partial r} + \boldsymbol{j}\frac{\partial}{\partial \theta} + \boldsymbol{k}\frac{\partial}{\partial z}\right) \cdot (\boldsymbol{i}a_r + \boldsymbol{j}a_\theta + \boldsymbol{k}a_z)$$

$$= \boldsymbol{i} \cdot \left(\boldsymbol{i}\frac{\partial a_r}{\partial r} + a_r\frac{\partial \boldsymbol{i}}{\partial r} + \boldsymbol{j}\frac{\partial a_\theta}{\partial r} + a_\theta\frac{\partial \boldsymbol{j}}{\partial r} + \boldsymbol{k}\frac{\partial a_z}{\partial r} + a_z\frac{\partial \boldsymbol{k}}{\partial z}\right)$$

$$+ \boldsymbol{j}\frac{1}{r} \cdot \left(\boldsymbol{i}\frac{\partial a_r}{\partial \theta} + a_r\frac{\partial \boldsymbol{i}}{\partial \theta} + \boldsymbol{j}\frac{\partial a_\theta}{\partial \theta} + a_\theta\frac{\partial \boldsymbol{j}}{\partial \theta} + \boldsymbol{k}\frac{\partial a_z}{\partial \theta} + a_z\frac{\partial \boldsymbol{k}}{\partial \theta}\right)$$

$$+ \boldsymbol{k} \cdot \left(\boldsymbol{i}\frac{\partial a_r}{\partial z} + a_r\frac{\partial \boldsymbol{i}}{\partial z} + \boldsymbol{j}\frac{\partial a_\theta}{\partial z} + a_\theta\frac{\partial \boldsymbol{j}}{\partial z} + \boldsymbol{k}\frac{\partial a_z}{\partial z} + a_z\frac{\partial \boldsymbol{k}}{\partial z}\right)$$

In this relation, six terms drop out immediately—the terms $\partial\boldsymbol{i}/\partial r = \partial\boldsymbol{j}/\partial r = \partial\boldsymbol{k}/\partial r = 0$—because, referring to Fig. A.12, it is seen that the unit vectors do not change with $\boldsymbol{r}$. The same is true for $\partial\boldsymbol{k}/\partial z = \partial\boldsymbol{j}/\partial z = \partial\boldsymbol{i}/\partial z = 0$; this eliminates six more terms. However, $\partial\boldsymbol{j}/\partial\theta \neq 0$, because from Fig. A.12(*a*) using Taylor's expansion $\boldsymbol{j}(\theta + d\theta) = \boldsymbol{j}(\theta) + \frac{\partial \boldsymbol{j}}{\partial \theta}d\theta$, and, consequently, $\boldsymbol{j}(\theta + d\theta) - \boldsymbol{j}(\theta) = \frac{\partial \boldsymbol{j}}{\partial \theta}d\theta\cdot$ This resultant vector is in the direction of $-\boldsymbol{i}$ and its magnitude is the sine of the angle or the angle. Thus, $\partial \boldsymbol{j}/\partial\theta = -\boldsymbol{i}$. From Fig. A.12(c) $\dfrac{\partial \boldsymbol{i}}{\partial\theta}\,d\theta = \boldsymbol{j}\,d\theta$ then giving $\partial \boldsymbol{i}/\partial\theta = \boldsymbol{j}$. The final quantity $\partial \boldsymbol{k}/\partial\theta = 0$. Now the divergence in cylindrical coordinate becomes

$$\nabla\cdot\boldsymbol{a} = \frac{\partial a_r}{\partial r} + \frac{a_r}{r} + \frac{1}{r}\frac{\partial a_\theta}{\partial\theta} + \frac{\partial a_z}{\partial z}$$

$$= \frac{1}{r}\frac{\partial}{\partial r}(ra_r) + \frac{1}{r}\frac{\partial a_\theta}{\partial\theta} + \frac{\partial a_z}{\partial z} \qquad \text{(A.46)}$$

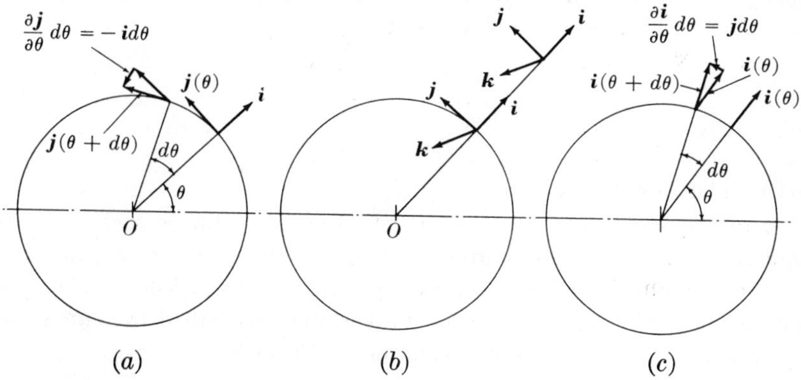

Figure A.12
Change of unit vector in a cylindrical frame.

In spherical coordinates the students should show that

$$\frac{\partial}{\partial r}(\boldsymbol{i},\boldsymbol{j},\boldsymbol{k}) = 0; \quad \frac{\partial \boldsymbol{i}}{\partial\theta} = \boldsymbol{j}; \quad \frac{\partial \boldsymbol{j}}{\partial\theta} = -\boldsymbol{i}; \quad \frac{\partial \boldsymbol{k}}{\partial\theta} = 0; \quad \frac{\partial \boldsymbol{i}}{\partial\alpha} = \boldsymbol{k};$$

$$\frac{\partial \boldsymbol{j}}{\partial\alpha} = \boldsymbol{k}\cos\theta, \quad \text{and} \quad \partial\boldsymbol{k}/\partial\alpha = -(\boldsymbol{i}\sin\theta + \boldsymbol{j}\cos\theta);$$

and, thus,

$$\nabla\cdot\boldsymbol{a} = \frac{1}{r^2}\frac{\partial}{\partial r}(r^2 a_r) + \frac{1}{r\sin\theta}\frac{\partial}{\partial\theta}(a_\theta\sin\theta) + \frac{1}{r\sin\theta}\frac{\partial a_\alpha}{\partial\alpha} = 0 \qquad \text{(A.47)}$$

One can show easily that the divergence of the sum of two vectors

$$\nabla\cdot(\boldsymbol{a} + \boldsymbol{b}) = \nabla\cdot\boldsymbol{a} + \nabla\cdot\boldsymbol{b} \qquad \text{(A.48)}$$

The divergence of the product of a scalar and a vector

$$\nabla\cdot(\phi\boldsymbol{a}) = \phi(\nabla\cdot\boldsymbol{a}) + (\nabla\phi)\cdot\boldsymbol{a} \qquad \text{(A.49)}$$

The divergence of a gradient of a scalar or the *Laplacian* of a scalar

$$\boldsymbol{\nabla}\cdot(\boldsymbol{\nabla}\phi) = \boldsymbol{\nabla}^2\phi = \frac{\partial^2\phi}{\partial x^2} + \frac{\partial^2\phi}{\partial y^2} + \frac{\partial^2\phi}{\partial z^2} \tag{A.50}$$

where

$$(\boldsymbol{\nabla}\cdot\boldsymbol{\nabla}) = \boldsymbol{\nabla}^2 \tag{A.51}$$

A vector whose divergence is equal to zero is called a *solenoidal vector*. If the velocity vector is such a vector, then from Eq. (A.45) one can see that the divergence will represent the sum of the changes of the velocity components away from a point which physically implies that the *net flux* of substance is zero. More physical significance of the divergence will be given in Sec. (4.16).

A.18 The Curl of a Vector

The vector operator $\boldsymbol{\nabla}$ has been used so far as a differential operation on a function giving the gradient and as a differential vector dotted to another vector giving a scalar quantity called the divergence. The cross product of $\boldsymbol{\nabla}$ and a vector gives a vector quantity called the ***curl*** which has a physical significance in mechanics. From Eq. [A.38(a)]

$$\begin{aligned}
\boldsymbol{\nabla}\times\boldsymbol{a} &= \textit{\textbf{curl a}} \\
&= \left(\boldsymbol{i}\frac{\partial}{\partial x} + \boldsymbol{j}\frac{\partial}{\partial y} + \boldsymbol{k}\frac{\partial}{\partial z}\right)\times(\boldsymbol{i}a_x + \boldsymbol{j}a_y + \boldsymbol{k}a_z) \\
&= \boldsymbol{i}\left(\frac{\partial a_z}{\partial y} - \frac{\partial a_y}{\partial z}\right) + \boldsymbol{j}\left(\frac{\partial a_x}{\partial z} - \frac{\partial a_z}{\partial x}\right) + \boldsymbol{k}\left(\frac{\partial a_y}{\partial x} - \frac{\partial a_x}{\partial y}\right) \qquad \text{(A.52)} \\
&= \begin{vmatrix} \boldsymbol{i} & \boldsymbol{j} & \boldsymbol{k} \\ \frac{\partial}{\partial x} & \frac{\partial}{\partial y} & \frac{\partial}{\partial z} \\ a_x & a_y & a_z \end{vmatrix} \\
&= \boldsymbol{i}\times\frac{\partial\boldsymbol{a}}{\partial x} + \boldsymbol{j}\times\frac{\partial\boldsymbol{a}}{\partial y} + \boldsymbol{k}\times\frac{\partial\boldsymbol{a}}{\partial z}
\end{aligned}$$

If $\boldsymbol{a}$ is the velocity vector, then the curl represents twice the angular velocity. This will be easily verified shortly after the triple vector product involving $\boldsymbol{\nabla}$ is introduced. First, it can easily be shown when differentiating by parts and using the triple scalar and vector products that

$$
\begin{aligned}
&(a)\ \nabla \times (\boldsymbol{a} + \boldsymbol{b}) = \nabla \times \boldsymbol{a} + \nabla \times \boldsymbol{b} \\
&(b)\ \nabla \times (\boldsymbol{a}\phi) = \phi(\nabla \times \boldsymbol{a}) + (\nabla\phi) \times \boldsymbol{a} \\
&(c)\ (\boldsymbol{a} \times \nabla)\cdot\boldsymbol{b} = \boldsymbol{a}\cdot(\nabla \times \boldsymbol{b}) \\
&(d)\ \nabla\cdot(\boldsymbol{a} \times \boldsymbol{b}) = \boldsymbol{b}\cdot(\nabla \times \boldsymbol{a}) - \boldsymbol{a}\cdot(\nabla \times \boldsymbol{b}) \\
&(e)\ \nabla \times (\boldsymbol{a} \times \boldsymbol{b}) = \boldsymbol{a}(\nabla\cdot\boldsymbol{b}) + (\boldsymbol{b}\cdot\nabla)\boldsymbol{a} - \boldsymbol{b}(\nabla\cdot\boldsymbol{a}) - (\boldsymbol{a}\cdot\nabla)\boldsymbol{b} \\
&(f)\ \nabla \times (\nabla\phi) = 0 \\
&(g)\ \nabla\cdot(\nabla \times \boldsymbol{a}) = 0 \\
&(h)\ \nabla \times (\nabla \times \boldsymbol{a}) = \nabla(\nabla\cdot\boldsymbol{a}) - \nabla^2\boldsymbol{a}
\end{aligned}
\tag{A.53}
$$

It would be interesting to incorporate proofs of all relations in Eq. (A.53). With the help of the principles of vectors treated so far, the student should be able to establish all these relations.[7]

To show the physical significance of the curl of the velocity, we choose a solid body rotating with a velocity according to

$$\boldsymbol{U} = \boldsymbol{\omega} \times \boldsymbol{r}$$

Consider the curl of $\boldsymbol{U}$

$$\nabla \times \boldsymbol{U} = \nabla \times (\boldsymbol{\omega} \times \boldsymbol{r})$$

Using Eq. [A.53(*e*)],

$$\nabla \times \boldsymbol{U} = \boldsymbol{\omega}(\nabla\cdot\boldsymbol{r}) + (\boldsymbol{r}\cdot\nabla)\boldsymbol{\omega} - \boldsymbol{r}(\nabla\cdot\boldsymbol{\omega}) - (\boldsymbol{\omega}\cdot\nabla)\boldsymbol{r}$$

The first term on the right hand side is easily seen to be $3\boldsymbol{\omega}$. The second and third terms are zero because there are no space variations of $\boldsymbol{\omega}$ on a rigid body. The last term is equal to $-\boldsymbol{\omega}$. Then

$$\nabla \times \boldsymbol{U} = 2\boldsymbol{\omega} \tag{A.54}$$

This expression could have been obtained just as easily from the last expression of Eq. (A.52). Then the curl of the velocity is twice the angular velocity. It is shown in Chap. (IV) that this concept is extended with more generality to fluid rotation as well.

A.19 Condition for Any Given Vector to Be the Gradient of a Scalar Function

Even though the gradient of a scalar function is a vector, not all vector fields can be represented as the gradient of a scalar field.

From Eq. [A.53(*f*)], for a vector $\boldsymbol{U}$ to be expressed as the gradient of ϕ it must follow that $\nabla \times \boldsymbol{U} = 0$. So conversely it can be said that

[7] Detailed proofs of these relations is given in the solution manual for this book. Most *vector calculus* books do treat these relations. For example see H. Lass, *Vector and Tensor Analysis*, McGraw-Hill Book Co., New York, 1950.

if the curl of a vector is zero then, because of the consequences of Eq. (A.53*f*) *the vector can be expressed as the gradient of some function* ϕ. This will be proven formally in Sec. A.22.

A.20 The Line Integral

Let $\boldsymbol{f}$ be a continuous vector field along a path AB represented by $\boldsymbol{r} = \boldsymbol{r}(s)$ where $\boldsymbol{r}$ is the radius vector from O to any point on the path and s the path length from a given origin. The infinitesimal arc length is $d\boldsymbol{r} = \boldsymbol{t}\, ds$ where $\boldsymbol{t}$ is the unit vector tagent to the path. The line integral is defined as

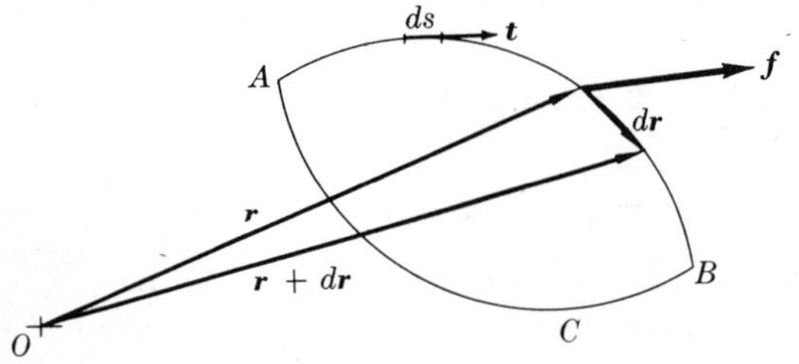

Figure A.13
The line integral.

$$\int_C \boldsymbol{f} \cdot d\boldsymbol{r} = \int_A^B \left(\boldsymbol{f} \cdot \frac{d\boldsymbol{r}}{ds}\right) ds = \int_A^B f_x\, dx + f_y\, dy + f_z\, dz \tag{A.55}$$

This integral appears, for instance, in mechanics where, if a fluid or solid particle moves along a path C under a force $\boldsymbol{f}$, the work done is given by Eq. (A.55). In general, this integral is a function of the path chosen from A to B; in other words, the work of all particles going from A to B may not be the same. There is, however, one condition for which this integral is independent of path, provided the end points are kept the same. Mathematically speaking, the product $\boldsymbol{f} \cdot d\boldsymbol{r}$ must be an exact differential. Looking at Eq. (A.36), we see that if $\boldsymbol{f}$ is the gradient of a scalar ϕ, then Eq. (A.55) can be written:

$$\int_C \boldsymbol{f} \cdot d\boldsymbol{r} = \int_C \nabla\phi \cdot d\boldsymbol{r} = \int_C d\phi = \phi_B - \phi_A$$

The result, then, is uniquely dependent on the values of ϕ at A and B and not on the path. If f is a force and can be expressed as $\nabla\phi$ then the force field is called *conservative*. The previous section already has shown under what condition f can be expressed as the gradient of a scalar function, since the integral from A to B for two different paths is the same for a conservative field.

$$\Gamma = \oint \boldsymbol{f} \cdot d\boldsymbol{r} = 0 \tag{A.56}$$

This integral sign indicates integration around a closed contour. This contour integration is called the *circulation* Γ.

A.21 Oriented Surface

We have seen in Sec. A.8, that a surface is oriented and that the orientation is dependent on the order of the cross product of its sides. The *surface vector* is in the direction normal to the surface established by the unit vector $\boldsymbol{n}$ and its magnitude is the value of the area. The infinitesimal surface vector is then $\boldsymbol{n}\, d\delta$ or $d\boldsymbol{\delta}$. This is shown in Fig. A.14.

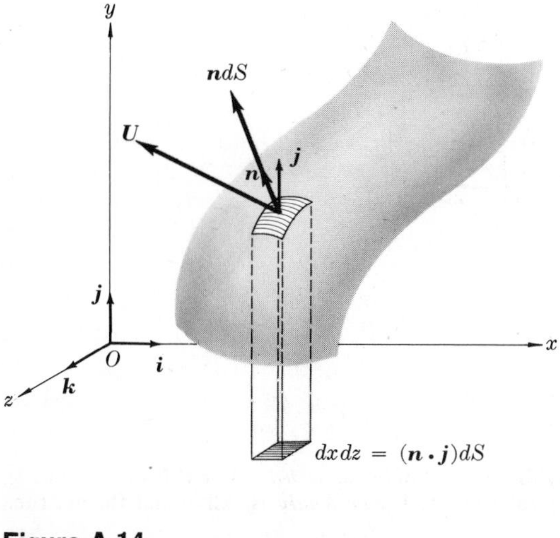

Figure A.14
Vector orientation of a surface.

If, at the point P, a vector, say the velocity $\boldsymbol{U}$, is defined, then the scalar quantity $\boldsymbol{n}\cdot\boldsymbol{U}\,d\delta$ by the scalar product rule, represents the component of $\boldsymbol{U}$ on $\boldsymbol{n}$ multiplied by the infinitesimal area or the projection of $\boldsymbol{n}\,d\delta$ normal to $\boldsymbol{U}$ multiplied by the magnitude of $\boldsymbol{U}$. By the same token, $(\boldsymbol{n}\,d\delta)\cdot\boldsymbol{j}$ is the projection area normal to $\boldsymbol{j}$. Since $\boldsymbol{n}\cdot\boldsymbol{j} = |n|\;|j| \cos\theta = \cos\theta$, then $(\boldsymbol{n}\,d\delta)\cdot\boldsymbol{j} = dS\cos\theta = dx\,dz$.

A.22 Stokes' Theorem. Line and Surface Integrals

Let S be a surface bounded by a closed curve C. Let $\boldsymbol{n}$ be the unit normal on the surface[8] defined in the outward direction as shown in Fig. A.15. If a vector field $\boldsymbol{U}$ and its derivatives are continuous and defined on the surface S then Stokes Theorem states that

$$\oint_C \boldsymbol{U}\cdot\boldsymbol{t}\,dc = \int_S \boldsymbol{n}\cdot(\nabla \times \boldsymbol{U})\,dS$$
$$\oint_C \boldsymbol{U}\cdot d\boldsymbol{c} = \int_S (\nabla \times \boldsymbol{U})\,dS \qquad \text{(A.57)}$$

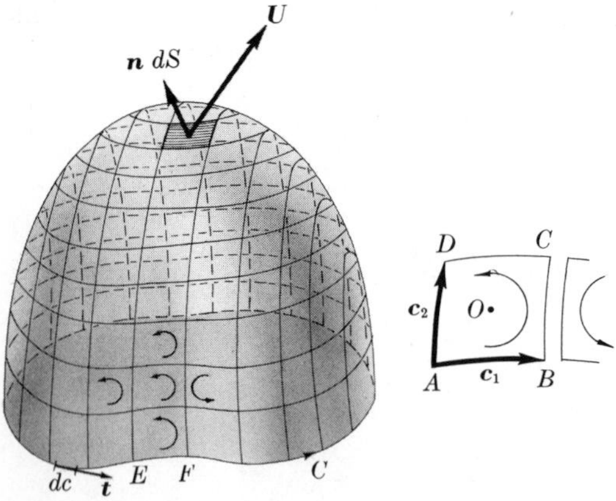

Figure A.15
Surface and contour in Stokes' theorem.

[8] This surface is arbitrary, provided it is *simply connected*. For this definition see, for instance, Harry F. Davis, *Introduction to Vector Analysis*, Allyn and Bacon, Inc., Boston, 1961, p. 130.

This is a relationship of the line integral of $\boldsymbol{U}$ around the closed contour C of infinitesimal length $\boldsymbol{t}\,dc = d\boldsymbol{c}$ in terms of the curl of $\boldsymbol{U}$ on any open surface S that ends on the contour C. The quantity $\boldsymbol{n}\,dS = d\boldsymbol{S}$ is the infinitesimal area vector normal to the surface while $\boldsymbol{t}$ is the unit vector tangent to C. This is a very important theorem in mathematics that applies to any vector field. Its use is very broad in engineering and physics.

To prove the theorem we proceed with the following geometrical proof, dividing the surface S into small meshes as shown and considering one such mesh $ABCD$. If the vector at the center of $ABCD$ is $\boldsymbol{U}$, then by Taylor's expansion, the corresponding quantities at all sides are

$$(\boldsymbol{U})_{AB} = \boldsymbol{U} - \tfrac{1}{2}(\boldsymbol{c}_2\cdot\nabla)\boldsymbol{U}$$

$$(\boldsymbol{U})_{DC} = \boldsymbol{U} + \tfrac{1}{2}(\boldsymbol{c}_2\cdot\nabla)\boldsymbol{U}$$

$$(\boldsymbol{U})_{AD} = \boldsymbol{U} - \tfrac{1}{2}(\boldsymbol{c}_1\cdot\nabla)\boldsymbol{U}$$

$$(\boldsymbol{U})_{BC} = \boldsymbol{U} + \tfrac{1}{2}(\boldsymbol{c}_1\cdot\nabla)\boldsymbol{U}$$

The circulation Γ, according to Eq. (A.56), around this small mesh is

$$\oint_{ABCD} \boldsymbol{U}\cdot d\boldsymbol{c} = (\boldsymbol{U})_{AB}\cdot\boldsymbol{c}_1 + (\boldsymbol{U})_{BC}\cdot\boldsymbol{c}_2 - (\boldsymbol{U})_{DC}\cdot\boldsymbol{c}_1 - (\boldsymbol{U})_{AD}\cdot\boldsymbol{c}_2$$

The negative signs on the last two terms appear because, if the integration is performed counterclockwise along CD and DA, the length vectors are negative. Evaluating this integral by substitution of the expanded vectors $\boldsymbol{U}$ at each edge,

$$\oint_{ABCD} \boldsymbol{U}\cdot d\boldsymbol{c} = \boldsymbol{c}_2\cdot[(\boldsymbol{c}_1\cdot\nabla)\boldsymbol{U} - \boldsymbol{c}_1\cdot(\boldsymbol{c}_2\cdot\nabla)\boldsymbol{U}]$$

From the rules of the triple vector product, Eq. (A.29), the previous equation for the circulation around $ABCD$ becomes

$$\oint_{ABCD} \boldsymbol{U}\cdot d\boldsymbol{c} = [(\boldsymbol{c}_1 \times \boldsymbol{c}_2) \times \nabla]\boldsymbol{U}$$

Now, according to permutations of the triple scalar product of vectors $(\boldsymbol{c}_1 \times \boldsymbol{c}_2)$, ∇, and $\boldsymbol{U}$,

$$\oint_{ABCD} \boldsymbol{U}\cdot d\boldsymbol{c} = (\boldsymbol{c}_1 \times \boldsymbol{c}_2)\cdot(\nabla \times \boldsymbol{U})$$

$$= (\nabla \times \boldsymbol{U})\cdot d\boldsymbol{S} \qquad \text{(A.58)}$$

This is very similar to Eq. (A.57). It applies just to the small mesh. Now, if a summation is performed one mesh after another, each edge, as AB, will be integrated twice, once in each direction and therefore cancelling, except for the edges EF along C which will not be common to two meshes. However, the right-hand side of Eq. (A.58) depends on the area of the mesh and in the summation these contributions add throughout the surface S. Thus,

$$\oint_C \boldsymbol{U} \cdot d\boldsymbol{c} = \int_S (\boldsymbol{\nabla} \times \boldsymbol{U})\, d\boldsymbol{S},$$

which is the proof of the theorem. From the triple scalar product $\boldsymbol{n} \cdot (\boldsymbol{\nabla} \times \boldsymbol{U}) = (\boldsymbol{n} \times \boldsymbol{\nabla})\,\boldsymbol{U}$, consequently Stokes' equation (A.57) can be written as

$$\oint_C \boldsymbol{U} \cdot d\boldsymbol{c} = \int_S (\boldsymbol{n} \times \boldsymbol{\nabla}) \cdot \boldsymbol{U}\, dS \qquad \text{(A.59)}$$

This theorem can be shown to extend also for scalar fields ϕ instead of vector field $\boldsymbol{U}$. Then

$$\int_C \phi\, d\boldsymbol{c} = \int_S (\boldsymbol{n} \times \boldsymbol{\nabla})\phi\, dS \qquad \text{(A.60)}$$

Also it could be shown to apply to the cross product

$$-\int_C \boldsymbol{U} \times d\boldsymbol{c} = \int_S (\boldsymbol{n} \times \boldsymbol{\nabla}) \times \boldsymbol{U}\, dS \qquad \text{(A.61)}$$

The condition for a vector field $\boldsymbol{U}$ to be represented as the gradient of a scalar field ϕ discussed in Sec. A.19 can be obtained formally here. It is seen immediately from Eq. (A.57) that if $\boldsymbol{U} = \boldsymbol{\nabla}\phi$, the left hand integral vanishes because of Eq. (A.56). Since for any S whose boundary is C the right hand integral is zero, then, the integrand must be zero: $\boldsymbol{\nabla} \times \boldsymbol{U} = 0$. So if in a region $\boldsymbol{\nabla} \times \boldsymbol{U} = 0$ then $\boldsymbol{U}$ can be represented in that region as the gradient of a scalar function.

A.23 The Divergence Theorem. Gauss's Theorem

This is one of the most important theorems[9] in vector analysis. It relates the vector field at a closed arbitrary surface to the vector field inside the surface. Given a continuously deferential vector $\boldsymbol{U}$ in a volume $\mathcal{V}$ bounded by a surface S, in which $\boldsymbol{n}$ is the unit outward normal,

$$\oint_S \boldsymbol{n} \cdot \boldsymbol{U}\, dS = \int_{\mathcal{V}} (\boldsymbol{\nabla} \cdot \boldsymbol{U})\, d\mathcal{V} \qquad \text{(A.62)}$$

The integral on the left is the so-called "net-flux integral" over the entire surface of the vector $\boldsymbol{U}$ crossing the surface S, which is by Eq. (A.62)

[9] Often the Stokes' theorem of Sect. A.21 is shown to be deduced from Gauss's theorem. For instance, see I. J. Sokolnikoff and R. M. Redheffer, *Mathematics of Physics and Modern Engineering*, McGraw-Hill Book Co., p. 391, New York, 1958.

equal to the summation of the divergence inside the volume. If a physical significance is attached to $\boldsymbol{U}$, say the velocity, then Eq. (A.62) states physically that in order to conserve mass, the net flux of mass across S, if not zero, must be equal to the summation of sources and sinks[10] in the volume. To prove this, we proceed as follows with the guide of Fig. A.16.

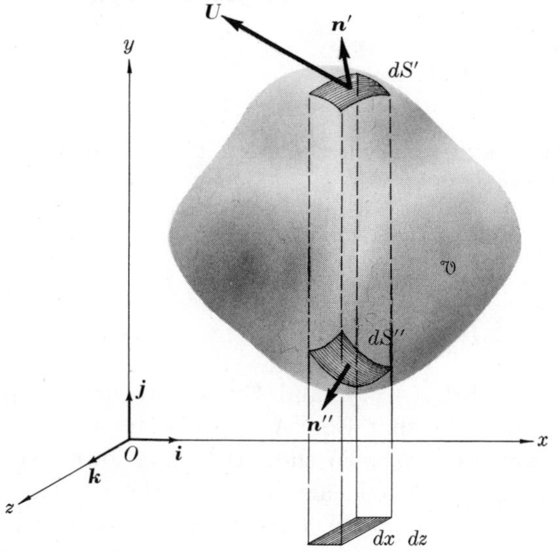

Figure A.16
Geometric representation for Gauss's theorem.

The integral

$$\oint_S \boldsymbol{n}\cdot\boldsymbol{U}\,dS = \oint_S [(\boldsymbol{n}\cdot\boldsymbol{i})u + (\boldsymbol{n}\cdot\boldsymbol{j})v + (\boldsymbol{n}\cdot\boldsymbol{k})w]\,dS \qquad \text{(A.63)}$$

if $\boldsymbol{U} = \boldsymbol{i}u + \boldsymbol{j}v + \boldsymbol{k}w$. Out of the arbitrary volume $\mathcal{V}$ consider an infinitesimal volume intersecting the surface S at dS' and dS''. Consider the second term in the last integral. The quantity $(\boldsymbol{n}\cdot\boldsymbol{j})\,dS = \boldsymbol{j}\cdot\boldsymbol{n}\,dS = \boldsymbol{j}\cdot d\boldsymbol{S} = dx\,dz$ by Sec. A.21. Then the contribution of the integral in the differential strip is $(\boldsymbol{n}''\cdot\boldsymbol{j})\,dS''v'' - (\boldsymbol{n}'\cdot\boldsymbol{j})\,dS'v'$ or $(v'' - v')\,dx\,dz$. By calculus:

$$v'' - v' = \int_{y'}^{y''} \frac{\partial v}{\partial y}\,dy$$

[10] The physical analogy, here, pertains to a fluid motion with constant density. A more thorough application of this theorem is given in Chap. IV.

Now if the strip is integrated in the whole surface, the contribution to the second term at the right of Eq. (A.63) is

$$\oint_S \int_{y'}^{y''} \left(\frac{\partial v}{\partial y}\, dy \right) dx\, dz$$

where the first integration is taken over from the xz projection of S and the second integration is taken from y'' to y'. This is exactly the volume integration of $\partial v/\partial y$

$$\oint_{\mathcal{V}} \frac{\partial v}{\partial y}\, d\mathcal{V}$$

The same reasoning can be carried out for the other two quantities in Eq. (A.63) and thus show that

$$\oint_S \boldsymbol{n} \cdot \boldsymbol{U}\, dS = \int_{\mathcal{V}} \left(\frac{\partial u}{\partial x} + \frac{\partial v}{\partial y} + \frac{\partial w}{\partial z} \right) d\mathcal{V}$$

$$= \int_{\mathcal{V}} (\boldsymbol{\nabla} \cdot \boldsymbol{U})\, d\mathcal{V}$$

—the proof of the theorem.

Finally Stokes' theorem, Eq. (A.57), and Green's theorem Eq. (A.62) could be combined to show that Eq. [A.53(g)] states that the divergence of the curl is always zero. To show this, if a lower half surface was drawn in Fig. A.15, it would also equal to the left hand side of Eq. (A.57). Therefore the complete closed integral

$$\oint_S \boldsymbol{n} \cdot (\boldsymbol{\nabla} \times \boldsymbol{U})\, dS = 0$$

Now in Eq. (A.62) for another vector $\boldsymbol{a}$ in the region,

$$\oint_S \boldsymbol{n} \cdot \boldsymbol{a}\, dS = \int_{\mathcal{V}} (\boldsymbol{\nabla} \cdot \boldsymbol{a})\, d\mathcal{V}$$

For $\boldsymbol{a} = \boldsymbol{\nabla} \times \boldsymbol{U}$, the divergence of $\boldsymbol{a}$ must be equal to zero, since for all $\mathcal{V}$ the answer would be the same. This, then, verifies that the divergence of the curl is always zero provided the vector fields and their derivatives are continuous in the volume $\mathcal{V}$.

A.24 Consequences of Gauss's Theorem

It can be shown easily that the generalized Gauss's theorem applies not only to the divergence but also to the gradient, the curl and the Laplacian.

$$\text{(a)} \qquad \oint_S \boldsymbol{n} \times \boldsymbol{U}\, dS = \int_{\mathcal{V}} \nabla \times \boldsymbol{U}\, d\mathcal{V}$$

$$\text{(b)} \qquad \oint_S \boldsymbol{n}\phi\, dS = \int_{\mathcal{V}} \nabla\phi\, d\mathcal{V}$$

$$\text{(c)} \qquad \oint_S (\boldsymbol{n}\cdot\nabla)\phi\, dS = \int_S \frac{\partial\phi}{\partial n}\, dS = \int_{\mathcal{V}} \nabla^2\phi\, d\mathcal{V} \qquad \text{(A.64)}$$

$$\text{(d)} \qquad \oint_S (\boldsymbol{n}\cdot\nabla)\boldsymbol{U}\, dS = \int \nabla^2\boldsymbol{U}\, d\mathcal{V}$$

Problems

A.1 If the four vectors $\boldsymbol{a}$, $\boldsymbol{b}$, $\boldsymbol{c}$, and $\boldsymbol{d}$ have the same origin O and lengths OA, OB, OC and OD, and if the relation $\boldsymbol{a} - \boldsymbol{b} = \boldsymbol{d} - \boldsymbol{c}$ show that $ABCD$ is a parallelogram.

A.2 Show that the absolute value of the sum of two vectors is less than or equal to the sum of their absolute values, in the same way show that the absolute value of the difference of two vectors is larger or equal to the difference of their absolute values.

A.3 If three points A, B, and C lie on a straight line, show that if $\boldsymbol{a}$, $\boldsymbol{b}$, and $\boldsymbol{c}$ are vectors extending from any arbitrary origin O to the three points, then

$$m\boldsymbol{a} + n\boldsymbol{b} + p\boldsymbol{c} = 0$$

$$m + n + p = 0$$

A.4 Show that the projection of the sum of two vectors on a line is the sum of their projection on that line.

A.5 Show that the distributive law applies for a scalar product

$$\boldsymbol{a}\cdot(\boldsymbol{b} + \boldsymbol{c}) = \boldsymbol{a}\cdot\boldsymbol{b} + \boldsymbol{a}\cdot\boldsymbol{c}$$

A.6 Show in a triangle with sides $\boldsymbol{a}$, $\boldsymbol{b}$, and $\boldsymbol{c}$ that

$$c^2 = a^2 + b^2 - 2ab\cos\theta$$

when θ is the angle between $\boldsymbol{a}$ and $\boldsymbol{b}$.

A.7 Through the use of the dot product show the trigonometric relation $\cos(\alpha - \beta) = \cos\alpha\cos\beta + \sin\alpha\sin\beta$.

A.8 If the cross product is taken of two vectors $(\boldsymbol{i}\cos\alpha + \boldsymbol{j}\sin\alpha)$ and $(\boldsymbol{i}\cos\beta + \boldsymbol{j}\sin\beta)$, show the trigonometric relation

$$\sin(\alpha - \beta) = \sin\alpha\cos\beta - \cos\alpha\sin\beta$$

A.9 Show that $\boldsymbol{a}\cdot(\boldsymbol{b}\times\boldsymbol{c})$ vanishes if two of these vectors are proportional to one another.

A.10 Show that $\boldsymbol{a}\times(\boldsymbol{b}\times\boldsymbol{c}) + \boldsymbol{b}\times(\boldsymbol{c}\times\boldsymbol{a}) + \boldsymbol{c}\times(\boldsymbol{a}\times\boldsymbol{b}) = 0$

A.11 Derive the identity

$$\begin{aligned}(\boldsymbol{a}\times\boldsymbol{b})\times(\boldsymbol{c}\times\boldsymbol{d}) &= [\boldsymbol{c}\cdot(\boldsymbol{d}\times\boldsymbol{a})]\boldsymbol{b} - [\boldsymbol{c}\cdot(\boldsymbol{d}\times\boldsymbol{b})]\boldsymbol{a}\\ &= [\boldsymbol{d}\cdot(\boldsymbol{a}\times\boldsymbol{b})]\boldsymbol{c} - [\boldsymbol{c}\cdot(\boldsymbol{a}\times\boldsymbol{b})]\boldsymbol{d}\end{aligned}$$

A.12 Show that

$$\begin{aligned}(\boldsymbol{a}\times\boldsymbol{b})\cdot(\boldsymbol{c}\times\boldsymbol{d}) &= \boldsymbol{a}\cdot\boldsymbol{b}\times(\boldsymbol{c}\times\boldsymbol{d})\\ &= \begin{vmatrix}\boldsymbol{a}\cdot\boldsymbol{c} & \boldsymbol{a}\cdot\boldsymbol{d}\\ \boldsymbol{b}\cdot\boldsymbol{c} & \boldsymbol{b}\cdot\boldsymbol{d}\end{vmatrix}\end{aligned}$$

A.13 Show that

$$\boldsymbol{a}\cdot[(\boldsymbol{b}\times\boldsymbol{c})\cdot\boldsymbol{d}] - \boldsymbol{b}\cdot[(\boldsymbol{c}\times\boldsymbol{d})\cdot\boldsymbol{a}] + \boldsymbol{c}\cdot[(\boldsymbol{d}\times\boldsymbol{a})\cdot\boldsymbol{b}] - \boldsymbol{d}\cdot[(\boldsymbol{a}\times\boldsymbol{b})\cdot\boldsymbol{c}] = 0$$

A.14 Show that

$$\begin{aligned}(\boldsymbol{a}\times\boldsymbol{b})\cdot(\boldsymbol{c}\times\boldsymbol{d}) &= \boldsymbol{c}\cdot[\boldsymbol{d}\times(\boldsymbol{a}\times\boldsymbol{b})]\\ &= (\boldsymbol{a}\cdot\boldsymbol{c})(\boldsymbol{b}\cdot\boldsymbol{d}) - (\boldsymbol{b}\cdot\boldsymbol{c})(\boldsymbol{a}\cdot\boldsymbol{d})\end{aligned}$$

(Lagrange's identity)

A.15 Given $\boldsymbol{a}\times\boldsymbol{b} = \boldsymbol{c}$, solve for $\boldsymbol{b}$ in terms of $\boldsymbol{a}$ and $\boldsymbol{c}$, showing that

$$\boldsymbol{b} = \frac{\boldsymbol{c}\times\boldsymbol{a}}{\boldsymbol{a}\cdot\boldsymbol{a}} + m\boldsymbol{a}$$

where m is an arbitrary constant.

A.16 If $\boldsymbol{a}\cdot\boldsymbol{b} = m$ and $\boldsymbol{a}\times\boldsymbol{b} = \boldsymbol{c}$, solve for $\boldsymbol{b}$, showing that

$$\boldsymbol{b} = \frac{\boldsymbol{c}\times\boldsymbol{a}}{\boldsymbol{a}^2} + \frac{m\boldsymbol{a}}{\boldsymbol{a}^2}$$

A.17 If $\boldsymbol{a}$, $\boldsymbol{b}$, and $\boldsymbol{c}$ are vectors from a given origin to points A, B, and C, show that the vector

$$(\boldsymbol{a}\times\boldsymbol{b}) + (\boldsymbol{b}\times\boldsymbol{c}) + (\boldsymbol{c}\times\boldsymbol{a})$$

is perpendicular to the plane ABC.

A.18 Prove that

$$(\boldsymbol{a}+\boldsymbol{b})\times(\boldsymbol{a}-\boldsymbol{b}) = -2\boldsymbol{a}\times\boldsymbol{b}$$

A.19 Show that

$$(\boldsymbol{a} \times \boldsymbol{b})\cdot(\boldsymbol{c} \times \boldsymbol{d}) + (\boldsymbol{b} \times \boldsymbol{c})\cdot(\boldsymbol{a} \times \boldsymbol{d}) + (\boldsymbol{c} \times \boldsymbol{a})\cdot(\boldsymbol{b} \times \boldsymbol{d}) = 0$$

A.20 $(\boldsymbol{a} - \boldsymbol{b})\cdot(\boldsymbol{d} - \boldsymbol{c}) + (\boldsymbol{b} - \boldsymbol{c})\cdot(\boldsymbol{d} - \boldsymbol{a}) + (\boldsymbol{d} - \boldsymbol{b})\cdot(\boldsymbol{c} - \boldsymbol{a}) = 0$

A.21 $(\boldsymbol{a} - \boldsymbol{d}) \times (\boldsymbol{b} - \boldsymbol{c}) + (\boldsymbol{b} - \boldsymbol{d}) \times (\boldsymbol{c} - \boldsymbol{a})$

$$+ (\boldsymbol{c} - \boldsymbol{d}) \times (\boldsymbol{a} - \boldsymbol{b}) = 2(\boldsymbol{a} \times \boldsymbol{b} + \boldsymbol{b} \times \boldsymbol{c} + \boldsymbol{c} \times \boldsymbol{a})$$

A.22 Prove that the area of the triangle whose vertices are at $\boldsymbol{a}$, $\boldsymbol{b}$, and $\boldsymbol{c}$ is the vector

$$\tfrac{1}{2}[(\boldsymbol{a} \times \boldsymbol{b}) + (\boldsymbol{b} \times \boldsymbol{c}) + (\boldsymbol{c} \times \boldsymbol{a})]$$

A.23 Prove the relationships of Eq. (A.34).

A.24 Show that for a vector to remain parallel to a fixed line the following relation must be true

$$\boldsymbol{a} \times \frac{d\boldsymbol{a}}{d\sigma}$$

where $\boldsymbol{a} = \boldsymbol{a}(\sigma)$ describes the vector field.

A.25 Expand $\dfrac{d}{d\sigma}[\boldsymbol{a} \times (\boldsymbol{b} \times \boldsymbol{c})]$.

A.26 If the rate of change of two vectors a and b is given as

$$\frac{d\boldsymbol{a}}{dt} = \boldsymbol{\omega} \times \boldsymbol{a} \quad \text{and} \quad \frac{d\boldsymbol{b}}{dt} = \boldsymbol{\omega} \times \boldsymbol{b},$$

show that

$$\frac{d}{dt}(\boldsymbol{a} \times \boldsymbol{b}) = \boldsymbol{\omega} \times (\boldsymbol{a} \times \boldsymbol{b})$$

A.27 Show that the divergence of a radius vector is equal to 3 and that the curl of a radius vector is zero.

A.28 Show that $(\boldsymbol{a}\cdot\boldsymbol{\nabla})\boldsymbol{r} = \boldsymbol{a}$.

Cartesian, Cylindrical and Spherical Coordinates

appendix B

Depending on the geometry of fluid motion and its boundary conditions, vectorial fluid properties and vectorial conservation equations are generally expressed in *Cartesian, cylindrical,* or *spherical* coordinates. It is the purpose of this appendix to tabulate these component equations in the coordinate systems mentioned. The contents in this appendix are limited to the quantities used in the text.

The space and velocity components in the three coordinate systems are shown in Figs. B.1, B.2, and B.3.

B.1 Space Coordinates

(*a*) *Cartesian Coordinates*

$$x, y, z$$

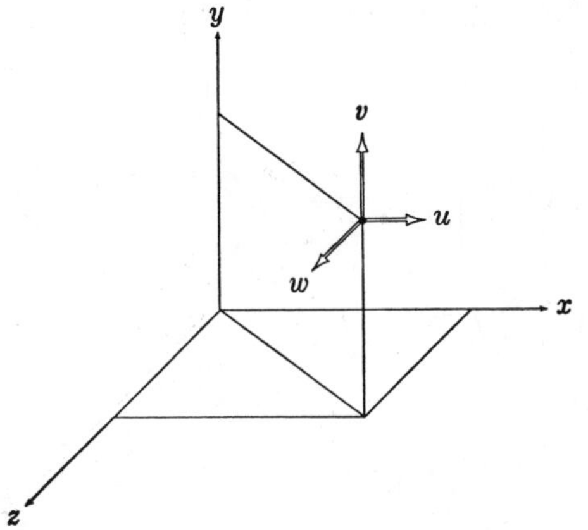

Figure B.1
Cartesian-coordinate representation.

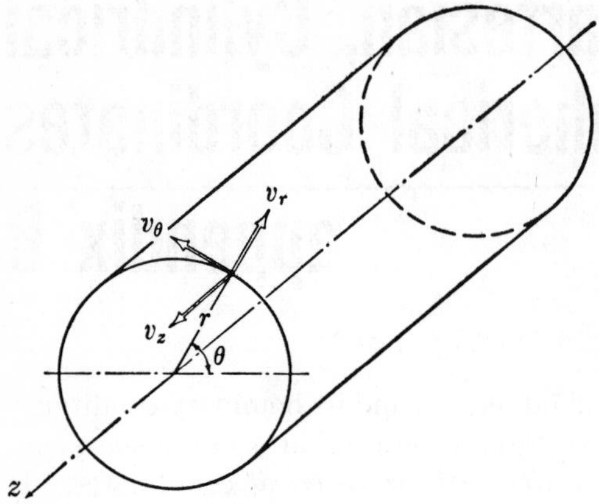

Figure B.2
Cylindrical-coordinate representation.

(*b*) *Cylindrical Coordinates*

$$r,\theta,z$$

(*c*) *Spherical Coordinates*

$$r,\theta,\alpha$$

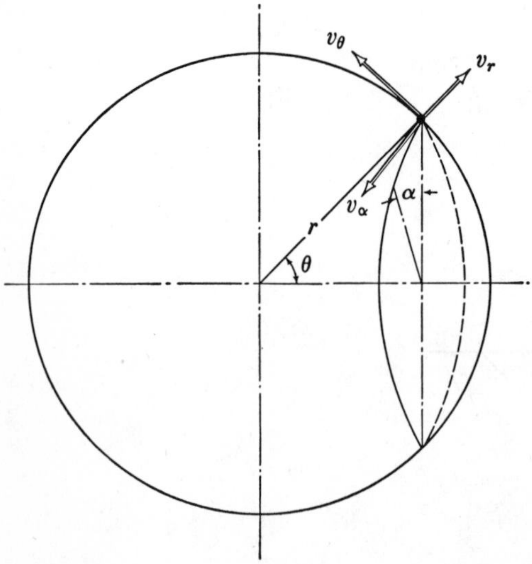

Figure B.3
Spherical-coordinate representation.

B.2 Velocity

(*a*) *Cartesian Coordinates*

$$u = \frac{dx}{dt}, \qquad v = \frac{dy}{dt}, \qquad w = \frac{dz}{dt}$$

(*b*) *Cylindrical Coordinates*

$$v_r = \frac{dr}{dt}, \qquad v_\theta = r\,\frac{d\theta}{dt}, \qquad v_z = \frac{dz}{dt}$$

(*c*) *Spherical Coordinates*

$$v_r = \frac{dr}{dt}, \qquad v_\theta = r\,\frac{d\theta}{dt}, \qquad v_\alpha = r\sin\theta\,\frac{d\alpha}{dt}$$

B.3 Acceleration

Since, in the Eulerian representation, each velocity component is a function of the space coordinates and time, as was shown in Sec. 4.2,

(*a*) *Cartesian Coordinates*

$$a_x = \frac{du}{dt} = \frac{\partial u}{\partial t} + u\,\frac{\partial u}{\partial x} + v\,\frac{\partial u}{\partial y} + w\,\frac{\partial u}{\partial z}$$

$$a_y = \frac{dv}{dt} = \frac{\partial v}{\partial t} + u\,\frac{\partial v}{\partial x} + v\,\frac{\partial v}{\partial y} + w\,\frac{\partial v}{\partial z}$$

$$a_z = \frac{dw}{dt} = \frac{\partial w}{\partial t} + u\,\frac{\partial w}{\partial x} + v\,\frac{\partial w}{\partial y} + w\,\frac{\partial w}{\partial z}$$

(*b*) *Cylindrical Coordinates*

$$a_r = \frac{\partial v_r}{\partial t} + v_r\,\frac{\partial v_r}{\partial r} + \frac{v_\theta}{r}\,\frac{\partial v_r}{\partial \theta} - \frac{v_\theta^2}{r} + v_z\,\frac{\partial v_r}{\partial z}$$

$$a_\theta = \frac{\partial v_\theta}{\partial t} + v_r\,\frac{\partial v_\theta}{\partial r} + \frac{v_\theta}{r}\,\frac{\partial v_\theta}{\partial \theta} + \frac{v_r v_\theta}{r} + v_z\,\frac{\partial v_\theta}{\partial z}$$

$$a_z = \frac{\partial v_z}{\partial t} + v_r\,\frac{\partial v_z}{\partial r} + \frac{v_\theta}{r}\,\frac{\partial v_z}{\partial \theta} + v_z\,\frac{\partial v_z}{\partial z}$$

(*c*) *Spherical Coordinates*

$$a_r = \frac{\partial v_r}{\partial t} + v_r \frac{\partial v_r}{\partial r} + \frac{v_\theta}{r}\frac{\partial v_r}{\partial \theta} + \frac{v_\alpha}{r \sin\theta}\frac{\partial v_r}{\partial \alpha} - \frac{v_\theta^2 + v_\alpha^2}{r}$$

$$a_\theta = \frac{\partial v_\theta}{\partial t} + v_r \frac{\partial v_\theta}{\partial r} + \frac{v_\theta}{r}\frac{\partial v_\theta}{\partial \theta} + \frac{v_\alpha}{r \sin\theta}\frac{\partial v_\theta}{\partial \alpha} + \frac{v_r v_\theta}{r} - \frac{v_\alpha^2 \cot\theta}{r}$$

$$a_\alpha = \frac{\partial v_\alpha}{\partial t} + v_r \frac{\partial v_\alpha}{\partial r} + \frac{v_\theta}{r}\frac{\partial v_\alpha}{\partial \theta} + \frac{v_\alpha}{r \sin\theta}\frac{\partial v_\alpha}{\partial \alpha} + \frac{v_\alpha v_r}{r} + \frac{v_\theta v_\alpha \cot\theta}{r}$$

B.4 Vorticity

(*a*) *Cartesian Coordinates*

$$\zeta_x = \frac{\partial w}{\partial y} - \frac{\partial v}{\partial z}$$

$$\zeta_y = \frac{\partial u}{\partial z} - \frac{\partial w}{\partial x}$$

$$\zeta_z = \frac{\partial v}{\partial x} - \frac{\partial u}{\partial y}$$

(*b*) *Cylindrical Coordinates*

$$\zeta_r = \frac{1}{r}\frac{\partial v_z}{\partial \theta} - \frac{\partial v_\theta}{\partial z}$$

$$\zeta_\theta = \frac{\partial v_r}{\partial z} - \frac{\partial v_z}{\partial r}$$

$$\zeta_z = \frac{1}{r}\frac{\partial}{\partial r}(r v_\theta) - \frac{1}{r}\frac{\partial v_r}{\partial \theta}$$

(*c*) *Spherical Coordinates*

$$\zeta_r = \frac{1}{r \sin\theta}\left[\frac{\partial}{\partial \theta}(v_\alpha \sin\theta) - \frac{\partial v_\theta}{\partial \alpha}\right]$$

$$\zeta_\theta = \frac{1}{r \sin\theta}\frac{\partial v_r}{\partial \alpha} - \frac{1}{r}\frac{\partial}{\partial r}(r v_\alpha)$$

$$\zeta_\alpha = \frac{1}{r}\frac{\partial}{\partial r}(r v_\theta) - \frac{1}{r}\frac{\partial v_r}{\partial \theta}$$

B.5 Mass-Continuity Equation

From inspection of Eq. (3.16), it is seen that the first term is not dependent on the space-coordinate system used, since it represents the change with time. The remaining three terms are called the divergence of the product of the density times the velocity vector whose components are different in different coordinate systems. For this reason it will suffice to express the divergence of the velocity vector alone, as in Eq. (3.17), which is valid for an incompressible flow. If the flow is compressible, then the quantity ρ can be added with every velocity component.

(*a*) *Cartesian Coordinates*

$$\frac{\partial u}{\partial x} + \frac{\partial v}{\partial y} + \frac{\partial w}{\partial z} = 0$$

(*b*) *Cylindrical Coordinates*

$$\frac{1}{r}\frac{\partial}{\partial r}(rv_r) + \frac{1}{r}\frac{\partial v_\theta}{\partial \theta} + \frac{\partial v_z}{\partial z} = 0$$

(*c*) *Spherical Coordinates*

$$\frac{1}{r^2}\frac{\partial}{\partial r}(r^2 v_r) + \frac{1}{r \sin\theta}\frac{\partial}{\partial \theta}(v_\theta \sin\theta) + \frac{1}{r\sin\theta}\frac{\partial v_\alpha}{\partial \alpha} = 0$$

B.6 The Shearing Stress

(*a*) *Cartesian Coordinates*

$$\tau_{xy} = \mu\left(\frac{\partial u}{\partial y} + \frac{\partial v}{\partial x}\right)$$

$$\tau_{zx} = \mu\left(\frac{\partial w}{\partial x} + \frac{\partial u}{\partial z}\right)$$

$$\tau_{yz} = \mu\left(\frac{\partial v}{\partial z} + \frac{\partial w}{\partial y}\right)$$

(*b*) *Cylindrical Coordinates*

$$\tau_{r\theta} = \mu\left[\frac{1}{r}\frac{\partial v_r}{\partial \theta} + r\frac{\partial}{\partial r}\left(\frac{v_\theta}{r}\right)\right]$$

$$\tau_{\theta z} = \mu\left(\frac{\partial v_\theta}{\partial z} + \frac{1}{r}\frac{\partial v_z}{\partial \theta}\right)$$

$$\tau_{zr} = \mu\left(\frac{\partial v_z}{\partial r} + \frac{\partial v_r}{\partial z}\right)$$

(*c*) *Spherical Coordinates*

$$\tau_{r\theta} = \mu\left[\frac{1}{r}\frac{\partial v_r}{\partial \theta} + r\frac{\partial}{\partial r}\left(\frac{v_\theta}{r}\right)\right]$$

$$\tau_{\theta\alpha} = \mu\left[\frac{1}{r\sin\theta}\frac{\partial v_\theta}{\partial \alpha} + \frac{\sin\theta}{r}\frac{\partial}{\partial \theta}\left(\frac{v_\alpha}{\sin\theta}\right)\right]$$

$$\tau_{\alpha r} = \mu\left[r\frac{\partial}{\partial r}\left(\frac{v_\alpha}{r}\right) + \frac{1}{r\sin\theta}\frac{\partial v_r}{\partial \alpha}\right]$$

B.7 The Equations of Motion for a Viscous, Incompressible Fluid

Similar to Eq. (9.13), in the absence of external body forces and surface tension, the equations of motion in various coordinate systems are

(*a*) *Cartesian Coordinates*

$$\frac{\partial u}{\partial t} + u\frac{\partial u}{\partial x} + v\frac{\partial u}{\partial y} + w\frac{\partial u}{\partial z} = -\frac{1}{\rho}\frac{\partial p}{\partial x} + \nu\nabla^2 u$$

$$\frac{\partial v}{\partial t} + u\frac{\partial v}{\partial x} + v\frac{\partial v}{\partial y} + w\frac{\partial v}{\partial z} = -\frac{1}{\rho}\frac{\partial p}{\partial y} + \nu\nabla^2 v$$

$$\frac{\partial w}{\partial t} + u\frac{\partial w}{\partial x} + v\frac{\partial w}{\partial y} + w\frac{\partial w}{\partial z} = -\frac{1}{\rho}\frac{\partial p}{\partial z} + \nu\nabla^2 w$$

where

$$\nabla^2 \equiv \frac{\partial^2}{\partial x^2} + \frac{\partial^2}{\partial y^2} + \frac{\partial^2}{\partial z^2}$$

(*b*) *Cylindrical Coordinates*

$$\frac{\partial v_r}{\partial t} + v_r\frac{\partial v_r}{\partial r} + \frac{v_\theta}{r}\frac{\partial v_r}{\partial \theta} - \frac{v_\theta^2}{r} + v_z\frac{\partial v_r}{\partial z} = -\frac{1}{\rho}\frac{\partial p}{\partial r} + \nu\left(\nabla^2 v_r - \frac{v_r}{r^2} - \frac{2}{r^2}\frac{\partial v_\theta}{\partial \theta}\right)$$

$$\frac{\partial v_\theta}{\partial t} + v_r\frac{\partial v_\theta}{\partial r} + \frac{v_\theta}{r}\frac{\partial v_\theta}{\partial \theta} + \frac{v_r v_\theta}{r} + v_z\frac{\partial v_\theta}{\partial z} = -\frac{1}{\rho}\frac{1}{r}\frac{\partial p}{\partial \theta} + \nu\left(\nabla^2 v_\theta + \frac{2}{r^2}\frac{\partial v_r}{\partial \theta} - \frac{v_\theta}{r^2}\right)$$

$$\frac{\partial v_z}{\partial t} + v_r\frac{\partial v_z}{\partial r} + \frac{v_\theta}{r}\frac{\partial v_z}{\partial \theta} + v_z\frac{\partial v_z}{\partial z} = -\frac{1}{\rho}\frac{\partial p}{\partial z} + \nu\nabla^2 v_z$$

where

$$\nabla^2 \equiv \frac{\partial^2}{\partial r^2} + \frac{1}{r}\frac{\partial}{\partial r} + \frac{1}{r^2}\frac{\partial^2}{\partial \theta^2} + \frac{\partial^2}{\partial z^2}$$

(*c*) *Spherical Coordinates*

$$\frac{\partial v_r}{\partial t} + v_r \frac{\partial v_r}{\partial r} + \frac{v_\theta}{r}\frac{\partial v_r}{\partial \theta} + \frac{v_\alpha}{r \sin\theta}\frac{\partial v_r}{\partial \alpha} - \frac{v_\theta^2 + v_\alpha^2}{r} = -\frac{1}{\rho}\frac{\partial p}{\partial r}$$
$$+ \nu\left(\nabla^2 v_r - \frac{2v_r}{r^2} - \frac{2}{r^2}\frac{\partial v_\theta}{\partial \theta} - \frac{2v_\theta \cot\theta}{r^2} - \frac{2}{r^2 \sin\theta}\frac{\partial v_\alpha}{\partial \alpha}\right)$$

$$\frac{\partial v_\theta}{\partial t} + v_r \frac{\partial v_\theta}{\partial r} + \frac{v_\theta}{r}\frac{\partial v_\theta}{\partial \theta} + \frac{v_\alpha}{r \sin\theta}\frac{\partial v_\theta}{\partial \alpha} + \frac{v_r v_\theta}{r} - \frac{v_\alpha^2 \cot\theta}{r} = -\frac{1}{\rho}\frac{1}{r}\frac{\partial p}{\partial \theta}$$
$$+ \nu\left(\nabla^2 v_\theta + \frac{2}{r^2}\frac{\partial v_r}{\partial \theta} - \frac{v_\theta}{r^2 \sin^2\theta} - \frac{2\cos\theta}{r^2 \sin^2\theta}\frac{\partial v_\alpha}{\partial \alpha}\right)$$

$$\frac{\partial v_\alpha}{\partial t} + v_r \frac{\partial v_\alpha}{\partial r} + \frac{v_\theta}{r}\frac{\partial v_\alpha}{\partial \theta} + \frac{v_\alpha}{r \sin\theta}\frac{\partial v_\alpha}{\partial \alpha} + \frac{v_\alpha v_r}{r} + \frac{v_\theta v_\alpha \cot\theta}{r} = -\frac{1}{\rho}\frac{1}{r \sin\theta}\frac{\partial p}{\partial \alpha}$$
$$+ \nu\left(\nabla^2 v_\alpha - \frac{v_\alpha}{r^2 \sin^2\theta} + \frac{2}{r^2 \sin\theta}\frac{\partial v_r}{\partial \alpha} + \frac{2\cos\theta}{r^2 \sin^2\theta}\frac{\partial v_\theta}{\partial \alpha}\right)$$

where

$$\nabla^2 \equiv \frac{1}{r^2}\frac{\partial}{\partial r}\left(r^2 \frac{\partial}{\partial r}\right) + \frac{1}{r^2 \sin\theta}\frac{\partial}{\partial \theta}\left(\sin\theta \frac{\partial}{\partial \theta}\right) + \frac{1}{r^2 \sin^2\theta}\frac{\partial^2}{\partial \alpha^2}$$

Index